be retu
ate stam

D1614410

MONOGRAPHS OF THE PHYSIOLOGICAL SOCIETY

Editors: H. Davson, A. D. M. Greenfield,
R. Whittam, G. S. Brindley

Number 23 MAMMALIAN MUSCLE RECEPTORS AND
THEIR CENTRAL ACTIONS

Volumes marked * are now out of print

MAMMALIAN MUSCLE RECEPTORS AND THEIR CENTRAL ACTIONS

PETER B. C. MATTHEWS

M.D. (Cantab.), D.Sc. (Oxon.)

Student of Christ Church and University Lecturer, Oxford

LONDON
EDWARD ARNOLD (PUBLISHERS) LTD

First published 1972
by Edward Arnold (Publishers) Ltd.,
41 Maddox Street,
London, WR1 0AN

ISBN 0 7131 4191 3

Printed in Great Britain by
The Camelot Press Ltd, London and Southampton

PREFACE

MUSCLE receptors and particularly the muscle spindle have now been studied more or less continuously for slightly over a century. Part of their attraction for successive generations of physiologists has been that they look simple enough for the answer to any question to be only just round the corner, but in fact they are sufficiently complex to have proved a continuing challenge to experimental skill and to have prevented the final word on any matter being said at too early a stage in the game. The muscle spindle, moreover, has the extra intellectual attraction of providing an accessible example for the study of the motor regulation of the responsiveness of a peripheral sense organ. The practical importance of all this work for clinical neurology needs no emphasis, since the muscle receptors are so intimately concerned with the reflex regulation of muscle tone. A knowledge of their behaviour and reflex actions in the experimental animal is the basis of any proper appreciation of the much more complicated problems presented by human disease and is a pre-requisite for elucidating the pathophysiology of the numerous neurological conditions which are accompanied by an abnormality of muscle tone.

The study of muscle receptors is also of interest in providing a starting point for further experiment on the central nervous system. The nerve fibres concerned with the major muscle receptors comfortably outnumber the ordinary α motor fibres which produce the overt muscular contractions by which so much central activity eventually expresses itself. This outnumbering of the ordinary motor fibres may be taken as a sign of the importance of proprioceptive feedback for the regulation of motor performance. Moreover, the study of these feedback mechanisms would appear to be an essential prelude to achieving an understanding of many of the motor regulatory systems existing within the central nervous system itself. The function of some central elements may be expected to be the combination of peripheral feedback with higher command in various sorts of way. For the time being attack on the peripherally coursing motor control loops offers the advantage of ease of access, with the added bonus that the patterns of firing can be more easily understood than can those recorded from within the depths of the central nervous system.

The last fifteen years have seen notable progress in understanding of peripheral mechanisms and would appear to have helped set the stage for further attack on what the central nervous system does with the flood of proprioceptive information that it continuously receives from the periphery. This book sets out to detail this newer knowledge for the use of all those who need to take an interest in the subject but who may not have been concerned with the actual work or had time to read the rapidly accumulating original literature. On the structural side, there has been the histological recognition of two kinds of intrafusal muscle fibre with a progressive hardening of the evidence for their being at least partly supplied by separate motor fibres. On the sensory side, there has been a rather full analysis of the functional differences between the primary and secondary endings which have for so long been recognised to be anatomically distinct. On the motor side, there has been the functional delimitation of two types of fusimotor fibre, the static and dynamic fibres, with a reasonably complete study of the effects of their stimulation; moreover, we at last appear to be reaching agreement on the way that they operate within the spindle to achieve their separate actions. On the reflex side, there has been the appreciation of the potential complexity and opportunity for higher control which is introduced by the presence of interneurones on all reflex pathways except that mediating the tendon jerk; this has helped lead to the suggestion that the spindle group II fibres from the secondary endings play a part in reflexly producing the hypertonia of the decerebrate preparation instead of merely contributing to a generalised flexor reflex as previously believed. On the control side, the hypothesis that movement may sometimes be produced by means of a 'follow-up' servo involving the muscle spindle has been with us long enough to have stimulated the performance of experiments which have led to its replacement by the related hypothesis of the servo-assistance of movement.

Almost every time progress has followed an erratic course with controversy and false turnings up to the very present. Matters which are so simple in concept that they can be taught to first year undergraduates when dogmatically presented have often only recently been established after careful experimental exclusion of equally plausible alternatives. The present account has not glossed over the difficulties and has followed the subject back to its beginnings in the last century. This should help those who have to delve into the older literature to appreciate which were the growing points and which were the dead ends. It is also hoped that discussion of the evidence and the way that ideas developed will increase awareness of why progress is often so slow and how a lifetime can be spent in finding out so little. Moreover, an analytical approach is potentially more interesting than a simple presentation of 'the facts' as we currently understand them. It naturally follows from all this that much which is here presented will in due course be replaced by something better.

For those who want to get to the gist of the matter reasonably quickly two ancillary devices have been employed. Each chapter begins with a list of its sub-headings, numbered by page, and terminates with a résumé of its salient points. The résumés have been written in ordinary prose rather than in summary form and can be used on their own without reference to the detailed text. When all ten are read consecutively they provide a review of some forty pages retailing the present state of affairs. But in spite of its size this book makes no claim to be so exhaustive as to cite every recent paper. Rather it brings together a wide variety of material in an attempt to form a connected account for those who wish to see the field as a whole.

April 1971   P. B. C. M.

ACKNOWLEDGEMENTS

Most of all I should like to thank the various colleagues I have worked with over the years who in a continuous dialogue have helped in the development of so much that is here described and which may seem to be presented as if it were solely my own thoughts about the subject. Dr. Per Andersen of Oslo and Dr. Michael Brown of Oxford both patiently read through the first draft of the book and gave me much valuable advice. Dr. Ian Donaldson, Mr. Guy Goodwin and Dr. Cathy MacLennan read smaller portions connected with their special interests. Miss Penny Paterson photographed the 181 illustrations, both to provide working prints and also those suitable for reproduction. Miss Jill Smith made several drawings for the book and re-drew a large number of graphs. Mrs. Shirley Greenslade and Miss Vivian Sandes between them typed something well over the 150,000 words that it has taken to cover the subject. Many of the illustrations have been taken from the literature and I am most grateful to the individual authors and also to numerous scientific journals for allowing their reproduction. The sources are all referred to in the individual legends and the bibliography. The reproduction of a figure will, it is hoped, provide a stimulus for the reader to turn to the original article and thereby show his and my gratitude to those who brought it to birth. To spell out my thanks in detail to each of the individual authors and publishers would serve little purpose since such a list rarely seems to be read.

CONTENTS

THE STRUCTURE OF THE RECEPTORS

As always in the study of the nervous system the description of structure which comprises this chapter provides the essential prelude to the study of function to which the rest of this monograph is devoted. Skeletal muscle is supplied with a wealth of afferent fibres varying in size from the very largest to the very smallest found in the mammalian body (0·2–20 μm) and considerably outnumbering the ordinary motor fibres. The large medullated afferent fibres terminate almost exclusively in specialised encapsulated end-organs, while the small medullated fibres and the non-medullated fibres terminate as free nerve endings; intermediate sized medullated fibres may terminate in either way. The chief specialised receptors are the muscle spindles and the tendon organs which are present in roughly equal numbers. In addition, there are occasionally a few typical large Pacinian corpuscles and more commonly a few smaller and more elongated paciniform corpuscles. Joints contain the specialised spray or Ruffini ending in their capsules, and tendon organs may occur in their ligaments. Pacinian corpuscles and paciniform corpuscles are also to be found in and near joint capsules.

These various specialised terminations have now been examined for slightly over a hundred years by successive generations of workers equipped with the light microscope. Even so, new features continue to be described on the basis of such observation and there has still been relatively little charting of simple quantitative matters such as the numbers of receptors in different muscles and the sizes of their nerve fibres. Electron microscopy is currently supplying further important detail but without as yet leading to any fundamental revision of pre-existing knowledge. The literature already contains numerous reviews of structural matters and some of the older ones may perhaps be found to provide more valuable reading than some of the newer, including the present account. (For example: Sherrington, 1894; Huber & DeWitt, 1897; Regaud & Favre, 1904; Hinsey, 1934; Barker, 1948; Tiegs, 1953; Matthews, 1964.) A very full bibliography on all the literature on muscle receptors up to 1966 has been compiled by Eldred, Yellin, Gadbois & Sweeney (1967) and Granit's recent book (1970) provides some additional recent references as well as some on certain related topics.

Free nerve endings

These are the most numerous of the muscle receptors and so merit first mention, even though there is little to say about them. Their presence has long been recognised and they have recently been re-examined by Stacey (1969). Under the light microscope free terminations are seen simply as fine varicose filaments which may terminate either by coming abruptly to an end or by gradually tapering to a point. Electron microscopy has yet to show whether there is any detectable structural specialisation at the terminals, and in particular whether there is any structural change corresponding to the functional transition which may be presumed to occur along a fibre as it changes from being primarily an agent for the conduction of an impulse to being primarily the site of transducer action and impulse initiation. Free endings are found in close association with practically every structure in muscle (muscle fibres, fascia, fat, blood vessels excluding capillaries, tendon organs and muscle spindles). They may well have different functions depending upon their location, though sometimes the branches originating from a single nerve fibre may be seen terminating in relation to more than one type of histologically identifiable cell. In addition, even when free terminals are similarly placed with respect to other tissues it remains an open question whether or not functional specialisations exist so that different free endings respond preferentially to different types or stimuli.

All non-medullated afferent fibres end as free endings, and since such fibres are numerous so also must be the number of free endings. Stacey (1969), on the basis of fibre enumeration in electron micrographs of a de-efferented and sympathectomised nerve, recently demonstrated that in the nerve to the tibialis posterior muscle the non-medullated afferent fibres outnumber the medullated ones by about 2:1. He claimed that in ordinary light micrographs it is impossible to distinguish and count every individual non-medullated fibre, and thus suggested that all previous estimates of their numbers are likely to have been appreciably too low. It would be useful to have electron-micrographic enumerations performed for a range of muscle nerves, particularly as the nerve to tibialis posterior has been suspected to supply extramuscular as well as intramuscular receptors (Boyd & Davey, 1968).

The smallest medullated fibres, namely those below about 5 μm total diameter and conventionally called group III, are also thought to terminate almost exclusively as free endings. This is because insufficient of the more specialised types of ending have been found for them to terminate in any other way; it may be noted, however, that some of the spindle secondary endings derive from fibres of less than 5 μm diameter at their point of entry to the spindle and so have the opportunity to be similarly thin in the main nerve trunk. A few of the larger medullated fibres in the main nerve trunk probably also supply free nerve endings after becoming suitably thin. Anatomical work cannot easily show just how commonly this occurs and the matter is discussed later in the light of the electrophysiological evidence (p. 233). Microscopic examination has shown, however, that unlike the afferents to the encapsulated receptors, the fibres of origin of free nerve terminals often branch profusely, and this is particularly clearly seen for the small medullated fibres in the nerve bundles running alongside blood vessels (Stacey, 1969). The extent of the ramifications of the branches of a single fibre would be interesting to know but is not easy to determine at all systematically; from examination of teased material, Stacey (1969) has noted individual 'endings' covering areas of from 10×110 μm to $300 \times 1,000$ μm.

Paciniform corpuscles

A few of these probably occur in all muscles of any size and some muscles contain an appreciable number. This statement is based on Barker's work (1962, 1967) for he alone appears to have attempted to count them. In the cat, he found an average of only two for the soleus muscle, while the Vth interosseus of the foot and the rectus femoris contained an average of 8 and 12 paciniform corpuscles respectively. These numbers are probably more meaningfully expressed as a percentage of the number of muscle spindles in the same muscles, when they become in turn 4%, 31% and 12%. Typical Pacinian corpuscles rarely if ever occur actually inside muscles, but some way may be found occasionally on fascial sheets between muscles and more frequently in the loose connective tissue near joints. About 60 Pacinian corpuscles are found on the interosseus membrane of the cat's hindlimb and further local assemblies of them may remain to be discovered in other muscular regions.

The paciniform corpuscles found in muscle do not appear to have been given a single comprehensive description in the literature. Like the true Pacinian corpuscles they are supplied by a medullated fibre which loses its myelin and then runs with a uniform diameter inside a lamellated sheath. Judging by isolated

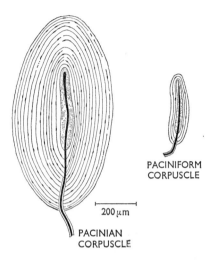

PACINIFORM
CORPUSCLE

200 μm

PACINIAN
CORPUSCLE

FIG. 1.1. Diagrammatic comparison of the relative sizes of the two kinds of lamellated end-organ found in relation to muscles and joints. (Based on descriptions cited in text.)

pictures (Barker, 1967; Stacey, 1969) the whole structure is 0·1–0·5 mm long and about 30 μm wide, and of fairly uniform diameter throughout its length. This contrasts with the typical Pacinian corpuscle which is 0·5–2 mm long and around 500 μm in diameter and is somewhat oval in longitudinal section. The paciniform corpuscle is thus altogether smaller and also relatively the much more elongated, with far fewer lamellae. The two kinds of corpuscle are illustrated diagrammatically in Fig. 1.1. Paciniform corpuscles are supplied by a medullated nerve fibre which is about 3 μm diameter along its terminal myelinated segment. Several nearby corpuscles are usually supplied by the branches of a single parent axon which is naturally usually appreciably thicker than its terminal branches. In two illustrated examples the stem fibres were 7 μm and 10·5 μm in diameter while still within 0·5 mm of their terminal corpuscles (Stacey, 1969). Paciniform corpuscles are found almost exclusively at the musculo-tendinous junction. They are particularly frequent in the immediate vicinity of tendon organs and more so than would be expected by chance (42 out of a sample of 65, Stacey, 1969).

Tendon organs

These were first properly described by Camillo Golgi in 1880 and are therefore often given his name. Cattaneo (1888) subsequently confirmed that they definitely were afferent end-organs, for in the one dog that he studied the nerve endings of the tendon organs persisted after section of the appropriate ventral roots had led to muscle atrophy. This finding was confirmed shortly afterwards by Sherrington (1894) working on the cat, and also by several others since (for example Boyd, 1962; Barker, 1962). The structure of tendon organs was subsequently described in great detail by Huber and DeWitt (1900) who also reviewed the previous literature. In view of their simplicity relatively little has remained to be added to the early descriptions and over half a century later Merrillees (1962) concluded, on presenting the first electron micrographs of a tendon organ, that there had been 'no major morphological contribution since 1900'.

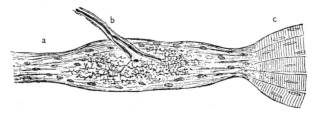

FIG. 1.2. The Golgi tendon organ as seen by Cajal. a, tendon; b, large afferent fibre breaking up into sensory terminals; c, muscle fibres. (Cajal, 1909, Fig. 199.)

Figure 1.2 illustrates the structure of the tendon organ as seen by Cajal in 1909 and plate I.1 shows a more recent microphotograph. Tendon organs usually lie at the musculo-tendinous junction rather than in the tendon proper; in the cat Barker (1967) found only 8% of them in the tendon itself. They occur both at the origin and insertion of a muscle and also at intermuscular septa. Consequently, as first emphasised over forty years ago by Hinsey (1927), ablation of the macroscopically visible portion of a tendon entirely fails to deprive a muscle of its tendon organs and so this procedure can provide no help in determining their function. In man, they may be up to 1 mm long, but in the cat the typical size is 0·5 mm by 0·1 mm (Barker, 1967; Ralston, Miller & Kasahera,

1960; Stilwell, 1957; Bridgman 1968). As Cajal's diagram shows any individual tendon organ is directly pulled upon only by a relatively small number of muscle fibres; in the cat, Barker (1967) puts the number at about 10. Recent electrophysiological evidence (Chap. 3) suggests that the tetanic contraction of any one of these muscle fibres is sufficient to excite an afferent discharge. The tendon organ is usually supplied by a single medullated nerve fibre of relatively large diameter (8–12 μm, see Chap. 2). In addition, Ruffini (1897) found the main fibre to some tendon organs to be accompanied by a thinner 'concomitant' myelinated fibre and similar fibres have been seen more recently by Wohlfart & Henriksson (1960). The role of these finer fibres is still in doubt, but as just noted paciniform corpuscles are often closely associated with tendon organs, as also are free nerve endings.

The main nerve fibre of the tendon organ breaks up into a series of non-medullated sprays which are closely applied to the surfaces of tendon fascicles. The whole ramification is enclosed in a delicate capsule which blends at either end with the connective tissue, and also with the sheath of Henle of the nerve fibre. The tendon bundles inside the capsule are smaller than those outside and are less closely packed; between them are thin processes of cytoplasm which are derived either from fibroblasts or from Schwann cells. This makes the tendon inside the capsule less 'compact' than that outside, and so presumably slightly weaker per unit of cross-section. Electron microscopy (Merrillees, 1962) shows that the plasma membrane of the nerve terminals is occasionally in direct contact with the tendon bundles, but more usually they are slightly separated by 'basement membrane' material or by Schwann cell cytoplasm. There are persistent reports in the literature that a tendon organ may be not uncommonly found near the end of a muscle spindle, as if the two lay in some kind of functional relation (cf. Cattaneo, 1888, p. 346; Ruffini, 1898, p. 196; Barker, 1948, p. 167). At present, however, this observation is unsupported by the quantitative observations needed to show whether this conjunction of the two kinds of sense ending occurs more frequently than would be expected by chance from their relative abundance.

Joint receptors

The connective tissue of joint capsules contain free nerve endings and two types of specialised ending. In addition, both internal and external joint ligaments may possess Golgi endings, very like those in tendons. The thin synovial membrane itself contains no specialised endings and few if any free terminals; the same is true for the cartilaginous articular surfaces. Because of their form and the large size of their supplying axon there has never been felt to be any doubt that all the specialised nerve endings are indeed afferent end-organs, rather than motor endings for which there is no reasonable function; but the matter does not seem to have been directly tested by degeneration experiments. Samuel (1952) showed that many of the free endings were also afferent by finding that they persisted after sympathectomy. Of course, some free terminals, particularly those on blood vessels, may be expected to be derived from sympathetic motor fibres. This should now be readily demonstrable histochemically by showing that they contain catecholamines.

The specialised endings were seen by various workers in the last century, notably by Rauber (1874) and by Krause (1874), and some discussion ensued on their morphological relationship to endings found in the skin and elsewhere. More recently there have been several accounts of the endings in the knee joint of the cat which has been chosen for histological study because it is convenient for electrophysiological work (Gardner, 1944, 1950; Boyd, 1954; Skoglund, 1956; Freeman & Wyke, 1967). These accounts are essentially complementary and form the basis of the following description. The Golgi endings present no significant differences from those found in tendons, and like them are supplied by a large medullated afferent nerve fibre (anything from 10 to 17 μm given by different authors). They lie in the ligaments, and are never found in unsupported regions of the capsule. The joint capsule contains a quite different kind of encapsulated ending which is smaller than the Golgi ending (100×40 μm as compared with 600×100 μm), and which has several spray terminals arranged in three dimensions in the connective tissue of the capsule, rather than running along fibrous slips as do the Golgi tendon organs. This spray ending is now usually referred to as the 'Ruffini ending' and this term will be adopted here. Freeman & Wyke (1967) proposed a numerical classification to replace such eponyms but this puts a greater burden on the memory! The term Ruffini ending was introduced by Sfameni in 1902 because the joint endings, as he saw them, resembled certain cutaneous endings which

Ruffini had described a few years beforehand (1894). It is ironic that Ruffini's name should be attached to a receptor to the study of which he made no particular contribution, while his work on the muscle spindle goes unrecognised in any such manner.

Figure 1.3 shows a drawing of a nerve fibre with several spray

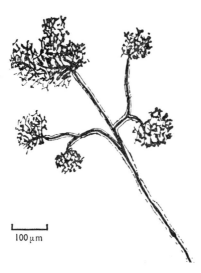

100 μm

FIG. 1.3. The Ruffini type ending found in joint capsules. A medium sized afferent fibre breaks up into several separate terminal ramifications. Drawing of ending stained with gold. (Skoglund, 1956, Fig. 9.)

endings attached to it. For the purposes of anatomical description it appears simplest to call each of the terminal spray arborisations a separate ending, but there appears to be no agreed usage on this matter. From the functional point of view the whole collection of sprays supplied by a single axon must comprise the sensory unit. Typically, a parent axon of 5–10 μm diameter divides once or twice and then each of the branches breaks up into a series of fine sprays. Each of the sets of sprays is enclosed by a delicate capsule which often fails to stain clearly. Sometimes the main afferent may be accompanied by a finer accessory nerve fibre which also runs into the capsule, though whether to supply intracapsular blood vessels or to mediate 'pain' is quite uncertain.

Joints also contain 'modified' small pacinian corpuscle type endings or 'lamellated endings' though these are appreciably less common than the Ruffini endings. The description usually given to them and their illustrated appearance are closely similar to that just given to the 'paciniform' corpuscle of muscle. This name will thus be used here for both such end-organs irrespective of whether they are located in joint capsules or in muscle. Freeman & Wyke (1967) describe the paciniform corpuscles of joints as being rather larger (280×120 μm) than those presently described for muscle (around 200×30 μm), but this is probably merely because they allocated more of the surrounding connective tissue to the sheath of the corpuscle than have other workers. The paciniform corpuscles of joints are seen to be supplied by medullated axons of some 7–12 μm diameter and which are on average slightly larger than those to the Ruffini endings. The free endings of joint capsules are supplied by small myelinated and by non-myelinated axons. A functionally important point is that the three kinds of specialised endings in joints are always found to be innervated independently of each other, though a single axon may supply several endings of one kind.

Muscle spindles

Finally we must turn to consideration at some length of the structure of the muscle spindles which are altogether more complicated than any of the other muscle and joint receptors. Indeed, in Ruffini's words of 1898 'apart from the organs of special sense (eye, ear, etc.) the body possesses no terminal organ that can compare with these in richness of nerve-fibres and nerve endings'. Their histological study has been pursued for over a hundred years and has been beset with controversy and false turnings up to the very present. It would be unwise to imagine that the last word has yet been said and it still seems possible as Tower presciently remarked in 1932 that their 'rich confusion of nerve fibres . . . has not yet been thoroughly analysed'.

Figure 1.4 shows a modern scale drawing of a fairly simple muscle spindle with only its afferent nerve endings, and partially illustrates the difficulties of histological study. Chief among these is the great length of the spindle, which may be over 10 mm. In addition, there is the large number of nerve fibres which supply it, of which there may be 10–20 overlapping in their distribution. Yet individual nerve fibres need to be followed throughout their

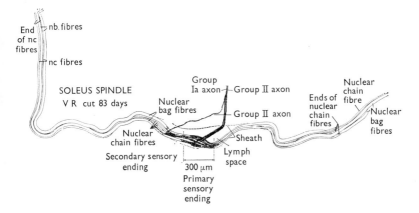

FIG. 1.4. Modern illustration of a cat muscle spindle drawn to scale to emphasise its great length. Only the afferent nerve endings are present. The numerous motor endings have degenerated following section of the ventral roots. (Boyd, 1962, Fig. 12.)

course to be sure of their place and mode of termination. This is a laborious and difficult task whether attempted on serial sections or on whole spindles isolated by teasing. The difficulty has been increased by the capriciousness of the classical methods of gold and silver staining used to demonstrate the nerve terminals. Indeed, it may even be doubted whether light microscopy can always settle whether a nerve fibre is making functional contact with an underlying intrafusal muscle fibre or is merely passing over it. Moreover, on using light microscopy the distinction between somatic motor, sensory and sympathetic fibres can only be made in the first place by coupling the histology with the appropriate degeneration experiments. Electron microscopy is currently providing an increasing contribution to the understanding of the structure of the intrafusal fibres and the nerve terminals. But the electron microscope may provide relatively little help in further unravelling the distribution of individual nerve fibres as the production of complete serial sections of a spindle would be a monumental undertaking.

Historical survey—the first 70 years

There have been four periods of relatively intense histological activity. The first was in the 1860's when the spindle was discovered. The second was in the 1890's when it was proved to be an afferent end-organ and two kinds of afferent ending were recognised within it. The third was in the late 1920's when the degeneration experiments were performed more adequately than before and so established the genuine existence of a motor supply; previously this had tended to be rather taken for granted. The fourth and most recent period began in 1956 with the recognition that there are two different kinds of intrafusal muscle fibre. It continues with the incompletely resolved controversy as to whether their motor nerves are shared in common, and if so how far. In addition, there is an increasing flow of electron-microscopic and histochemical contributions. It seems salutary to review some of the earlier work in outline as this provides a more balanced understanding than can be obtained from a simple description of the present position.

The essential feature of the muscle spindle is that it contains both nervous and muscular elements. The first descriptions of the muscle spindle as an entity which included both these components were given by Kölliker for the frog (1862 *a,b*) and by Kühne for the mammal (1863 *a,b*). The intrafusal bundle of slender muscle fibres had been noticed a few years earlier by Hassall (in 1851 according to Ruffini, 1898) and subsequently described in more detail by Weismann (1861). Immediately there was controversy about their nature. Following Weismann, Kölliker interpreted them as growth centres persisting in the adult; this was because of the small size of the intrafusal fibres and their rich content of nuclei. Consequently he called them 'muscle-buds' (*Muskelknospen*) and according to Sherrington he was continuing to propagate this view nearly 30 years later in the 1889 edition of his handbook of histology. Kühne was more guarded and simply called the new structures muscle spindles (*Muskelspindeln*) by virtue of their shape. This non-committal name has come to be generally used by English-writing authors in spite of the subsequent plea from Ruffini (1898) that the term 'neuromuscular spindle' was more appropriate; French writers, however, do prefer to call them *fuseaux neuromusculaire*.

From the time of their discovery until 1890 little more seems to have been learnt about spindles even though by then they had been studied by several workers. At that time three views prevailed about their function, that they were growth centres, that they were pathological foci of inflammation, and that they were sense endings under motor control. The last view was forcibly propounded on morphological grounds by Kerschner in 1888, but like the two others it lacked any experimental foundation. Cajal made the same suggestion at the same time (1888) for frog muscle spindles but his paper appears to have initially passed unnoticed so he republished the main findings 10 years later (1897) and again in his book (1909). In 1890, Onanoff in an unillustrated note of a single page described how section of the ventral spinal roots in the dog caused the atrophy of only a few of the nerve fibres of the muscle spindle, while destruction of the dorsal root ganglia caused nearly all of them to degenerate. On this direct evidence he suggested that the muscle spindle was a sense organ under motor control. But his contemporaries appear to have overlooked his work and there is no mention of it in the subsequent influential papers by Sherrington (1894) and by Ruffini (1898).

Shortly afterwards, Sherrington (1894) published a very full description for the cat and the monkey of the effects of intradural section of both the dorsal and the ventral spinal roots at the same time. This causes degeneration of the motor fibres while leaving the peripheral afferent fibres unaffected, because they remain connected to the dorsal root ganglion. By this means he demonstrated that the muscle spindle received one or more large myelinated afferent fibres whose diameter ranged from 7 to 18 μm. He concluded that 'the muscle-spindle proves therefore to be a sensorial organ'. He believed that 'the stimulus to which these organs are specially adapted is mechanical in quality' and that they possibly signalled stretch and/or contraction of the muscle. At about the same time, Ruffini (1893, 1897, 1898) made a detailed study of the appearance of the nerve terminals within the spindle using gold chloride impregnation and published fuller descriptions and better illustrations than any before. From the unique structure and mode of termination of the endings he independently concluded that the spindles were 'special nerve-organs entrusted with some peculiar sensorial function' (1893, Sherrington's 1894 translation), but he refused to speculate on their precise function for 'to do so would be to go beyond the field of anatomical analysis where prudence bids me remain' (1898). He also disputed whether Kerschner's preparations had been adequate for him to have been justified in reaching the same conclusion beforehand!

Thus after thirty years of uncertainty a few crucial observations established the mammalian muscle spindle as an afferent end-organ.

The establishment of the existence of a motor supply to the mammalian spindle, however, proceeded less satisfactorily. Kerschner (1888 *a,b*), stated that there was one, but had no firm evidence for the belief which rested only on his interpretation of structure. Onanoff (1890) was overlooked and had moreover given so brief a description of his work that its significance is still difficult to assess in view of the possibilities of artefact. Ruffini (1898) debated the matter at length but concluded on morphological grounds that none of the endings he described were motor, for even the endings he called plate endings showed definite differences from the ordinary motor end-plates on extrafusal fibres and he believed that Kerschner was mistaken in seeing similarities. Cipollone (1898) found that a short period of aortic compression in the rabbit led to a degeneration of the plate endings but not of the large afferent endings and felt that this demonstrated that the former were motor. Sherrington initially implied (1894) that there was no motor supply to the spindle. This was because 150 days after excising a portion of the sciatic nerve he could find no change in the intrafusal muscle fibres, whereas the extrafusal muscle fibres were grossly atrophied. Subsequently, however, intrafusal atrophy has been shown to occur (Tower, 1932; Boyd, 1962).

By 1900, however, Sherrington appears to have shifted his ground for in writing a textbook account he stated that of the numerous spindle nerve fibres 'some were probably motor' as also were Ruffini's plate endings. This view seems to have gained general acceptance, though with the exception of the neglected Onanoff the only really cogent evidence for a motor supply was in the lizard. In this species motor nerve fibres had been seen to branch, with one branch supplying an ordinary extrafusal end-plate and with another branch ending on an intrafusal muscle fibre (Cipollone, 1898; Perroncito, 1901). This, however, can hardly be taken to have settled the matter in the mammal but no further experiments to resolve the problem seem to have been attempted for a further thirty years. Then there was a rush of comprehensive degeneration work and in a couple of years the existence of a motor supply to the spindle was established beyond question, but it remained an open question whether this was private to the spindle, or whether it was shared with the ordinary extrafusal muscle fibres as in the lizard. Thus Boeke (1927) found plate endings degenerating on intrafusal muscle fibres shortly after sectioning both dorsal and ventral roots proximal (cord-wards) to the dorsal root ganglion in the cat. Hinsey (1927) and Hines & Tower (1928) showed that the plate endings persisted after removal of both the sympathetic and the dorsal root ganglia, but degenerated after ventral root section. Cuajunco (1932) confirmed the persistence of a motor supply after ablation of dorsal root ganglia. Thus the forty-year-old belief (Kerschner, 1888 *a,b*) that the mammalian spindle was a sense organ under motor control was finally vindicated and the text-book descriptions happily proved correct.

The classical picture of spindle structure

The more recent stages in the development of knowledge can best be appreciated on the basis of a description of the structure of the mammalian spindle as it was understood at the turn of the last century. This may be termed the 'classical picture' of spindle structure because it held sway from approximately 1900 to 1960 and formed the basis for most physiological thinking over this period. The classical picture shows the spindle as a sense ending under motor control and allows it two kinds of afferent ending but only a single kind of intrafusal fibre with a single type of motor fibre.

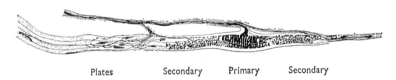

Plates   Secondary   Primary   Secondary

FIG. 1.5. The muscle spindle as seen by Ruffini and epitomising the classical view of its structure. As can be judged from Fig. 1.4 this drawing shows only the more central part of the spindle and is probably not precisely to scale. (Ruffini, 1898, Fig. 1, heavily retouched and slight amount of adventitious detail removed.)

It derives largely from the detailed descriptions given by Sherrington in 1894 of the general form of the spindle and by Ruffini in 1893–1898 of the nerve endings, but several other workers of that period contributed to it as fully described in Regaud & Favre's excellent annotated bibliography (1904). The classical picture was fortified half a century after its inception by Barker's (1948) detailed descriptions and illustrations which essentially agreed with what had gone before. In retrospect, it can be seen that he was unfortunate to have chosen to work mainly on the rabbit for the spindles of this species have proved to be slightly different in appearance from those of most other mammals, thus possibly leading to an unnecessary prolongation of the life of the classical picture. Fortunately, the deficiencies of the classical picture have proved to be errors of omission and undue simplification rather than straight errors of description or interpretation. Thus the classical picture still provides a useful starting point for present thought, and little past physiological work has been vitiated by reliance upon it.

The classical picture of the spindle is epitomised by Ruffini's well known drawing which is reproduced in Fig. 1.5. The whole structure is several millimetres long and contains from 2 to 12 intrafusal muscle fibres whose diameters may vary from 6 to 28 μm. The distribution of the actual numbers of intrafusal fibres per spindle for all the spindles of a single medial gastrocnemius muscle of the cat is shown in Fig. 6. This emphasises that there are marked

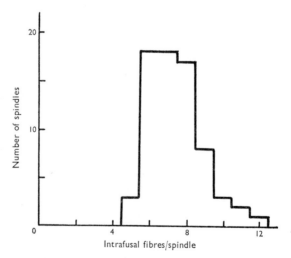

FIG. 1.6. The number of intrafusal fibres per muscle spindle found in the 70 spindles of a particular medial gastrocnemius muscle of the cat. (Swett & Eldred, 1960*b*, Fig. 1, redrawn.)

differences in this respect between different spindles, which may perhaps be related to differences in function. Along the central third or so of the spindle the intrafusal fibres are surrounded by fluid contained in a connective tissue capsule. Elsewhere the intrafusal muscle fibres lie immediately alongside the extrafusal fibres until at their very ends the intrafusal fibres are directly attached to the extrafusal fibres or to tendinous slips. More recent work has shown that both the capsule and the intrafusal fibres are given resilience by having elastic fibres running along much, but not all, of their length (Cooper & Daniel, 1967). The capsule with its contained fluid makes the central or equatorial region of the spindle rather thicker than its poles and so gives the spindle the fusiform shape upon which Kühne (1863) christened it. The intrafusal bundle, however, varies relatively little in diameter throughout its course, and is only about 30 μm in diameter; the capsule may be 80–200 μm across at its widest point. Sherrington believed that the capsular fluid was lymph, because as he said 'I have succeeded in injecting it by injecting the lymphatics of the leg' (1894). On this view, it is hard to see why the capsular fluid is not squeezed out when the muscle contracts. More recently, Brzezinski (1961) has found that unlike lymph the fluid contains a large amount of hyaluronic acid, and so suggested that it was 'probably formed by the spindle sheath' and was not in communication with the lymphatics. The intrafusal muscle fibres are well striated at their ends, but in their most central 400 μm or so they contain a conglomeration of nuclei and under the light microscope their striations are poorly seen if at all. The nuclei, however, never show mitotic figures and so there is no suggestion that the intrafusal fibres are still engaged in growing, whether longitudinally or by subdividing themselves transversely.

Ruffini (1893, 1897, 1898) described three morphologically distinct kinds of nerve ending terminating within the spindle and surmised that they were functionally distinct entities; time has proved him correct. He named them the primary ending, the secondary ending and the plate ending. These names are still applicable and are to be preferred to the various alternatives which have been used from time to time. The primary ending, which Ruffini also called the annulo-spiral ending, is formed by the branched terminals of a single large medullated afferent fibre. It lies in the centre of the spindle and consists of spirals and rings wrapped round each one of the individual intrafusal muscle fibres thereby forming an ending which is quite unlike any other in the body. The 'regularity and elegance' of its structure may be seen in the photomicrograph of plate I.4. There is never more than one primary ending inside an individual spindle capsule. The secondary ending lies to one or other side of the centre of the spindle, usually contiguous with the primary ending, and is not always present. Ruffini gave it the alternative names of 'flower-wreath', 'flower-spray' or 'flowered' ending (1897, 1898). It is supplied by a medium sized medullated afferent fibre and consists of varicose filaments of diverse form running along the intrafusal fibres and sometimes around them. As more recent work has emphasised there is, however, no absolute division between the form of the individual terminal filaments of primary and secondary endings for both may show spirals and both may show sprays (Barker, 1948; Cooper & Daniel, 1963). Ruffini appears to have chosen to emphasise the extreme forms which are well shown in the cat. The plate ending is a discrete ending, much smaller than the other two, and not unlike an ordinary motor end-plate on extrafusal muscle fibres though the spindle plate ending is often two or three times the larger. There are always several of them in any muscle spindle, lying on both sides of the equator, and they are supplied by smaller nerve fibres than those to either the primary or the secondary endings. Unlike the other endings they often lie at the poles of the spindle, sometimes inside and sometimes outside the capsule. Ruffini also described, but did not name, 'one or two extremely minute myelinate fibres' ending inside the spindle.

Ruffini emphasised that different muscle spindles differed greatly in their complexity even though they came from the same muscle. He divided spindles into those with simple, those with intermediate, and those with complex nerve endings. Simple spindles have a single primary ending and several plate endings, but no secondary endings. Intermediate spindles have one secondary ending, and complex spindles more than one secondary ending, in addition to their normal complement of a single primary ending and several plate endings. The primary ending always occupies the central 300 μm of the length of the spindle. Each of any secondary endings occupies a length of about 400 μm and does not overlap with the primary ending or any other secondary ending in its distribution. Moreover, a secondary ending is only found in an outlying region of the spindle when the more central regions in the same half of the spindle are also occupied. These further details were described much more recently by Boyd (1962) who has used them as the basis of a rapid and convenient way of classifying the endings in any particular spindle. The successive 400 μm lengths of intrafusal fibre lying on each side of the primary ending are called the S_1, S_2 and S_3 regions and any secondary endings lying on them the S_1, S_2 or S_3 endings respectively. Thus, for example, a complex spindle with four secondary endings may be rapidly and more fully described by calling it an $S_2PS_1S_2S_3$ spindle.

Ruffini (1898) concluded on morphological grounds that all three of the endings he described were afferent, but as already noted his contemporaries soon decided that the plate endings were really motor, as was subsequently proved by degeneration experiments. Ruffini's primary ending was immediately established as an afferent ending by the prior degeneration experiments of Sherrington (1894) which had shown that de-efferented spindles retained afferent fibres which were up to 18 μm diameter and which supplied the spindle equator. These could only have terminated in the primary ending as Sherrington himself concluded on the basis of Ruffini's preliminary reports. In addition, Sherrington's (1894) experiments made it virtually certain that Ruffini's secondary endings were afferent also, for the spindle was shown to receive several afferent fibres ranging in diameter from 7 μm upwards and only one of these could have supplied the single primary ending of the spindle. Much later, the afferent origin of the primary ending was re-affirmed by degeneration experiments combined with staining of the nerve terminals by gold or methylene blue, rather than simply with staining of the afferent fibres with osmium as Sherrington appears to have done. The primary ending was then seen to degenerate after removal of the dorsal root ganglia but to survive ventral root section (Hinsey, 1927; Hines & Tower, 1928; Cuajunco, 1932). The secondary ending, however, received rather little attention in these various experiments and only Hinsey specifically stated that it persisted after ventral root section but degenerated after dorsal root section. Hines & Tower talked only of 'the equatorial ending', and appear to have regarded any 'flower-spray' terminals they saw as part of the primary ending.

This slight lack of clarity in the degeneration experiments produced an echo many years later when Cöers & Durand (1956) felt able to challenge the conventional view and suggest that most, if not all, of the sprays of secondary endings were motor rather than sensory. This was because the juxta-equatorial region of the spindle where the secondary endings lie is stained when treated histochemically for cholinesterase. Subsequently, however, irrefutable degeneration experiments (Boyd, 1962; Barker, Ip & Adal, 1962; Barker, 1967, Fig. 5) have closed the matter and shown that the classical belief was correct, namely that there are indeed two morphologically distinct kinds of afferent ending corresponding to Ruffini's primary and secondary endings. At the same time it has become clear that the motor innervation of the spindle is appreciably more complex than that given in the classical picture, and all fine 'spray-like' terminals are not necessarily sensory.

The present picture of spindle structure

The recognition of morphologically distinct intrafusal muscle fibres

Different intrafusal muscle fibres within a single spindle have long been known to differ considerably in diameter, and this is well shown in the illustrations of Sherrington's paper of 1894 (Figs. 14–17). Until quite recently, however, no particular attention appears to have been paid to these differences, and in his classical paper on the development of the spindle Cuajunco (1927) suggested that even in the adult different sizes of intrafusal fibre should be 'looked upon as different stages in the development of the muscle-fibres'. In 1956, in preliminary communications mainly devoted to other matters, Boyd working on the cat and Cooper & Daniel working on human material independently described differences between intrafusal fibres which suggested that they might fall into two morphologically distinct classes. By the time they had published full papers establishing their initial suggestions (Boyd, 1962; Cooper & Daniel, 1963) their main observations had already been confirmed by others (Barker & Gidumal, 1961; Swett & Eldred, 1960b; Walker, 1958).

All subsequent workers appear to have accepted that intrafusal fibres fall more or less clearly into two separate natural groups. The two kinds of intrafusal fibres were named *nuclear bag fibres* and *nuclear chain fibres* by Boyd in 1960 on the basis of the arrangement of nuclei in their central regions, which had been first described by Cooper & Daniel (1956). These names have subsequently been generally adopted. The scale drawings of Figs. 1.7 and 1.8 show

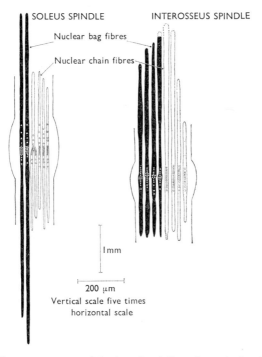

FIG. 1.7. The arrangement of the intrafusal fibres in typical spindles from two different cat muscles. The drawings are to scale and are based on serial tranverse sections like those in Fig. 1.8. The nuclear bag and nuclear chain regions are indicated diagrammatically. Bag fibres, black; chain fibres, stippled. The outermost line shows the position of the spindle capsule. The interosseus spindle was from adductor digiti longus V. (Boyd, 1962, Fig. 2, redrawn.)

the general arrangement of the nuclear bag fibres (black) and the nuclear chain fibres (stippled) in two individual spindles from two different muscles of the cat. The most comprehensive description of the morphological differences between the bag and chain fibres is still to be found in Boyd's long paper of 1962 which probably did the most to establish the two kinds of fibre as separate entities. The distinguishing features of the nuclear bag and the

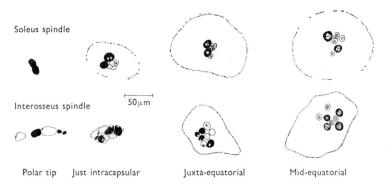

FIG. 1.8. Transverse sections at various levels of the two spindles of Fig. 1.7. Bag fibres, black; chain fibres, stippled. (Redrawn from Boyd, 1962, Figs. 1, 2 and 4.)

nuclear chain fibres are best discussed under several separate headings. This is especially so as in some muscles the two kinds of intrafusal fibre can be differentiated by features which in other muscles are useless for discriminating between them, as may be seen in Figs. 1.7 and 1.8. Indeed, it seems likely that fundamental difference between the two kinds of intrafusal fibre is primarily a functional rather than a structural one and resides in as yet incompletely explored differences in their contractile properties. These may regularly express themselves ultrastructurally, but the relatively gross morphological differences which have attracted most attention hitherto may well be to some extent accidental features. This would explain why the latter may show appreciable variation with spindles from different sources in spite of the apparent existence of a consistent duality of intrafusal function.

Distinguishing features of bag and chain fibres

(a) *Nuclear arrangement.* This is the feature by which each kind of intrafusal fibre was originally characterised, though the difference between them in this respect is found for only a short part of their length, namely at the equator of the spindle, as shown in Fig. 1.7. The poles of either kind of intrafusal fibre contain a number of scattered nuclei, mostly at their periphery as in ordinary striated muscle. As the intrafusal fibres enter the capsule additional nuclei are found, and these are mostly placed centrally as occurs in cardiac muscle and in the 'myotubes' of developing skeletal muscle. The nuclei reach their highest density at the very middle of the encapsulated region of the spindle where some fibres are crammed so full of nuclei that any cross-section of the fibre cuts across several of them, all packed so closely together that little else can be seen of the fibre. Barker (1948) introduced the term 'nuclear bag' for this region of an intrafusal fibre, and any fibre which shows this feature is by definition a nuclear bag fibre. In spite of the name, the concatenation of nuclei is not enclosed in any special 'bag' other than the sarcolemma of the intrafusal fibre itself, and there is no appreciable swelling of the fibre in this region. Other intrafusal fibres, which are usually thinner, have a more modest concentration of nuclei at the spindle equator and these lie in a continuous single file to form a 'chain' rather than a 'bag', so that it is rare to see more than a single nucleus in any cross-section of a fibre. Such fibres are called nuclear chain fibres. Boyd (1962) contended that in the muscles he studied every intrafusal fibre which was traced for an adequate distance could be readily categorised as either a bag or a chain fibre solely on this criterion of nuclear arrangement, and other histologists appear to have fallen in with this proposition. Thus, by implication, if the density of nuclei in a fibre could be assessed in some suitable quantitative manner the distribution of nuclear densities of a population of intrafusal fibres should consist of two well separated peaks, one for each kind of fibre, and there should be no inter-mediate fibres; it would be valuable to have this demonstrated experimentally.

The central most densely nucleated region of either kind of fibre is only about 300 μm long and corresponds approximately to the region occupied by the primary ending. Immediately adjacent to this region the nuclei in the bag fibre are arranged as a central core in the fibre, sometimes only one nucleus wide, and with an appreciable surround of cytoplasm and myofilaments. This is sometimes called the 'myotube' region (Barker, 1948) and appears to be somewhat longer in the rabbit than in the cat; there is no sharp demarcation between the myotube and the bag regions of a fibre. The diameters of all the individual intrafusal fibres stay approximately constant throughout their course so the local excess of nuclei at the spindle equator can only be accommodated at the expense of normal cytoplasmic constituents, most notably the myofilaments. Consequently, the equatorial regions of both

BM

kinds of fibre appear poorly striated when seen in the light microscope, though with care a thin rim of myofilaments may be detected (Cooper & Daniel, 1963). The equatorially persisting myofilaments can be better demonstrated by electron microscopy (Landon, 1966, Adal, 1969; Corvaja, Marinozzi & Pompeiano, 1969). This has also shown that these residual myofilaments are more prominent in the chain than in the bag fibres, and that in the latter may be split up into separate strands rather than forming a complete annulus surrounding the nuclei. This is illustrated in Fig. 1.9.

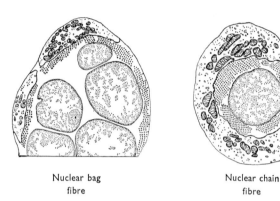

Nuclear bag
fibre

Nuclear chain
fibre

FIG. 1.9. The arrangement of nuclei and of myofibrils seen in electron-micrographs of transverse sections of the equatorial region of the two kinds of intrafusal fibre. The nuclei are surrounded by a layer of myo-fibrils, which are relatively more numerous in the chain fibre. Outside this is a sensory ending containing prominent mitochondria. The chain fibre is shown at about twice the scale of the bag fibre; both are from the cat tenuissimus. (Drawing based on Fig. 2. Adal, 1969.)

(b) *Diameter of fibres.* In many muscles the nuclear bag intra-fusal fibres are appreciably thicker than the nuclear chain fibres and this is true throughout the whole of their length. For example, in the soleus of the cat the average diameter of the bag fibres is about 30 μm and that of the chain fibres is 14 μm, and there is no overlap in the diameters of the two kinds of fibres. This is illustra-ted in the top histogram of Fig. 1.10 which is based on measure-ments of the fibres taken near the end of the lymph space and as seen in transverse sections, which probably have about 20%

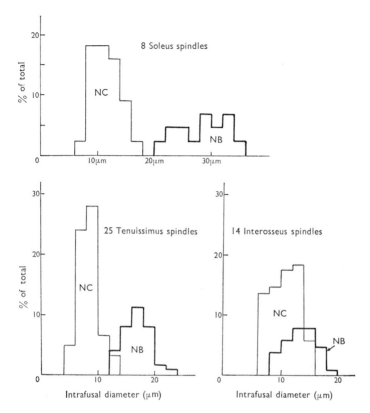

FIG. 1.10. The distribution of the diameters of the two kinds of intrafusal fibre in the spindles of three different muscles of the cat. The measurements were made on transverse sections from close to the end of the lymph space. NC = nuclear chain fibres; NB = nuclear bag fibres. (Boyd, 1962, Fig. 7, redrawn.)

shrinkage from the living value (Boyd, 1962). In the tenuissimus muscle the mean diameters of the two kinds of fibre lie closer together (21 μm and 11 μm for bag and chain fibres respectively in life, 16·9 and 8·9 μm in Fig. 1.9), though they still form two distinct populations. In the Vth interosseus the diameters of the two kinds of fibre overlap almost completely, and the means differ only very slightly (22 μm and 18 μm for bag and chain fibres respectively in life, and 13·9 μm and 10·7 μm in Fig. 1.9). Histograms published by other workers of the diameters of all the intrafusal fibres lumped together in the cat soleus, gastrocnemius and rectus femoris muscles have shown a bimodality but not an absolute separation into two kinds of fibre with different diameter (Barker & Gidumal, 1961; Swett & Eldred, 1960b; Eldred, Bridgman, Swett & Eldred, 1962). Other workers who have looked at individual spindles without systematic measurement have usually noted distinct large and small intrafusal fibres, usually with the appropriate equatorial nuclear arrangement (Adal, 1969, cat; Landon, 1966, rat; Cooper & Daniel, 1963, man; Jones, 1966, opossum; Porayko & Smith, 1968, rat; Corvaja, Marinozzi & Pompeiano, 1967, 1969, cat). It may be concluded that when the intrafusal fibres in an individual spindle can be separated into large and small fibres then these may be taken to correspond to the nuclear bag and nuclear chain fibres respectively; but the absence of such a segregation of diameter cannot be taken to show that all the fibres are of the same kind. In other words, measurement of intrafusal diameter alone does not regularly provide a basis for the classification of intrafusal fibres, as may be seen in Figs. 1.7, 1.8 and 1.10.

(c) *Length of Fibres*. The nuclear bag fibres are usually rather longer than the nuclear chain fibres. In the cat soleus the mean length of the bag fibres is 7 mm (range 4–13 mm) and of the chain fibres 4 mm (range 2·5–5·5 mm, Boyd, 1962). In a single human first lumbrical muscle spindle the bag fibres were 5 mm long and the chain fibres 3·5 mm (Cooper & Daniel, 1963), and in the rat lumbrical the mean values are 1·5 and 1·2 mm respectively (Porayko & Smith, 1968). However, the cat interosseus spindles are again anomalous and the two kinds of fibre are about the same length as well as diameter (mean value 5 mm, range 2–8 mm, Boyd, 1962, see present Fig. 1.8). The nuclear bag fibres always extend an appreciable distance beyond the spindle capsule (i.e. 1–2 mm at either end of a large cat spindle). The nuclear chain fibres may end with the capsule, but usually also project somewhat beyond it (see illustrations in Boyd, 1962, and Barker & Gidumal, 1961; also statements by Cooper & Daniel, 1963, and Porayko & Smith, 1968).

(d) *Response to de-efferentation*. Boyd (1962) studied three cats 2–3 months after ventral root section and found definite differences between the degree of atrophy of the two kinds of intrafusal fibre. He concluded that on average the nuclear chain fibres had shrunk to about 65% of their normal diameter, whereas the nuclear bag fibres remained at 90% of their normal size; the extrafusal muscle fibres in the same muscles had atrophied to about half their original size. Thus the normal difference in diameter between the bag and the chain fibres was accentuated after de-efferentation, and became prominent even in spindles from the interosseus muscle in which it was normally almost absent; this provided further evidence that the bag and chain fibres were functionally distinct. In addition, these experiments showed that in their trophic dependence upon a motor innervation the chain fibres more closely resembled the extrafusal fibres than did the bag fibres. It would, however, be valuable to have these conclusions confirmed in a wider series of experiments using a wider range of degeneration times, especially as in one of the illustrated examples both kinds of intrafusal fibre appear to have atrophied to a nearly similar degree (Boyd, 1962, Fig. 7, chains 65%, bags 69% of normal after de-efferentation.). Very much earlier, Sherrington (1894) failed to observe any changes 5 months after nerve section, probably because he devoted his main attention to the capsule which may even hypertrophy slightly. However, later Tower (1932) in detailed experiments on forelimb interosseus spindles found marked intrafusal atrophy, especially at the spindle poles, 4–12 months after simple de-efferentation by ventral root section. Interestingly, Tower (1932) further showed that de-afferentation also produces characteristic changes in the intrafusal fibres. Dorsal root ablation leads to a gradual disappearance of the normal concentration of nuclei in the equatorial regions of the intrafusal fibres with the simultaneous appearance of more myofilaments, as judged by the more ready visibility of cross-striations. Boyd (1962) noted additionally that after de-afferentation the diameters of the two kinds of intrafusal fibre tend to become more alike.

(e) *Myofibrillar arrangement, particularly as seen with the electron microscope.* Extrafusal muscle fibres have long been subdivided into those with uniformly arranged myofibrils of constant size and with little sarcoplasm (*Fibrillenstruktur*), and those with larger myofibrils of varying size scattered somewhat irregularly in a relatively larger amount of sarcoplasm (*Felderstruktur*). Such differences were first recognised on the basis of light microscopy but are now better demonstrated with the electron microscope. In the particular case of the frog, the fast or twitch fibres have been conclusively shown to have a *Fibrillenstruktur* while the slow or tonic fibres have a *Felderstruktur* (Peachey & Huxley, 1962), thus encouraging speculations about function on the basis of the arrangement of myofibrils in every other species. Boyd (1962) found that the bag and chain intrafusal fibres differed in their appearance in cross-section, as observed with the light microscope, and that the bag fibres were 'filled with numerous myofibrils of uniform size, uniformly distributed throughout the sarcoplasm', whereas the chain fibres contained relatively fewer myofibrils and these were less regularly arranged in a relatively larger amount of sarcoplasm. Thus the bag fibres showed something akin to *Fibrillenstruktur* and the chain fibres something like *Felderstruktur*. Barker & Gidumal (1961), on the other hand, thought that an individual intrafusal fibre could show different types of myofibrillar arrangement at different places along its length and that there was no systematic difference between bag and chain fibres in this respect and that both were predominantly fibrillar.

However, on the basis of more recent electron microscopic studies there now seems to be agreement that myofibrils in the bag fibres are indeed more regularly ordered than those in the chain fibres, while the chain fibres contain appreciably more sarcoplasm, as represented by mitochondria (Adal, 1969; Corvaja, Marinozzi & Pompeiano, 1969; Landon, 1966). On this criterion alone the bag fibres would appear more like the frog twitch fibres and the chain fibres the more like the frog slow fibres. On the other hand, the chain fibres possess a well marked M line like that seen in the frog twitch fibres, while the bag fibres completely lack an M line as do the frog slow fibres (Adal, 1969, Corvaja *et al.*, 1969, Landon, 1966). The M line, it will be remembered, is a dark line in the middle of the clearer H zone which lies at the centre of the sarcomere. In addition, the H zone is somewhat better marked in the chain fibres than in the bag fibres. These differences between bag and chain fibres were seen throughout their length. In another respect both kinds of intrafusal fibre resemble the frog slow fibres rather than the twitch fibres, for Adal (1969) found that 'transverse tubules and triads were rarely seen in either type' of intrafusal fibre; these are prominent in the frog twitch fibres but not in the slow fibres. Corvaja *et al.* (1969) largely concur with this finding for though they regularly saw triads in both kinds of intrafusal fibre they found them to be appreciably the more numerous in the chain fibres.

On all this the chain fibres may reasonably be suggested to be 'faster' than the bag fibres. But it is probably a fruitless exercise to attempt simply to equate the two kinds of mammalian intrafusal fibre with the two kinds of frog extrafusal fibre, and to hope thereby to decide upon the mode of contraction of the intrafusal fibres and whether contraction is 'fast' or 'slow', and whether it is initiated by local or by propagated potentials. Mammalian intrafusal fibres may well differ in the details of their working from both kinds of frog fibre, and the determination of their precise mode of action has now become a matter for experiment rather than for deduction from structure. This is not to decry the value of histological and particularly ultrastructural observation, but is a plea that functional deductions should be made with suitable caution and only after comparisons have been made with the extrafusal fibres of a range of species and not just those of the frog. A further structural observation of interest is that the nuclear bag fibres tend to have longer sarcomeres than do the nuclear chain fibres (Sybil Cooper, 1970, personal communication); in the crayfish greater sarcomere length is associated with slower contraction, as judged by the rate of development of tension under isometric conditions (Jahromi & Atwood, 1969).

(f) *Histochemical reactions.* As just noted electron-microscopic observation shows that the nuclear chain fibres contain a higher density of mitochondria than do the nuclear bag fibres. The chain fibres might therefore be expected to stain the more readily on using histochemical methods based upon mitchondrial activity, and this has proved to be so in the particular cases of staining for 'mitochondrial ATP'ase' and for succinic dehydrogenase (Henneman & Olson, 1965; Barker, Stacey & Adal, 1970). Myofibrillar ATP'ase is also more active in the chain than in the bag fibres (Spiro & Beilin, 1969a; Nyström, 1967). The nuclear bag fibres, however, contain more myoglobin than do the nuclear chain fibres (James, 1968). The preceding workers appeared content to accept that intrafusal fibres fell into two main classes, but Yellin

(1969) who stained for both phosphorylase and succinic dehydro-genase divided intrafusal fibres into four types and suggested that 'perhaps even other fiber types are observable'. Most of these workers have compared the staining of the intrafusal fibres with that of extrafusal fibres and have usually felt it to be incumbent upon themselves to attempt to deduce whether the intrafusal are 'fast' or 'slow', often with contradictory conclusions. This need occasion no surprise in view of the inadequacy of the evidence in relation to the complexity of the situation.

Cholinesterase staining was first applied by Cöers & Durand (1956; Cöers, 1962) and beautifully demonstrates the location of the motor terminals, all of which may be presumed to be cholin-ergic. They found that the whole of the spindle is stained except for the capsule and for the equatorial portion of the intrafusal fibres where the primary ending lies. Since then, the technique has been applied several times for the more detailed demonstration of the motor terminals (see for example Barker, Stacey & Adal, 1970).

(g) *Suspected branching.* Whether or not an intrafusal fibre may ever branch has been debated sporadically ever since the intra-fusal bundle was seen by Weismann in 1861 and thought to be a growth centre. More recently, Boyd (1962) and Barker & Gidumal (1961) managed for once to agree in concluding that branching of nuclear bag fibres was so rare as to be negligible but that nuclear chain fibres sometimes did so. This thus appeared to be a minor point of difference between the two kinds of fibre. Electron-microscopic studies have now put a new complexion on the matter by showing that two previously separate nuclear chain fibres may sometimes come into such close apposition along part of their length that under the light microscope they must inevitably appear to have fused, even though the electron microscope clearly shows that each fibre retains a separate plasma membrane (Adal, 1969; Corvaja, Marinozzi & Pompeiano, 1967, 1969). The paired fibres may come to within 200 Å of each other and without any basement membrane intervening. Certain specialised regions of contact have been seen between the paired fibres, but according to Corvaja *et al.* (1967) these regions are quite distinct from the 'tight' junctions across which impulse activity may be transmitted electrically, and they interpreted them simply as 'specialised sites of firmer attachment between the opposing membranes'. At any rate, whatever the precise nature of the junctions, the closeness of such paired nuclear chain fibres must mean that they are unable to change their length independently. In contrast, nuclear bag fibres have not as yet been seen to pair with each other or with the nuclear bag fibres and so can be presumed to be able to act more independently. This fits in with direct observations of the behaviour of living spindles.

(h) *Arrangement of sensory terminals upon the intrafusal fibres.* The large afferent fibre which subdivides to form the primary ending sends a branch to terminate upon every intrafusal fibre running through the centre of the spindle, irrespective of whether it is a bag or a chain fibre. Moreover, the structure of the primary terminals lying on each kind of intrafusal fibre appears to be the same. In the light microscope the terminations are seen to consist predominantly of spirals and incomplete rings with few sprays (Boyd, 1962; Cooper & Daniel, 1963). Because of the size of the underlying intrafusal fibre the diameter of the spirals on the bag fibres is inevitably greater than of those on the chain fibres, but the pitch of the spirals on the two kinds of fibre does not appear to differ, at any rate judging from Boyd's (1962) photomicrographs.

In contrast, the secondary afferent ending is very differently disposed with regard to the two kinds of intrafusal fibre for it always lies predominantly, and sometimes lies exclusively, upon the nuclear chain fibres (Boyd, 1962; Cooper & Daniel, 1963; Barker, 1967). The secondary terminals on the chain fibres often have a spiral arrangement, but those few on the bag fibre usually consist of sprays. Fig. 1.11 illustrates this uncontroversial finding on the differential distribution of the secondary ending on the two kinds of intrafusal fibre. It provides cogent evidence, quite independent of the structural differences between the intrafusal fibres themselves, that the subdivision into nuclear bag and nuclear chain fibres is real and likely to be functionally meaningful from the point of view of central neurophysiology. The arrangement of motor terminals upon the two kinds of intrafusal fibre is probably also different, but the present position is still too controversial for it to be possible to obtain any worthwhile evidence from this line of argument either for or against the validity of the simple bifid classification of intrafusal fibres.

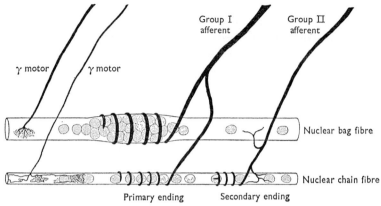

Group I
afferent

Group II
afferent

γ motor   γ motor

Nuclear bag fibre

Nuclear chain fibre

Primary ending   Secondary ending

FIG. 1.11. Simplified diagram of the central region of the muscle spindle to show the relation of the two kinds of afferent ending to the two kinds of intrafusal fibre. (Matthews, 1964, Fig. 1.)

Universality of classification

With one exception it has so far proved possible to subdivide the intrafusal muscle fibres of a wide variety of mammals into nuclear bag and nuclear chain types on the basis of relatively gross morphological features. The distinction was originally made in the phylogenetically distant species of *Felix domesticus* and *Homo sapiens*. The two kinds of fibre have since been recognised in the rat (Landon, 1966; Porayko & Smith, 1968), the sheep somatic and extraocular muscles (Barker, 1968), the hedgehog, the tree shrew, the armadillo (Barker & Hunt, 1964) and the marsupial opossum (Jones, 1966). The relative numbers of the two kinds of intrafusal fibre differ both for the same muscle in different species and for different muscles in the same species. In the muscles of the cat and man the chain fibres typically outnumber the bag fibres by about two to one, but the absolute numbers of each vary in different spindles and there may be between 1 and 4 bag fibres and up to 10 chain fibres per spindle. Spindles in the rat lumbrical muscle usually contain two fibres of each kind (Porayko & Smith, 1968).

For the last half of the 1960's the rabbit spindle was thought to provide an exception to the general rule, for when Barker & Hunt (1964) examined it with the light microscope they could usually find only a single kind of intrafusal fibre. More recently the usual duality of intrafusal fibres has been amply demonstrated by histochemical and ultrastructural techniques and so no exception remains. However, it still seems worth reviewing the initial failure to recognise two kinds of intrafusal fibre for it led to much unnecessary confusion and so helped to distort physiological thought from 1964 to 1970. Barker & Hunt (1964) traced individual intrafusal fibres from end to end in serial sections of fourteen spindles from hindlimb muscles and found that every fibre possessed a 'nuclear bag' in the equatorial region; the same was found for 3 hindlimb spindles from the hare. However, of six forelimb rabbit spindles three contained only nuclear bag fibres but three contained additionally one or two nuclear chain fibres, identified apparently on their nuclear arrangement. Barker & Hunt (1964) thus suggested that the nuclear bag fibres were the 'basic component of the mammalian spindle' while the nuclear chain fibres appeared to be something of an optional extra.

The question immediately arose as to whether the apparent structural deficit of the majority of rabbit spindles was matched by any corresponding functional deficit. At the time no physiological data were available to attempt to answer this question but the new histological findings stimulated Laporte and his colleagues to fill the gap, and show that in several essential respects rabbit spindles could match the cat spindle in the range of effects produced by fusimotor stimulation. In particular, they succeeded in isolating two functionally distinct kinds of fusimotor fibre in the rabbit corresponding to the static and the dynamic fusimotor fibres previously distinguished in the cat (Chap. 5). For the subsequent few years the supposed existence of only a single kind of intrafusal fibre in the rabbit became a stumbling block militating against the acceptance of the idea that the static and dynamic fusimotor fibres achieved their separate actions by each exciting a different kind of intrafusal fibre. The difficulty was always more apparent than real for the objection rested insecurely on the premise that the functional and contractile differences between the bag and chain fibres were inviolably linked to particular forms of nuclear arrangement; and one, moreover, which occurred only in a short region of the spindle (cf. Fig. 1.7). As the role of the nuclei is quite obscure it has long seemed equally possible that their precise arrangement is no more than an epiphenomenon which bears no regular relation to the contractile

properties of different intrafusal fibres. This view suddenly
gained widespread acceptance with the demonstration that in the
rabbit as in other mammals the intrafusal fibres fell into two groups
when examined with the appropriate histochemical or ultrastructural technique. Spiro & Beilin (1969b) stained rabbit spindles
for 'myofibrillary adenosine triphosphatase' and found that
virtually every spindle contained 'two distinctly different histochemical types' of intrafusal fibre even though all the fibres
possessed nuclear bags; they thus suggested that 'differences in
the contractile elements exist in spindle fibres which appear
morphologically similar'. At about the same time Düring &
Andres (1969) and Corvaja & Pompeiano (1970) found that different rabbit intrafusal fibres differ in the prominence of their M
bands and in other ultrastructural details in the same way as do
the bag and chain fibres in the other species. Barker & Stacey
(1970) then re-examined the rabbit and agreed that the earlier
view had been too simple, but now felt that three kinds of intrafusal fibre were distinguishable by a combination of histochemical
and ultrastructural studies!

At any rate, there is no longer any obstacle to concluding that
muscle spindles throughout the *Mammalia* contain two distinct
types of intrafusal fibre, which may be differentiated by appropriate
morphological and histochemical techniques, and which may
reasonably be presumed to be functionally distinct. In spite of the
smallness of the sample of species studied the generality of the
conclusion is favoured by the wide and approximately random
distribution of the sample over the mammalian kindgom. It
would, however, be of value to have detailed studies made of the
spindles from yet further types of animal.

It naturally remains an open question as to whether further
physiologically meaningful subdivisions of intrafusal fibre have
yet to be recognised. In the cat, Barker & Gidumal (1961) described a rare type of fibre which was intermediate between the
bag and chain fibres in its gross morphological features. In the
rabbit, as just noted, three kinds of intrafusal have now been
suggested to exist. Yellin (1969), as also previously mentioned, felt
that in the rat several kinds of intrafusal fibre could be distinguished
by an appropriate battery of histochemical tests. For the time
being, however, it seems enough to settle for a simple dual classification and to put the onus of establishing the consistency and

functional significance of any new classification upon its proposer. In particular, any fresh subdivision should desirably be based upon a bimodal distribution of some measurable intrafusal property. Otherwise any newly observed intrafusal difference may merely reflect normal biological variability in a structural feature which is unrelated to major function.

The motor innervation

On the classical picture, the motor innervation of the spindle was considered to consist solely of plate type endings lying predominantly towards the spindle poles. Further, following the physiological demonstration that in the cat the γ efferent fibres are exclusively devoted to supplying muscle spindles it tended to be assumed that all the plate endings were derived from branches of γ fibres. This simple view has now been destroyed, but agreement has still to be reached over the details of the more complicated arrangements which certainly prevail.

Recognition of trail endings. One new feature on which there is general agreement is that the intrafusal motor endings within the spindle cannot all be properly described as 'plate endings', looking something like the motor end-plates on extrafusal muscle fibres. There are also more diffuse motor terminations, somewhat resembling the '*en grappe*' endings seen in many lower animals, for example perhaps most familiarly on the slow muscle fibres of the frog. These endings were initially shown up as motor in the cholinesterase preparations of Cöers & Durand (1956) which demonstrated that the motor innervation of the spindle occupied a far greater part of its length than the polar regions classically supposed to contain the plate endings. In their preparations the whole of the spindle stained for cholinesterase except for the central 300 μm where the primary ending lies. Shortly afterwards Hess (1961), also using cholinesterase staining, confirmed that there were two types of motor endings, one relatively near the poles consisting of 'discrete motor endplates', and the other adjacent to the equatorial region consisting of 'diffuse multi-terminal endings'. The existence of a diffuse motor ending was soon more firmly established by degeneration experiments, particularly by Boyd (1962; also Barker, 1967).

Boyd (1962) called the diffuse ending the 'γ_2 network'. Perhaps he used the term 'network' because he was unable to trace its details in the gold impregnated preparations which he studied. At any rate this name carried with it unfortunate overtones of a neural network in which the separate fibres of origin come into functional if not cytoplasmic continuity. Barker & Ip (1965), using a newly developed method of silver impregnation, which gave better resolution of detail than before, could find no sign of a true network and introduced the term 'trail ending' for what may be presumed to be the same terminations. After some public discussion (Granit, 1966, p. 119) Boyd concurred in the change of terminology. The name 'trail ending' may therefore now be considered as the accepted term for any spindle motor ending which cannot be classed as a plate ending, though perhaps this need not exclude the parallel use of such phrases as 'diffuse ending' (Cooper & Daniel, 1963) and 'diffuse multiterminal ending' (Hess, 1961). Barker has subsequently described the morphological differences between plate and trail endings in some detail, including between their ultrastructural appearances (Barker, 1967; Barker, Stacey & Adal 1970; see also Corvaja, Marinozzi & Pompeiano, 1969, and Hennig, 1969). Under the light microscope, the difference is simply that the plate endings consist of discrete plates whereas the trail endings wander over a large area of intrafusal surface. This is illustrated in Fig. 1.12. Under the electron microscope both kinds of motor ending can be seen to contain typical synaptic vesicles

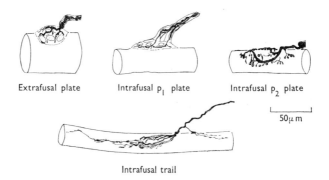

FIG. 1.12. Drawings of the gross structure of the various types of motor ending as seen on light microscopic observation of silver-stained preparations. (Tracings of endings selected from Barker, Stacey & Adal, 1970, Figs. 2 and 5.)

and to be separated from the underlying intrafusal fibres by a more or less continuous basement membrane. The chief ultra-structural difference between them is that post-junctional folding of the intrafusal surface is present beneath plate endings but not beneath trail endings. An additional complication is provided by the recent differentiation of plate endings into two subgroups termed p_1 and p_2 plates (see p. 42).

The next question is how widely the two major types of motor ending are distributed upon the two types of intrafusal fibres. The resolution of this problem is still not complete and its discussion has generated an unfortunate amount of heat which has done little to clarify the issue. However, it now seems to be currently agreed among histologists that of the motor terminations on the nuclear bag fibres the majority may be classified as plates, though a few trail endings also occur. Conversely, most of the endings on the nuclear chain fibres are of the trail type, though there is also a significant scattering of plates. Boyd (1962) initially believed that, almost without exception, the plate endings were restricted to the bag fibres and the trail endings to the chain fibres. But by 1966 he was 'prepared to concede that innervation of an intrafusal fibre by both types of motor ending may occur more frequently than I thought previously', though he still maintained 'that selective innervation of nuclear bag and nuclear chain intrafusal fibres by γ_1 end-plates (γ-plates) and by diffuse γ_2 endings (γ-trails) respectively is common' (in Granit, 1966, p. 67).

Problem of cross-innervation of bag and chain fibres. Quite apart from the precise appearance of the motor terminals, the abandonment of the classical picture of the spindle with its single kind of intrafusal fibre raised a major new problem which is still only partly resolved. This is whether the nuclear bag and the nuclear chain intrafusal muscle fibres are usually supplied by separate motor fibres, or whether they are both commonly supplied by branches of the same single axon. In other words, is the peripheral machinery available to enable the central nervous system to control each kind of intrafusal fibre independently of the other, and incidentally also of the ordinary α motor fibres? Rather surprisingly, this problem does not seem to be easily resolvable by histological means alone, and the attempt to do so has become obscured in relative side issues such as the morphological details of the motor terminations and the size and degree of myelination of different motor fibres.

When Boyd (1962) originally published his detailed description of the two kinds of intrafusal muscle fibre he specified that they were completely separately innervated. In doing this he stated that the motor fibres to bag fibres always ended in plate endings (his γ_1 plates) and those to the chain fibres in trail endings (his γ_2 network) and that the diameters of the two kinds of motor fibre were systematically different when measured at their point of entry to the spindle (γ_1, medullated 2–4 μm, γ_2 usually non-medullated about 1 μm). He speculated at some length on the size of the γ_1 and γ_2 fibres when they were in the main nerve trunk some distance from the spindle, and perhaps over-pressed the case for their being of different diameter and degree of myelination at this site also (Boyd & Davey, 1962); though he never claimed to have proved it. Barker (1962) immediately challenged Boyd's description of the motor innervation of the spindle, stating that it was over-simplified, and has continued to disagree with it more or less ever since (1966, 1967; Barker, Stacey & Adal, 1970). However, most of Barker's initial attack on Boyd's scheme was devoted to points which are comparatively immaterial for the major issue, namely the degree of independence of the motor innervation of the nuclear bag and nuclear chain fibres. For

PLATE I.1. A Golgi tendon organ stained with gold. It lay on a slip of tendon arising from an interosseus muscle of the cat's hindlimb. It is rather longer and narrower than most of those found in the cat. (Boyd, 1962, Fig. 76.)

PLATE I.2. A cat muscle spindle stained with silver. It was isolated from the peroneus longus muscle by teasing. The intrafusal fibres extended considerably outside the present picture, but received no further inner-vation. P = Primary ending. S = Secondary ending. cp. = capsule. tr.e.a. = trail endings. p_2 pl. = a p_2 plate ending. Ia and II = group Ia and II afferent fibres respectively. tr.f. = motor fibres terminating as trail endings. (Barker, Stacey & Adal, 1970, Fig. 13.)

PLATE I.3. The centre of a teased spindle which has been stained with gold to show the two kinds of afferent ending. The primary ending has spirals on every one of the intrafusal fibres, whereas the secondary ending lies largely if not entirely upon the smaller nuclear chain intrafusal fibres. The spindle is from the soleus muscle of the cat. All motor innervation has been removed by cutting the ventral roots nearly 3 months beforehand. (Boyd, 1962, Fig. 64.)

PLATE I.4. A silver stained primary ending in a spindle teased from the peroneus brevis muscle of the cat. (Barker, 1967, Fig. 19.)

PLATE I. AFFERENT ENDINGS

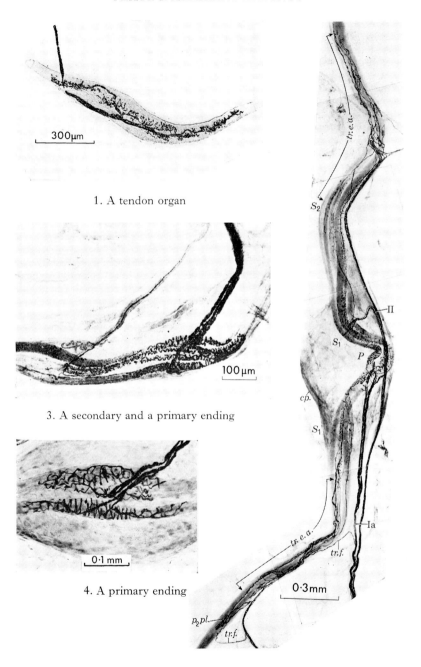

1. A tendon organ

3. A secondary and a primary ending

4. A primary ending

2. A nearly complete spindle

PLATE III. MOTOR ENDINGS

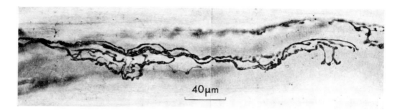

9. A trail ending

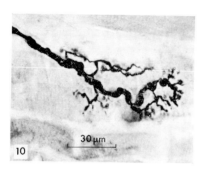

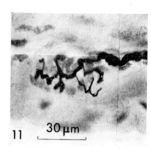

10. A p₂ plate

11. A p₁ plate

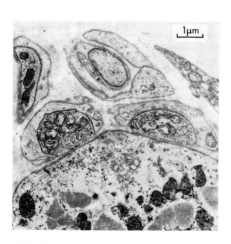

12. Ultrastructure of trail

of plate

instance, Adal & Barker (1965) traced individual motor fibres for long distances and showed that there was no consistent relation between their diameter in the nerve trunk and their diameter on entry into the spindle. In addition, Barker found some trail endings on bag fibres and some plate endings on chain fibres, thus further upsetting Boyd's simple comprehensive dichotomy.

In place of Boyd's subdivision, Barker instead proposed that the functionally meaningful dichotomy resided in the morphological appearance of the motor terminals rather than upon which fibres they occurred. This is to say that the important feature about a motor fibre was whether its endings were of plate or trail type, rather than whether they lay on a bag or a chain fibre (Barker & Ip, 1965; Barker, 1966, 1967), and he continued to propagate this view at any rate until 1970 (Barker, Stacey & Adal, 1970). An essential pre-requisite for such a position is that any particular motor fibre must always terminate in the same manner, whether as plate or trail, at all its branches; but though there are plenty of illustrations showing this in individual cases, there appears to be no general statement on the matter backed by quantitative data. Such specificity of the terminations of individual fusimotor fibres was of course an implicit part of Boyd's more far-reaching scheme, but with the apparent failure of some of its other details to be confirmed this particular component of the scheme inevitably loses some of its certainty when considered in isolation.

Working on the rat lumbrical, Porayko & Smith (1968) found

PLATE III.9. A trail type of motor ending seen stained with silver. This ending lay at the top end of the spindle shown in plate I.2. (Barker, Stacey & Adal, 1970, Fig. 16.)

PLATE III.10. A p_2 plate type of motor ending seen stained with silver. This ending lay in a spindle of the peroneus longus muscle of the cat. (Barker, Stacey & Adal, 1970, Fig. 49.)

PLATE III.11. A p_1 plate type of motor ending seen stained with silver. This ending lay on a nuclear bag fibre in a spindle of the flexor hallucis longus muscle of the cat. (Barker, Stacey & Adal, 1970, Fig. 68.)

PLATE III.12. Two adjacent trail endings seen under the electron microscope. Note the absence of post-junctional folding. From a de-afferented and sympathectomised spindle of the peroneus longus of the cat. (Barker, Stacey & Adal, 1970, Fig. 44.)

PLATE III.13. A p_1 plate ending seen under the electron microscope. Note prominent post-junctional folds. The spindle lay in a deep lumbrical muscle of the cat. Magnification twice III. 12. (Barker, Stacey & Adal, 1970, Fig. 60.)

that both kinds of intrafusal fibre might have either kind of motor termination upon them. But more importantly they found that there were only two motor fibres to the spindle, one of which supplied exclusively nuclear bag fibres and the other nuclear chain fibres, so that a given motor fibre could terminate in both kinds of ending. In this case, therefore, functional importance can only be attached to the separate innervation of the two kinds of intrafusal fibre; and the precise appearance of the terminations, at any rate as seen by Porayko & Smith, would appear to be irrelevant. In the opossum, there also seems to be a high degree of independence of the innervation of bag and chain fibres, for Jones (1966) found that a majority of fusimotor axons were small at the point of entry to the spindle and that 'nuclear bag and nuclear chain motor endings always received different small axons'. In addition, however, in about a third of spindles there was a large motor axon which supplied both bag and chain fibres, apparently then sometimes terminating with plates on bag fibres and both plates and trails (his 'sprays') on chain fibres (his Fig. 29). Thus certain observers using relatively gross methods have failed to find an absolute specificity of appearance of the terminals of single axon. It is, however, very difficult for an outside observer to decide how much weight can be given to this kind of finding when experts can write, 'It is now clear to us that the majority of terminals which we earlier identified as belonging to p_2 plates in fact belong to trail junctions in which irregular folding is present' (Barker, Stacey & Adal, 1970, p. 331). Indeed one is inevitably left wondering whether the classification of any particular motor ending as of p_1, p_2 or trail type is not rather more arbitrary than might at first be supposed, and whether this has contributed to some of the confusion and disagreement.

Returning to the major point, Barker has consistently stated that branches of a single motor axon commonly do supply both bag and chain fibres. Moreover he has published several diagrams apparently showing this as the standard arrangement, as well as producing numerous drawings illustrating its occurrence in individual histological preparations. However, Barker has also simultaneously implied that there is an appreciable independence of innervation of bag and chain fibres, with plates predominantly on bag fibres and trails predominantly on chain fibres. The controversy does not warrant further analysis, and it seems likely that there is some truth on both sides. Boyd himself seems to have felt this for after the controversy had continued for some years he stated in a review (Boyd & Davey, 1968), 'It is also clear, however, that the morphological concept on which these proposals were based, namely that the two types of intrafusal muscle fibre are selectively innervated by two types of small motor fibres (Boyd, 1962), does not apply universally.'

The physiological findings to be described later strongly suggest that Boyd was originally right in principle and that the bag and chain fibres have a sufficiently separate innervation for this to be one of the key features in the design of the spindle. Yet he would appear to have over-elaborated his scheme by linking its various components while simultaneously over-simplifying its details. This produced a conceptually simple picture, but one which failed to withstand scrutiny in its entirety; thus unnecessary doubt tended to be cast on features which were actually nearly correct. However, it must now be believed that some cross-innervation does occur on occasion and the present uncertainty is as to its precise extent and as to how far it has functional significance. On past showing such questions will not be rapidly settled by purely histological work and the attack is now being mounted by a combination of histological and experimental methods. Thus very recently the occurrence of cross-innnervation has been confirmed by observing it in spindles in which only a single fusimotor fibre has been allowed to survive. This was done by allowing time for degeneration after cutting the ventral root filaments containing all but one of the fusimotor fibres to the tenuissimus muscle; the fibre was identified electrophysiologically (Barker, Emonet-Dénand, Laporte, Proske & Stacey, 1970). So far all of the surviving fibres studied have happened to be of the static type. It was found firstly, that all terminated as trail rather than as plate endings, and secondly that these lay on nuclear bag as well as on nuclear chain intrafusal muscle fibres; but the relative density of the innervation of the two kinds of intrafusal fibre remains to be described. It was felt that the 9–12 days allowed for degeneration was insufficient to have allowed for the development of new connections by sprouting of the fibre. Within the next few years the continued progress of such combined experimental–morphological attack seems likely to resolve most of the controversial points just discussed.

Skeleto-fusimotor or β fibres. Another addition to the classical picture is the recent demonstration that the intrafusal fibres may be sporadically supplied by branches of the ordinary motor fibres as well as by specifically fusimotor fibres. Such skeleto-fusimotor cross-innervation is of course the usual arrangement in many lower animals (frog, lizard, snake), but for the 20 years following the demonstration of the specifically fusimotor function of the γ efferents it had been thought unlikely to occur in the mammal. It has now, however, been demonstrated by both anatomical and physiological methods. Following physiological work showing its existence in the lumbrical muscle of the cat (see Chap. 5), Adal & Barker (1965) studied the same muscle histologically. Aided by the small number of fibres in its nerve, they succeeded in tracing most of the branches of individual motor fibres to their destination in the muscle. For a number of fibres one branch was found to terminate as an extrafusal end-plate and another branch to enter a spindle; this has also been seen on a few occasions in the rat and in the opossum (Porayko & Smith, 1968; Berndt, Oswald-Cruz & Rocha-Miranda, 1969). Subsequently, the intrafusal branch of such a fibre was seen on 3–4 occasions to terminate as a p_1 type ending lying on a nuclear bag intrafusal fibre (Barker, Stacey & Adal, 1970). For no logically defensible reason such mixed skeleto-fusimotor fibres are now usually called β fibres and the term is so convenient that it seems likely to stay. The frequency of their occurrence probably varies from muscle to muscle and species to species.

Accepted at its face value certain morphological evidence (Barker, Stacey & Adal, 1970) suggests that β innervation may be relatively common in a wide range of muscles. The argument starts from the subdivision of intrafusal plate endings into two morphologically distinct types, namely p_1 and p_2 plates. The p_1 plates are closely similar to extrafusal motor end-plates, and have a well nucleated sole-plate. The p_2 plates are about twice as large as p_1 plates, and lack a sole-plate (see Fig. 1.12). The two kinds of plate ending are similarly distributed and may lie anywhere along the length of the spindle except for its central third or so. In addition the post-junctional folding seen with the EM is appreciably less prominent for p_2 plates than it is for p_1 plates. The argument proceeds on the belief that the p_1 plates arise solely from β fibres, and the p_2 plates solely from specifically fusimotor γ efferents. As p_1 plates are to be found in most cat spindles this leads to the conclusion that β innervation is widespread, including in the large limb muscles as well as in the small foot muscles in which they have hitherto been directly demonstrated. The chief evidence that p_1 and p_2 plates are derived from different kinds of motor fibre has been obtained by studying their rate of degeneration following motor nerve section. The p_1 plates and their nerves then degenerated after about 50 hours as also did the ordinary α motor fibres, whereas the p_2 plates and the trail endings did not degenerate until after 70–80 hours. As Barker *et al.* (1970) recognised, a difficulty for their view arose from the extreme preponderance of p_1 plates in certain muscles. For example, in the flexor hallucis longus they found 7 times as many fibres supplying p_1 plates as there were supplying p_2 plates so that on the above view the γ fibres would have to be presumed to supply an almost insignificant proportion of the plate endings, which would mean that this muscle possessed practically no specific dynamic fusimotor fibres. This is a sufficiently surprising conclusion for it to be reasonable to question the basic assumptions and to suspend judgement on the origin of the p_1 plates until the matter can be confirmed by some other method. Indeed, given the tangled story from Ruffini onwards of the elucidation of the nature of the motor supply to the spindle, the experimental physiologist may be perhaps permitted to wonder how far the precise appearance of motor terminations invariably provides a true guide to their origin and function. This is especially so as intermediate types of ending may also exist, some of which may be fibres in the course of degeneration and regeneration (Barker & Ip, 1966) and which may perhaps be passing over the underlying intrafusal fibres without making functional contact.

Another twist is added to the argument by the suggestion that in the lumbrical muscles of the rabbit the β fibres may have completely taken over from γ fibres in the innervation of the spindle; they may certainly have both static and dynamic actions (Emonet-Dénand, Jankowska & Laporte, 1970). This suggestion was based on the regular isolation of β fibres in electrophysiological experiments coupled with the inability to find any γ fibres. Thus it is not unreasonable to believe that in the cat also there may be large differences in the relative preponderance of the β and γ supply of different muscles. The rabbit findings also raise the question whether the β fibres with a static action may terminate in trail endings even though they may be presumed to terminate in ordinary end-plates on extrafusal muscle fibres. Clearly, histological problems are far from exhausted.

Question of sympathetic motor supply

A residual question on the motor side is whether the muscle spindle possesses a significant sympathetic innervation, and if so whether it terminates on the intrafusal muscle fibres themselves or merely upon the intracapsular blood vessels. At present the evidence is against the existence of any sympathetic innervation of the intrafusal fibres themselves, but the presumption rests on negative evidence and will become stronger when current histochemical techniques for the demonstration of catecholamines have been applied to the spindle. The fine non-medullated nerve branches which supply most of the trail endings are certainly somatic motor and not sympathetic motor in origin because Boyd (1962) found that they degenerated after cutting the ventral roots while leaving the relevant rami communicantes and sympathetic ganglia intact. He further concluded (1962, p. 108) that 'in general, no nerve fibres to spindles with an axon diameter less than 2 μ are present' after such a somatic de-efferentation 'and any other small nerve fibres (axon diameter 2 to 5 μ) which remain can be traced to secondary sensory endings'. Thus fine nerve fibres observed in the intact spindle must usually if not invariably be somatic motor fibres supplying the trail endings. Rather earlier, Hinsey (1927) saw presumed sympathetic fibres innervating blood vessels within the spindle capsule after ablating both the ventral roots and the dorsal root ganglia. Hines & Tower (1928) found no residual spindle innervation persisting after a similar ablation. However, the spindle does have a rich blood supply (Barker, 1948) and there are capillaries running alongside the intrafusal muscle fibres, so an intrafusal as well as a capsular sympathetic innervation would not seem finally eliminated.

Distinctiveness of primary and secondary afferent endings

In spite of a certain amount of re-iteration it seems convenient to collect together the various morphological differences between the primary and secondary endings. As already noted the most important difference is probably their different arrangement with regard to the two kinds of intrafusal fibre. The primary ending lies upon every one of the individual intrafusal fibres in any particular spindle, however many there are and irrespective of whether they are nuclear bag or nuclear chain fibres. In contrast, the secondary ending lies predominantly and sometimes entirely on nuclear chain fibres; it may surround the chain fibres in spirals but only put sprays on to the bag fibres (Boyd, 1962). Thus almost inevitably the two kinds of afferent would be expected to be influenced differently by the contraction of the two kinds of intrafusal fibre.

The next important difference is that the primary ending lies on a region of intrafusal fibre which is grossly deficient in myofibrils compared with the rest of the fibre, whereas the secondary ending lies on a region which is not nearly so deficient in myofibrils if it is at all. The central equatorial regions of both bag and chain fibres upon which the primary ending lies has only a thin rim of myofibrils, thinner for bag fibres than for chain fibres. Thus even if an intrafusal fibre were to be uniformly activated along its length by a propagated potential the contraction of the centre of the spindle would be expected to be weaker than that of its poles. Hence when the intrafusal fibres contract under isometric conditions the region occupied by the primary ending would be expected to be forcibly stretched by the greater contractile strength of the rest of the fibre. Interestingly there are apparently also fewer elastic fibres on the equator of the bag fibres than there are for the chain fibres (Cooper & Daniel, 1967).

The density of intrafusal myofibrils underlying a secondary ending depends upon how far away from the equator it is placed. When it lies immediately next to the primary ending then there may be a slight concentration of nuclei beneath the secondary ending with a corresponding deficiency of myofibrils; this occurs particularly in the bag fibres (myotube region of Barker, 1948). The contraction of the fibre below the ending would then be expected to be slightly weaker than elsewhere. When there are several secondary endings in a spindle, those furthest away from the equator will lie on regions of intrafusal fibre which have no excess of nuclei and so should be as strong as any other part of the fibre. A further complication in assessing the regional strength of contraction is the degree to which the intrafusal fibre is activated. If it is activated by local rather than propagated potentials then differences in regional strength will arise depending upon the precise location of the motor endings and the space constant of the fibre. In this respect it is interesting that when there are several secondary endings the ones which are furthest off-centre may overlap with trail-type motor terminals. This difference between the presumed contractility of the regions of intrafusal fibre underlying primary and secondary endings may be presumed to be of functional importance, but in precisely what way remains to be established (see Chap. 6).

A further difference between the primary and secondary endings lies in the size of their afferent fibres at their point of entry to the spindle. From Ruffini onwards it has been agreed that at this site the afferent supplying the primary is larger than that supplying the secondary ending (cat, Ruffini, 1898, Boyd, 1962; man, Cooper & Daniel, 1963; rabbit, Barker, 1948). In the cat, the primary afferent range from 6 to 18 μm in diameter and the secondary afferents from 4 to 10 μm, with only a slight overlap between the two populations (Fig. 2.8). This difference in afferent diameter fortunately occurs also in the main nerve trunk (see later) and has been of the greatest value for physiological experimentation; but it would not appear to be as fundamental as the difference in the intrafusal location of the two kinds of ending. Indeed at present there seems to be no compelling reason why spindles should not exist with two kinds of afferent ending which differ in their location and behaviour in the same way as the primary and secondary endings, but which do not differ in afferent fibre diameter.

The difference between the endings that Ruffini (1898) particularly emphasised, namely whether the axons terminated in spirals or sprays, is now felt to be unimportant if not misleading. In the rabbit, Barker found that 'both endings have an annulo-spiral form' (1948, p. 172). In the cat, secondary endings may consist solely of sprays but Boyd found that many of them were 'definitely of spiral form' with the spirals on the nuclear chain fibres (1962, p. 106). In man, Cooper & Daniel found that for the secondary ending 'the most common form of these is a short spray', but they also noted for the primary endings that 'the whole ending is less regular than the well-known spiral in some animal spindles' (1963, p. 581).

For the understanding of function, the ultrastructural appearance of the nerve terminations would seem to be at least as important as the light microscopic appearance after silver or gold impregnation. Under the electron microscope the nerve terminals of the primary and secondary endings appear just the same except for their size (Merrillees, 1960; Adal, 1969; Landon, 1966; Corvaja, Marinozzi & Pompeiano, 1969). Both kinds of ending are closely apposed to the surface of the intrafusal fibres with the muscular and neural membranes separated by only 100–200 Å. The closeness of the contact is often increased by either kind of nerve terminals lying in a groove on the surface of the muscle fibres, sometimes with lips of intrafusal sacroplasm partly over-lying the sensory terminal. The basement membrane belonging to the muscle fibres runs over the outside surface of the sensory terminal, and not between the muscle and nerve plasma mem-branes as it does at the motor end-plate and at all of the intrafusal motor endings. There is no sign of any functionally specialised areas of contact between the muscle fibre membrane and the sensory membrane, and neither 'tight junctions' nor mechanical bridges have been seen; the latter have been seen in the frog (Katz, 1961), but appear to be functionally unnecessary in the mammal in view of the greater closeness of contact. The nerve terminals themselves contain frequent mitochondria up to 3 μm long and various vesicles of 20–200 Å diameter, and a few of which contain dense bodies. Neither kind of afferent possesses the beaded-chain structure of the frog terminals in which bulbous expansions of the terminal are connected by a thin cylinder (Katz, 1961).

Distribution of muscle spindles

With the exception of a few muscles innervated by cranial nerves, muscle spindles have now been found in every striated muscle of every species of mammal in which they have been appropriately sought. They are in no way particularly concerned with postural muscles as they are found in both the flexors and extensors of any joint. However, different muscles do differ in the richness of their supply of spindles. This has been shown particularly by Voss's extensive counts on a wide variety of muscles in the newborn human infant where the problem of finding the needles in the haystack is to some extent eased (Voss, 1937, 1956, 1957, 1958, 1959). Spindles are particularly conspicuous in many small muscles concerned with the regulation of fine movements, such as the human lumbrical muscles and the small muscles of the neck. Large muscles operating on proximal joints tend to contain relatively few spindles in relation to their bulk. For example, the human latissimus dorsi contains only nine times as many spindles as the abductor pollicis brevis (368 to 80) though it is nearly 140 times the heavier (Voss, 1956; Schulze, 1955).

One way of expressing such differences is to measure the 'density' of spindles per gram of muscle. This works out at 29 spindles per gram of muscle for the abductor pollicis and 1·4 for the latissimus dorsi; further values are given in Table 1.1. As the number of spindles in a muscle stays constant with its growth these values have been calculated using the adult weight of the muscles even when the actual counts were made on the newborn. Similarly, in the cat, the lateral gastrocnemius contains 5 spindles/g,

TABLE 1.1. Values of 'spindle densities' in certain human muscles, arranged in order of decreasing density

Muscle	No. of spindles	Weight (g)	Density spindles/g
Obliquus capitis superior	141	3·3	42·7
Rectus capitis post. major	122	4·0	30·5
Abductor pollicis brevis	80	2·7	29·3
1st lumbrical, foot	36	1·7	21·0
2nd lumbrical, hand	36	1·8	19·7
Opponens pollicis	44	2·5	17·3
1st lumbrical, hand	51	3·1	16·5
Masseter, deep portion	42	3·8	11·2
Biceps brachii	320	164	1·95
Pectoralis major	450	296	1·5
Triceps brachii	520	364	1·4
Latissimus dorsi	368	246	1·4
Teres major	44	123	0·36

Data from Voss, 1937, 1956, 1958; Schulze, 1955; Freimann, 1954; Körner, 1960.

the soleus 23, while the Vth interosseus of the forepaw contains 119 spindles/g (Chin, Cope & Pang, 1962). The intercostal muscles are also richly supplied with spindles while the diaphragm is not (Huber & DeWitt, 1897; Dogiel, 1902). Table 1.1 also shows that the absolute numbers of spindles in different muscles differ considerably, though if the spindles were merely monitoring the length of a muscle the same absolute number might seem adequate for any and every muscle whatever its size. Large muscles tend to have large motor units with a relatively large number of muscle fibres, so that the spindle content of different muscles becomes more similar when expressed as the number of spindles per hundred large motor fibres rather than just the number per gram. But even on this basis, differences are still found between muscles. For example, the cat soleus has 30–35 spindles/100 α motor fibres while the medial gastrocnemius has only 15–25 (figures taken from Hagbarth & Wohlfahrt, 1952; Swett & Eldred, 1960a; Boyd & Davey, 1968; see also Cooper, 1966).

Muscles also appear to differ in the average degree of complexity of their spindles, and in particular with regard to the number of secondary endings; in any individual spindle this may vary from 0 to 5. On endeavouring to count all the endings in a series of muscles Barker (1962) found an average of about one secondary ending per primary ending. Boyd (1962) on a possibly less random sample of soleus, tenuissimus and interosseus spindles found 1·5 secondary endings per primary ending, though he later appears to have preferred Barker's figure for he subsequently stated that 'on average each spindle contains one secondary ending' (Boyd & Davey, 1968). Barker's (1962) figures for certain muscles are given in Table 1.2 and in spite of their unknown degree of error may be taken to show a significant difference in the relative numbers of secondary to primary endings in different muscles (compare the interosseus with the intercostal). All these figures may reasonably be suspected to be on the low side for it must be easier to miss seeing a secondary ending than to mistakenly count some other structure as one. Cooper (1960) suggested that complex spindles (i.e. with several secondary endings) are particularly numerous in tonic muscles, while short simple spindles are more often found in flexors which tend to be phasic. The average length of spindles from different muscles may also differ, even when the extra-fusal fibres are long enough not to compulsorily restrict the length of the spindle (cf. Swett & Eldred, 1960b). In addition, some muscles contain relatively more 'tandem spindles' in which two or more capsules are spaced along a single intrafusal bundle (Barker & Ip, 1961). The muscular continuity between the capsules is provided by one or two nuclear bag fibres while the nuclear chain fibres terminate shortly beyond each capsule. For purposes of spindle counts tandem spindles have usually been treated as so

TABLE 1.2. Average numbers of different kinds of ending in various muscles of the cat. The last two columns show the numbers of secondary endings and tendon organs expressed as a percentage of the number of primary endings. The data can be considered only approximate both because of the failure to find all the endings in an individual muscle, and because there are wide variations between the numbers in the same muscle in different cats.

Muscle	No. studied	Average no. endings per muscle			S/P%	G/P%
		Primary	Secondary	Golgi		
Rectus femoris	9	102	100	78	98	76
Soleus	3	55	43	31	78	56
Soleus*	1	53	—	45	—	85
Semitendinosus	3	137	162	85	118	62
Medial flexor digitorum longus	1	51	47	17	92	33
Vth pes interosseus	1	27	16	25	59	92
IVth intercostal (external + internal)	1	49	67	17	137	35

Data from Barker (1962) who counted the number of endings in teased muscles except for soleus* which was from Swett & Eldred (1960a) who used serial sections.

many separate spindles, one for each capsule. This seems physiologically meaningful as each capsule contains a primary ending with or without accompanying secondary endings—as do individual spindles.

The number of tendon organs in a muscle has been determined relatively infrequently. In several muscles of the cat tendon organs are usually rather less numerous than spindles as may be seen in Table 1.2. The same is true of the medial gastrocnemius muscle of the mouse (Wohlfart & Henriksson, 1960). According to Barker (1966) some small muscles completely lack tendon organs even though they contain a few muscle spindles; an example is provided by the deep lumbrical muscles of the cat. In larger muscles the number of tendon organs varies roughly in sympathy with the number of spindles, but an exact ratio is not maintained (Table 1.2). Further quantitative data on the entire proprioceptive equipment of different muscles might well throw light on function, but in view of the labour involved is not likely to be rapidly forthcoming.

The positions where the muscle spindles lie within various muscles have been charted several times (Hagbarth & Wohlfart,

1952; Swett & Eldred, 1960*a*; Boyd, 1962; Chin, Cope & Pang, 1962). Fig. 1.13 shows two examples of the position of every

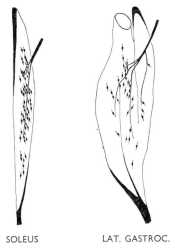

SOLEUS   LAT. GASTROC.

FIG. 1.13. The position of the spindles in two muscles of the cat. The position of each spindle capsule is indicated by a small ellipse. The intrafusal fibres, however, would have extended several times further than indicated by the short tails. The capsular positions were determined on serial transverse sections of kitten muscles. In the adult, both muscles are about 5 cm long and the total length of the spindles is about 7 mm. (Chin, Cope & Pang, 1962, Figs. 2 and 4 redrawn.)

spindle capsule in an individual muscle. The intrafusal fibres stretch 2–3 mm either side of the capsule, so that in the soleus muscle the number of spindles or parts of spindles found in any volume of muscle will be very much the same. In gastrocnemius, however, quite large parts of the muscle would appear to be almost devoid of spindles. More recently, Yellin (1969) found that in some muscles of the rat the spindles were concentrated in the 'slow' regions of the muscle which contain the histochemically recognised types B and C 'red' fibres, whereas they were absent from the 'fast' regions of the muscle containing the 'white' A fibres. If this is a common arrangement it has interesting implications for the functional role of the spindle.

Extraocular muscles

Muscle spindles appear to be completely absent from certain

muscles innervated by cranial nerves as they have been diligently
sought without being found. The deficiency is not a general
one for all cranially innervated muscles, for many of them contain
numerous spindles which are quite typical of those elsewhere
(Cooper, 1960). The best documented and most interesting
example of muscles without spindles are the external ocular
muscles of many species including the cat, dog, rabbit and horse
(Sherrington, 1897; Cilimbaris, 1910; Cooper & Daniel, 1949;
Cooper, Daniel & Whitteridge, 1955). On the other hand, man,
the chimpanzee, and many ungulates possess numerous spindles
in the same muscles (Cilimbaris, 1910; Cooper & Daniel, 1949);
the ungulates in which they have been looked for and found are the
goat, sheep, pig, cow, deer, giraffe and white-tailed gnu. For several
reasons, the histological demonstration of spindles in extraocular
muscles is not always easy. The spindles tend to be appreciably
shorter than those of limb muscles. In man, many are only about
500 μm in length and few are longer than 1 mm (Cooper & Daniel,
1949); also they usually have a rather thin capsule which makes
them harder to spot. In addition, as may be seen in Fig. 1.14,
they are not distributed evenly throughout the muscle but tend to
be concentrated near its origin and insertion, and in man are completely absent from much of the main belly of the muscle so that
they can only be found by a systematic search. Interestingly, in
man and in the Macaque monkey the spindles lie in regions where
the extrafusal muscle fibres are mostly rather small (about 10 μm
in diameter instead of 30–50 μm) and may be 'slow' fibres with
a distributed motor innervation and probably contracting in
response to local rather than propagated potentials. In the goat,
however, the spindles are more widely scattered throughout the
muscle. It has been suggested (Barker, 1968) that the extraocular
spindles receive their motor innervation entirely from collaterals
of the motor fibres to the extrafusal muscle fibres rather than from
a specific γ efferent supply; if so, there is no conceptual problem
about the nuclear bag and nuclear chain fibres being separately
innervated since there are separate fast and slow extrafusal muscle
fibres in mammalian extraocular muscles, each presumably with
its own motor supply.

In both man and goat the spindles are rather numerous; a
human inferior rectus was found to contain 47 spindles (Cooper
& Daniel, 1949), a goat inferior oblique contained 120 and a

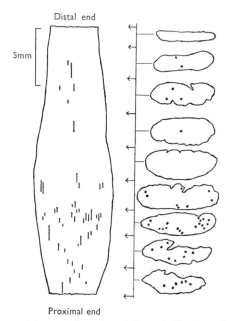

5mm

Proximal end

FIG. 1.14. The position and lengths of the spindles in a human inferior rectus muscle. On the left, a plan drawing of the muscle showing each spindle as a line. On the right, cross-sectional drawings of the muscle with the spindles shown as black dots; each of these sections includes every spindle found in the longitudinal segment of muscle indicated by the adjacent arrows. (Cooper & Daniel, 1949, Fig. 1, redrawn.)

sheep lateral rectus 281 (Cilimbaris, 1910; Cooper, Daniel & Whitteridge, 1951). Assuming the weight of the human muscle to have been about 0·37 g (Voss, 1957) this would give a spindle density of around 130 spindles/g which is much higher than in any other human muscle so far studied (Voss, 1937; Schulze, 1955). The density in the ungulates must be even higher. There seems little doubt, therefore, that in spite of the difficulties, the reported absence of spindles in certain species can be accepted at its face value, for the negative findings have been made by the same workers at the same time as they were making positive findings in different species (Cilimbaris, 1910; Cooper & Daniel, 1949). In a few cases, however, the reported absence may turn out to be only a gross deficiency, for up to 6 spindles per muscle have recently been seen in the recti of the Macaque monkey (Greene & Jampel, 1966), though they had previously been reported to be absent (Sherrington, 1897; Cooper & Daniel, 1949).

It would be particularly interesting to know whether the extra-ocular muscles that are deficient in spindles are also deficient in all afferent nerve fibres and sense endings that could perform the normal functions of spindles. Unfortunately, the anatomical arrangement of the cranial nerves does not permit the ready quantitative demonstration of the number of afferent fibres, as can be obtained for ordinary somatic muscles by cutting the ventral roots and allowing the motor fibres to degenerate. The precise route taken by the afferent fibres from the extraocular muscles on their passage to the brain is still a matter for discussion (Bach-y-Rita, 1959; Cooper, Daniel & Whitteridge, 1955; Hosokawa, 1961, Manni, Desole & Palmieri, 1970). In the goat, recording has shown that some of the proprioceptive fibres from the superior oblique muscle enter the brainstem via the Vth nerve, though whether by the sensory or the motor root is uncertain, and in this species there are obvious connections between the oculomotor nerves and the branches of the Vth nerve (Whitteridge, 1955). It also seems possible though unlikely that some of the cell bodies of the spindle afferent fibres lie in the mesencephalic tract of the Vth nerve as do those from the muscles of mastication. How far the afferent fibres of different species enter the brain independently of their own motor fibres is a question of considerable interest for the design of future experiments. In the cat, which lacks spindles, what may be presumed to be afferent terminals may be seen histologically in the extraocular muscles, and electro-physiological recording has shown that there are low threshold 'stretch receptors' in these muscles (Cooper & Fillenz, 1955; Bach-y-Rita & Ito, 1966). For the time being the presence of muscle spindles in the extraocular muscles of some species and not others finds no ready explanation, but one feels that when supple-mented by further evidence on differences in extraocular motor control it might provide a clue on the general function and use made of spindles everywhere in the body.

Other muscles. There are a number of other muscles in which spindles have been reported to be absent. This must mean at the least that any spindles are either rather uncommon or that their structure is sufficiently atypical for them to have failed to be recognised with the techniques used. The number of supposedly spindle-free muscles is, however, currently, on the decrease as successive investigations pursue the search in ever more detail. The following synopsis is based on Cooper's review (1960) which gives full references as also does that by Hosokawa (1961). Spindles are present in the masseter, temporal, medial pterygoid and the anterior belly of the digastric but have not been found in the mylohyoid or the posterior belly of the digastric; recently a few have been discovered in the lateral pterygoid where they were earlier thought to be absent (Gill, 1971). A few have been found in the human and rabbit facial muscles and they have also been seen in human intra-auricular muscles but not those of the cat (Winckler, 1959; Blevins, 1964), all the laryngeal muscles (Lucas Keene, 1961), the infrahyoid muscles (Fernand, 1970), the striated muscles of the oesophagus and perhaps unexpectedly in the human cremaster. Their absence or deficiency presumably means either that the muscle concerned has other stretch receptors which take their place or that it is not under significant proprioceptive control. Such control might perhaps be dispensed with either because no fine regulation is required or because there is some alternative source of feedback to the CNS on the state of the muscle or the effect of its contraction. Further searches for spindles are to be welcomed, particularly if accompanied by determination of their precise number in different muscles.

Résumé of receptor structure

Muscle contains muscle spindles, Golgi tendon organs, free nerve endings and a few paciniform corpuscles. Joints contain free endings and Ruffini spray endings in their capsules and Golgi endings, like those in tendons, in their ligaments. Because of its complexity the muscle spindle has attracted the bulk of attention. Although it was first described in 1861 and has been studied more or less continuously ever since, certain details of its structure remain to be resolved.

The classical picture of the spindle. What may be termed the classical picture of the structure of the spindle held sway from 1900 to 1960. In this the spindle is seen as a bundle of about 6 striated intrafusal muscle fibres, all of the same kind, surrounded by a fluid-filled capsule over the central third of its length. It is supplied by three kinds of nerve fibre, two sensory and one

Cm

motor. The whole structure is several millimetres long but only slightly over 100 μm across at its broadest. The intrafusal muscle fibres are appreciably thinner than the extrafusal muscle fibres. For a length of about 300 μm at the centre of the capsule they lose their striations and instead are filled with a collection of nuclei. The primary afferent ending, of which there is only one in any spindle, lies on this central equatorial region. It is derived from a large medullated afferent fibre which subdivides and sends non-medullated spirals round each one of the intrafusal muscle fibres. The secondary afferent endings, of which there may be 0 to 5 within any particular spindle, lie on either side of the primary ending on regions of intrafusal fibre which are moderately well striated. They are supplied by medium-sized medullated afferent fibres which break up to end in a mixture of spirals and sprays. Modern work has tended to play down the spiral/spray dichotomy originally described for the two kinds of ending; moreover, there is no ultrastructural difference to be seen between the terminals of primary and secondary endings. In addition to their afferent innervation the intrafusal fibres have a rich innervation consisting of 'plate' endings mostly lying towards the pole of their spindle. Any one spindle is supplied by several motor fibres. Individual intrafusal fibres may have one or two plate endings at either end, apparently often arising from different motor fibres.

The two kinds of intrafusal muscle fibre. The classical picture remains correct as far as it goes but since about 1960 certain additional features have been recognised; these have important functional implications. To begin with, all mammals studied have now been found to have two distinct kinds of intrafusal muscle fibre. These are called the nuclear bag fibres and the nuclear chain fibres after the arrangement of nuclei found in their equatorial regions. Here the bag fibres have a cluster of nuclei lying 2 or 3 abreast, while those of the chain fibres lie in single file. Elsewhere along the length of the spindle there are similarly few nuclei in both kinds of intrafusal fibre. The bag fibres are also frequently longer and thicker than the chain fibres, though this is not universal. Features seen with the light microscope, however, appear to some extent to be epi-phonomena only distantly related to function, for they may show appreciable variation for spindles from different muscles of the same animal, and also between species. Most notably, the intrafusal fibres of the rabbit all appear to be of the 'bag' type when examined with classical techniques and for a time this confused the issue. Electron-microscopic examination, however, has now shown two kinds of intrafusal fibre in all the species so far examined, including the rabbit. The bag fibres have a regularly arranged array of myofilaments, contain rather little sarcoplasm with few mitochondria, lack the M line at the centre of each sarcomere, often have poorly developed H lines, and have very few triads. The chain fibres have a less regular array of myofilaments, possess an appreciable amount of sarcoplasm containing prominent mitochondria, have well developed M and H lines, and have rather more triads than the bag fibres though they are not so numerous as in the frog twitch fibres. The difference in the band structure of the two kinds of fibre suggest that the chain fibres contract the more quickly. Various histochemical differences have also been described between the bag and chain fibres, in particular the chain fibres are richer in both mitochondrial and myofibrillar ATP'ase. The morphological duality of the intrafusal fibres may thus now be considered to be firmly established and is of sufficient degree to betoken a functional duality. The occasional description of intermediate types of fibre appears of much less importance, and may probably be safely neglected for the time being.

Innervation of bag and chain fibres. There is no fuzziness in the new picture about the arrangement of the afferent terminals. The primary ending encircles both kinds of intrafusal fibre whereas the secondary ending lies predominantly on the chain fibres; as in the classical picture they lie equatorially and juxta-equatorially respectively. The arrangement of the motor endings is less certain. It is generally agreed that in addition to the plate endings of the classical picture there are also more diffuse endings somewhat resembling those on the slow fibres of the frog. These are now termed the 'trail endings'; an earlier but now discarded name for them was the 'γ_2 network'. The plate endings have also become more complicated for they have been subdivided into two kinds named p_1 and p_2 plates. p_1 plates closely resemble ordinary motor end-plates. p_2 plates are about twice as long as p_1 plates and are associated with rather less infolding of the underlying intrafusal membrane and fewer sole plate nuclei. Very occasionally a p_1

plate has been seen to be derived from a branch of a motor fibre which also supplies extrafusal muscle fibres; whether all p_1 plates are so derived is an open question though it has been suggested. Such mixed skeleto-fusimotor fibres are now commonly called β fibres. The p_2 plates and the trail endings are both thought to be derived from γ motor fibres. A given fusimotor fibre is believed to have all of its terminations of the same morphological kind. All three kinds of ending have been seen on both kinds of intrafusal fibre, but in the main the plate endings occur on bag fibres and trail endings on chain fibres. The chief present uncertainty is as to the extent of the cross-innervation of the two kinds of intrafusal fibre by single fusimotor fibres. The balance of evidence would appear to be that the two kinds of intrafusal fibre are largely innervated independently, that is to receive separate motor fibres, but that a certain amount of cross-innervation does occur on occasion. In other words, the peripheral machinery, would appear to be available to enable the central nervous system to control each kind of intrafusal fibre largely independently of the other, and this is supported by the physiological findings discussed later.

Distribution of spindles. Muscle spindles are ubiquitous and occur in every somatic muscle of the body and not only the postural ones. The only well-established exception are the extraocular muscles of some animals, such as the cat and dog, which completely lack spindles; but typical spindles occur in the extraocular muscles of some other species, such as man and the goat. The number of spindles in different muscles naturally varies with their size. Only 1–2 are found in the very smallest muscles, such as those in the rat's tail, while several hundred are present in the large somatic muscles of man. However, the density of spindles, that is the number per gram of muscle, tends to be particularly high in small mucles subserving fine movements such as those of the hand or the deep muscles of the neck. This alone suggests that spindles have an important role to play in the regulation of fibre movements, whether voluntary or automatic.

References

The numbers in square brackets indicate the pages on which the reference is cited.

Adal, M. N. (1969). The fine structure of the sensory region of cat muscle spindles. *J. ultrastruct. Res.* **26**, 332–354.   [24–30, 47]

Adal, M. N. & Barker, D. (1965). Intramuscular branching of fusimotor fibres. *J. Physiol.* **177**, 288–299.   [39, 42]

Bach-y-Rita, P. (1959). Extraocular proprioception. *Acta neurol. lat.-am.* **5**, 17–39.   [54]

Bach-y-Rita, P. & Ito, F. (1966). Properties of stretch receptors in cat extraocular muscles. *J. Physiol.* **186**, 663–688.   [54]

Barker, D. (1948). The innervation of the muscle-spindle. *Q. Jl. microsc. Sci.* **89**, 143–186.   [2, 7, 16, 18, 23, 44–46, 52]

— (1962). The structure and distribution of muscle receptors. In *Symposium on Muscle Receptors*, ed. Barker, D., pp. 227–240. Hong Kong: Hong Kong University Press.   [4, 6, 38, 49, 50]

— (1966). The motor innervation of the mammalian muscle spindle. In *Muscular Afferents and Motor Control*, ed. Granit, R., pp. 51–58. Stockholm: Almqvist & Wiksell.   [38, 39, 50]

— (1967). The innervation of mammalian skeletal muscle. In *Myotatic, Kinesthetic and Vestibular Mechanisms*, ed. de Reuck, A. V. S. & Knight, J. pp. 3–15. London: Churchill.   [4–7, 20, 31, 35–39]

— (1968). L'innervation motrice du muscle strié des vertébrés. *Actualités neuro-physiol.* **8**, 23–71.   [32]

Barker, D., Emonet-Dénand, F., Laporte, Y., Proske, U. & Stacey, M. (1970). Identification des terminaisons motrices des fibres fusimotrices statiques chez le chat. *C.r. hebd. Séanc. Acad. Sci., Paris* **271**, 1203–1206.   [41]

Barker, D. & Gidumal, J. L. (1961). The morphology of intrafusal muscle fibres in the cat. *J. Physiol.* **157**, 513–528.   [20, 26, 28, 30, 34]

Barker, D. & Hunt, J. P. (1964). Mammalian intrafusal muscle fibres. *Nature (Lond.)* **203**, 1193.   [32, 33]

Barker, D. & Ip, M. C. (1961). A study of single and tandem types of muscle-spindle in the cat. *Proc. R. Soc.* B **154**, 377–397.   [49, 50]

— (1965). The motor innervation of cat and rabbit muscle spindles. *J. Physiol.* **177**, 27P.   [36, 39]

— (1966). Sprouting and degeneration of mammalian motor axons in normal and de-afferentated skeletal muscle. *Proc. R. Soc.* B **163**, 538–554.   [43]

Barker, D., Ip, M. C. & Adal, M. N. (1962). A correlation between the receptor population of the cat's soleus muscle and the afferent fibre diameter spectrum of the nerve supplying it. In *Symposium on Muscle Receptors*, ed. Barker, D. pp. 257–261. Hong Kong: Hong Kong University Press.   [20]

Barker, D. & Stacey, M. J. (1970). Rabbit intrafusal fibres. *J. Physiol.* **210**, 70–72P.   [34]

60   1. RECEPTOR STRUCTURE

Barker, D., Stacey, M. J. & Adal, M. N. (1970). Fusimotor innervation in the cat. *Phil. Trans. R. Soc.* B **258**, 315–346.   [29, 30, 36–43]

Berndt, J. M., Oswaldo-Cruz, E. & Rocha-Miranda, C. E. (1969). Identification of beta fibres at spindle entry. *J. comp. Neurol.* **136**, 419–422.   [42]

Blevins, C. E. (1964). Studies on the innervation of the stapedius muscle of the cat. *Anat. Rec.* **149**, 157–172.   [55]

Boeke, J. (1927). Die morphologische Grundlage der sympathischen Innervation der quergestreiften Muskelfasern. *Z. Mikrosk.-anat. Forsch.* **8**, 561–639.   [15]

Boyd, I. A. (1954). The histological structure of the receptors in the knee-joint of the cat correlated with their physiological response. *J. Physiol.* **124**, 476–488.   [8]

— (1956). The tenuissimus muscle of the cat. *J. Physiol.* **133**, 35–36P.   [20]

— (1960). The diameter and distribution of the nuclear bag and nuclear chain muscle fibres in the muscle spindles of the cat. *J. Physiol.* **153**, 23–24P.   [20]

— (1962). The structure and innervation of the nuclear bag muscle fibres system and the nuclear chain muscle fibre system in mammalian muscle spindles. *Phil. Trans. R. Soc.* B **245**, 81–136.   [6, 11, 14, 19–51]

Boyd, I. A. & Davey, M. R. (1962). The groups of origin in the nerves to skeletal muscle of γ_1 and γ_2 fusimotor fibres present close to, and within mammalian muscle spindles. In *Symposium on Muscle Receptors*, ed. Barker, D. pp. 191–198. Hong Kong: Hong Kong University Press.   [38]

— (1968). *Composition of Peripheral Nerves.* 57 pp. Edinburgh: Livingstone.   [3, 41, 49]

Bridgman C. F. (1968). The structure of tendon organs in the cat: A proposed mechanism for responding to muscle tension. *Anat. Rec.* **162**, 209–220   [7]

Brzezinski, D. K. von. (1961). Untersuchungen zur Histochemie der Muskelspindeln. II. Mitteilüng: Zur Topochemie und Funktion des Spindelraumes und der Spindelkapsel. *Acta histochem.* **12**, 277–288.   [17]

Cajal, S. R. (1888). Terminaciones nerviosas en los husos musculares de la rana. *Riv. trim. Histol. norm. y patol.* **1**, cited by Cajal, 1909.   [13]

— (1897). Terminaciones nerviosas en los husos musculares de la rana. *Rev. trim. microgr.* **2**, 181–185. Cited by Cajal, 1909.   [13]

— (1909). *Histologie du Systeme Nerveux de l'Homme et des Vertébrés*, Vol. 1, pp. 485–489. Paris: Maloine.   [6, 13]

Cattaneo, A. (1888). Organes nerveux terminaux musculo-tendineux, leurs conditions normales et leur manière de se comporter après la section des racines nerveuses et des nerfs spinaux. *Archs ital. Biol.* **10**, 337–357.   [6, 7]

Chin, N. K., Cope, M. & Pang, M. (1962). Number and distribution of spindle capsules in seven hind-limb muscles of the cat. In *Symposium on Muscle Receptors*, ed. Barker, D. pp. 241–248. Hong Kong: Hong Kong University Press. [48, 51]

Cilimbaris, P. A. (1910). Histologische Untersuchungen über die Muskelspindeln der Augenmuskeln. *Arch. mikrosk. Anat. EntwMech.* **75**, 692–747. [52, 53]

Cipollone, L. T. (1898). Nuove ricerche sul fuso neuromuscolare. *Ann. Med. nav Colon.* **4**, 461–514. [14]

Coërs, C. (1962). Histochemical identification of motor nerve endings in muscle spindles. In *Symposium on Muscle Receptors*, ed. Barker, D. pp. 221–226. Hong Kong: Hong Kong University Press. [30]

Coërs, C. & Durand, J. (1956). Données morphologiques nouvelles sur l'innervation des fuseaux neuromusculaires. *Archs Biol., Liège* **67**, 685–715. [20, 30, 35]

Cooper, S. (1960). Muscle spindles and other muscle receptors. In *The Structure and Function of Muscle*, ed. Bourne, G. H., Vol. 1, pp. 381–420. New York: Academic Press. [49, 52, 55]

— (1966). Muscle spindles and motor units. In *Control and Innervation of Skeletal Muscle*, ed. Andrew, B. L. pp. 9–15. Dundee: Thomson. [49]

Cooper, S. & Daniel, P. M. (1949). Muscle spindles in human extrinsic eye muscles. *Brain* **72**, 1–24. [52–54]

— (1956). Human muscle spindles. *J. Physiol.* **133**, 1–3P. [20, 21]

— (1963). Muscle spindles in man; their morphology in the lumbricals and the deep muscles of the neck. *Brain* **86**, 563–586. [18–26, 31, 36, 46]

— (1967). Elastic tissue in muscle spindles of man and the rat. *J. Physiol.* **192**, 10–11P. [17, 45]

Cooper, S., Daniel, P. M. & Whitteridge, D. (1951). Afferent impulses in the occulomotor nerve, from the extrinsic eye muscles. *J. Physiol.* **113**, 463–474. [53]

— (1955). Muscle spindles and other sensory endings in the extrinsic eye muscles; the physiology and anatomy of these receptors and of their connections with the brainstem. *Brain* **78**, 564–583. [52, 54]

Cooper, S. & Fillenz, M. (1955). Afferent discharges in response to stretch from the extraocular muscles of the cat and monkey and the innervation of these muscles. *J. Physiol.* **127**, 400–413. [54]

Corvaja, N., Marinozzi, V. & Pompeiano, O. (1967). Close appositions and tight junctions of plasma membranes of intrafusal fibres in mammalian muscle spindles. *Pflügers Arch. ges. Physiol.* **296**, 337–345. [26, 30]

— (1969). Muscle spindles in the lumbrical muscle of the adult cat. Electron microscopic observations and functional considerations. *Archs ital. Biol.* **107**, 365–543. [24–30, 36, 47]

Corvaja, N. & Pompeiano, O. (1970). The differentiation of two types of intrafusal fibres in rabbit muscle spindles. *Pflügers Arch. ges. Physiol.* **317**, 187–197. [34]

Cuajunco, F. (1927). Embryology of the neuromuscular spindle *Contr.*
Embryol. Carnegie Inst. **99**, 19, 45–72.   [20]
— (1932). The plurisegmental innervation of neuromuscular spindles.
J. comp. Neurol. **54**, 205–235.   [15, 19]
Dogiel, A. S. (1902). Die Nervenendigungen in Bauchfell, in den Sehnen,
den Muskelspindeln und dem Centrum tendineum des Diaphragma
beim Menschen und bei Säugethieren. *Arch. mikrosk. Anat. Entw-
Mech.* **59**, 1–31.   [48]
Düring, M.v. & Andres, K. H. (1969). Zur Feinstruktur der Muskelspindeln von Mammalia. *Anat. Anz.* **124**, 566–573.   [34]
Eldred, E., Bridgman, C. F., Swett, J. E. & Eldred, B. (1962). Quantita-
tive comparisons of muscle receptors of the cat's medial gastrocnemius, soleus, and extensor digitorum brevis muscles. In *Sym-
posium on Muscle Receptors*, ed. Barker, D. pp. 207–213. Hong
Kong: Hong Kong University Press.   [26]
Eldred, E., Yellin, H., Gadbois, L. & Sweeney, S. (1967). Bibliography on
muscle receptors; their morphology, pathology and physiology.
Expl. Neurol. Suppl. 3, 1–154.   [2]
Emonet-Dénand, F., Jankowska, E. & Laporte, Y. (1970). Skeleto-
fusimotor fibres in the rabbit. *J. Physiol.* **210**, 669–680.   [43]
Fernand, V. S. V. (1970). The afferent innervation of two infrahyoid
muscles of the cat. *J. Physiol.* **208**, 757–771.   [55]
Freeman, M. A. R. & Wyke, B. (1967). The innervation of the knee joint.
An anatomical and histological study in the cat. *J. Anat.* **101**,
505–532.   [8, 10]
Freimann, R. (1954). Untersuchungen über Zahl und Anordnung der
Muskelspindeln in den Kaumuskeln des Menschen. *Anat. Anz.* **100**,
258–264.   [48]
Gardner, E. (1944). The distribution and termination of nerves in the
knee-joint of the cat. *J. comp. Neurol.* **80**, 11–32.   [8]
— (1950). Physiology of movable joints. *Physiol. Rev.* **30**, 127–176. [8]
Gill, H. I. (1971). Neuromuscular spindles in human lateral pterygoid
muscles. *J. Anat.* **109**, 157–167.   [55]
Golgi, C. (1880). Sui nervi dei tendini dell'uomo e di altri vertebrati e di un
nuovo organo nervoso terminale musculo-tendineo. Reprinted in his
Opera Omnia, 1903, Vol. 1, pp. 171–198. Milan: Ulrico Hoepli.   [6]
Granit, R. ed. (1966). *Muscular Afferents and Motor Control.* 466 pp.
Stockholm: Almqvist & Wiksell.   [36, 37]
— (1970). *The Basis of Motor Control.* 346 pp. London & New York:
Academic Press.   [2]
Greene, T. & Jampel, R. (1966). Muscle spindles in the extraocular
muscles of the Macaque. *J. comp. Neurol.* **126**, 547–549.   [53]
Hagbarth, K. E. & Wohlfart, G. (1952). The number of muscle-spindles
in certain muscles in cat in relation to the composition of the muscle
nerves. *Acta anat.* **15**, 85–104.   [49, 50]
Henneman, E. & Olsen, C. B. (1965). Relations between structure and
function in the design of skeletal muscles. *J. Neurophysiol.* **28**, 581–
598.   [29]

Hennig, G. (1969). Die Nervenendingungen der Rattemuskelspindel im elektronen und phasekontrastmikroskopischen Bild. *Z. Zellforsch. Mikrosk. Anat.* **96**, 275–294. [36]

Hess, A. (1961). Two kinds of motor nerve endings on mammalian intrafusal muscle fibres revealed by the cholinesterase technique. *Anat. Rec.* **139**, 173–184. [35, 36]

Hines, M. & Tower, S. S. (1928). Studies on the innervation of skeletal muscles. II. Of muscle spindles in certain muscles of the kitten. *Bull. John Hopkins Hosp.* **42**, 264–307. [15, 19, 44]

Hinsey, J. C. (1927). Some observations on the innervation of skeletal muscle of the cat. *J. comp. Neurol.* **44**, 87–195. [6, 15, 19, 44]

— (1934). The innervation of skeletal muscle. *Physiol. Rev.* **14**, 514–585. [2]

Hosokawa, H. (1961). Proprioceptive innervation of striated muscles in the territory of cranial nerves. *Tex. Rep. Biol. Med.* **19**, 405–464. [54, 55]

Huber, G. C. & DeWitt, L. M. A. (1897). A contribution on the motor nerve-ending and on the nerve-endings in the muscle-spindles. *J. comp. Neurol.* **7**, 169–230. [2, 48]

— (1900). A contribution on the nerve terminations in neuro-tendinous end organs. *J. comp. Neurol.* **10**, 159–208. [6]

Jahromi, S. S. & Atwood, H. L. (1969). Tension and structure in crustacean fast and slow muscle fibres. *Experientia* **25**, 1046. [29]

James, N. T. (1968). Histochemical demonstration of myoglobin in skeletal muscle fibres and muscle spindles. *Nature (Lond.)* **219**, 1174–1175. [29]

Jones, E. G. (1966). The innervation of muscle spindles in the Australian opossum, *Trichosurus vulpecula*, with special reference to the motor nerve endings. *J. Anat.* **100**, 733–759. [26, 32, 40]

Katz, B. (1961). The termination of the afferent nerve fibres in the muscle spindle of the frog. *Phil. Trans. R. Soc.* B **243**, 221–240. [47]

Kerschner, L. (1888*a*). Bemerkungen über ein besonders Muskelsystem im willkürlichen Muskel. *Anat. Anz.* **3**, 126–132. [14, 15]

— (1888*b*). Beiträge zur Kenntniss der sensiblen Endorgane. *Anat. Anz.* **3**, 288–296. [14, 15]

Kölliker, A. (1862*a*). Untersuchungen über die letzten Endigungen der Nerven. *Z. wiss. Zool.* **12**, 149–164. [12]

— (1862*b*). On the terminations of nerves in muscles, as observed in the frog: and on the disposition of the nerves in the frog's heart. *Proc. R. Soc.* **12**, 65–84. [12]

Körner, G. (1960). Untersuchüngen über Zahl, Anordnung und Länge der Muskelspindeln in einegen Schulterei, den Oberarmmuskeln und im Muskulus sternalis des Menschen. *Anat. Anz.* **108**, 99–103. [48]

Krause, W. (1874). Histologische Notizen. *Zentbl. med. Wiss.* **12**, 211–212. [8]

Kühne, W. (1863*a*). Uber die Endigung der Nerven in den Muskeln. *Virchows Arch. path. Anat. Physiol.* **27**, 508–523. [12, 17]

Kühne, W. (1863b). Die Muskelspindeln. Ein Beitrag zur Lehre von der Entwickelung der Muskeln und Nervenfasern. *Virchows Arch. path. Anat. Physiol.* **28**, 528–538. [12, 17]
Landon, D. N. (1966). Electron microscopy of muscle spindles. In *Control and Innervation of Skeletal Muscle*, ed. Andrew, B. L. pp. 96–110. Dundee: Thomson. [24–28, 32, 47]
Lucas Keene, M. F. (1961). Muscle spindles in human laryngeal muscles. *J. Anat.* **95**, 25–29. [55]
Manni, E., Desole, C. & Palmieri, G. (1970). On whether eye muscle spindles are innervated by ganglion cells located along the occulo-motor nerves. *Expl. Neurol.* **28**, 333–343. [54]
Matthews, P. B. C. (1964). Muscle spindles and their motor control. *Physiol. Rev.* **44**, 219–288. [2, 32]
Merrillees, N. C. R. (1960). The fine structure of muscle spindles in the lumbrical muscles of the rat. *J. biophys. biochem. Cytol.* **7**, 725–742. [6, 47]
— (1962). Some observations on the fine structure of a Golgi tendon organ of a rat. In *Symposium on Muscle Receptors*, ed. Barker, D. pp. 199–205. Hong Kong: Hong Kong University Press. [7]
Nyström, B. (1967). Muscle-spindle histochemistry. *Science, N.Y.* **155**, 1424–1426. [29]
Onanoff, M. I. (1890). Sur la nature des faisceux neuromusculaires. *C. r. Séanc. Soc. Biol.* **42**, 432–433. [13, 14]
Peachey, L. D. & Huxley, A. F. (1962). Structural identification of twitch and slow striated muscle fibres of the frog. *J. cell Biol.* **13**, 177–180. [28]
Perroncito, A. (1901). Sur la terminaison des nerfs dans les fibres musculaire striées. *Archs ital. Biol.* **36**, 245–254. [14]
Porayko, O. & Smith, R. S. (1968). Morphology of muscle spindles in the rat. *Experientia* **24**, 588–589. [26, 32, 39, 42]
Ralston, H. J., Miller, M. R. & Kasahara, M. (1960). Nerve endings in human fasciae, tendons, ligaments, periosteum, and synovial joint membrane. *Anat. Rec.* **136**, 137–147. [6]
Rauber, A. (1874). Über die Vater'schen Körper der Gelenkkapseln. *Zentbl. med. Wiss.* **12**, 305–306. [8]
Regaud, C. & Favre, M. (1904). Les terminaisons nerveuses et les organes nerveux sensitifs de l'appareil locomoteur. *Rev. gen. histol.* **1**, 1–140. [2, 16]
Ruffini, A. (1893). Sur la terminaison nerveuse dans les faisceux musculaires et leur signification physiologique. *Archs ital. Biol.* **18**, 106–114. [13, 17]
— (1894). Sur un nouvel organe nerveux terminal et sur la présence des corpuscles Golgi–Mazzoni dans le conjunctif sous-cutané de la pulpe des doigts de l'homme. *Archs ital. Biol.* **21**, 249–265. [9]
— (1897). Observations on sensory nerve-endings in voluntary muscles. *Brain* **20**, 368–374 [7, 13, 17, 18]

Ruffini, A. (1898). On the minute anatomy of the neuromuscular spindles of the cat, and on their physiological significance. *J. Physiol.* **23**, 190–208. [10–19, 46]

Samuel, E. P. (1952). The autonomic and capsular innervation of the articular capsule. *Anat. Rec.* **113**, 52–70. [8]

Schulze, M. L. (1955). Die absolute und relative Zahl der Muskelspindeln in den Kurzen Daumenmuskeln des Menschen. *Anat. Anz.* **102**, 290–291. [48, 53]

Sfameni, A. (1902). Recherches anatomiques sur l'existence des nerfs et sur leur mode de se terminer dans le tissu adipeux, dans le périoste, dans le périchondre et dans les tissus qui renforcent les articulations. *Archs ital. Biol.* **38**, 49–101. [8]

Sherrington, C. S. (1894). On the anatomical constitution of nerves of skeletal muscles; with remarks on recurrent fibres in the ventral spinal nerve-root. *J. Physiol.* **17**, 211–258. [2, 6, 13–20, 27]

— (1897). Further note on the sensory nerves of muscles. *Proc. R. Soc.* **61**, 247–249. [52, 54]

— (1900). The muscular sense. In *Textbook of Physiology*, Vol. 2, ed. Schäfer, E. A., pp. 1002–1025. Edinburgh and London: Pentland. [14]

Skoglund, S. (1956). Anatomical and physiological studies of knee joint innervation in the cat. *Acta. physiol. scand.* **36**, Suppl. 124, pp. 101. [8, 9]

Spiro, A. J. & Beilin, R. L. (1969a). Human muscle spindle histochemistry. *Arch. Neurol. Psychiat., Chicago* **20**, 271–275. [29]

— (1969b). Histochemical duality of rabbit intrafusal fibres. *J. Histochem. Cytochem.* **17**, 348–349. [34]

Stacey, M. J. (1969). Free nerve endings in skeletal muscle of the cat. *J. Anat.* **105**, 231–254. [3, 4, 5]

Stilwell, D. L. (1957). The innervation of tendons and aponeuroses. *Am. J. Anat.* **100**, 289–317. [7]

Swett, J. E. & Eldred, E. (1960a). Distribution and numbers of stretch receptors in medial gastrocnemius and soleus muscles of the cat. *Anat. Rec.* **137**, 453–560. [49–51]

— (1960b). Comparisons in structure of stretch receptors in medial gastrocnemius and soleus muscles of the cat. *Anat. Rec.* **137**, 461–473. [16, 20, 26, 49, 50]

Tiegs, O. W. (1953). The innervation of voluntary muscle. *Physiol. Rev.* **33**, 90–144. [2]

Tower, S. H. (1932). Atrophy and degeneration in the muscle spindle. *Brain* **55**, 77–90. [14, 27]

Voss, H. (1937). Untersuchungen über Zahl, Anordnung und Länge der Muskelspindeln in den Lumbricalmuskeln des Menschen und einiger Tiere. *Z. mikrosk.-anat. Forsch.* **42**, 509–524. [47, 48, 53]

— (1956). Zahl und Anordnung der Muskelspindeln in den oberen Zungennbeinmuskeln, im M. trapezius und M. latissimus dorsi. *Anat. Anz.* **103**, 443–446 [47, 48]

Voss, H. (1957). Beiträge zur mikroskopischen Anatomie der Augenmuskeln des Menschen. (Fasedike, Muskelspindeln, Ringbinden).
Anat. Anz. **104**, 345–355.   [47, 53]
— (1958). Zahl und Anordnung der Muskelsplndein in den unteren
Zungenbeinmuskeln, dem M. sternocleidomastoideus und den
Brauch- und tiefen Nackenmuskeln. *Anat. Anz.* **105**, 265–275.
                                                                  [47, 48]
— (1959). Weitere Untersuchungen über die absolute und relative Zahl
der Muskelspindeln in verschiednen Muskelgruppen (Huft, Ober-,
schenkelund Untermuskeln) des Menschen. *Anat. Anz.* **107**,
190–197.   [47]
Walker, L. B. (1958). Diameter spectrum of intrafusal muscle fibres in
muscle spindles of the dog. *Anat. Rec.* **130**, 385.   [20]
Weismann, A. (1861). Uber das Wachsen der quergestreiften Muskeln
nach Beobachtungen am Frosch. *Z. Rat. Med.* **10**, 263–284.
                                                                  [12, 30]
Whitteridge, D. (1955). A separate afferent nerve supply from the extraocular muscles of goats. *Q. Jl. exp. Physiol.* **40**, 331–336. [54]
Winckler, G. (1959). Remarques sur l'innervation proprioceptive du
muscle du marteau. *Arch. Anat. Pathol.* **7**, 170–173.   [55]
Wohlfart, G. & Henriksson, K. G. (1960). Observations on the distribution, number and innervation of Golgi musculo-tendinous organs.
Acta anat. **41**, 192–194.   [7, 50]
Yellin, H. (1969). A histochemical study of muscle spindles and their
relationship to extrafusal fibre types in the rat. *Am. J. Anat.* **125**,
31–37.   [29, 34, 51]

2

MUSCLE NERVE FIBRES—THEIR
NUMBERS AND DIAMETERS

Usefulness of fibre spectra

THE tedious job of fibre counting has provided the physiologist
with the raw material out of which he has been able to fashion a
variety of experimental tools. The first stage of investigation
consists simply of determining the numbers and range of diameters
of all the fibres in a variety of muscular nerves. Such data may be
most simply displayed by plotting a histogram of the number of
fibres of each size against their diameter; this is conveniently
referred to as a fibre spectrum. The next stage is to determine
separate spectra for each of the functionally distinct kinds of fibre
which are found in muscle nerves. The combination of these
functionally-specific spectra with a knowledge of the patterns of
discharge of the various fibres should eventually make it possible
to give a complete quantitative description of the nervous traffic
between a muscle and its controlling spinal centres, and thus assist
understanding of the nervous co-ordination of movement.

In the past, fibre spectra of whole nerves have provided important clues to function, for they showed multimodal distributions which were correctly suspected to arise from the combination of two or more unimodal distributions, each contributed by fibres of a different function. This has provided a continuing stream of neurophysiological investigation ever since the various waves of the compound action potential of the bullfrog sciatic were first seen and realised to be attributable to fibres of different conduction velocity (cf. Erlanger & Gasser, 1937). Now that the individual distributions are becoming well established they provide the basis of much physiological experimentation. This is because the two physiologically significant parameters of conduction velocity and electrical excitability vary systematically with fibre diameter. Thus the identification of any single unit, recorded from electrophysiologically, may be furthered by measuring its conduction velocity; and nerve volleys of different functional composition may be initiated by shocks of different strength. In addition, various kinds of nerve block may preferentially paralyse fibres of different size, and so may be used to eliminate the activity of certain kinds of fibre selectively. Thus for these largely practical reasons the growth of electrophysiology has encouraged a good deal of fibre charting. In retrospect, the surprising thing is the confidence with which in the past electrical stimulation was used as a tool to produce a presumed functionally selective excitation of different kinds of nerve fibre, even though the data had yet to be gathered to show how far it actually did so. This partly arose because histological work on its own cannot provide the required answers, and apparently premature physiological work has actually been essential in establishing the significance of variations in fibre size.

Histological study can provide functionally specific spectra of nerve fibres close to their termination, as here fibres can be divided into functional groups on the basis of being seen to supply different structures. For the main nerve trunks, histology can usually provide only a single overall spectrum, as at this site the fibres cannot be divided by function since it is then usually impossible to trace an individual fibre to its termination. Indeed even the spectra obtained for the same population of nerve fibres at different points along their course cannot be directly correlated without ancillary evidence, for different kinds of nerve fibre may taper and branch to a different degree. Even the simple assumption that fibres which are the same diameter at one level will have the same diameter at another level is contradicted by the differing behaviour of the α and γ motor fibres (Fig. 2.4).

Under these circumstances the basic argument underlying physiological work inevitably becomes somewhat circular. In the first place, physiological experiments are performed to follow up a classification suggested on the basis of anatomical work. Later, the physiological findings are used to validate the provisional anatomical classification and provide the more crucial measure of how far fibres of different function are segregated into groups of separate size. To aid thinking, there has often been an unwarranted tendency to simplify the classifications and to suppose that the dividing lines are sharper than has ever been shown experimentally. Confusion may also arise because there are undoubted differences in fibre composition between nerves to different muscles in the same animal, between the same nerve in different animals of the same species, and even more so between similar nerves in different species. Moreover, on the technical side there is the ever-present danger of shrinkage of the fibres in their preparation for histological study. Shrinkage may sometimes be as much as 20% and so could easily lead to discrepancies between different descriptions of the absolute sizes of various kinds of fibre; probably, however, the relative sizes of the fibres in a given individual nerve must be less altered by the fixation and dehydration required for histology. Because of such variability fibre counts cannot be widely generalised. This, together with the imprecision with which fibres of different function are segregated by diameter, sets a limit to the accuracy of much physiological experimentation and hence to the practical utility of determining yet further precise fibre spectra.

Recognition of distinctiveness of large and small motor fibres

Fortunately, motor and sensory fibres can be studied independently either by performing the appropriate degeneration experiments, or by examining the spinal nerve roots. The motor fibres will be dealt with initially, as they are the simpler and provide the clearer example of the physiological importance of a multimodal distribution of diameters. They were first charted in detail in de-afferented preparations by Eccles & Sherrington (1930) one of whose histograms is shown in Fig. 2.2. Figure 2.1. shows a transverse section of a de-afferented muscle nerve. Both figures

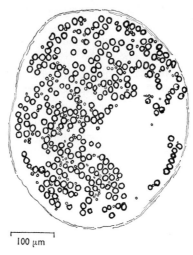

100 μm

FIG. 2.1. The motor fibres to the medial head of gastrocnemius seen in an osmium stained cross-section of its nerve after degeneration of the afferent fibres. The clear area is due to degeneration of some of the motor fibres, as well as the sensory fibres, as a result of damage to the ventral root. (Tracing of much enlarged copy of Fig. 8, Eccles & Sherrington, 1930.)

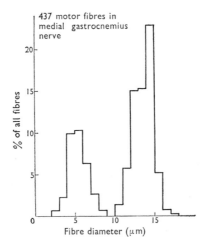

FIG. 2.2. The distribution of the diameters of the motor fibres to the medial head of gastrocnemius. The diameter plotted is the total diameter, including the myelin sheath. (Re-drawn from chart 1, Eccles & Sherrington, 1930; different nerve from that shown in Fig. 2.1.)

demonstrate the strikingly bimodal distribution of motor fibres with peaks at 16 and 6 μm. Eccles & Sherrington suggested that the bimodality was due to the combination of two separate unimodal populations, rather than due to branching of a single set of fibres, for a similar bimodal distribution was obtained for fibres in the ventral root where branching would not have occurred (Fig. 2.3). Careful fibre counts in the peripheral nerve did show,

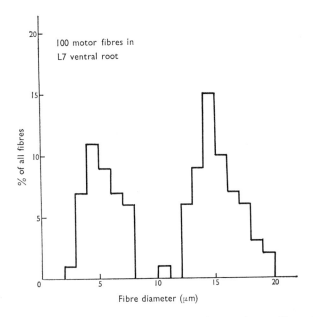

FIG. 2.3. The distribution of the diameters of ventral root fibres in the same preparation as Fig. 2.2. (Re-drawn from chart 5, Eccles & Sherrington, 1930.)

however, that some large motor fibres began to branch while the nerve was still more than 1 cm away from the muscle. In addition, Eccles & Sherrington demonstrated that the small fibres were not autonomic for they survived sympathectomy but were destroyed by combined section of the dorsal and ventral roots.

At the time, Eccles & Sherrington were engaged in furthering the Oxford school's detailed myographic analysis of reflex action by determining the average tension produced by contraction of the motor unit. To obtain the required value they merely divided the total tension which the muscle could develop by the total number of its motor fibres, irrespective of whether the fibres were large or small. They believed that the smaller fibres branched less than the larger ones and so supplied fewer muscle fibres, and they entirely overlooked the possibility that the two completely different sizes of motor fibre might have quite different functions. This is especially remarkable as a few years earlier, working only 80 miles away in Cambridge, Langley (1922) had noted the subdivision of myelinated ventral root fibres into two sizes and suggested that the small motor fibres might 'perhaps form the small nerve endings in muscle spindles'. Langley has proved to be right, leaving Eccles and Sherrington's paper as a now classic example of the dangers in scientific research of the undue attention to the particular, for they refused to be diverted from their set purpose; their oversight also incidentally provides encouragement for lesser men. As described in Chap. 5 electrophysiological work was required to demonstrate the specific fusimotor function for the small fibres and an ordinary motor function for the large ones.

An unexpected anatomical finding is illustrated in Fig. 2.4, namely that the distribution of the diameters of fusimotor fibres (measured at their point of entry to the spindle) and that of ordinary motor fibres (measured in the fine intramuscular nerve bundles near their termination) are very similar, even though there is so much difference between their stem fibres in the peripheral nerve. This is not entirely surprising as the α motor fibres divide to produce upwards of 100 terminal branches while individual fusimotor fibre supply only a few different muscle spindles and so need to branch correspondingly less. In practice, branching seems to regularly lead to each of a pair of daughter fibres being thinner than the original single parent fibre. It should also be noted that though strikingly bimodal distributions of motor fibres are widely found in the nerves to large limb muscles of the cat (see for example Boyd & Davey, 1968), smaller muscles from different species may have nerves which are less clearly subdivided. While it seems to be universally true that small nerve fibres are exclusively fusimotor, it is not universally true that large fibres are always exclusively skeletomotor. Occasionally, the branches of an individual large fibre supply both extrafusal and intrafusal muscle fibres. Thus each new muscle nerve needs to be approached on its own merits.

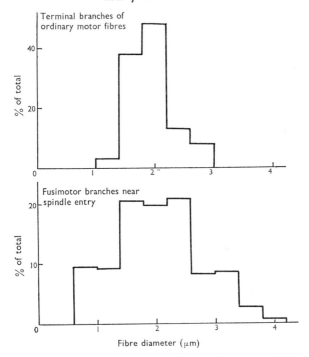

FIG. 2.4. The distribution of diameters of motor fibres near their termination in the peroneal muscles. Most of the fibres below 1·2 μm in diameter were non-myelinated. (From data in Fig. 1, Barker, Stacey & Adal, 1970. The upper histogram is a direct plot of their findings. The lower histogram is obtained by summing their results for the motor fibres to p_1, p_2, and trail endings, and using as weighting factors the relative frequency with which they observed nerve fibres to the three kinds of ending, namely 0·15, 0·15 and 0·70 respectively. Related histograms, differing in the width of spread of the fusimotor fibres are to be found in Fig. 1, Barker, 1962b and Fig. 10, Boyd, 1962.)

Introduction of terms α motor and γ motor

A nomenclature whose rationale should now be outlined is the use of the prefixes 'alpha' and 'gamma' to distinguish the large from the small motor fibres, and also their respective motoneurones; the terms are often conveniently abbreviated by the greek symbols α and γ. The term α for the large motor fibres arises from the demonstration by Erlanger, Bishop & Gasser (1926) on recording from the spinal nerve roots of the frog that the large motor fibres contribute to the first peak of the compound action potential of the sciatic nerve which had already been named the α peak (in due course to become the Aα peak as smaller and later waves were distinguished in the compound potential). In his classical lectures with Gasser (1937), Erlanger later summarised this and related findings, some for the mammal, and gave a diagram in which the large motor fibres themselves are implicitly given the name α, rather than just the wave to which they contribute. In this diagram the conduction velocities of the various sized fibres were normalised so as to give the fastest fibres 'a conduction rate of 100' in arbitrary units and it was held to be applicable to mammals as well as frogs. Erlanger partly chose a value of 100 for the maximum velocity because '100 m.p.s. very commonly approximates the conduction rate of the fastest fibre in warm-blooded animals'. His diagram, however, did not recognise the existence of small motor fibres and so at that time they were left without a specific name. Moreover, the term α motor does not appear to have come immediately into general use because few then felt the need to sub-classify motoneurones.

Nearly ten years later, Leksell (1945) set out to study the physiology of the small motor fibres and immediately needed a convenient name to distinguish them from the large ones. He adopted the term α without comment but specifically introduced the terms 'efferent gamma fibres' and 'efferent gamma wave' for the small fibres and their contribution to the compound action potential in the cat. He did this on the basis of Erlanger's diagram in which the start of the sensory gamma wave had a normalised velocity of 40, which corresponded 'closely' with the start of his own efferent gamma wave relative to an assumed conduction velocity of the fastest motor fibres of 100 m/sec. The numerous subsequent publications on motor mechanisms from Granit's laboratory continued to employ the terms alpha and gamma thus leading to their widespread adoption; this was also favoured by their brevity. However, the parallel terms large and small motor fibres are sometimes still used as precise anatomical synonyms in the mammal. The functional term fusimotor was introduced by Hunt & Paintal (1958) for any specific motor fibre to the muscle spindles. It is also frequently used for the gamma efferents now that they have been shown to be exclusively motor to the muscle spindles. The frog also possesses separate large and small motor nerve fibres, but in this species both supply extrafusal muscle fibres and neither is exclusively fusimotor; whether they, also, should be termed α and γ does not yet seem to be established either by general usage or by the dictation of a leader of fashion.

Attempted anatomical subdivision of γ efferents

The next question is whether the small motor fibres in the muscle nerve can be subdivided into two groups corresponding to the presumed independent nerve fibres to the two kinds of intrafusal muscle fibre. The present answer to this question is quite simply that no such subdivision has yet been convincingly made and it seems unlikely that any absolute anatomical division exists. In his full paper of 1962 Boyd left the matter open though he did describe two groups of fibres at their point of entry to the muscle spindle. These were his γ_1 fibres which were relatively thick and which were supposed to provide the sole motor supply to the nuclear bag intrafusal fibres, and his γ_2 fibres which were relatively thin and which were supposed to supply solely the nuclear chain fibres. However, Boyd considered that the terminally thinner γ_2 fibres came from stem fibres which had branched more profusely than the terminally thicker γ_1 fibres so that 'in the intramuscular nerve branches two groups of fusimotor axon are not obvious'. Thus whatever view is taken of the site of termination of Boyd's γ_1 and γ_2 fibres there seems no particular reason to expect them to give rise to histologically distinct populations of nerve fibres in the main nerve trunk. This view was fortified by Adal & Barker (1965) who traced individual motor fibres for some distance and found no systematic relation between their diameter in the main nerve trunk and that on their entry into the spindle capsule. Naturally no nerve fibre increased in diameter on coursing peripherally, but a thin fibre entering the spindle could be derived either from a stem fibre in the nerve which was initially thick and branched, or from one which was thin throughout its course. Their exacting experiments were done on the 1st and 2nd deep lumbrical muscles of the cat, each of which is supplied by only about 10 motor fibres altogether, thus making reliable fibre tracing possible. As discussed in Chap. 5 electrophysiological experiments independently suggest that there is no absolute separation of conduction velocity, and hence of diameter, between the γ efferents supplying nuclear bag fibres and those supplying nuclear chain intrafusal muscle fibres (i.e. presumed to correspond to dynamic and static fusimotor fibres respectively). Thus the question seems best closed until new evidence is forthcoming.

Boyd & Davey (1962, 1966 a,b, 1968), however, have propounded a yet further anatomical subdivision of small motor fibres, presumed fusimotor, which has yet to be confirmed by other workers or given physiological significance. The division is based on their observations on the thickness of the myelin sheath of different fibres as they run in the muscle nerve and as seen using light microscopy of serial sections some 7 μm thick stained with osmium tetroxide. Those they called the thinly myelinated γ fibres had a sheath which 'was between 0·3 and 0·4 μ in thickness in most cases and never more than 0·6μ' while the thickness of the sheath of those they called the thickly myelinated fibres 'was relatively constant between 1·0 μ to 1·5 μ' (Boyd & Davey, 1968, p. 13). The diameters of the central axis cylinders were however very similar for the two kinds of fibre ranging from 1 to 5 μm for the thinly myelinated fibres and from 2 to 6 μm for the thickly myelinated ones. Thus histograms of the total diameters of all the fibres together might be slightly bimodal, whereas those for the axis cylinders alone were not. On average there were about as many thickly myelinated fibres but the relative proportions of the two kind of fibres varied appreciably in different muscle nerves; thin fibres were particularly numerous in the nerves to the popliteus and the tibialis posterior muscles and particularly scanty in the nerves to plantaris and the lateral head of flexor digitorum longus. Collateral experiments showed that neither kind of fibre was sympathetic and they felt that fixation and staining artefacts had been excluded. However, their work would appear to be at the limit for accurate observation with the light microscope particularly when the sections studied are relatively thick. Their conclusions could usefully be confirmed by systematic measurement of low magnification electron micrographs of thinner sections and a recent preliminary study has failed to do so (Barker, Harker, Stacey & Smith, 1971); nor could an earlier independent study do so (Becker & Wiesendanger 1967). At present, the division of small motor fibres into separate thickly and thinly myelinated populations would appear to rest mainly on the visual impression of the original two authors for they state that 'it proved difficult, however, to demonstrate the difference between thickly and thinly myelinated γ fibres in photographs, except in a few cases'. Further, some of their published examples appear to show fibres with such thin axis cylinders and such thick myelin sheaths that their efficacy as conducting units is open to question on biophysical grounds (cf. Rushton, 1951).

Boyd & Davey supported their histological division by electrophysiological experiments in which they recorded the compound action potentials set up in muscle nerves on stimulating ventral roots, and vice versa. These experiments certainly showed that there were some motor fibres conducting as slowly as 10–12 m/sec, but they would not appear to have furthered solution of the problem as to whether or not there are two separate populations of γ motor fibres. To prove their point the compound action potential should consist of two well-separated 'γ' peaks each with a relatively smooth profile. Instead, like others before them, Boyd & Davey recorded a succession of irregular deflections with no obvious natural dividing line between fast and slow γ fibres. It may be readily accepted that γ motor fibres do range in size and degree of myelination and that there are interesting differences between different nerves in the relative numbers of different sized γ fibres. But the case has yet to be established that they can be classified on these criteria into two separate populations which are sufficiently distinct to be presumed to have quite different functions.

Diameters of afferent fibres

The wide range of diameter of the various afferent fibres supplying muscle was shown 75 years ago by Sherrington (1894) at the same time as he proved the muscle spindle to be a sense ending. After ventral root section he found that the persisting medullated fibres had diameters of from 1·5 to 20 μm. Many years later he quantified this observation by publishing a complete histogram of the distribution of diameters of the afferent fibres to a single muscle. This is reproduced in Fig. 2.5 and is essentially similar to those obtained more recently for the same nerve (Lloyd and Chang, 1948; Rexed & Therman, 1948; Hagbarth & Wohlfart, 1952; Boyd & Davey, 1968; see also O'Leary, Heinbecker & Bishop, 1935, whose method of plotting impedes comparison with other data). As might be immediately suspected, the broad histogram showing a relative excess of both large and small fibres has proved to be composed of a number of narrower unimodal distributions,

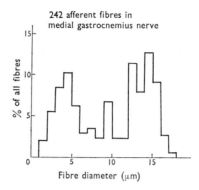

FIG. 2.5. The distribution of the diameters of the medullated afferent fibres to the gastrocnemius muscle. (Redrawn from chart 7, Eccles & Sherrington, 1930.)

one for each of the groups of afferent fibres from the various functionally distinct types of receptor. The establishment of this point and the elucidation of the distributions for each kind of receptor have proceeded fitfully and still cannot be regarded as quite complete. It may be noted that the problem is more severe than that for the motor fibres because the number of separate components contributing to the compound histogram is greater. Confusion has also arisen because the usual classification of muscular afferents into four groups seems sometimes to have been used as a strictly anatomical classification of fibre size, and sometimes as a physiological classification—based either on the type of receptor supplied by the afferents in question or on the central actions of the fibres. These two physiological criteria are operationally distinct though obviously they are closely related in the results they give. Mixtures of physiological and anatomical bases of classifications also seem to have been used.

Lloyd's classification into groups I–IV

The standard classification of muscle afferent fibres into groups I to IV was introduced by Lloyd in 1943 as an aid in the codification of the reflex responses obtained on stimulating various nerves. In spite of certain difficulties with the classification its merits have ensured its universal employment more or less ever since. Lloyd found that a weak shock to a muscle nerve monosynaptically excited the motoneurones of the same muscle. Increase of the strength of the stimulus beyond a certain low limit produced no further increase in the initial monosynaptic excitation, but it did initiate a later polysynaptically mediated discharge of motoneurones to flexor muscles. Stimulation of cutaneous nerves elicited only a flexor discharge. He thus demonstrated that afferent fibres of different sizes could elicit qualitatively different reflex effects, and in order to handle this important finding he subdivided somatic afferent fibres into four groups on the basis of their size. At the time he completely lacked the comprehensive histological and physiological data required to give precision to such a classification, but subsequent workers have found it useful for muscle nerves because it has proved to be reasonably closely related to receptor function. The classification can best be introduced in the words Lloyd used on its first promulgation:

For the purposes of the present discussion the afferent fibers will be classified into groups, each group being marked by a peak in the fiber distribution plots of one or another of the several peripheral nerves. Group I consists of the largest afferent fibers, which are to be found only among the afferent fibers arising from muscle. Approximately these fibers range from 20 μ to 12 μ in diameter, with a distribution peak at 15 to 16 μ. Group II contains fibers of approximately 12 μ to 6 μ in diameter, with a mode at 8 to 9 μ. These fibers form a prominent peak in the fiber distribution plots of cutaneous nerves, but they are poorly represented among the muscle afferent fibers. Group III consists of fibers gathered about a peak at 3 to 4 μ (the delta pile). These last are to be found in both muscle and cutaneous nerves. Another category, to consist of C fibers the afferent and reflex function of which is proven, should be included as Group IV.

In his initial paper, at any rate, Lloyd clearly equated all afferents of the same size irrespective of their origin for he further stated that 'since group I and group II fibers are the lowest threshold fibers in muscle and cutaneous nerves respectively, they may be excited in isolation by the simple expedient of selecting the appropriate nerves for stimulation'. It is certainly true that under his particular conditions stimulation of 'group II' fibres from muscle and from skin may produce much the same effect, but few would now wish to equate them, and Lloyd's attempt to provide a unitary classification of all somatic afferents has been largely abandoned. Cutaneous afferents are now rarely subdivided into Lloyd's groups, partly because this mode of classification does such scant justice to the differences of function which may be found between different cutaneous fibres of the same diameter, and partly because the equally imprecise classification of fibres in Aα, $\beta\gamma$ and δ groups had already taken precedence. It may be noted incidentally, however, that Lloyd's influence seems to have been strong enough to prevent the α, β, γ classification ever being systematically applied to muscular afferents. This has created the present thoroughly illogical situation in which a motor fibre of around 5 μm diameter is normally called a γ efferent whereas an afferent fibre of the same diameter to the same muscle is called a group II afferent and not a γ afferent; moreover a similar sized cutaneous afferent fibre may be referred to as a delta fibre.

The initial inclusion of cutaneous fibres into Lloyd's groups has, however, had a lasting effect, for these appear to have been the fibres which he used to characterise the group II peak in the position in which it is still usually given for muscular afferents. Eccles and Sherrington's histogram, which is given in the present Fig. 2.5, was one of the very few spectra available to Lloyd for a muscle nerve. As Lloyd fully recognised it shows a paucity of medium sized fibres, and there are certainly too few of them to characterise a well marked peak. His recognition of a group II peak can only have been derived from a study of cutaneous nerves, like the digital nerve illustrated in Fig. 2.6. The derivation of group I and

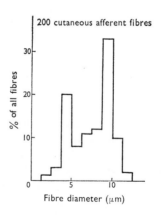

FIG. 2.6. The diameters of the afferent fibres in a largely cutaneous 'dorsal digital nerve' in the hindlimb of the cat. (Re-drawn from chart 7, Eccles & Sherrington, 1930.)

group III peaks for the gastrocnemius nerve is reasonable enough. However, on such data the allocation of an exact range of fibre diameter for each group is clearly somewhat arbitrary. What is more serious is that by his precise choice of words Lloyd skated over the crucial question as to whether the classification is purely an anatomical one based solely on fibre size, when overlap of diameter between the groups cannot occur, or whether it is really meant to be a functional classification, when overlap is clearly allowable. In the latter case it would be meaningful but confusing to say, for example, that a small group I fibre was smaller than a large group II fibre. One suspects that Lloyd was aiming at a functional classification, but if so little remains of its initial appearance of clarity. In any case, his initial obscurity has continued to creep through the literature.

Afferent spectra. The deficiency of fibre spectra for muscle afferents which existed when Lloyd made his classification led him to chart a variety of de-efferented muscle nerves (Lloyd & Chang, 1948) and several other similar studies have also been made since (Rexed & Therman, 1948; Hagbarth & Wohlfart, 1952; Boyd & Davey, 1968). In view of the paucity of Lloyd's original evidence it is remarkable that peaks often do occur in the afferent histograms of a variety of muscle nerves at approximately the places he had originally designated, though this is not invariable (Boyd & Davey, 1968). One of the best and most widely quoted examples of trimodality is shown in Fig. 2.7. As a result of all this histological work, but without explicit statement, the position of the boundary between groups II and III appears to have been quietly shifted downwards by 2 μm to make it correspond more exactly with the appropriate trough in histograms like that of Fig. 2.7. In 1943, Lloyd placed the boundary at approximately 6 μm. By 1954, Hunt, writing from the same laboratory as Lloyd, stated without comment that group II consisted of fibres of 12–4 μm and group III of fibres of 4–1 μm. This revised definition of the limits of the two groups is now firmly established in the literature. Subsequent physiological recording of afferent discharges has left no doubt that trimodality such as that seen in Fig. 2.7 is the expression of an important segregation of fibres from different receptors into restricted bands of diameter and that Lloyd had therefore been right in principle. Anatomical work on its

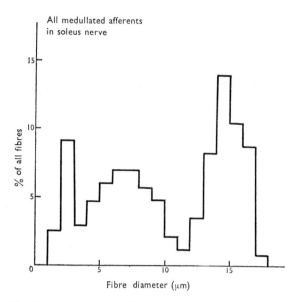

FIG. 2.7. The diameters of the afferent fibres in the nerve to the soleus muscle. The distribution is markedly trimodal. (Re-drawn from Fig. 2, Lloyd & Chang, 1948.)

own cannot show this to be so for the main nerve trunk, though it can provide separate histograms of the diameters of the nerve fibres from each kind of receptor measured close to the receptors themselves deep in the muscle.

Figure 2.8 shows such spectra for the afferents from the three main mechanoreceptors and is taken from Barker's work; essentially similar histograms for the spindle afferents have also been published by Boyd (1962; Boyd & Davey, 1968). Near their respective receptors the afferents from spindle primaries and from tendon organs are about the same size (6–16 μm) and both are larger than the afferents from the spindle secondaries (4–10 μm). Thus on the assumption that the three kinds of afferent do not change in their relative size as they become thicker on their way to the spinal cord, it follows that the spindle primaries and the tendon organs are responsible for the group I peak in the muscle nerve and the spindle secondaries for the group II peak. The group III fibres are left as a repository for axons terminating as free nerve endings. Fig. 2.9 introduces a slight doubt into the argument by showing

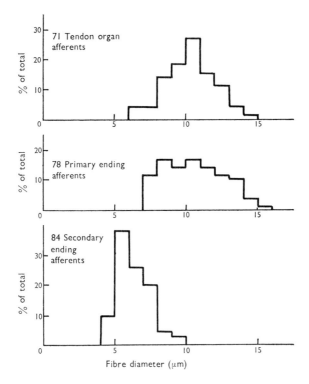

FIG. 2.8. The diameters of the fibres to the three main types of muscle afferent ending, measured close to the receptor in a teased rectus femoris muscle. (Data from Adal & Barker, 1962.)

that the spectrum of the nerve is wider than that measured near to the receptors and has acquired more prominent peaks, thus suggesting that there may have been some change in the relative sizes of different fibres. This leaves open the question of the degree of overlap in the main nerve between the diameters of the functionally different types of afferent. At the receptor level there is virtually complete overlap between the diameters of afferents from spindle primaries and those from tendon organs, so much the same might perhaps be anticipated in the nerve trunk.

A more interesting finding is that there is also a definite overlap between the afferents from the spindle primaries and those from the secondaries when they are all measured close to the spindle. One reason why such overlap arises is that primary endings in

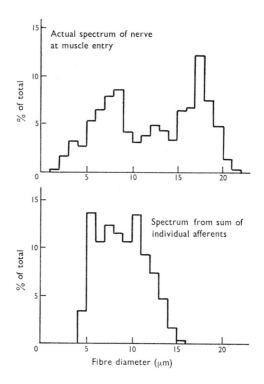

FIG. 2.9. Comparison of the fibre spectrum of the nerve to a de-efferented
rectus femoris muscle (above) with the synthetic spectrum (below) produced by summing the spectra shown in Fig. 2.8 for the same muscle for
the afferents from spindle primary and secondary endings and from tendon
organs. (Re-drawn from Fig. 4, Adal & Barker, 1962. The fibres in the
nerve trunk were stained with osmium, whereas when near the receptor
they were stained with gold chloride. The measurements made with the
two methods were thought to be directly comparable.)

simple spindles, which lack secondaries, have afferents which are
smaller than average as illustrated in Fig. 2.10 (Adal & Barker,
1962). In addition, secondary endings lying immediately next to the
primary ending tend to have afferents which are larger than average
(see discussion in Barker 1962a, p. 281). Thus overlap of the diameters of the afferents from primary and secondary endings does
not occur for any individual spindle, though it does for the population as a whole.

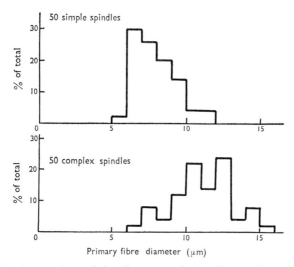

FIG. 2.10. Comparison of the diameters of the afferent fibres from the primary endings of simple spindles (i.e. lacking secondary endings) with those from complex spindles (i.e. containing more than one secondary ending). The measurements were made near to the point of entry of the fibres to the spindle. (Re-drawn from Fig. 3, Adal & Barker, 1962.)

How far overlap occurs in the main nerve trunk is unknown, but it seems unlikely that a classification based strictly on fibre size can ever give precisely the same result at the border line between groups I and II as one based on receptor type. Nor is it possible to overcome such incompatibility between the two modes of classification by shifting the somewhat arbitrary anatomical dividing line from one diameter to another. Most authors avoid grappling with this problem directly, but the sense of much recent literature is that fibres from spindle primaries and from Golgi tendon organs are allocated to group I irrespective of their precise size and called Ia and Ib fibres respectively; thus a functional classification is often tacitly adopted. The usage of the term group II is usually less explicit and only an assessment of context can show whether an author means it anatomically, physiologically or in some intermediate sense defying precise analysis. In the present work the terms Ia, Ib and spindle group II afferent will be used in a physiological sense to refer to the afferents from spindle primary endings, tendon organs and spindle secondary endings respectively. The unqualified use of the phrases group I and group II fibres will be used to refer to large or to medium sized muscle afferents, irrespective of their receptor of origin.

'Contamination' of group I and II by afferents from receptors insensitive to stretch

This leads on to the question as to whether there are fibres of group I and II diameter which arise outside spindles and tendon organs. Again, anatomical work cannot provide a universal answer but it does suggest that such fibres exist in many if not all nerves, though in variable numbers. The simplest example of such contamination of the group I and II range is by joint afferents. Gross dissection showed long ago that joint nerves may fuse with muscular nerves and this may occur on too fine a scale to be always macroscopically identifiable (Hilton's law, cf. Freeman & Wyke, 1967). One clear case is the contamination of the quadriceps nerve by fibres from the knee joint (Skoglund, 1956; Freeman & Wyke, 1967). The posterior articular nerve of the knee joint, which joins the tibial nerve, contains afferents of all sizes from 18 μm downwards as shown in Fig. 2.11 (Skoglund, 1956; Freeman & Wyke,

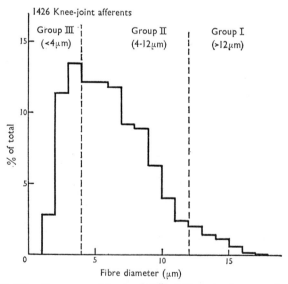

FIG. 2.11. The diameters of the medullated fibres in the posterior nerve to the knee joint. The fibre counts from ten cats were pooled to give a single histogram. (Data from Table 2, Skoglund, 1956.)

1967; Boyd & Davey, 1968, Fig. 29b). This argues that joint afferents may contribute to both groups I and II of the quadriceps nerve in particular, and to muscular nerves in general. Another well known example of contamination is the union of the fine nerve from the interosseus membrane of the cat's leg with the nerve to the flexor longus digitorum. This may contribute fibres of up to 16 μm diameter to the otherwise pure muscle nerve thereby contaminating both groups I and II (Hunt & McIntyre, 1960; Boyd & Davey, 1968, Fig. 29d). Many muscle nerves may well prove to be spared gross contamination by being joined by an extraneous nerve filament but each case needs to be assessed on its own.

The more serious problem is whether a significant number of group I and II fibres arise from the muscle itself and its immediately surrounding tissues, other than from spindles and tendon organs. There is no doubt that except for the well-known encapsulated endings (including paciniform corpuscles) large and medium medullated nerve fibres do not terminate suddenly in a localised region of the muscle, for such termination could hardly have escaped discovery. This, however, does not preclude group I and II nerve fibres from ending as relatively fine free terminals after reducing their diameter by extensive branching, and three probable examples of this have recently been documented (Stacey, 1969).

The chief anatomical line of attack on the problem of how often this happens has been to count the number of spindles and tendon organs in a muscle and then to compare the number of afferent fibres needed to supply these known receptors with the number of afferent fibres actually found in the muscle nerve. Any excess of afferent fibres in the nerve can then be allocated to unidentified receptors, presumably free nerve endings. The two main groups who have made such computations have reached somewhat different conclusions (Barker, 1962b; Barker, Ip & Adal, 1962; Boyd & Davey, 1968) and in any case the potential sources of error are so numerous that all results need to be accepted with caution.

Some of the sources of error are as follows. First, the counting of known receptors must tend to give too low a value because some of them are overlooked. This is likely to be particularly severe for the secondary endings sought in teased material because the end of the spindle which contains them may break off. When serial sections are used for counting then the number of spindle capsules is usually all that can be determined because the appropriate stains for nerve terminals are not then usually readily employable. This does, however, provide a reliable estimate of primary endings because there is only one per capsule. But an assessment of the number of secondary endings can only be arrived at on the basis of an independent estimation of the average number of secondary endings per spindle for the muscle in question. As already noted such estimates vary appreciably, with consequent effect on the afferent requirements.

Second, when the number of receptors has been successfully agreed upon it becomes necessary to estimate the degree of branching of the original stem fibres before it is possible to decide how many afferents are required to supply the observed number of endings. There is no difficulty in this respect for the afferents to the primary endings because, although they branch repeatedly on reaching the individual spindles, they do not do so earlier, and an individual Ia fibre almost invariably supplies only a single spindle. This statement is based partly on observations on teased material (Boyd, 1962; Barker, 1962b), partly on the slight amount of branching of afferents of about 10 μm diameter which occurs in the main nerve trunk (Eccles & Sherrington, 1930), and partly on a single occasion in which a Ia afferent was traced from a spindle in the piriformis muscle to the dorsal root ganglion (von Thiel, 1959). The position is more complicated for the afferents to tendon organs and to spindle secondaries since these have been seen to branch so as to supply more than one receptor. Moreover, assessments of the precise degree of branching usually rely upon a circular argument which starts by assuming that all group I and II fibres in a muscle nerve arise from known receptors. Barker, on the basis of the amount of branching seen close to the nerve terminations, has adopted a receptor/afferent fibre ratio of 1·2:1·0 for tendon organs and 1:1 for secondary endings (Barker, Ip & Adal, 1962).

Third, unless all the measurements are made on the self-same muscle the results may be vitiated by the quite large variations which occur in the numbers of spindles lying in corresponding muscles in different animals. Barker & Chin (1960) counted the spindles in 40 different tibialis anterior muscles and found the number varied from 52 to 89. In addition, any count of afferent fibres has to be made on a de-efferented preparation and so is liable to give a value which is too low in comparison with the normal. This is because a few afferent fibres are almost inevitably damaged in the ventral rhizotomy needed to display them in isolation from the motor fibres. Thus afferent fibre counts cannot properly be compared with the receptor population of a normal muscle. Finally, as a preliminary to performing the quantitative comparison of receptors and afferents, it is necessary either to start with an arbitrary subdivision of the afferent spectrum into groups I, II and III, or to use electrophysiological data on the distribution of conduction velocity of the afferents of different receptors.

The experiments of Barker, Ip & Adal (1962) appear to have come closest to overcoming all the various difficulties though perhaps not sufficiently so to guarantee their conclusions. These were that for the 4 soleus muscles which they studied about 10% of the group I fibres could not be allocated to a known encapsulated receptor nor could about 35% of the group II fibres. These are remarkably high figures in the light of Hunt's (1954) electrophysio-logical work which was also on soleus and which suggested that an insignificant number of group I and II fibres arose outside spindles and tendon organs, as has since also been found by others (see later). Boyd & Davey (1968), on comparing their own afferent spectra with receptor counts from the literature, were content to state 'it can be seen that nearly all the I and II fibres in the nerves to the medial head of gastrocnemius, soleus, semitendinosus, tenuissimus and flexor digitorum longus are accounted for. Thus, in these nerves the group II peak consists almost entirely of fibres from muscle spindles' (their p. 32). On the other hand, Boyd & Davey considered that various other muscle nerves contained appreciably more afferents, particularly in the group II range, than could be allocated to the known receptors and felt these afferents arose partly from free endings in the muscles and partly from receptors outside the muscles themselves. These 'contamina-ted' nerves were also found to contain a relatively large number of afferent fibres in relation to the number of motor fibres and to have fibre spectra in which trimodality was inconspicuous. Particular examples were the nerves to the popliteus, tibialis anterior, tibialis posterior and extensor digitorum longus muscles.

Thus there is far from being a secure anatomical basis for the common supposition that muscular nerve fibres of different function are always sharply segregated by diameter. There is, however, enough truth behind the belief for its retention to be desirable provided its limitations are recognised. Table 2.1 sum-marises what may be called the conventional classification and provides a useful starting point for thought, even though it largely begs the important question of the degree of overlap of diameter of fibres with different functions.

Applicability of classification outside cat hindlimb

Finally, it should be emphasised that all that has just been said is based on studies of the pattern of innervation of large muscles of the hindlimb of the cat. Even here there are differences from muscle to muscle in the precise position of the group I and the α peaks,

TABLE 2.1. Conventional classification of proprioceptive afferent fibres

Name	Diameter	Velocity	Muscle receptors supplied	Joint receptors supplied
Group I (Thick medullated)	12–20 μm	72–120 m/sec	Spindle primaries (by Ia) Tendon organs (by Ib) ? Occasional free endings	Some Golgi endings
Group II (Medium medullated)	4–12 μm	24–72 m/sec	Spindle secondaries Paciniform corpuscles Some free endings (number very variable with particular nerve)	More Golgi endings Ruffini endings Some free endings Paciniform corpuscles
Group III (Fine medullated)	1–4 μm	6–24 m/sec (? may be as low as 2 m/sec)	Free endings (? of diverse kinds)	Free endings
Group IV (Non-medullated)	Below 1 μm	<2 m/sec	Free endings	Free endings

These values refer only to the hindlimb of the cat and even here cannot be considered precise. They are derived partly from the histological work described in Chap. 2 and partly from the electrophysiological work described in Chaps. 3 and 4. The diameters and velocities refer to measurements made on the fibres where they run in main nerve trunks. The values near the receptors would all be lower, not necessarily in simple proportion. On the motor side, the α fibres have velocities of 50–120 m/sec and the γ fibres of about 10–50 m/sec; these correspond to diameters of 8–20 μm and 2–8 μm respectively.

and thus also of the troughs between each of them and the immediately following group of smaller fibres. For example, both the largest sensory and the largest motor fibres to soleus are significantly smaller than the corresponding fibres to gastrocnemius. To be specific, Eccles & Sherrington (1930) found that the largest motor fibres to medial gastrocnemius were 17 μm in diameter while those to soleus were only 14 μm, though the position of the γ peak was the same for both muscles. Lloyd & Chang (1948) found the largest soleus afferent to be 17·5 μm and the largest gastrocnemius afferent to be 21 μm. The largest motor fibres to the cat lumbrical muscles are only 13·5 μm in diameter (Adal & Barker, 1965), while their Ia afferent fibres may be up to 17 μm as judged by their conduction velocity. Further examples can be found in Boyd & Davey, 1968. A minor problem is that different workers have given histograms for the same nerves which differ slightly in the precise positions of the various peaks and troughs, possibly because of differences between individual animals or because of different degrees of shrinkage in the preparation of the nerves for histological study. In young animals, of course, all fibres are smaller and so the spectra must differ from those of the adult.

Turning to different species it appears that the whole pattern of fibre distribution may be scaled down from that in the cat, but as yet there is little exact information as to whether it may also be qualitatively transformed. In the rat the fastest muscular afferent nerve fibres conduct at only 60–80 m/sec instead of 100–120 m/sec as in the cat (Hník, 1970). In man and monkey, in spite of their greater body size, the largest fibres are also slightly smaller and more slowly conducting than in the cat and the conduction velocity of both their largest motor and the largest muscle afferent fibres is somewhat below 90 m/sec (Mayer & Mawdsley, 1965; Koeze, 1968; Clough, Kernell & Phillips, 1968). Thus the direct transference of the cat classification to other species is fraught with danger.

When in doubt it seems best to specify groups of fibres by their function first and their conduction velocity second. The terms α for ordinary motor fibres and γ for smaller specific fusimotor fibres have a sufficiently established functional meaning for their use to be safely continued whatever the absolute size of the fibres concerned. Likewise the term β fibre will probably also prove

widely acceptable for fibres which supply both intrafusal and extrafusal muscle fibres. On the afferent side, however, the classification
into groups I to IV should properly only be used after specifying
whether it is meant in an anatomical or in a physiological sense.
For example, it has recently been suggested from a study of their
functional properties that the afferents from the spindle secondary
endings of muscles in the rat's tail might have similar conduction
velocities to the afferents from the spindle primaries in the same
muscle, whereas for muscles of the leg the familiar situation prevails as in the cat (Andrew, Leslie & Thompson, 1970). Discussion
of such a suggestion becomes almost impossible if it is attempted
with the terms group I and II used in the familiar way without
specifying whether they are meant anatomically or physiologically.
In difficult cases a minimum of three pieces of information are
required about an afferent fibre to place it in relation to other
afferent fibres; its receptor of origin, its diameter, and the diameter
of the largest nerve fibre of the same animal.

*Pattern of muscle innervation illustrated by description of that of
the cat soleus*

It seems helpful to draw together much that has already been
said by giving a dogmatic and simplified description of the nerve
supply to the soleus muscle of the cat. The general arrangement
is outlined in Fig. 2.12. This muscle has been studied intensively

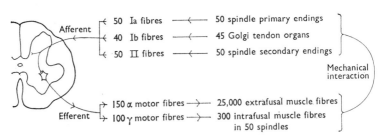

Thus :   240 fibres for control (Ia, Ib, II, and γ)
           150 fibres for direct action (α).

FIG. 2.12. The major neural equipment of the cat soleus muscle drawn so
as to emphasise the large number of fibres devoted to the regulation of
muscle rather than to the direct production of contraction. All values
approximate.

by anatomical methods, partly because it has frequently been used for physiological experimentation. It is peculiar in being a rather red muscle with a correspondingly slow contraction, and consists almost entirely of the type B fibre recognisable histologically (Henneman & Olson, 1965), but its innervation does not appear to differ from that of faster muscles; its homogeneity facilitates the interpretation of physiological findings. In the adult cat the soleus weighs about 2·5 g, is about 5 cm long, and is roughly cylindrical with a maximum diameter of about 8 mm. It is made up of around 25,000 extrafusal muscle fibres each of which is about 60 μm in diameter and 3 cm long; the fibres are shorter than the whole muscle because they run somewhat obliquely from an extended tendon of origin to the extended tendon of insertion. About 50 muscle spindles are scattered fairly uniformly among the muscle fibres, running parallel to them and with their capsules all more than about 5 mm from the ends of the muscle fibres. The ends of the spindles blend with the connective tissue around the muscle fibres. The muscle also contains about 45 Golgi tendon organs which lie at the musculo-tendinous junctions at either end of the muscle; slightly more tendon organs are found at the insertion of the muscle fibres into the main tendon than are found at the origin. The tendon organs are only about 0·5 mm long whereas the spindles average about 7 mm. Each spindle contains 2–3 nuclear bag intrafusal fibres of 30 μm diameter and each of which stretches the full length of the spindle. It also contains 4–6 nuclear chain fibres of 14 μm diameter. These are only about 4 mm long and are placed symmetrically so that they occupy the central two thirds of the length of the spindle.

The 45 tendon organs are supplied by about 40 Ib afferent fibres which are 12–20 μm diameter in the main nerve and a few of which branch to supply more than one tendon organ. The 50 spindles, however, are supplied by slightly over 200 nerve fibres, approximately half of which are motor while the rest are afferent. The afferent fibres comprise 50 Ia fibres of 12–20 μm diameter to the primary endings and 50 group II fibres of 4–12 μm diameter to the secondary endings. By and large each of these afferents supplies only a single ending. Every spindle contains a single primary ending but the number of secondary endings may vary from 0 to 5. In addition, there may be 2–3 medium sized medullated fibres supplying paciniform corpuscles and there are always some 20–40 medullated fibres, mostly below 6 μm in diameter, which terminate as free nerve endings after branching extensively. On top of the 170 or so medullated afferent fibres to the muscle there are likely to be another 200–400 non-medullated afferent fibres terminating as free endings, though no count of their numbers has yet been made for the soleus.

In comparison with the 50 muscle spindles with their 200 nerve fibres, the 25,000 ordinary muscle fibres are relatively neglected by the central nervous system. There are only 150 large α motor fibres devoted to their direct activation. Each muscle fibre is innervated by a single branch of a single motor fibre so that simple division is enough to show that the motor unit contains on average some 170 muscle fibres. Physiological work suggest that the extreme values vary from 40 to 500 fibres, but that most motor units contain between 60 and 300 fibres. The average tension developed by a motor unit when tetanically activated is 16 g wt., giving a contractile force of about 100 mg wt. per muscle fibre. The 50 spindles of soleus are supplied by just over 100 small γ motor fibres which are exclusively devoted to their innervation; this is 40% of the total somatic motor supply to soleus.

On average there are just two fusimotor fibres per spindle, but histological examination shows that each spindle actually receives 6–12 apparently quite separate fusimotor fibres. Thus, each of the original 100 stem γ fibres must divide well before reaching the spindles to produce 3–6 separate branches (i.e. over 1 mm beforehand). Physiological work has shown that the different branches of any particular γ stem fibre commonly go to separate muscle spindles. Individual spindle afferents are regularly found to be influenced by 5 or more separate fusimotor fibres (isolated in the ventral root) instead of just the two allowed on average, and individual fusimotor fibres have frequently been shown to influence the primary endings of several different spindles. There is further fusimotor branching within any particular spindle so that a single fusimotor fibre typically supplies several of its intrafusal fibres, often with more than one localised termination upon each. Conversely, any particular intrafusal muscle fibre is usually supplied by several different fusimotor fibres. The precise degree of such overlap of innervation between and within spindles has not yet been fully charted, and may be different for the two kinds of fusimotor fibre presumed to be supplying the two kinds of intrafusal muscle fibre. Physiological experiments suggest that there may be 2–3 times as many stem γ fibres supplying nuclear chain fibres as there are to nuclear bag fibres for this is the relative frequency with which static and dynamic fusimotor fibres have been isolated in ventral root filaments. In addition, it seems likely that there may be sporadic branches from α motor fibres also supplying a few spindles.

The amount of overlap of innervation which occurs is sufficient to make the concept of the 'motor unit' unhelpful when applied to a fusimotor fibre and either the muscle spindles or the particular intrafusal fibres that it supplies. On average an individual fusimotor fibre is responsible for only 3–4 intrafusal fibres and half a muscle spindle, but in practice each one supplies some 15–30 intrafusal fibres scattered in some 4 or more different spindles. The main muscle can usefully be treated as a series of independent motor units whose effects sum more or less arithmetically, and this provides the basis for the use of isometric myographic recording to deduce the quantity of a motor discharge occurring under various circumstances. But the muscle spindles cannot be dealt with so simply; it remains for experiment to show the best way to handle the statistical relations between the fusimotor input to the spindles and the resulting effect on their afferent output.

Finally, it should be emphasised that the various numerical values of this section have all been rounded off to help produce a simple general picture. They are orders of magnitude and not precise values for direct comparison with particular experimental findings. They are derived from the following papers which give more specific figures, but not all of which are in agreement (Barker, 1962*b*; Boyd, 1962; Boyd & Davey, 1968; Clark, 1931; Crowe & Matthews, 1964; Bessou & Laporte, 1966; McPhedran, Wuerker & Henneman, 1965; Rack & Westbury, 1969; Swett & Eldred, 1960).

Résumé of standard classification of muscle nerve fibres

The histogram produced by plotting the number of fibres of each size in a muscle nerve against their diameter provides what is called a fibre spectrum. In the past the observation that the spectra of both the afferent and the efferent fibres possessed more than one peak provided an important clue that fibres with different functions tend to be of different sizes. Knowledge of such differences is now important for a number of physiological purposes, such as the identification of single fibres by measurement of their conduction velocity, and the recruitment of functionally different sets of fibres by increasing the strength of an electrical stimulus.

Motor fibres. The motor fibres may be divided into large α fibres which supply ordinary extrafusal muscle fibres and smaller γ fibres which supply exclusively the muscle spindles. The α fibres have diameters of 8–20 μm and conduct at 50–120 m/sec. The γ fibres have diameters of 2–8 μm and velocities of 10–50 m/sec. These figures refer to the main nerve trunks. The differences between α and γ fibres are no longer so obvious near their terminations because the α fibres branch so much the more freely. Attempts to anatomically subdivide the γ fibres where they run in the main nerve trunk have yet to be brought to a successful conclusion. Motor fibres which supply both intrafusal and extrafusal muscle fibres are usually called β fibres irrespective of their precise size.

Afferent fibres. These are classified into groups I to IV rather than by being referred to by Greek letters. This illogically different nomenclature from that of the motor fibres has arisen for historical reasons. Group I consists of fibres of 12–20 μm diameter (72–120 m/sec) and is contributed to equally by fibres from spindle primary endings (Ia fibres) and those from Golgi tendon organs (Ib fibres). Group II consists of fibres of 4–12 μm in diameter (24–72 m/sec) and mostly arises from spindle secondary endings. However, for some nerves such as that to tibialis anterior an appreciable fraction of the group II fibres supply free nerve endings. Group III and IV comprise the smallest medullated fibres and the non-medullated fibres respectively. They both terminate exclusively as free nerve endings. Joints are supplied predominantly by fibres of group II and III diameter, but also by a few fibres of up to 16 μm diameter. This has important practical consequences as joint afferents may run in apparently pure muscle nerves and so contaminate all groups of muscle afferents.

Limitations of classifications. The above dogmatic and simplified description is based on electrophysiological as well as histological study. Histological work alone can provide functionally specific spectra only for fibres near their termination deep in the muscle.

In the nerve trunk all fibres tend to be thicker and can only be allocated a function by electrophysiological work. The motor classification is a reasonably precise one since in most muscle nerves there is a complete deficiency of fibres of a size in between that of the α and γ fibres. For the afferent spectrum, however, the troughs between the various peaks never come right down to the baseline. This raises the problem of how to classify such intermediate fibres and more fundamentally whether when the classification of afferent fibres into four groups is put to the test it is envisaged as primarily an anatomical one or primarily a physiological one. This uncertainty was not resolved when the classification was originally introduced and as no general agreement has yet been reached upon the matter it has continued to produce confusion ever since.

Definition. In the present work the terms group I, II, III and IV will be used in a strictly anatomical sense. On the other hand, the terms Ia, Ib and spindle group II will be used in a physiological sense for the afferent fibres from spindle primaries, from tendon organs and spindle secondaries respectively. These latter terms will be adhered to even if the diameters of the fibres concerned should stray slightly outside their proper anatomical boundaries.

All the above applies strictly only to nerves supplying the larger muscles of the cat's hindlimb. Other nerves and other species may have different sizes of fibres subserving the same functions. On the assumption that the difference is chiefly one of scaling, applicable to all sizes of fibres, the above classification may reasonably be stretched so as to cover other cases and the usual names applied to fibres of the right function falling into the right peaks of the spectrum even though their absolute size is wrong. However, unless care is taken to explain precisely what is being done this can lead to yet further confusion. In spite of all these difficulties the α–γ and groups I–IV classifications have proved so verbally convenient and have been so widely adopted that there seems little prospect of their being displaced by a more rationally based system. Provided their imprecisions are recognised they can usually be employed so as to clarify rather than confuse, and have become a useful form of shorthand as summarised and illustrated in Table 2.1 and Fig. 2.12.

References

Adal, M. N. & Barker, D. (1962). Intramuscular diameters of afferent nerve fibres in the rectus femoris muscle of the cat. In *Symposium on Muscle Receptors*, ed. Barker, D. pp. 249–256. Hong Kong: Hong Kong University Press. [83–85]

— (1965). Intramuscular branching of fusimotor fibres. *J. Physiol.* **177**, 288–299. [75, 91]

Andrew, B. L., Leslie, G. C. & Thompson, J. (1970). Characteristics of secondary endings in muscle spindles in caudal segmental muscles of the rat. *J. Physiol.* **206**, 31–32P. [92]

Barker, D. ed. (1962a). *Symposium on Muscle Receptors*. Hong Kong: Hong Kong University Press. [84]

— (1962b). The structure and distribution of muscle receptors. In *Symposium on Muscle Receptors*, ed. Barker, D. pp. 227–240. Hong Kong: Hong Kong University Press. [73, 87, 88, 95]

Barker, D. & Chin, N. K. (1960). The number and distribution of muscle-spindles in certain muscles of the cat. *J. Anat.* **94**, 473–486. [88]

Barker, D., Harker, D., Stacey, M. J. & Smith, C. R. (1971). Fusimotor innervation. In *Research in muscle development and the muscle spindle*, Excerpta medica, Amsterdam. In the press. [76]

Barker, D., Ip, M. C. & Adal, M. N. (1962). A correlation between the receptor population of the cat's soleus muscle and the afferent fibre diameter spectrum of the nerve supplying it. In *Symposium on Muscle Receptors*, ed. Barker, D. pp. 257–261. Hong Kong: Hong Kong University Press. [87, 88]

Barker, D., Stacey, M. J. & Adal, M. N. (1970). Fusimotor innervation in the cat. *Phil. Trans. R. Soc.* B **258**, 315–346. [73]

Becker, H. W. & Wiesendanger, M. (1967). Electrophysiologische und elektronmikroskopische charakterisierung der efferenten Innervation des M. tenuissimus der Katze. *Helv. physiol. pharmac. Acta* **25**, 262–286. [76]

Bessou, P. & Laporte, Y. (1966). Observations on static fusimotor fibres. In *Muscular Afferents and Motor Control*, ed. Granit, R. pp. 81–89. Stockholm: Almqvist & Wiksell. [95]

Boyd, I. A. (1962). The structure and innervation of the nuclear bag muscle fibre system and the nuclear chain muscle fibre system in mammalian muscle spindles. *Phil. Trans. R. Soc.* B **245**, 81–136. [73, 75, 82, 88, 95]

Boyd, I. A. & Davey, M. R. (1962). The groups of origin in the nerves to skeletal muscle of the γ_1 and γ_2 fusimotor fibres present close to, and within mammalian muscle spindles. In *Symposium on Muscle Receptors*, ed. Barker, D. pp. 191–198. Hong Kong: Hong Kong University Press. [76]

Boyd, I. A. & Davey, M. R. (1966a). The distribution of two types of small motor nerve fibre to different muscles in the hind limb of the cat. In *Muscular Afferents and Motor Control*, ed. Granit, R. pp. 59–68. Stockholm: Almqvist & Wiksell. [76]

— (1966b). The composition of peripheral nerves. In *Control and Innervation of Skeletal Muscle*, ed. Andrew, B. L. pp. 18–31. Dundee: Thomson. [76]

— (1968). *Composition of Peripheral Nerves*. 57 pp. Edinburgh: Livingstone. [72, 76–82, 87–91, 95]

Clarke, D. A. (1931). Muscle counts of motor units—a study in innervation ratios. *Am. J. Physiol.* **96**, 296–304. [95]

Clough, J. F. M., Kernell, D. & Phillips, C. G. (1968). Conduction velocity in proximal and distal portions of forelimb axons in the baboon. *J. Physiol.* **198**, 167–178. [91]

Crowe, A. & Matthews, P. B. C. (1964). Further studies of static and dynamic fusimotor fibres. *J. Physiol.* **174**, 132–151. [95]

Eccles, J. C. & Sherrington, C. S. (1930). Numbers and contraction-values of individual motor-units examined in some muscles of the limb. *Proc. R. Soc.* B **106**, 326–357. [69–71, 78, 80, 88, 91]

Erlanger, J., Bishop, G. H. & Gasser, H. S. (1926). The action potential waves transmitted between the sciatic nerve and its spinal roots. *Am. J. Physiol.* **78**, 574–591. [73]

Erlanger, J. & Gasser, H. S. (1937). *Electrical Signs of Nervous Activity*. Philadelphia: University of Pennsylvania Press. [68, 74]

Freeman, M. A. R. & Wyke, B. (1967). The innervation of the knee joint. An anatomical and histological study in the cat. *J. Anat.* **101**, 505–532. [86]

Hagbarth, K. E. & Wohlfart, G. (1952). The number of muscle-spindles in certain muscles in cat in relation to the composition of the muscle nerves. *Acta Anat.* **15**, 85–104. [77, 81]

Henneman, E. & Olson, C. B. (1965). Relations between structure and function in the design of skeletal muscles. *J. Neurophysiol.* **28**, 581–598. [93]

Hník, P. (1970). The increased response of chronically de-efferented rat muscle spindles to stretch. *Brain Res.* **21**, 448–451. [91]

Hunt, C. C. (1954). Relation of function to diameter in afferent fibres of muscle nerves. *J. gen. Physiol.* **38**, 117–131. [89]

Hunt, C. C. & McIntyre, A. K. (1960). Characteristics of responses from receptors from the flexor longus digitorum muscle and adjoining interosseus region of the cat. *J. Physiol.* **153**, 74–87. [87]

Hunt, C. C. & Paintal, A. S. (1958). Spinal reflex regulation of fusimotor neurones. *J. Physiol.* **143**, 195–212. [74]

Koeze, T. H. (1968). The response to stretch of muscle spindle afferents of baboon's tibialis anticus and the effect of fusimotor stimulation. *J. Physiol.* **197**, 107–121. [91]

Langley, J. N. (1922). The nerve fibre constitution of peripheral nerves and of nerve roots. *J. Physiol.* **56**, 382–396. [72]

Leksell, L. (1945). The action potentials and excitatory effects of the small ventral root fibres to skeletal muscle. *Acta physiol. scand.* **10,** Suppl. 31, 1–84. [74]

Lloyd, D. P. C. (1943). Neuron patterns controlling transmission of ipsilateral hind limb reflexes in cat. *J. Neurophysiol.* **6,** 293–315. [78–81]

Lloyd, D. P. C. & Chang, H. T. (1948). Afferent fibres in muscle nerves. *J. Neurophysiol.* **11,** 199–208. [77, 81, 82, 91]

McPhedran, A. M., Wuerker, R. B. & Henneman, E. (1965). Properties of motor units in a homogeneous red muscle (soleus) of the cat. *J. Neurophysiol.* **28,** 71–84. [95]

Mayer, R. F. & Mawdsley, C. (1965). Studies in man and cat of the significance of the H wave. *J. Neurol. Neurosurg. Psychiat.* **28,** 201–211. [91]

O'Leary, J., Heinbecker, P. & Bishop, G. H. (1935). Analysis of function of a nerve to a muscle. *Am. J. Physiol.* **110,** 636–658. [77]

Rack, P. M. H. & Westbury, D. R. (1969). The effects of length and stimulus rate on tension in the isometric cat soleus muscle. *J. Physiol.* **204,** 443–460. [95]

Rexed, B. & Therman, P. O. (1948). Calibre spectra of motor and sensory nerve fibres to flexor and extensor muscles. *J. Neurophysiol.* **11,** 133–140. [77, 81]

Rushton, W. A. H. (1951). A theory of the effects of fibre size in medullated nerve. *J. Physiol.* **115,** 101–122. [77]

Sherrington, C. S. (1894). On the anatomical constitution of nerves of skeletal muscles; with remarks on recurrent fibres in the ventral spinal nerve-root. *J. Physiol.* **17,** 211–258. [77]

Skoglund, S. (1956). Anatomical and physiological studies of knee joint innervation in the cat. *Acta physiol. scand.* **36,** Suppl. 124, 1–101. [86]

Stacey, M. J. (1969). Free nerve endings in skeletal muscle of the cat. *J. Anat.* **105,** 231–254. [87]

Swett, J. E. & Eldred, E. (1960). Distribution and numbers of stretch receptors in medial gastrocnemius and soleus muscles of the cat. *Anat. Rec.* **137,** 453–460. [95]

Thiel, W. von. (1959). Bau und funktionell Bedeutung einiger isolierter markhaltiger Nervenfasern des Musculus piriformis der Katze. *Acta Anat.* **37,** 137–153. [88]

3

PATTERNS OF AFFERENT RESPONSE

As so often in the study of the nervous system, histological investigation raises questions that require other methods for their solution
and which may have to await development by a later generation.
The classical histologists demonstrated the range of afferent
endings that occur in muscles and joints, and thus set the stage
for the era of single unit recording which has been with us for the
last 45 years. The era was initiated by Adrian & Zotterman
(1926) who recorded from the nerve to the sterno-cutaneus muscle
of the frog with an early home-made valve amplifier and the now
long-obsolete capillary electrometer. By cutting successive slices
off the muscle they were able to reduce the otherwise unanalysably
complex nervous activity to a regular train of similar 'all-or-
nothing' waves; these they showed to be the impulses generated

in a single nerve fibre by the activity of a single afferent ending. Adrian & Zotterman were thus the first ever to record a single unit discharge from a nervous structure and they thereby opened the way for finding out what is 'happening in each fibre' under a variety of conditions. Figure 3.1 reproduces one of their records as

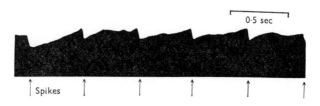

FIG. 3.1. One of the earliest single fibre recordings of the discharge of a stretch receptor in muscle (sterno-cutaneus of frog). The long duration of the individual spikes may be presumed to be due to the inertia of the recording instrument; this was a capillary electrometer in which the amplified potential alters the surface tension across a mercury–sulphuric acid interface and thus causes a small movement which is photographed under the microscope. (Adrian & Zotterman, 1926, Fig. 1D, heavily retouched.)

an act of sentiment, and to remind ourselves how much we are now helped by the advances of technology. Quite reasonably, Adrian & Zotterman were content to show that the frequency of discharge of the unknown end-organ they studied increased when the load was increased, and decreased by adaptation with the passage of time when the load was kept constant. The subsequent problem was, and still is, to determine the differences in functional specificity which may be presumed to exist between each of the anatomically recognisable types of afferent ending; in addition, functional differences may possibly also exist between some receptors which are not histologically differentiable.

The problem of identifying the pattern of response of each of the histologically identifiable endings

The elucidation of the patterns of response of the various endings hangs on the resolution of three kinds of difficulty. First, it depends upon the ability to record electrophysiologically from the requisite single fibres. This has become commonplace for the larger medullated fibres which are now usually isolated as functionally single units by splitting the dorsal spinal roots into fine filaments; this is easier than splitting peripheral nerves because the spinal roots contain less connective tissue. The recording of single unit discharges from finer medullated fibres and from non-medullated fibres, however, still poses considerable technical difficulties; this is because of the greater fragility of fine fibres and the smaller size of their externally recordable action potential. Thus any electrophysiological study of muscle afferents is liable to produce a sample which is more or less biassed in favour of large fibres. In consequence any patterns of behaviour which are shown mainly by smaller fibres are the more easily overlooked by the experimenter, though *a priori* they should be suspected of being of equal importance to the central nervous system.

Sampling errors may also arise as a result of the particular method used to first detect the fibres which are to be subsequently isolated. If the endings are detected by virtue of a spontaneous discharge, or by their response to some particular physiological stimulus, then endings with no spontaneous discharge or a high threshold to the chosen stimulus can the more easily be missed. Samples of single units which are random with regard to receptor type, as opposed to fibre size, are perhaps most readily obtained by using an electrical stimulus to excite fibres of all sizes and so detect units for isolation, and to follow the progress of the dissection. The physiological responsiveness of the afferent is then studied after isolation is complete. One way of attempting to decide upon the degree of bias in a sample of afferent fibres is to convert conduction velocity to diameter and so produce a synthetic fibre spectrum which may be compared with the histologically determined fibre spectrum for the same nerve, though only too often this is taken from another animal. Some deficiency of small fibres is then usually apparent, but it is doubtful if the comparison is sufficiently reliable for all departures from random sampling to be immediately apparent.

Second, there is the problem of correlating the various patterns of discharge which are shown by different single afferent fibres with the various types of histologically identifiable terminal. In the first place this tends to be done by *ad hoc* arguments. Ideally, however, a physiological stimulus should be shown to evoke a characterised type of response from a localised region of tissue which subsequent histological examination demonstrates to contain only a single receptor. Until the recent experimentation on isolated living muscle spindles such direct correlation has only rarely been achieved. Hitherto most of the correlations have been established on the basis of less direct evidence, and in particular on arguments based on a knowledge of the fibre spectra and on the measurement of the conduction velocity of the single afferent fibres from which recordings have been made. However, once a characteristic pattern of discharge has been allocated to a particular kind of receptor then the pattern itself becomes sufficient for receptor identification in subsequent single unit recordings.

Third, there is the problem of supplying each end-organ with an appropriate range of physiological stimuli (i.e. natural or adequate stimuli) for it to be able to display the essential features of the role for which it is functionally specialised. The technical aspect of the problem is the manufacture of mechanical stimulators and the like which are sufficiently versatile to match the sensitivity and range of response of the various end-organs. For example, the primary endings of the spindles in the soleus muscle of the cat respond with a progressive increase in firing to steady stretches of up to 10–15 mm, but they are also excited by superimposed high frequency vibration (100–300 Hz) of an amplitude of 5 μm or less (peak-to-peak). Thus to avoid artefactual excitation by vibration a muscle stretcher should have a peak-to-peak noise level of less than 0·05% of its maximum movement. This is easily achieved by simple mechanical devices but these will not produce a sufficiently wide range of dynamic stimuli for many purposes. The electro-magnetic, hydraulic and pneumatic devices which allow rapid stretches of large amplitude to be applied to a whole muscle need careful design to avoid stray noise. The technical problems, however, are generally soluble once they have been recognised. What is more serious is the conceptual aspect of the problem of providing suitable adequate stimuli. This is rarely explicitly recognised, even though in the past it has been the more important in impeding the advance of knowledge about peripheral receptors and seems likely to be long with us in the investigation of single units within the CNS which respond to proprioceptive stimuli. The conceptual problem is simply that an experimenter needs to visualise the appropriate stimuli to use before he can design an apparatus for their generation; otherwise only chance will decide whether or not a specialised functional unit, be it neurone or end-organ, is given an opportunity to display its specialised function. Furthermore, the generation of suitable stimuli needs to be accompanied by suitable analysis of the resulting response, for the essential point may be not whether a unit responds at all, but the quantitative way in which its response is related to the stimulus.

The above points may now seem self-evident but this has not always been so. The differences between the behaviour of the primary and secondary spindle endings only became apparent as controlled dynamic stimuli came to be employed, and the recent use of small-amplitude sinusoidal stretching has added fresh understanding of the role of the primary ending and its fusimotor control. Both cases required the generation of suitable mechanical stimuli combined with a suitable quantitative analysis of the responses. Simple observation of afferent responses restricted to periods of static stretch of a muscle can lead only to the classification of all mechanically excitable endings as 'stretch receptors'. The problem of deciding upon appropriate stimuli *de novo* admits of no general solution, and of course becomes progressively more serious in studying the responses of single units within the central nervous system. For cutaneous receptors simple introspection tells one which stimuli lead to conscious sensation and so should be investigated in the first place. The discharges of many muscle afferent fibres, however, do not appear to influence consciousness, and so relatively little help has been available from this quarter. Up to the present, physiologists have been working through the obvious mechanical variables describing the state of a muscle such as its length, velocity of movement and the preceding acceleration, and the tension and its derivatives. But there can be no certainty that all the appropriate stimuli have yet been employed, at any rate for the humoral or metabolic excitation of free nerve endings. However, for the last decade it has been possible to allocate a different pattern of firing to all the various kinds of muscle and joint afferent which are supplied by large nerve fibres. Each of them appears to transmit a signal about a different facet of the mechanical state of a muscle or the position of a joint, and so to this extent a satisfyingly simple view of their function has now been established. Whether the central nervous system uses the afferent information in relation to the stimuli to which the physiologist currently attaches most importance remains for the future to show.

*The first mammalian study and the classification of receptors
into types A, B and C*

B. H. C. Matthews (1933) was the first to record the discharge
of single afferent fibres from receptors in muscle and he provided
a comprehensive description of their behaviour to which little
was added over the following 20 years. It is thus helpful for an
appreciation of the earlier literature to consider his experiments
in detail and in particular to outline his terminology which had a
widespread if somewhat temporary usefulness. Moreover his work
illustrates several of the problems which have just been discussed.
Matthews subdivided the nerve to a variety of muscles in the cat
(usually the soleus or the peroneus longus) at a point between the
muscle and the recording electrodes until only one afferent fibre
remained intact in the dissected region. This was shown by the
regularity of rhythm and uniformity of size of the action potentials
which he recorded from the whole nerve beyond the point at which
it had been cut down. Matthews was immediately faced with the
problem which has just been discussed, namely of deducing the
histological nature of the receptor connected to any particular
afferent fibre from which he was recording. He distinguished three
main patterns of discharge and suggested that they arose from three
different types of receptor, temporarily named A, B and C. On the
basis of certain features of the responses he suggested that the
A endings were muscle spindle endings, the B endings were Golgi
tendon organs and the C endings were in the muscle fascia.

The C endings were only occasionally isolated in his preparations. They fired 5–20 impulses during the application of a stretch
to the muscle and sometimes also on the release of a pre-existing
stretch, but they adapted rapidly so that there was no continued
response during a steady stretch; nor were they active during a
maintained contraction of the muscle elicited by stimulation of its
nerve, though they might fire a few impulses on the rising or the
falling phase of the contraction. C endings were not found if the
fascia was cleared away from the muscle, and were felt to be of
relatively little importance. Matthews did not attempt to equate
the C endings with any of the histologically known structures, but
it seems likely that they were free nerve endings. The behaviour
of these is discussed later in more detail (p. 117).

Type A and B endings were both excited by steady stretch of

the muscle, but the threshold stretch required to excite the B endings was usually far the higher. The A endings often fired spontaneously in the absence of any external stretch at all and always fired rhythmically when the tension in the muscle was raised to 5–10 g as a result of stretching it. In contrast, a tension of 20–200 g was usually required to excite the B endings and sometimes the threshold tension was as much as 700 g. The more crucial difference, however, between the A and the B endings lay in their response to a contraction of the muscle elicited by weak stimulation of its nerve. Any pre-existing discharge of A endings was then diminished or abolished. In contrast, during contraction the B endings were excited to discharge more rapidly than before or to fire if they were previously silent. This is illustrated in Fig. 3.2 for

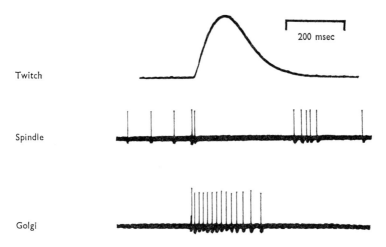

FIG. 3.2. The contrasting responses of a spindle ending and a tendon organ during a twitch contraction.

twitch contractions. Fulton & Pi-Suñer (1928) had previously pointed out on theoretical grounds that such a difference in behaviour was to be expected between the tendon organ and the muscle spindle receptors. Fig. 3.3 shows their classical diagram. The tendon organs lie in series with the muscle fibres and so would be pulled upon by muscle contraction in much the same way as by stretch of the muscle. The spindles, however, lie in parallel with the main muscle fibres so that muscle contraction and muscle stretch

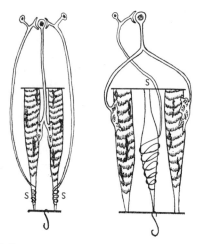

FIG. 3.3. Classical diagram contrasting the 'in-series' arrangement of the tendon organ (left) with the 'in-parallel' arrangement of the muscle spindle (right); the sense organ is labelled *s* in each case. The synaptic connections were drawn to show how the spindle, but not the tendon organ, could give rise both to a stretch reflex on simple stretch and to a silent period in the electromyogram during a superadded twitch. (Fulton & Pi-Suñer, 1928, Figs. 2 and 3.)

should have opposite effects upon them, even though both procedures increase the tension in the muscle as a whole. Stretch of the muscle will of course stretch the spindle, but contraction will slightly slacken it. This is because even under isometric conditions some muscle fibre shortening will still be allowed through a slight yielding of the tendon. This will partially unload the muscle spindles and relieve them of any pre-existing stretch stimulus— assuming of course that the effects of any intrafusal contraction are insufficient to compensate for the shortening.

The differentiation of spindle afferents from tendon organ afferents by their responses during muscle contraction has come to be generally accepted and is still regularly employed. The validity of the method has been strengthened by the finding that only the A endings, as defined above, are influenced by the stimulation of isolated γ efferents (Hunt & Kuffler, 1951). The practical value of this functional difference between spindle and tendon organ endings should not be allowed to obscure recognition of its fundamental importance from the point of view of the information that the two kinds of receptor signal to the central nervous system. It is interesting that this functional differentiation is achieved merely by virtue of a different anatomical arrangement and thus mechanical coupling of the two end-organs with the ordinary muscle fibres, rather than by any differences between the properties of the nerve terminals themselves.

It is easily overlooked that there are several factors which may complicate the experimental application of Fulton & Pi-Suñer's criterion. In the first place if only a small part of a muscle is activated, as by stimulation of a ventral root filament, the resulting asymmetrical contraction may 'accidentally' pull upon certain spindles. An asymmetrical contraction may also fail to pull upon certain tendon organs or even relieve them of pre-existing strain so that their discharge slows and they improperly mimic the response of a spindle (Houk & Henneman, 1967). Even when the whole muscle is activated some spindles may well still be 'accidentally' excited by the extrafusal contraction, though how far this occurs is a matter for debate. Such stray effects on spindles may be largely eliminated by working under semi-isotonic conditions rather than strictly isometric conditions, for this ensures an adequate muscle shortening to unload spindles while still producing an increase of tension to excite tendon organs.

A more serious potential complication is that if intrafusal fibres are activated simultaneously with the extrafusal fibres there is no longer any theoretical reason to expect spindle silence during muscle contraction. In preparations in which the muscle spindles are supplied by separate and smaller motor fibres than are the extrafusal fibres, intrafusal contraction is readily avoided by using suitably weak stimuli. In some muscles of some species, however, the intrafusal fibres may be supplied by branches of the motor fibres to extrafusal muscle fibres so that the two kinds of muscle fibre are inevitably activated together on nerve stimulation. The identification of spindle afferents then becomes more complex and each case must be considered on its own (see later discussion on evidence for common innervation). Fortunately, intrafusal contraction tends to be relatively ineffective at exciting the afferent endings when only a single stimulus is applied to the nerve. Thus it is rare for intrafusal contraction to be able to fill in the characteristic pause of the spindle afferent during a twitch contraction of the muscle, though it may readily do so for tetanic contractions, particularly those evoked by high-frequency stimulation (c.f. Harvey & Matthews, 1961).

B. H. C. Matthews (1933) found a further important functional difference between spindle endings and tendon organs by observing their response to a rapidly applied stretch. This is illustrated in Fig. 3.4 which shows that during the phase of dynamic stretching the spindle ending fired far more rapidly than it did at the final

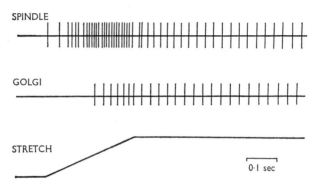

FIG. 3.4. The contrasting sensitivities to a dynamic stimulus of a spindle ending and a Golgi tendon organ. The spindle ending may be presumed to have been a primary ending. (Matthews, B. H. C., 1933, tracings of Figs. 5B and 16B respectively, showing responses on comparable stretching of the soleus muscle of the cat in two different preparations.)

length, whereas the tendon organ did not. Matthews concluded that 'the response of the B ending seems to depend on the tension at any moment and to be only slightly affected by the rate of stretch, whereas that of the A ending is largely dependent on the rate of stretch' rather than its absolute value (1933, p. 28). This difference between their behaviour probably also has a mechanical rather than a strictly neural basis. The velocity sensitivity of the spindle endings which B. H. C. Matthews found to distinguish them from the tendon organ endings is now, however, known to be a property solely of the primary endings and is not shown by the secondary endings which in this respect behave very like the tendon organs.

Demonstration of fusimotor excitation and the obsolete subdivision of A endings into types A1 and A2

A generation before B. H. C. Matthews' work Ruffini had described the histologically distinct primary and secondary afferent endings of the spindle and so it was natural for Matthews to attempt to subdivide the spindle endings into two kinds. On increasing the strength of a repetitive stimulus to the nerve slightly above that needed to elicit a maximal muscle contraction he found that some A endings then fired more rapidly than before, whereas other endings were silenced just as they were with weaker stimuli. He attributed the acceleration, when present, to the effects of 'contraction of the intrafusal fibres' as a result of their motor fibres being excited. On Ruffini's findings these fusimotor fibres were believed to be smaller than and separate from those to the ordinary muscle fibres so that they would be excited by stimuli which were supramaximal for muscle contraction but not by those which were submaximal. Figure 3.5 shows the different effects of maximal

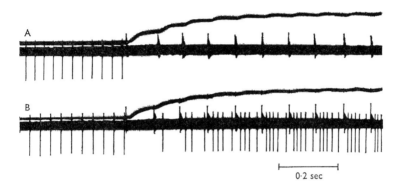

FIG. 3.5. B. H. C. Matthews' demonstration of the spindle excitation which is produced by supramaximal stimulation of the muscle nerve and which may be attributed to fusimotor excitation. A, silencing of spindle discharge by stimulation which just produced a maximal contraction of the main muscle (tension above, spikes below accompanied by smaller stimulus artefacts). B, acceleration of discharge on slightly supramaximal stimulation. This is the so-called A2 response which under B. H. C. Matthews' particular conditions was only given by about a third of the spindle endings. The majority were silenced by contraction for all the limited range of stimuli then employed; these were his A1 endings. The classification of spindle afferents on such a basis has now been abandoned. (B. H. C. Matthews, 1933, Fig. 12, retouched. The original stimulus artefacts were too large and too faint to be accurately reproduced so they have been retouched in a stylised manner.)

and of supramaximal stimuli on one of his A endings. There can be no doubt that the increased afferent discharge evoked by the stronger stimuli was indeed due to fusimotor excitation and the consequent intrafusal contraction (Harvey & P. B. C. Matthews, 1961). As the primary endings lie on a poorly striated region of intrafusal fibres and the secondary endings lie on a well-striated region Matthews suggested that only the primary endings would be excited by intrafusal contraction. On the basis of this belief and certain ancillary evidence he equated the fusimotor excited afferents (his A2 endings) with the primary endings, and the unexcited ones (his A1 endings) with the secondary endings. This did not, however, lead him to elucidate any further functional differences between them.

Unfortunately, more recent work has entirely failed to support this method for identifying the afferents from primary and from secondary endings, and so the classification of spindle afferent endings into types A1 and A2 has been tacitly abandoned. Reading B. H. C. Matthews' (1933) paper in the light of present knowledge suggests that most of his spindle endings, whether A1 or A2, were probably primary endings and the division into types A1 and A2 would appear to have been largely fortuitous. Matthews' method of isolating single units, like others, may have discriminated against afferents with small spikes. Anyhow, the foundering of the A1/A2 subdivision of spindle afferents after 20 or more years of acceptance illustrates the dangers besetting classifications based on functional properties, for they depend both upon the comprehensiveness of the sampling of different fibres and upon the adequacy of the range of stimuli employed, both of which can only usually be established retrospectively.

The detailed reasons for dismissing the A1/A2 classification seem worthy of brief summary as functional meaning has yet to be given to the different degree of striation of the regions of intrafusal fibre beneath the two kinds of ending. Thus the earlier classification might be suggested to be based upon, and to demonstrate, a truth which has more recently come to be overlooked. The dismissal rests on the acceptance of the present method of classifying spindle afferents into those from primary and secondary endings on the basis of measurements of their conduction velocity (see Chap. 4), for in the following essential respects the functional properties of the primary and secondary endings thereby elucidated fail to conform to those described by Matthews.

1. *Threshold.* B. H. C. Matthews' presumed secondary endings (A1 endings) had a very low threshold to mechanical stretch, often discharged spontaneously when the muscle was not loaded, and many of them were excited by arterial pulsation to discharge one or two impulses on each heart beat. For the cat soleus, which was one of the muscles used originally, these are all now recognisable as characteristics of primary endings and not of secondary endings. The slightly higher threshold of B. H. C. Matthews' presumed primary endings (A2 endings) were low enough for there to be no objection to their also being currently accepted as primary endings.

2. *Dynamic sensitivity.* The A1 and A2 endings responded 'practically

identically' on stretch of the muscle. B. H. C. Matthews laid great stress on the high frequency of firing of his presumed secondary endings (A1) during the dynamic phase of a stretch, as illustrated in the present Fig. 3.4. Such behaviour is now seen as characteristic of the primary ending, but not of the secondary ending. Matthews did not specifically illustrate the dynamic behaviour of his presumed primary endings (A2), but by implication they behaved in the way which we still believe primary endings to behave.

3. *Response to fusimotor stimulation.* Both primary and secondary endings have now repeatedly been found to be excited on stimulation of single fusimotor fibres. Moreover, both may be induced to give the A2 type of response on tetanic stimulation of the muscle nerve, provided the stimulus intensity and the initial muscle tension are adequate. In the original study the stimuli may simply not have been strong enough nor of suitably high frequency. This and other points are discussed in some detail by Harvey and P. B. C. Matthews (1961).

The deduction of fibre size from the measurement of conduction velocity—Hursh's conversion factor

The foregoing description of the first study of mammalian muscle receptors illustrates the need for additional criteria for characterising single units studied electrophysiologically. One criterion which is now routine is the measurement of the conduction velocity of the fibre in question. This allows an estimate to be made of the fibre's diameter for the classical studies of the compound action potential firmly established that large fibres conduct more rapidly than small ones (Erlanger & Gasser, 1937). Thus attempts can be made to correlate the conduction velocities of the fibres studied with the diameters of the nerve fibres seen to be supplying particular kinds of receptor. One flaw in this approach is, of course, that the conduction velocity is measured in the main nerve trunk while the functionally different fibres can only be identified and measured at their termination, where they will be thinner to a variable degree.

In the classical studies on the frog there was a good deal of discussion about the precise relation between diameter and velocity and whether or not it was linear. In the mammal it has become standard to take the diameter of the fibre, expressed in micra (μm), as one sixth of the value of the conduction velocity, expressed in metres/sec. This practice stems from Hursh's (1939) work on the kitten and cat in which for a variety of nerves of diverse function he measured, first the velocity of the fastest fibre in life, and second the size of the largest fibre of the self-same nerve after histological preparation; he assumed that both figures of a pair applied to the same fibre. (The nerves used were the peroneal, sural, saphenous, vagus, cervical sympathetic and the hypogastric.) Figure 3.6

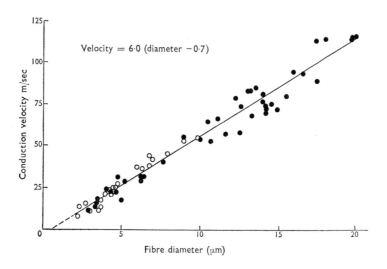

FIG. 3.6. Hursh's data showing a linear relation between diameter and conduction velocity for cat medullated nerve fibres. The full circles were obtained using nerves from adult cats and the open circles were obtained from those of kittens. The figures for the diameters of the fibres include their myelin sheaths. (Replotted from Fig. 2, Hursh, 1939.)

is a direct re-plot of his results and demonstrates a linear relation between velocity and total fibre diameter with a constant of proportionality of 6 metres $\sec^{-1} \mu m^{-1}$. Hursh's line, however, did not quite pass through the origin but crossed the X-axis at 0·7 μm diameter. Using the proportionality factor of 6 and neglecting the end correction of 0·7 μm, Hunt (1954) produced a synthetic fibre spectrum for the de-efferented nerves to the soleus and medial gastrocnemius muscles from measurement of the conduction velocities of about 600 afferent fibres; these had been isolated from the dorsal roots by a method which was believed to give random sampling both with regard to receptor type and fibre size above about 4 μm. The artificial spectra so obtained agreed suffi- ciently well with the real histological spectra obtained earlier for it to appear that both the linear relationship and Hursh's particular conversion factor had been validated for application to muscle nerves. Since then the conversion factor of 6 has been sanctified by repeated use but has only rarely been put to any further test.

Inexactness of ratio. It now appears, however, that Hursh's particular ratio is not applicable to the small nerve fibres in an adult muscle nerve as well as to the large ones. Boyd & Davey (1968) have suggested that for γ motor fibres the appropriate conversion factor from diameter to velocity may be about 4·5 rather than 6, though they still consider the latter value to be appropriate for the large fibres. This view was based on comparisons of the compound action potential recorded in the ventral root on stimulating various de-afferented muscle nerves with the subsequently determined fibre spectra of the self-same nerves. Boyd & Davey found that the conversion factor still varied with fibre size when they measured the diameter of the axon cylinder rather than total fibre diameter. Bessou & Perl (1966) also considered that for small medullated fibres the factor should be below 6, and said that for their results the 'fit is best with a figure approximating to 3'. They studied afferent fibres conducting at 5–10 m/sec which supplied mechanoreceptors in the cat's intestine, and made approximate correlations between the velocities of single units and the various diameters of the small number of fibres found in the actual nerves studied electrophysiologically. More recently, Coppin & Jack (1972) have argued that for muscle afferents also the conversion factor gets smaller with diminishing fibre size. This was based on comparisons of the conduction velocities of individual fibres with their internodal spacing, determined by means of a movable stimulating electrode, plus the assumption that the internodal spacing was proportional to diameter. The observed increase in the value of the conversion factor with the size of the fibre of course shows that conduction velocity increases more rapidly than linearly with diameter. Thus exact interconversion between velocity and diameter awaits the experimental determination of the true relationship between them. Until then a variety of *ad hoc* 'Hursh factors' will have to be employed, one for each range of fibre size. Coppin & Jack (1972) considered that their results would be best fitted by the power relation, conduction velocity $= 1·5 \times$ (external fibre diameter)$^{1·5}$.

As the conversion factor for small medullated fibres now appears to be rather lower than the figure of 6 which has hitherto been assumed, all past studies must prove to have been optimistic about the smallness of the fibres that were successfully isolated. For example, taking a Hursh factor of 4 rather than 6 shifts the estimated conduction velocity of a 4 μm fibre from 24 to 16 m/sec, and thus also the dividing line in conduction velocity between afferent fibres of groups II and III as defined histologically. Even on Hursh's actual results, with a factor of 6 and a positive intercept of 0·7 μm, the dividing line between groups II and III should be put at 20 m/sec rather than the usual 24 m/sec though nobody seems to have bothered to do this. However, few workers have acted upon the supposition that the old conversion ratio was exact so that little is lost if it has to be changed.

Difficulties of determination. It may also be noted that the experimental determination of the conduction velocity of a single fibre is often far from exact. It is usually based on measurements of the stimulus-response interval for a single conduction distance, namely from muscle nerve to spinal root. This can only give an average conduction velocity which need not be directly relatable to the diameter at the point of stimulation, for different fibres may taper or branch to a different degree. Preferably for comparisons with histological data the local conduction velocity at the region examined microscopically should also be determined by moving one pair of electrodes. For characterising a fibre in other ways, however, the value averaged over a long length of nerve seems the more valuable. Different authors vary in whether or not they make an allowance, conventionally of 0·1 msec (Hunt, 1954), for the delay between the stimulus and the initiation of the spike, and also on whether or not they standardise the strength of the stimulus so as to reduce this initial delay to a constant value; these are however second order corrections which cannot greatly affect the result. Variations of temperature, both along the course of a nerve in a single experiment and between animals in different experiments provide a further source of variability. Even measurement of the conduction distance is not without error, for it is not always easy to measure a nerve *in situ* or to apply the right amount of stretch to straighten it out when it is removed from the body. In making comparisons with histological findings, however, far greater errors than any of the above are liable to arise from shrinkage of nerve fibres in preparing them for microscopy; some degree of shrinkage is difficult if not impossible to prevent and after the event it is often hard to establish just how much has occurred.

Thus the commonplace deduction of fibre size from fibre velocity is often far from precise, and the values obtained should be treated with caution, particularly when comparing different sets of experiments. None the less, in any individual preparation it seems safe to assume that there is a unique monotonic relation between velocity and diameter, so that fibres ranked in order of increasing velocity will also be ranked in order of increasing size; for many purposes this is sufficient. Moreover, the range of diameter and corresponding velocities of different medullated fibres is so great (2–20 μm, 5–120 m/sec) that the values for different kinds of fibres often differ by so much that they cannot possibly be confused in spite of the various inaccuracies of measurement. By and large, present practice has been adequate for the rather limited conclusions so far drawn though these have often been dressed up with a spurious appearance of accuracy. At any rate, it has helped the characterisation of the responses of the various different kinds of afferent ending, particularly the free endings which are dealt with next.

The behaviour of free nerve endings

Histological work indicates that some of the free endings are derived from non-medullated fibres and some by fine medullated fibres. This means that when in an electrophysiological experiment an afferent fibre is found to conduct at below about 15 m/sec then it can be virtually guaranteed to terminate as a free ending; the afferents to spindles and to tendon organs are regularly seen to be thicker than 5 μm near their entry into their respective endorgans. Thus free endings can be studied electrophysiologically by selecting afferents with an appropriately low conduction velocity. Whether all free endings in muscle behave broadly similarly or whether they perform a range of specialised functions as they do in the skin remains an open question. Those supplied by non-medullated fibres have as yet been barely studied.

Free endings with non-medullated afferents. Iggo (1960) isolated an undisclosed but presumably small number of single muscular afferents conducting at 0·4 to 1·6 m/sec and which may be presumed to have been non-medullated fibres supplying free endings, as these velocities are too low for any medullated fibre. None of the afferents could be excited either by stretch or by contraction of the muscle studied. They could, however, be excited by local mechanical stimulation of the surface of the muscle, by the intramuscular injection of hypertonic saline, and more weakly by the muscle ischaemia produced by vascular occlusion combined with tetanic contraction of the muscle; they were sometimes also excited by temperatures departing appreciably from normal (above 41°C and below 25°C).

Bessou & Laporte (1958) studied the muscle C fibres in the mass by using the technique introduced by Douglas & Ritchie (1957). This consists of recording the size of a compound action potential after it has propagated antidromically against an asynchronous stream of dromically conducted action potentials, set up by adequate activation of receptors. The greater the physiologically induced discharge the greater are the number of collisions between dromically and antidromically conducted spikes, and so the smaller is the compound action potential. Bessou & Laporte found that simple stretch of the muscle produced no change in the size of the C fibre potential showing that an inappreciable proportion of the endings supplied by C fibres were stretch receptors. However, they did find a reduction in the potential on making the muscle ischaemic by stimulating it after occluding the circulation. Thus both these studies suggest that some at least of the free endings supplied by non-medullated fibres are nociceptors, for they are excited by a range of stimuli which are painful in man; on the other hand some or other of them may equally provide the specialised afferent limb of a cardiovascular or respiratory regulatory reflex.

Free endings with medullated afferents. The behaviour of the free endings derived from fine medullated fibres has been investigated with broadly similar results in two careful sets of single unit studies performed simultaneously in widely separated laboratories (Paintal, 1960, in Delhi; Bessou & Laporte, 1961, in Toulouse). In both cases the declared aim was to determine the pattern of behaviour of the endings supplied by Lloyd's group III fibres. For this purpose group III afferents were defined as those conducting at below 24 m/sec, which was presumed to correspond to fibres with diameters of less than about 4 μm. A few of the afferents supplied stretch receptors which were classified on their behaviour as either spindle endings (presumably secondary endings—see later) or in one or two cases as tendon organs. About 15% of the afferents isolated could not be excited by any of the mechanical stimuli tested (15/127 for Bessou & Laporte and 6/31 for Paintal). It remains quite uncertain whether these endings were mechanically inexcitable for some trivial reason, such as damage or a failure to locate their receptive field, or for the fundamental reason that their endings were specialised to receive some quite different form of stimulus.

The majority of the group III afferents supplied mechano-receptors which could be excited by pressure locally applied to the surface of the muscle but which could not be significantly excited by muscle stretch or by muscle contraction. Because of their low conduction velocity and their functional differences from the A and B receptors, these afferents may be presumed to have supplied free nerve endings. They differed markedly from each other, however, in their threshold, their rate of adaptation and in the size of their receptive field. The threshold of even the most sensitive of the endings appears to have been rather high in comparison with that of sensitive mechanoreceptors such as the spindle primary ending, the Pacinian corpuscle or cutaneous touch corpuscles all of which may be excited by displacements of a few μm. Thus Paintal (1960, p. 255) stated of group III afferents: 'While some were stimulated by pressing the appropriate region of the muscle gently with a glass rod, others could be stimulated only by squeezing the muscle between finger and thumb.' Rather similarly, Bessou & Laporte (1961) could excite some fibres by the pressure of a stylus of 2 mm^2 tip loaded with 10 g while others required 'assez forte' compression of the musculo-tendinous junction 'entre le pouce et l'index'. Some fibres had a receptive field which embraced virtually the whole of the muscle. Others could be excited from pressure applied over an area of only a few square millimetres. These were found more commonly at the origin and insertion of the muscle. Paintal found that most of his fibres adapted rapidly, 'the discharge ceasing in about 0·5–2 sec after its onset', on the application of a maintained stimulus. Some, however, adapted very slowly and Bessou & Laporte illustrate

EM

one which was still firing at 5/sec some 30 sec after applying a steady pressure by a load of 100 g over an area of 12 mm². Bessou & Laporte only rarely observed peak frequencies of firing above 30/sec, while Paintal observed some afferents which fired briefly at 100–150/sec. These are all low values compared to those obtainable from spindle endings and tendon organs.

Most of the group III fibres were not excited to discharge a single impulse either by a strong rapid stretch of the muscle or on its maximal contraction; nor were they excited by muscle vibration (Paintal, 1962). Of those which could be excited by the classical proprioceptive stimuli rather more seem to have been excited by muscle contraction than by muscle stretch. In both cases, however, the responses were of low frequency relative to that evoked by local pressure and do not appear to have been closely related to the stimulus parameters.

From all this it may reasonably be concluded that few if any of the free endings function as stretch or contraction receptors playing a part in signalling the mechanical state of the muscle to the central nervous system. This is not, however, the same thing as saying that their occasional weak excitation by stretch or contraction can always be overlooked. Occasionally, perhaps, under the artificialities of certain experimental situations some of the central effects of such mechanical stimuli may be mediated by group III discharges rather than by the more familiar group I and II discharges. However, in life, group III afferents must be mainly excited by pressure on the muscle or by firm squeezing, both of which excite a sensation which is quite different from that experienced during normal use of a muscle when its stretch receptors will be the ones which are predominantly excited.

Paintal (1960) also injected hypertonic NaC1 solutions (0·5 ml. of 6%) into the muscle and found that this procedure excited group III afferents, while control injections of isotonic saline did not. He believed this effect was specific for the group III fibres for in his preparations he could not excite the larger afferents by this means. Iggo (1960), however, stated that in his hands the injection of hypertonic saline excited all sizes of afferents so the interpretation of Paintal's finding remains in doubt. Paintal further found that asphyxia did not excite the group III endings he studied. The asphyxia was produced by ceasing to ventilate the preparations which were both curarised and anaesthetised; it would be interesting to have such metabolic stimuli investigated under a wider range of conditions. Thus the majority of the free endings supplied by fine medullated fibres would seem to be reasonably established as mechanoreceptors excited by moderate to high pressures applied locally to the surface of the muscle, particularly at the musculo-tendinous junction. As yet, however, investigation has been insufficiently thorough to show whether or not some of these mechanoreceptors also subserve some more interesting function, and the role of the mechanically inexcitable free endings remains obscure.

The Golgi tendon organ and the lowness of its threshold in relation to the strength of muscle contraction

As already noted, B. H. C. Matthews (1933) showed that the tendon organs are slowly adapting tension receptors, with a relatively low sensitivity to the rate of change of tension. He found that they never fired spontaneously in the absence of stretch and that to excite them a steady passive stretch usually had to develop a tension of 20–200 g (soleus and peroneus longus muscles). In his hands, 'the rate of response at any tension' was 'practically the same' whether it was produced by active contraction or passive stretch (p. 29). Many years later, Hunt & Kuffler (1951) again using the soleus of the cat found rather similarly that 'in general' tendon organs 'had a high threshold to stretch, and many gave no steady discharge with a maintained external tension of 100–200 g' though an occasional one was 'found to discharge continuously even at 5–10 g tension' (1951, p. 306). They do not appear to have investigated the behaviour of tendon organs during muscular contraction. On these limited findings of a 'high threshold' for tendon organs it seems to have become widely believed that their function was simply to signal dangerously high tensions in a muscle, and that they had no part to play in the moment-to-moment control of normal muscle contraction. This view was never very convincing, for a tension of 200 g is not particularly high in a muscle which can develop 2 kg tension on maximal activation. More recent work has shown that tendon organs are indeed sufficiently sensitive to play a part in the continuous regulation of muscle contraction for they may be excited by the contraction of a single appropriately placed motor unit.

Jansen & Rudjord (1964) were the first to re-open the question of the functional role of tendon organs. They noted that those of the soleus were invariably excited by quite small muscle twitches even though some of them were relatively inexcitable on maintained passive stretch or during a slowly applied stretch. This is illustrated in Fig. 3.7 which compares the threshold tensions for excitation

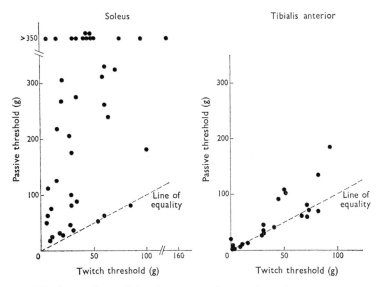

FIG. 3.7. Comparison of the thresholds of a number of tendon organs to twitch contractions and to simple stretch. The twitch threshold was determined by grading the strength of the stimulus to the muscle nerve and measuring the peak tension of the smallest twitch which would excite the ending. The passive threshold was measured by stretching the muscle by a considerable amount at 18 mm/sec and observing the tension at which the first spike was excited. (Data for soleus replotted from Fig. 5, Jansen & Rudjord, 1964, and for tibialis anterior from Fig. 2, Alnaes, 1967.)

in the two cases. The greater efficacy of the twitch was believed to be partly due to its being a more powerful dynamic stimulus and partly due to its being an 'active' tension rather than a passive tension. Because of the closeness of the mechanical coupling found histologically between muscle fibres and tendon organs, active tension was seen as having an inevitable direct action upon the tendon receptor terminals, whereas passive tension might be partly transmitted from the tendon of the muscle to its origin by connective tissue, and so by-pass the muscle fibres and their terminally arranged tendon organs. At any rate, the responsiveness to small twitches showed that the endings could not be considered to have so high a threshold as to be merely providing the afferent limb of a reflexly activated safety stop. Jansen & Rudjord (1964) showed further that those endings which had particularly high passive thresholds tended to lie at the proximal end of the muscle near its origin, and in line with the above they presumed that passively developed tension was never transmitted to these endings themselves. In the soleus muscle, therefore, active and passive tension would not appear to be equipotent stimuli and many endings are not excited by simple passive stretch limited to the physiological range of movement. They have, however, since been shown to be excited during the dynamic phase of passive stretches applied at physiologically natural velocities and within the physiological range of movement; moreover, the threshold tension then required to excite a discharge is nearly the same for passive stretches and for twitch contractions (Stuart, Goslow, Mosher & Reinking, 1970).

Soon after Jansen & Rudjord's original experiments, Alnaes (1967) working in the same laboratory endeavoured to extend these results to another muscle, the tibialis anterior, and immediately came across important differences of detail. First, all the tendon organs he studied were excited by 'passive stretching of the muscle within its physiological limits' and 4 out of 22 discharged spontaneously in the absence of stretch. Second, the differences in threshold to twitches and to slow passive stretches were insignificant, as illustrated in Fig. 3.7. This is a useful warning of the dangers of restricting observation to a single muscle, and one is left uncomfortably aware of how much other neurophysiological generalisation is poised on a similarly narrow base. In this case, the results on both muscles fortunately argue in the same direction, namely for a regulatory rather than emergency role for the tendon organs.

Action of single motor units. This view has now been greatly furthered by Houk & Henneman (1967) who performed a crucial experiment which in retrospect appears both simple and obvious as the necessary techniques had long been to hand. Using the soleus muscle they stimulated single large motor fibres, isolated in the ventral roots, and found that when the right one was obtained the contraction of a single motor unit was sufficient to excite a Golgi tendon organ. Figure 3.8 illustrates one such excita-

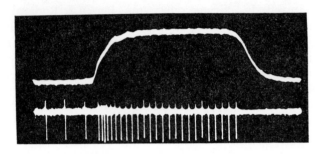

FIG. 3.8. The excitation of a tendon organ in soleus by the tetanic contraction of a single motor unit on stimulating a single α fibre in a ventral root filament. Below, afferent discharge. Above, tension. The contraction developed 18 g tension and lasted about 1 sec. (Houk & Henneman, 1967, Fig. 1.)

tion. By systematic searching they were able to isolate from 4 to 15 different motor fibres influencing a particular tendon organ, and any one of which was able to excite the ending on its own. On histological evidence they believed that each tendon organ was directly pulled upon by from 3 to 25 muscle fibres. In conjunction with the previous figures this shows that the tendon organ must usually respond to the contraction of no more than two muscle fibres and possibly often to that of one alone (i.e. for example, if 15 motor fibres can each excite a tendon organ which is pulled upon by 15 muscle fibres then each muscle fibre on its own must be able to excite the receptor since each muscle fibre is supplied by only a single motor fibre). This would make the threshold of the tendon organ only about 0·1 g applied to its particular piece of tendon. Thus the tendon organ is now firmly established as a 'low threshold' receptor for its preferred mode of stimulation, namely muscle contraction. Before all this work it often appears to have been tacitly assumed that the threshold of the tendon organ was so high that it could only be excited by the contraction of nearly all the particular muscle fibres which pulled upon it. Rather earlier, Hunt (1954) showed that, in line with the histology, the afferent fibres from tendon organs from soleus and gastrocnemius all conduct rapidly enough to fall in the group I range (72 m/sec), and so they are well placed to mediate a high-speed reflex control of muscle.

There are still, however, a number of points about tendon organs on which it would be nice to have more information. First, a wider range of muscles could usefully be studied to see how far their tendon organs are excited by passive stretch limited to the physiological range, and how far they function purely as 'contraction receptors'. From the point of view of muscle control the total tension in a muscle (active +passive) would seem to be the important variable, and on anatomical grounds this is what the tendon organs would be expected to be excited by, provided that the passive tension is due to strain of intramuscular structures and not of surrounding connective tissue. Second, though it is clear that increasing muscular tension causes increasing tendon organ discharge there is the problem of the nature of the scale with which tension is signalled.

Jansen & Rudjord (1964) chose to fit the best straight lines they could to plots of frequency of firing against the tension in the soleus. They then found that for different endings the slope ranged from 2 to 18 impulses sec^{-1} $(100 \text{ g})^{-1}$ for both active and passive tensions. Alnaes (1967), using the tibialis anterior muscle, found that on a linear–linear plot the points of frequency against tension lay on a curve of progressively decreasing slope, but that on a double logarithmic plot the relation became linear. He considered, therefore, that the relation between frequency and tension was best expressed as a power function (i.e. frequency = constant × tension^{n}) and found values for the exponent (n) ranging from 0·4 to 0·6. Jansen (1967) subsequently suggested that a power function relation would probably also be found to be appropriate for the tendon organs in the soleus if a sufficiently wide range of stimuli were to be explored. Houk & Simon (1967) treated the response of the ending as directly proportional to the tension, but they explicitly stated that they considered this an approximation valid only for small signals. More significantly, Houk & Henneman (1967) showed that the simultaneous activation of a pair of motor units both of which excited the same tendon organ produced an effect which was greater than that of either alone, but which was less than the arithmetical sum of their individual actions. On the assumption that the tension applied to the tendon organs did sum arithmetically this would suggest a logarithmic relation or a power relation with exponent less than 1 between frequency and tension, rather than a linear one. This view would have been strengthened if the description of the work had included some observations on the effectiveness of the summation of the tension produced in the whole tendon on stimulating different motor units separately and in combination. Of course, any particular tendon organ is only sampling a small fraction of the tension in a muscle, so there are actually two related but distinct things that one wishes to know. First, what is the behaviour of individual tendon organs. Second, what are the statistical relations between the massed discharge of all the tendon organs and the overall muscle tension in a progressively increasing contraction.

In this respect it has yet to be shown whether tendon organs have any preference for the tension generated by fast or by slow motor units and indeed, whether an individual tendon organ is pulled upon by fibres all of one kind or whether it is summing the action of muscle fibres with a range of contractile properties (M. C. Brown suggested this point). Such matters require study to achieve a quantitative understanding of the regulatory role of the tendon organs.

Joint receptors and the problem of which if any of them are responsible for an accurate position sense

Psycho-physical studies show that the angle of a joint can be accurately appreciated and this is believed to be due to the signals sent by joint receptors. The actual study of the discharges of joint afferents has been virtually confined to those from the knee joint of the cat, and until very recently the findings appeared to provide a sound basis for the accuracy of human position sense. In 1969, however, Burgess & Clark in a comprehensive study were unable to confirm much that had been hitherto rather lightly accepted, nor did their results lead to a satisfying alternative scheme. At present all that is possible is to summarise the various results and to hope that further insight will shortly be forthcoming.

Work of the 1950's. The knee joint of the cat is supplied by two separate nerves lending themselves to electrophysiological experimentation, as well as by several less accessible branches of muscular nerve trunks (cf. Freeman & Wyke, 1967); the two macroscopically obvious nerves are called the medial and the posterior articular nerves. In 1953, in independent studies, Andrew & Dodt recorded discharges of single units in the medial nerve and Boyd & Roberts in the posterior nerve. Both sets of workers regularly found slowly adapting discharges which were excited by movement of the joint or by local pressure on the joint capsule. They both found that different endings differed in the angle at which they were excited and considered that this distribution of thresholds would provide a ready basis for the central appreciation of joint angle by the recognition of which receptors were active. Moreover, they both considered that the endings were excited over a comparatively small range of joint positions. Thus Andrew & Dodt (1953) stated that the endings 'seem to be arranged so that each has an arc of maximum sensitivity covering a few degrees of angular movement but these ranges are different for individual endings' (p. 296). Boyd & Roberts (1953) said that individual endings 'show characteristic frequencies for particular positions of the joint' (p. 57) and that though 'the ranges over which the individual end organs have been found to be active show considerable overlapping' there was also 'much dispersion' in the threshold angles required to excite them. Three years later, Skoglund (1956) illustrated such behaviour in more detail, as shown in Fig. 3.9. The graphs show the adapted frequency of

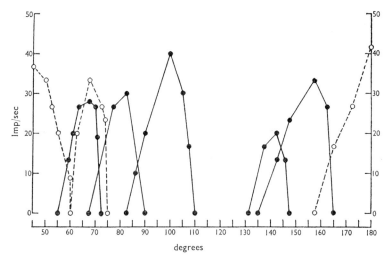

FIG. 3.9. The adapted frequencies of firing of a number of knee joint afferents at different positions of the knee. The lines join the various points obtained for each of 8 different single afferent fibres which were studied in two different experiments (solid and broken lines). In other experiments of the same series endings firing at one or other extreme of movement were found to be much commoner than those firing at intermediate positions. (Skoglund, 1956, Fig. 19.)

discharge which often appeared to be maintained 'indefinitely with very small variations of frequency' and which was sometimes observed for 4–5 hours.

In addition to being sensitive to the absolute value of the angle of the joint the endings were also sensitive to the angular velocity of movement, the discharge being increased for movements towards the angle of maximum excitation and decreased for movements away from it, whatever the actual direction of movement. Figure 3.10 shows that during movement the frequency varied systematically with the angular velocity, but that the adapted

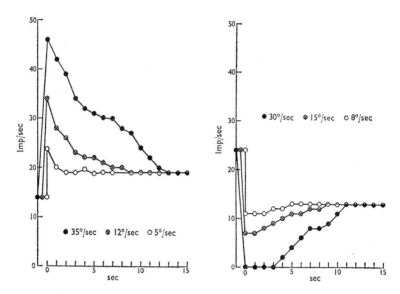

FIG. 3.10. The velocity sensitivity of a joint ending which was presumed to be of the Ruffini type. (*a*) Response to a movement of 5° at three different velocities from the same initial to the same final position. (*b*) Response to a similar movement in the opposite direction. (Skoglund, 1956, Figs. 18 and 19.)

discharge at the final position was independent of the preceding velocity. The angle over which an ending could be excited (cf. Fig. 3.9) was not invariant but depended partly on any twisting of the tibia and partly on any muscular tension exerted on the joint capsule. An increase in muscle tension tended also to increase the afferent discharge for all positions, thus extending the range of angles over which the ending was active. This was shown by pulling on muscles or by causing them to contract by stimulation, and perhaps more significantly by a decrease in joint afferent discharge occurring in the decerebrate cat on denervating the quadriceps muscle and so abolishing its pre-existing tone (Skoglund, 1956, Figs. 29 and 30).

The velocity-sensitive but otherwise slowly adapting receptors were shown both by Skoglund (1956) and by Boyd (1954) to be the Ruffini type of ending. This was done by locating them in an electrophysiological experiment by gentle probing of the joint capsule with a glass rod and then ablating the region and staining it with gold chloride. In addition, both workers also recorded a rapidly adapting discharge which was present only during movement of the joint and which they found to arise from paciniform endings. Skoglund (1956) recognised a further category of slowly adapting receptors which he thought arose from Golgi tendon organ type endings lying either in the internal or external ligaments and which had earlier been studied by Andrew (1954). The anatomical localisation was based on the findings that the endings could be influenced by sectioning or by pulling the ligaments rather than the capsule, and that the Golgi endings are the only ones in the ligaments. Their behaviour differed from that of the presumed Ruffini endings in two important respects: first, like the tendon organs in muscle they were rather insensitive to the velocity of movement (see Fig. 3.4); second, they were largely uninfluenced by contraction of the surrounding muscles. Both these features made the Golgi endings appear the more suitable for recording 'the exact position of the joint' (Skoglund, 1956); by implication the sensitive ranges of the Golgi endings were supposed to be scattered rather similarly to those in Fig. 3.9 though this does not seem to have been stated explicitly. The Ruffini endings were thought by Skoglund to be most effective in signalling 'minor variations of position' as they were sensitive to both velocity and position. The paciniform corpuscles were thought to possibly serve 'as an acceleration receptor' and as they were rather sensitive to vibration would certainly signal whenever movement was occurring.

All this made a conceptually satisfying background for thinking about 'position sense', which is no longer believed to be the province of the purely muscular receptors. Unfortunately, it is possible that the usual assessment of these results may have taken too little account of the limitations of the actual experimental data. Because of the positioning of their recording electrodes Boyd & Roberts (1953) and Andrew & Dodt (1953) could investigate movements of only a few tens of degrees and could not study the extremes. Thus they were unable to check how far each ending could fire outside this limited range, and in particular at the extremes of movement. Skoglund (1956) could investigate wide ranges of movement and on the basis of recording from the intact joint nerves stated that endings firing at one or other extreme of movement 'are by far the most numerous' in comparison with those firing at intermediate angles, but he did not provide a precise figure of the relative frequency of endings excited at different angles; his single unit studies appear to have been concentrated on endings with intermediate angles which were away from the extremes.

A disturbing recent investigation. The difficulties arising from sampling errors and a limited range of movement have been overcome in the recent experiments by Burgess & Clark (1969) who recorded from units isolated from dorsal root filaments rather than the muscle nerve. This allowed complete freedom of movement at the knee joint and the isolation of afferents with a wide range of conduction velocities; moreover the initial recognition of the afferents for subsequent isolation was based on electrical stimulation of the joint nerve so that the endings should have been selected quite independently of their preferred mode of physiological activation. Burgess & Clark recorded from 278 single afferent fibres running in the posterior articular nerve of the knee and which had conduction velocities ranging from 10 to 110 m/sec. Three quarters of the afferents (209) supplied slowly adapting endings which presumably included both Ruffini and Golgi endings. Unexpectedly, a completely insignificant proportion of these endings (4/209) were found to be maximally activated at some intermediate joint angle rather than at the extremes of the physiological range of movement of the joint. To make matters worse for the understanding of the origin of position sense, the majority of the slowly adapting endings (140/209) were found to be activated both at full flexion and at full extension of the joint but were completely silent for most intermediate positions of the joint. Thus even when these flexion–extension units were excited they would appear to provide ambiguous information about the angle of the joint at any time. Forty-seven of the remainder of the slowly adapting endings were active on flexion but not extension and 12 were active on extension but not flexion; these endings otherwise behaved similarly to those responding on both flexion and extension. The responses of all these endings was influenced by twisting the tibia as well as bending the knee. In addition, they were mostly sensitive, though in variable degree, to the rate of movement as well as to the absolute angle of the joint in the manner already noted by Skoglund (see Fig. 3.10).

Another 30 receptors (11% of total) were classified as 'phasic joint receptors' because they 'responded primarily to joint movement' though some of them would fire tonically for certain knee angles combined with twisting of the tibia, and all but 3 of them could be excited to discharge steadily by pressing on the knee joint. With the tibia untwisted, knee movements caused a transient response at the extremes of flexion and extension, but with the tibia twisted nearly all of them gave a transient discharge for movements at any point in the physiological range. Another 14 receptors gave a response 'characteristic of that described for Pacinian corpuscles' and were excited by light tapping of the leg and by rapid joint movement in either direction and regardless of position. No evidence was available to show whether these receptors were paciniform corpuscles or true Pacinian corpuscles, but on the basis of previous work the former seems the more likely. Another 11 fibres responded only to 'bending or twisting procedures which could be considered noxious' and may well have terminated as free endings; so also may have a further 14 fibres which were not excited by any means studied. A further 6 slowly adapting endings were presumed to lie in muscle spindles for they were excited by the intravenous injection of suxemethonium which excites spindle endings more readily than other endings (Kidd & Kučera, 1969), and which in the doses used did not excite the other joint afferents. Most of these presumed spindle afferents were tonically active over much of the physiological range of movement.

Figure 3.11 shows the range of conduction velocities of the major types of afferent studied by Burgess & Clark (1969) and emphasises the adequacy of their sample with regard to fibre size. Thus the major finding of this comprehensive single unit study is that an insignificant afferent discharge is excited over a wide range of joint angles; this was confirmed by recording from the whole of either the medial or the posterior joint nerve and finding virtually no activity in either when the joint was near its mid position. Accepting these results at their face value the nervous mechanism responsible for appreciation of joint position in the middle of the physiological range would have to be considered unknown. Moreover much of the nervous discharge which Burgess & Clark found to occur at the extremes of movement appears irrelevant for the measurement of joint position, for individual afferents did not distinguish between flexion and extension. This is such an unsatisfying position that it is to be hoped that some crucial factor has been overlooked in the most recent experiments. One conceivable possibility is that in the more intact animal muscle tone tenses the joint capsule in such a way as to significantly alter the range of response of the endings, as Skoglund (1956) found to occur for

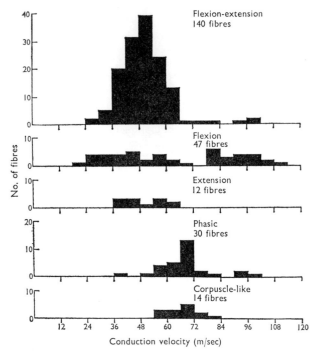

FIG. 3.11. The distribution of the conduction velocities of a number of joint afferents classified according to their functional properties. (Burgess & Clark, 1969, Fig. 4.)

some Ruffini endings. Alternatively other unsuspected factors may be at work in the normal animal maintaining intracapsular tension and with it the sensitivity of joint receptors. The experiments of Burgess & Clark (1969) were performed on anaesthetised cats with widespread denervation of the muscles acting at the knee joint. Conceivably again, free nerve endings with non-medullated afferent fibres might be providing accurate positional information by recording the stress in the joint capsule; in skin, some free endings are now established to be low threshold mechanoreceptors rather than nociceptors.

A pointer that the behaviour of joint receptors may be generally simpler than would appear from the most recent study on the knee joint is provided by some findings on receptors in the costo-vertebral joints (Godwin-Austen, 1969). These receptors, like those in the knee, were slowly adapting with a superadded sensitivity to movement. Again like those in the knee they were maximally excited on extreme displacement of the joint and were never optimally excited with the rib at an intermediate position. Unlike those in the knee, however, any particular ending was maximally excited by maximal displacement in one direction only, though some fibres were excited by displacement in one direction and some in the other. Moreover, whichever their preferred direction of displacement for maximal excitation the majority of endings were excited throughout the 'range of movement of the rib encompassed during spontaneous breathing' (Godwin-Austen, p. 741). Their adapted frequency was linearly related to the joint angle so that a peripheral signal of joint angle was provided to the CNS throughout the physiological range.

A clue that receptors in various other joints may behave as simply, and provide as accurate a basis for position sense, is provided by recordings from single neurones in the thalamus of the monkey which were excited on movement of one or other of a number of hinge joints including the knee (Mountcastle, Poggio & Werner, 1963). As with the peripheral afferent fibres the cells fired at a mean rate dependent on the position of the joint. The maximum discharge of any cell occurred at one other extreme position of the joint, but not at both, and the discharge fell monotonically as the joint was moved away from its extreme position. Most cells were excited over a range of joint angles which covered more than half the total range of movement, so that there was still a considerable neural activity with the joint near its mid position. The behaviour of the thalamic neurones would be most simply explained if the peripheral afferents behaved somewhat similarly and each fired over a wide range of joint angles and with optimal excitation at one or other extreme. There would then be no need to postulate the subtle transformations of the patterns of nervous activity which were earlier thought necessary when individual receptors were believed to discharge over only a small range of movement and to have their optimal angles scattered throughout the physiological range.

Résumé of patterns of afferent response of all the various receptors except for the recent work on spindles

The initial problem is to correlate the various patterns of discharge recordable electrophysiologically with the various kinds of receptor observed histologically.

A, B and C endings. In the first electrophysiological study of mammalian muscle receptors in 1933 three types of discharge were recognised and attributed to different endings, temporarily called A, B and C. The C endings appeared to lie in the surrounding fascia rather than the muscle proper and were probably free endings. The A endings were suggested to correspond to muscle spindle endings and the B endings to Golgi tendon organs. This was because the A endings behaved as if they lay 'in parallel' with the main muscle fibres and stopped firing when the muscle was made to contract, while the B endings behaved as if they lay 'in series' with the muscle fibres and increased their firing during muscle contraction. These patterns of behaviour corresponded to those which had already been predicted for spindles and tendon organs respectively. Experiments showed, in addition, that the spindle endings had a lower threshold and were more dynamically sensitive than the Golgi tendon organs. The spindle endings were originally further subdivided into types A1 and A2 which were thought to correspond to the secondary and the primary endings respectively. This sub-classification has now been discarded as it has failed to agree with more recent work on primary and secondary endings. However, the recognition of A or B behaviour still provides the standard way of distinguishing between spindle and tendon organ afferents studied in an electrophysiological experiment.

Conversion of conduction velocity to diameter. Modern practice usually also further characterises single afferent fibres studied electrophysiologically by measurement of their conduction velocity. The larger the fibre the more rapidly it conducts, and thus correlations may be attempted between the velocities of fibres studied electrophysiologically and fibre spectra determined histologically. It has become usual to believe that the relation between velocity and diameter is linear, and that the velocity in m/sec equals six times the total fibre diameter in μm. In reality, however, the factor of 6 appears to apply only to the larger medullated fibres. For smaller fibres the conversion factor is probably nearer 4, but the matter awaits detailed investigation. Thus estimates of fibre diameter can be considered to be only approximate; but the range of fibre diameter and conduction velocity is so wide that such uncertainty has so far proved immaterial for most practical purposes.

Behaviour of free endings. Those supplied by non-medullated fibres may be identified electrophysiologically by the very slow conduction velocity of their afferent fibres (below 1 m/sec) for all non-medullated afferents terminate as free endings. The limited work performed hitherto suggests that they are not excited by either stretch or muscle contraction but that they are excited by a range of nociceptive stimuli (ischaemia, hypertonic saline, squeezing). Free endings supplied by fine medullated fibres may be recognised electrophysiologically by having fibres conducting at below about 24 m/sec (group III), and by their behaving differently from the A and B endings. They are only rarely excited by muscle stretch or contraction, and then but weakly; but they are regularly excited by mechanical stimulation of the surface of an exposed muscle. Many of them then have rather high thresholds thus justifying the name 'pressure–pain receptors', but some of them are excited by quite gentle stimuli. It remains to be tested whether any of the free endings are preferentially sensitive to humoral or metabolic stimuli, and thus fitted to provide the afferent limb of respiratory or cardiovascular reflexes.

Tendon organs. Simple passive stretch of a non-contracting muscle often excites an appreciable number of tendon organs only when quite a large tension has been built up, and the muscle stretched beyond its maximum length in the body. The early recognition of such behaviour for the tendon organs of the soleus muscle led to the widespread characterisation of tendon organs as 'high threshold receptors' with their function presumed to be restricted to reflexly shutting off α motor discharge when the tension in a muscle became dangerously high. This view has now collapsed with the demonstration that tendon organs always have a low threshold for their preferred stimulus, namely tension produced by muscle contraction. Such active tension inevitably pulls directly upon the tendon organs which lie at the musculo-tendinous junction. The passive tension produced by simple stretch of a muscle is often partly borne by fascial sheaths around the muscle rather than by the muscle fibres themselves and so may fail to be transmitted to the tendon organs. However, there appear to be marked differences between different muscles; all the tendon organs in the tibialis anterior can be excited by passive stretches limited to the physiological range. In contrast, active tension is always effective and the contraction of any one of the 15 or so muscle fibres directly inserted into a tendon organ appears to be enough to make it fire. Any particular Golgi tendon organ is regularly found to be excited by the contraction of each of about 10 different motor units, provided that they are the right ones. Thus tendon organs are now seen as receptors with a low threshold for their appropriate stimulus and as providing the CNS with a signal which is suitable for helping continuously to regulate the strength of muscle contraction.

Joint receptors. In the mid-1950's a satisfyingly simple view was built up of the behaviour of the various endings, but it has recently had slight doubt cast upon it. The discharge patterns of the various receptors was established by ablating regions of joint capsule or ligament which had just been studied electrophysiologically and then studying them histologically to identify the type of receptor present. The Ruffini endings were found to give a signal related both to the position and to the velocity of angular movement of a joint. Each one was thought to fire over only rather a restricted range of joint angles, and the optimum angles for different endings were usually thought to be spread throughout the physio-logical range. Golgi endings in the ligaments were thought to behave similarly, except that they lacked any appreciable velocity sensitivity. Thus the CNS was supposed to be able to determine the angle of a joint by detecting which of the afferent fibres were firing, and by already knowing the optimum angle of excitation of each one. Paciniform corpuscles responded during the dynamic phase of a movement or to any externally applied vibration.

Unfortunately, a study performed in 1969 has disturbed these simple views without immediately replacing them by any alterna-tive concrete suggestions of how the CNS detects the angle of a joint. This study showed that for the cat's knee virtually all end-ings had optimal angles at the extremes of movement, and that there were practically none with preferred angles in between. To make matters worse for functional understanding, the majority of the endings were completely silent when the knee was held almost anywhere between the two extremes, so that no nervous signal at all then appeared to be being sent to the CNS from the joint. In addition, a large number of the receptors fired equally well both at full flexion and at full extension so that their signals would appear to have been irrelevant in helping the CNS decide between these two contrasting positions. At first sight the work appears impeccable, but the findings are so distasteful that it is to be hoped that some essential factor has been overlooked. In the costo-vertebral joints the endings behave more sensibly. Each is maximally excited at one or other extreme, but not at both. Moreover, each fires at a frequency proportional to angle throughout a wide range of angles, so that a signal of joint angle is never withheld from the CNS.

References

Adrian, E. D. & Zotterman, Y. (1926). The impulses produced by sensory nerve endings. Pt. 2. The response of a single end-organ. *J. Physiol.* **61,** 151–171. [101, 102]

Alnaes, E. (1967). Static and dynamic properties of Golgi tendon organs in the anterior tibial and soleus muscles of the cat. *Acta physiol. scand.* **70,** 176–187. [122–125]

Andrew, B. L. (1954). The sensory innervation of the medial ligament of the knee joint. *J. Physiol.* **123,** 241–250. [129]

Andrew, B. L. & Dodt, E. (1953). The deployment of sensory nerve endings at the knee joint of the cat. *Acta physiol. scand.* **28,** 287–296. [126, 129]

Bessou, P. & Laporte, Y. (1958). Activation des fibres afferentes amyelinques d'origine musculaire. *C.r. Séanc. Soc. Biol.* **152,** 1587–1590. [118]

— (1961). Étude des récepteurs musculaires innervés par les fibres afférentes du groupe III (fibres myelinisées fines), chez le chat. *Archs Ital. Biol.* **99,** 293–321. [118, 119]

Bessou, P. & Perl, E. R. (1966). A movement receptor of the small intestine. *J. Physiol.* **182,** 404–426. [115]

Boyd, I. A. (1954). The histological structure of the receptors in the knee joint of the cat correlated with their physiological response. *J. Physiol.* **124,** 476–488. [128]

Boyd, I. A. & Davey, M. R. (1968). *Composition of Peripheral Nerves.* 57 pp. Edinburgh: Livingstone. [115]

Boyd, I. A. & Roberts, T. D. M. (1953). Proprioceptive discharges from stretch-receptors in the knee joint of the cat correlated with their physiological response. *J. Physiol.* **124,** 476–488. [126, 129]

Burgess, P. R. & Clark, J. F. (1969). Characteristics of knee joint receptors in the cat. *J. Physiol.* **203,** 317–335. [126, 130–132]

Coppin, C. M. L. & Jack, J. J. B. (1972). Internodal length and conduction velocity of cat muscle afferent nerve fibres. *J. Physiol.* Proceedings. In the press. [115]

Douglas, W. W. & Ritchie, J. M. (1957). A technique for recording functional activity in specific groups of medullated and non-medullated fibres in whole nerve trunks. *J. Physiol.* **138**, 19–30.
[118]

Erlanger, J. & Gasser, H. S. (1937). *Electrical Signs of Nervous Activity.* 221 pp. Philadelphia: University of Pennsylvania Press.   [113]

Freeman, M. A. R. & Wyke, B. (1967). The innervation of the knee joint. An anatomical and histological study in the cat. *J. Anat.* **101**, 505–532.   [126]

Fulton, J. F. & Pi-Suñer, J. (1928). A note concerning the probable function of various afferent end-organs in skeletal muscle. *Am. J. Physiol.* **83**, 554–562.   [107, 108]

Godwin-Austen, R. B. (1969). The mechanoreceptors of the costo-vertebral joints. *J. Physiol.* **202**, 737–753.   [132, 133]

Harvey, R. J. & Matthews, P. B. C. (1961). Some effects of stimulation of the muscle nerve on afferent endings of muscle spindles, and the classification of their responses into types A1 and A2. *J. Physiol.* **156**, 470–497.   [109, 111, 113]

Houk, J. & Henneman, E. (1967). Responses of Golgi tendon organs to active contractions of the soleus muscle of the cat. *J. Neurophysiol.* **30**, 466–481.   [109, 123–125]

Houk, J. & Simon, W. (1967). Responses of Golgi tendon organs to forces applied to muscle tendon. *J. Neurophysiol.* **30**, 1466–1481.   [125]

Hunt, C. C. (1954). Relation of function to diameter in afferent fibres of muscle nerves. *J. gen. Physiol.* **38**, 117–131.   [114, 116, 124]

Hunt, C. C. & Kuffler, S. W. (1951). Stretch receptor discharges during muscle contraction. *J. Physiol.* **113**, 298–315.   [108, 121]

Hursh, J. B. (1939). Conduction velocity and diameter of nerve fibres. *Am. J. Physiol.* **127**, 131–139.   [113, 114]

Iggo, A. (1960). Non-myelinated afferent fibres from mammalian skeletal muscle. *J. Physiol.* **155**, 52–53P.   [117, 120]

Jansen, J. K. S. (1967). On the functional properties of stretch receptors of mammalian skeletal muscles. In *Myotatic, Kinesthetic and Vestibular Mechanisms*, eds. de Reuck, A. V. S. and Knight, J. pp. 20–34. London: Churchill.   [125]

Jansen, J. K. S. & Rudjord, T. (1964). On the silent period and Golgi tendon organs of the soleus muscle of the cat. *Acta physiol. scand.* **62**, 364–379.   [121–125]

Kidd, G. L. & Kučera, J. (1969). The excitation by suxamethonium of non-proprioceptive afferents from caudal muscles of the rat. *Experientia* **25**, 158–160.   [131]

Matthews, B. H. C. (1933). Nerve endings in mammalian muscle. *J. Physiol.* **78**, 1–53.   [106–112, 121]

Mountcastle, V. B., Poggio, G. F. & Werner, G. (1963). The relation of thalamic cell response to peripheral stimuli varied over an intensive continuum. *J. Neurophysiol.* **26**, 807–834.   [133]

Paintal, A. S. (1960). Functional analysis of group III afferent fibres of mammalian muscles. *J. Physiol.* **152**, 250–270.   [118–120]

Paintal, A. S. (1962). Responses and reflex effects of pressure–pain receptors of mammalian muscles. In *Symposium on Muscle Receptors*, ed. Barker, D. pp. 133–142. Hong Kong: Hong Kong University Press. [120]

Skoglund, S. (1956). Anatomical and physiological studies of knee joint innervation in the cat. *Acta physiol. scand.* **36,** suppl. 124, 1–101. [127–131]

Stuart, D. G., Goslow, G. E., Mosher, C. G. & Reinking, R. M. (1970). Stretch responsiveness of Golgi tendon organs. *Expl. Brain Res.* **10,** 463–476. [123]

4

THE FUNCTIONAL DISTINCTIVENESS OF THE PRIMARY AND SECONDARY SPINDLE ENDINGS

EVER since Ruffini described the morphologically distinct primary and secondary endings of the muscle spindle the presumption has been that they have different functions. That this is so and that they send rather different signals to the CNS has only been firmly established in the last decade. It is true that 40 years ago B. H. C. Matthews subdivided A endings into two groups which he believed corresponded to the two kinds of afferent ending, but as already noted (p. 112) the passage of time has failed to substantiate his method of classification. In any case, it did not lead on to any further differentiation between the behaviour of the two kinds of ending, over and above that required to classify them.

The anatomical basis for the presumption of different functions for the primary and secondary endings is simply that they are rather differently disposed in relation to the intrafusal fibres. The primary ending lies equatorially on both kinds of intrafusal fibre on regions which are poorly striated. The secondary endings lie juxta-equatorially, predominantly on the chain fibres, on regions which are well striated. In addition, the fact that the primary and secondary endings are supplied by quite different sizes of afferent fibre supports the idea that they are functionally distinct entities. This is further indicated by the well known finding that only the large spindle afferents make monosynaptic connections with motoneurones, while the smaller spindle afferents produce their reflex effects through one or more interneurones. In modern jargon, which begs most of the present questions, this is expressed by saying that the monosynaptic excitatory pathway is the prerogative of the Ia fibres from the spindle primaries, while the group II afferents from the spindle secondaries produce their effects polysynaptically. Such a differentiation of central action would be functionally pointless unless the two kinds of afferent transmitted different signals about the state of the muscle. This has proved to be so and may be summarised to a first approximation by the statement that for stretches of appreciable size the primary ending is very much more sensitive than the secondary ending to the velocity component of the movement, but that they are about equally sensitive to change in length of the muscle *per se*.

As yet, however, it remains impossible to make any one single general statement, like the one above, which will embrace every difference in behaviour between the two kinds of ending. Nor has their behaviour yet proved to be fully describable by a mathematical equation or by the construction of a physical model of the spindle, including if necessary non-linear elements. When such approaches can be brought to fruition it should prove possible to characterise the behaviour of each of the endings, and likewise the differences between them, in terms of a limited number of measurable parameters. For the time being, however, all that can be done is to give a catalogue of the way each kind of ending behaves under a variety of circumstances. The present chapter is devoted to such a detailed description and thus provides the background for endeavouring to understand the uses to which the spindle is put by the CNS.

Comparison of the behaviour of the two kinds of ending is complicated by the fact that both of them are under fusimotor control, and as a result can alter their response to the same stimulus applied under different conditions. The present chapter will concentrate on the way the endings behave when they are de-efferented, and the various effects of fusimotor stimulation are deferred until the next one. In life, however, some background fusimotor discharge is probably almost always going on, and the de-efferented spindle shows certain peculiarities of behaviour which are not found during such background firing, and whose relevance for normal function may therefore be questioned. The criticism that everything described for the de-efferented spindle is irrelevant for consideration of normal function is obviated whenever possible in the present chapter by describing also the way in which the two kinds of endings respond to the various stimuli when they are applied in the decerebrate cat with intact ventral roots. In this preparation there is a steady fusimotor discharge to extensor muscles and so their spindles may well be behaving more typically of the normal than those studied in the complete absence of intrafusal tone. In passing, it may be noted that the spontaneous fusimotor discharge of the decerebrate usually involves both kinds of functionally distinguishable fusimotor fibres, that is both the static and the dynamic fusimotor fibres.

The range of behaviour seen in the decerebrate and de-efferented preparation need not, however, span the full extent of the possible physiological behaviour of the endings and so the present chapter makes no claim to say all there is to say about them. For example, high-frequency stimulation of static fusimotor fibres suppresses the normally marked dynamic responsiveness of the primary endings to large stretches, and in this respect leads them to behave rather like secondary endings. Chapter 6 will deal with the intricate mechanisms within the spindle which can bring about such dramatic changes in afferent responsiveness and it will also discuss the related mechanisms underlying the functional differences between the two kinds of ending. By then, the effects of fusimotor stimulation will have been described in detail and so the problems can be seen in proper perspective. The present chapter merely presents the results of 'black-box' studies of the spindle afferents and relates the afferent output to the mechanical input. It would be more logical to present the patterns of afferent response as necessary consequences of established intrafusal mechanisms but it is still premature to attempt this. Fortunately, the present descriptive approach seems likely to continue to fill a certain need even after the more logical approach begins to become possible. This is because the CNS also can only see the spindle as a 'black box', and is concerned solely with the signals the spindle transmits rather than with how it does its business. But it should be emphasised at the outset, before we are lost in detail, that some of the differences which are detectable between the behaviour of the primary and secondary endings may in themselves prove to be of no functional concern to the body, but merely represent the irrelevant consequences of the spindle being asked to perform some quite different and functionally important job. The fact that a physiologist equipped with the modern armoury of instruments can recognise a particular difference between the two kinds of ending obviously provides no guarantee that it is one to which the CNS pays any attention, nor even that it is detectable by the particular mechanisms employed by the CNS to decode afferent signals and put them to functional use.

Classification of the endings on the basis of the conduction velocity of their afferent fibres

The elucidation of the various functional differences between the behaviour of primary and secondary endings has been crucially aided by the use of an independent criterion for their indentification—namely the measurement of the conduction velocity of each single afferent fibre studied. This permits an estimate of its size which can then be related to the histologically measured diameters of the afferent fibres to primary and secondary endings as they are seen on their point of entry to the spindle. At this site the primary afferent is appreciably the larger. In order to get under way with experimentation the same is assumed to hold true for the two kinds of afferent throughout their course, though as already indicated histological work alone can provide little guarantee that this is so, nor show precisely where the boundary should be placed in terms of conduction velocity.

In 1954, Hunt made the first systematic study of the behaviour of primary and secondary endings after identifying them by means of the conduction velocities of their afferent fibres. He isolated a large number of single muscle afferent fibres in dorsal root filaments and determined for each one, firstly its conduction velocity and, secondly, the behaviour of the ending it supplied. All but 3 of the 628 fibres he studied originated from stretch receptors. As usual these were classifiable into spindle endings and tendon organs on the basis of whether they showed 'in-parallel' or 'in-series' behaviour during a muscle contraction. Figure 4.1 shows

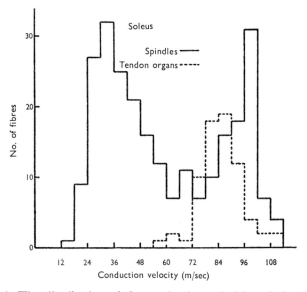

FIG. 4.1. The distribution of the conduction velocities of the afferent fibres from spindles and from tendon organs in the soleus muscle of the cat determined electrophysiologically. The afferents were isolated as functionally single units in dorsal root filaments and the sampling was believed to be random with regard to receptor type and fibre size for all fibres conducting at above about 24 m/sec. (Hunt, 1954, Fig. 3.)

the distribution of velocities that Hunt found for these two kinds of afferent. The tendon organ afferents showed a unimodal distribution of velocities. In contrast, the distribution for the spindle endings was bimodal, thus fitting in with the idea that there are two kinds of spindle afferent fibre. Following Lloyd, Hunt classified the afferents into groups I and II and arbitrarily placed the dividing line between them at a velocity of 72 m/sec which was presumed to correspond to a diameter of 12 μm. Fortunately it also corresponded to the middle of the trough between his group I and group II peaks. Hunt suggested that spindle fibres of group I diameter 'probably terminate in primary endings while group II fibres probably terminate as secondary endings within the spindles' (1954, p. 125). He found that on average the presumed secondary endings had a slightly higher threshold to stretch than did the presumed primary endings (19 g to 3·3 g tension respectively) though the thresholds of the two populations overlapped considerably. It should be noted that although such a difference has been confirmed for the soleus and tenuissimus muscles it does not appear to be invariable. In the tibialis anterior of the cat, secondary endings tend to have a resting discharge more frequently than do the primary endings, and when one is present it is of higher frequency for the secondaries than the primaries (Fehr, 1962; Alnaes, Jansen & Rudjord, 1965); the same is found for spindles in the gastrocnemius and plantaris muscles of the rabbit (Diete-Spiff, 1961).

Hunt had no evidence to show how far primary and secondary afferents could be segregated by any single dividing line of velocity, or whether the division at 72 m/sec was placed at the most appropriate position. He himself stated that more information was 'needed before the above correlation can be regarded as definite'. None the less the figure of 72 m/sec seems to have passed into much of the literature as if it were inviolable, and though it has been hallowed by repeated use much of the data obtained thereby are insufficiently cogent to be used to argue either for or against a precise dividing line at this or any other particular position. The only definite conclusion which can reasonably be reached from the combination of the histological data and Hunt's work, is that most of the large fibres must come from primary endings and that most of the small fibres from secondary endings. This is simply because it seems most unlikely that a fibre will ever get thinner on its way from the periphery to the spinal cord. Thus if some tolerably consistent functional difference can be found between the receptors with large axons and receptors with small axons then this should correspond to the difference between primary and secondary endings and once such a difference can be established it should be usable in its own right as a criterion for classification.

In practice, in moving along these lines, most workers seem to have accepted that if an afferent fibre has a conduction velocity considerably above the dividing line (say above about 80 m/sec) it can fairly confidently be attributed to a primary ending, and if its conduction velocity is considerably below the dividing line (say below about 60 m/sec) it may be attributed to a secondary ending. As will become clear the application of this criterion to the hindlimb muscles of the cat has been remarkably successful in dividing spindle endings into two groups with quite different functional properties. But even now, an afferent fibre with a conduction velocity of between 60 and 80 m/sec cannot be confidently attributed to one or other kind of ending depending upon whether it lies just above or just below 72 m/sec or any other dividing line. The reliability of velocity measurements could, however, probably be slightly improved by expressing them in terms of that of the fastest fibres present in each particular preparation. On the traditional view a factor of 0·6 would then seem appropriate for separating the afferents from primary and secondary endings. This should do something to overcome the scatter introduced by experimenting upon cats of different size, but of course can do nothing to overcome the effects of a true overlap of diameter of the two kinds of afferent occurring within a single preparation.

Responsiveness to stretches of large amplitude

Dynamic sensitivity and its assessment by the 'dynamic index'

Five years after Hunt's work, Cooper (1959, 1961) again used the criterion of conduction velocity to identify the afferents from primary and secondary endings in the soleus muscle. She then studied their responses to stretches of 4 mm applied at a constant velocity, which was controllable over a wide range. Like Hunt, she noted that the primary endings had a lower threshold than the secondary endings, but more significantly she found that only the primary endings possessed the great sensitivity to dynamic stimuli which was familiar from B. H. C. Matthews' work of 25 years earlier. For the 8 secondary endings which she studied in detail she found that 'during the application of stretch the rate hardly exceeds that reached during a maintained stretch', whatever the velocity of stretching. Hunt had apparently studied the spindle endings only under static conditions and so had failed to give the two kinds of ending an opportunity to demonstrate their very real physiological differences.

Cooper studied decerebrate cats with 'good tone' of the soleus muscle and in which 'an active intrafusal motor supply could be assumed'. Several other workers have now confirmed and extended her striking result using a sufficient number of different preparations and different modes of stretching to show that the greater dynamic sensitivity of the primary ending is an omnipresent difference, and is not essentially dependent upon intrafusal contraction or the precise waveform of the stimulus. Thus shortly afterwards Harvey & Matthews (1961) and Matthews (1963) obtained the same result for a larger number of secondary endings studied in the same muscle (soleus) after de-efferentation to eliminate fusimotor activity, and with a wide range of constant velocity stretches. Renkin & Vallbo (1964) extended the findings to spindle endings lying in the gastrocnemius as well as the soleus muscle. Bessou & Laporte (1962) did the same for the tenuissimus and Alnaes, Jansen & Rudjord (1965) did so for the tibialis anterior. Rather later, Lennerstrand (1968) obtained essentially similar results for the soleus on using 'triangular stretching' in which the muscle is alternately stretched and released without any intervening period of rest in between. Other workers have usually preferred to use 'ramp stretches' in which the muscle is stretched or released at a constant velocity from one position of rest to another.

Figure 4.2 shows the responses of a primary and of a secondary ending to a relatively rapid stretch applied both during a steady level of fusimotor discharge (V.R. intact) and in its absence (V.R. cut). Figure 4.3 contrasts the behaviour of de-efferented primary and secondary endings to a slowly applied stretch and release. The abrupt change in the firing frequency of the primary ending at the moment the velocity changes, namely at the end of the stretching and the beginning of releasing, contrasts with the nearly smooth change of firing of the secondary ending with the progressive change of length. It may be noted, however, that in the decerebrate the primary ending usually fires during the first part of a slow release. Figure 4.4 shows similar responses from de-efferented endings in the tibialis posterior muscle to two rates of stretching, and demonstrates that the fall in the discharge on completion of stretching becomes more marked as the velocity is increased.

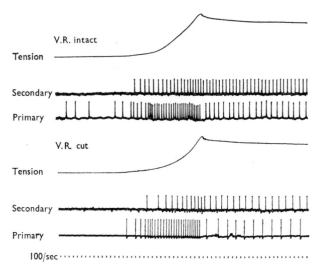

FIG. 4.2. The contrasting responses of spindle primary and secondary endings to a rapidly applied stretch (approximately 14 mm at 70 mm/sec) shown both in the presence and absence of fusimotor activity. The endings lay in the soleus muscle of the same decerebrate cat; their responses were recorded together both before and after cutting the ventral roots to eliminate fusimotor activity. The stretch was applied manually by pulling upon a lever which then moved from one stop to another; when the stretch was complete the muscle was approximately at the greatest length that it could take up in the body and it developed a tension of about 300 g. The conduction velocities of the afferent fibres were 85 and 44 m/sec for the primary and secondary ending respectively. (Previously unpublished record from experiments of Jansen & Matthews, 1962a.)

The dynamic index. The frequency of discharge occurring a second or so after reaching the final length is largely independent of the velocity used to stretch the muscle. Thus the magnitude of the sudden diminution of the discharge on completion of the dynamic phase of stretching provides a convenient way of assessing the velocity responsiveness of an ending, over and above its responsiveness to a change of length. On completion of the stretching the velocity falls abruptly from a finite value to nothing while the length of the muscle remains constant. Conventionally, the decrease in frequency occurring in the first 0·5 sec after completion of stretching is measured and called the 'dynamic index'. This is illustrated in Fig. 4.4 (Crowe & Matthews, 1964; Jansen

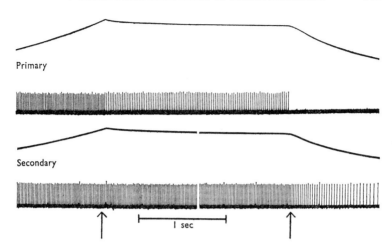

Primary

Secondary

I sec

FIG. 4.3. The contrasting responses of spindle primary and secondary endings in the de-efferented preparation to a slowly applied stretch and release. The records show the termination of a 12 mm stretch at 2·3 mm/sec and the beginning of a release at the same velocity. Results from two different preparations of the cat soleus. A 1 sec portion has been removed from the discharge of the secondary ending. (Harvey & Matthews, 1961, Fig. 9.)

& Matthews, 1962a, called the same measure the 'dynamic response' as it was the increase in firing above the static level, produced by the dynamic stimulus).

There is no particular significance in the choice of 0·5 sec as a period of measurement and different times would give somewhat different figures, depending upon how rapidly the endings adapt with time. None the less, by virtue of its simplicity the dynamic index has provided a continuingly useful measure of velocity responsiveness and its changes with fusimotor activity. It should, however, be regarded as an interim measure due for replacement in the fullness of time by one or more parameters giving a more exact description of the response of the endings to various patterns of stretching. Figure 4.4 also helps illustrate that measurement of the response of the endings at the beginning of a constant velocity stretch is less readily employed than the dynamic index, though *a priori* it might have been supposed to be the more sensible measure. Sometimes the endings fail to fire at the initial length employed and so any measurement should properly start

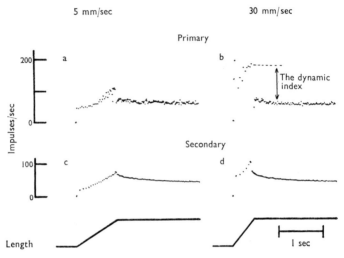

FIG. 4.4. Comparison of the responses of de-efferented primary and secondary endings to a ramp stretch by means of a direct display of their 'instantaneous' frequency of firing. Each spot represents an action potential and its vertical displacement is proportional to the reciprocal of the time interval since the immediately preceding spike. The measurement of the arbitrary 'dynamic index' is illustrated at the top right; it is simply the difference in frequency between the discharge near the termination of the dynamic phase of stretching and that occurring when the muscle has been maintained at the final length for 0·5 sec. Results from a single preparation of the tibialis posterior muscle. The stretch was 3 mm applied at either 5 mm/sec (left) or 30 mm/sec (right). The 1 sec time marker applies only while the muscle is at a constant length; during the phase of dynamic stretching the time scale is somewhat expanded. (Brown, Crowe & Matthews, 1965, Fig. 1.)

from a negative value, but precisely what this should be is not immediately apparent. Sometimes the initial response to the stimulus of velocity is obscured by an initial high-frequency burst of impulses apparently related to the initial acceleration rather than to velocity alone and which therefore should not be included in the measurements (see later).

Figure 4.5 contrasts the effects of a range of velocities of stretching on the dynamic indices of a primary and a secondary ending, identified on the conduction velocities of their afferent fibres. For both, increasing the velocity of stretching increases the dynamic index, but for any particular velocity its value is always consistently

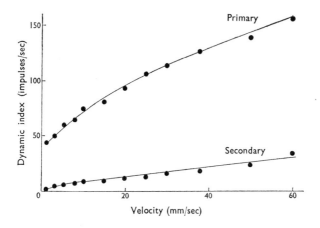

FIG. 4.5. The relation between the dynamic index and the velocity of stretching for a primary and a secondary ending in the same soleus muscle. De-efferented preparation stretched by 6 mm with a ramp waveform as in Fig. 4.4. (Matthews, 1963, Fig. 11, re-drawn.)

greater for the primary ending than for the secondary ending. It should be noted also that the value of the dynamic index of an ending is usually largely independent of the degree of stretching of the muscle, though this is usually more nearly true for the decerebrate than for the de-efferented preparation. Such constancy of the dynamic index with length is illustrated in Fig. 4.6 which shows the response of a primary ending to successive increments of stretch applied in the decerebrate cat under three different sets of conditions with different, but unknown, amounts of fusimotor activity. The variable time-course of the decay of the discharge on completion of each period of stretching emphasises that no single index could be sufficient on its own to describe the dynamic behaviour of the ending. None the less the dynamic index is the simplest measure currently available, and so continues to retain a certain usefulness.

Figure 4.7 shows the dynamic indices of a number of de-efferented soleus endings plotted against the conduction velocity of their afferent fibres. There is a clear tendency for their velocity responsiveness, assessed by this means, to increase with fibre size but no absolute division is apparent for afferents above and below a dividing line of 72 m/sec. This is so both on 3 and 30

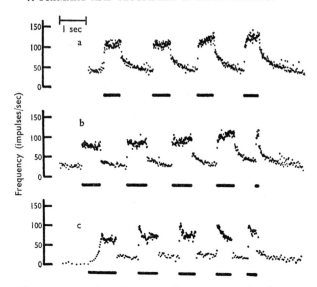

FIG. 4.6. The response of a primary ending to successive increments of stretch, each of about 2 mm. This was done for three different levels of background fusimotor activity (a, b, c) occurring in the decerebrate cat with intact ventral roots; the level of fusimotor activity was altered reflexly. During the bars the muscle (soleus) was stretched at 3 mm/sec; in between, it was held at the final length reached by the preceding stretch. The records demonstrate: first, the dynamic index is approximately the same at different lengths of the muscle; second, the time-course of decline of frequency on completion of the dynamic phase of stretching may vary with the background fusimotor activity. (Jansen & Matthews, 1962a, Fig. 8.)

mm/sec stretching and also for the difference between the dynamic indices found for the two velocities (C). The difference value provides a two-point measure of the average slope of the relation between dynamic index and velocity, and thus perhaps provides a truer measure of velocity-sensitivity than a single measure of dynamic index. The static responsiveness of the same afferents was assessed by measuring their frequency of discharge at the final length of the muscle. As can be seen in Fig. 4.7D this did not differ appreciably for different sized afferents. Rather similar results were obtained for spindle endings in the tibialis anterior muscle (Alnaes, Jansen & Rudjord, 1965), though in this muscle there was a rather greater overlap in the velocity responsiveness of primary and secondary endings.

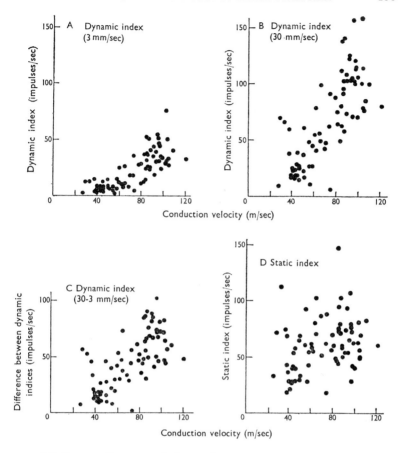

FIG. 4.7. Scatter diagrams relating various responses of spindle endings in the de-efferented soleus muscle to the conduction velocities of their afferent fibres. *A, B, C*, the dynamic indices on 3 and 30 mm/sec stretching, and their difference. *D*, the frequency of firing at the final length 0·5 sec after completing the extension. Ramp stretches of 6 mm extent terminating at the maximum physiological length of the muscle. (Matthews, 1963, Fig. 12.)

Position-sensitivity. Another measure of static responsiveness can be obtained by plotting the frequency of steady firing of an ending against the length of the muscle for each of a number of different lengths. This was first done by Eldred, Granit & Merton (1953) who showed that the relationship was often approximately linear.

The slope of the best-fitting line is sometimes called the position-sensitivity of the ending and its value seems important for assessing the part played by the endings in the reflex control of posture. Thus it is interesting that the values are usually approximately the same for primary and secondary endings (Harvey & Matthews, 1961; Renkin & Vallbo, 1964; Alnaes, Rudjord & Jansen, 1965; Lennerstrand, 1968). This is illustrated in Fig. 4.8 for a pair of

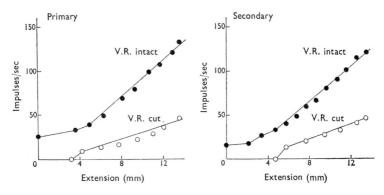

FIG. 4.8. The relation between the frequency of static firing and the extension, determined on stretching the muscle to a series of different lengths. This was done for a pair of endings in the soleus muscle of the same decerebrate cat both in the presence of spontaneous fusimotor activity (V.R. intact) and after its abolition by ventral root section (V.R. cut). The measurements were made 0·5 sec after completing each of a series of incremental stretches as in Fig. 4.6; measurement at a later time would have given a flatter relation, especially during fusimotor activity. Similar curves may be obtained by applying stretches of different sizes all starting from the same initial length. (Jansen & Matthews, 1962*b*; Fig. 4.)

endings which were studied together in a decerebrate preparation first with the ventral roots intact, when both the endings were appreciably excited by the steady fusimotor activity of this preparation, and again after de-efferenting the spindles by ventral root section. During fusimotor activity the position-sensitivity was about 10 impulses sec^{-1} mm^{-1} while in its absence the value was about 4 impulses sec^{-1} mm^{-1}; the value with fusimotor activity is higher than that often found, while the value for the de-efferented endings is typical.

Comparison of the responses of a primary and of a secondary ending lying within the same spindle. Much of the scatter seen in Fig. 4.7 for the responsiveness of different endings probably simply reflects the fact that the results were obtained from a number of different preparations. A more crucial approach was introduced by Bessou & Laporte (1962) who simultaneously recorded the responses of a pair of afferent fibres one supplying a primary ending and the other a secondary ending and which both lay in the same muscle spindle. They achieved this by using the tenuissimus muscle which is very long and thin, and at the ends of which the spindles may lie so far apart that only one is found in any cross-section of the muscle. Boyd's diagram illustrating this arrangement is shown in Fig. 4.9. Bessou & Laporte argued, therefore, that if a

Pelvic end   Tibial end

L 1 cm ⌐

FIG. 4.9. The arrangement of the spindles in the tenuissimus muscle of the cat. The diagram shows the length of each spindle and the position of its capsular swelling. It was constructed from serial transverse sections of a complete muscle. The scale applies longitudinally but not transversely. (Traced from Boyd, 1962, Fig. 31a.)

primary and a secondary ending could be found which were excited from the same locus then they would be known to be in the same spindle. Figure 4.10 shows the high degree of localisation of the endings that they could obtain on lightly poking the muscle with a vibrissa which exerted a pressure that 'was barely felt when it was applied to the back of the hand' (their p. 106). They also used an electrical stimulus to localise the endings by determining the point along the muscle at which they ceased to be able to stimulate any afferent fibre studied; they presumed that this corresponded to its termination. They studied the endings under a variety of conditions and confirmed the existence of a greater dynamic sensitivity for the primary ending during slow stretches of several millimetres extent, during sudden stretches of 1–2 mm, and during approximately sinusoidal stretching of the muscle at several Hz. Their striking record of the last effect is shown in Fig. 4.11 and was taken to show a difference in the response of the endings to 'phasic changes of length'.

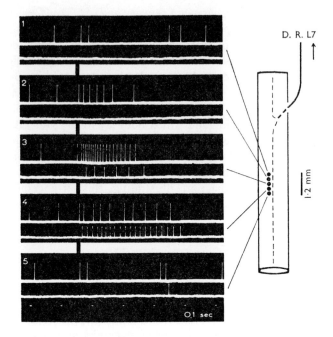

FIG. 4.10. Method of localising a primary and a secondary ending lying in the same tenuissimus muscle spindle. The records show the responses of a primary ending (above in each pair) and of a secondary ending (below) on touching the muscle with a fine probe at the series of points indicated on the diagram. (Bessou & Laporte, 1962, Fig. 2.)

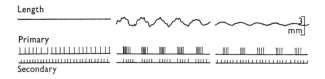

FIG. 4.11. Responses of a primary and a secondary ending lying in the same spindle to cyclic stretching at 13 Hz. Increasing stretch gives a downwards deflection on the length record. (Traced from Bessou & Laporte, 1962, Fig. 6.)

Thus it is now firmly established that 'typical' primary and secondary endings with afferents well above and below the dividing line show quite different behaviour. Their 'typical' responses are diagrammatically brought together in Fig. 4.12 which may be summarised to a first approximation by saying that at any time the secondary ending signals simply the length of the muscle, whereas the primary ending sends a signal dependent both upon the length of the muscle and its rate of change. However, the typical differences need not be prominent under all conditions, and during powerful static fusimotor activation (see Chap. 5) the primary ending loses its normally characteristic velocity responsiveness and behaves rather like a secondary ending. It may also be noted that at high velocities of stretching the velocity response of the primary ending is often so much larger than its length response that it may become impossible to say whether the ending is still responding to both the length and the velocity or whether just to the velocity alone. Occasionally a spindle is found which even on low velocity stretching fails to show a progressive increase in firing during the progressive stretching, and so seems to switch from being a length recorder to being a velocity recorder.

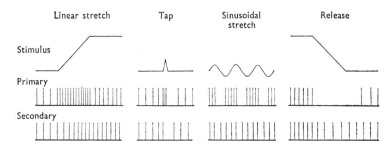

FIG. 4.12. Diagrammatic comparison of the typical responses of primary and secondary endings to large stretches applied in the absence of fusi-motor activity. (Matthews, 1964, Fig. 2.)

Endings with afferents of intermediate conduction velocity. This leaves open the question as to how far endings with afferents near the dividing line behave typically in one respect or other, and there is as yet no final solution to this problem. The first point which may be made is that the bimodal distribution of diameters of spindle afferents (Fig. 4.1) with its marked dip near the dividing line means that the majority of afferents are either large or small, and so come from endings with well differentiated properties.

Those near the dividing line and possibly with intermediate properties are in the minority and so are presumably of less functional significance. Second, many endings with afferents near the dividing line none the less have properties characteristic of the main mass of either primaries or secondaries. Some, however, do appear to have intermediate properties when studied in the de-efferented preparation (cf. Matthews, 1963; Brown, Engberg & Matthews, 1967).

It is possible that such intermediate types of behaviour are seen because the endings are being studied in an unphysiological state with quiescent intrafusal fibres. Under natural conditions there is always likely to be some intrafusal 'tone' influencing both primary and secondary endings and perhaps helping them to show their properly distinct forms of behaviour. This view was advanced by Rack & Westbury (1966) who studied the response of spindles to stretching (5–10 mm at 20 mm/sec) before and after giving suxamethonium or acetylcholine to produce intrafusal contraction. Before the injection, 16 afferents of intermediate conduction velocity showed dynamic behaviour intermediate between that of the main masses of primary and secondary endings, classified on the basis of the well separated conduction velocities of their afferent fibres. During the intrafusal contraction these intermediate endings changed their behaviour so that they then all fitted into one or other of the two main groups of endings. This led Rack & Westbury to suggest that, functionally, spindle endings do indeed 'form two distinct groups without any truly intermediate form' (1966, p. 712). For the time being this seems the simplest view to adopt.

It would be interesting to know also whether the synaptic connections made inside the spinal cord by spindle afferents fall cleanly into two classes only, or whether the central nervous system can make specific use of the information of any endings with behaviour intermediate between that of the main masses of primary and secondary endings. Another unsolved problem is whether either the primary or the secondary endings require to be sub-divided into further functionally distinct groups as has been variously attempted (Granit & Van der Meulen, 1962; Bianconi & Van der Meulen, 1963; Haase & Ortgieze, 1966). The difficulty so far has been that the endings do not usually appear to have fallen cleanly into the classes described and as yet there has been no parallel histological study of the particular endings studied to see whether the functional differences could be correlated with structural differences. In view of the morphological differences between different spindles minor functional differences between different primary and different secondary endings would almost certainly be expected to occur. Primary endings may occur in simple, complex or tandem spindles, and the number of intrafusal fibres of either kind in the spindle may vary. Secondary endings may be placed at various distances from the equatorial region of the spindle and hence lie on regions of intrafusal fibre with varying densities of myofibrils and which thus presumably differ in their contractile strength. In addition to their invariable termination on the nuclear chain fibres secondary endings may have a few inconstant terminations on the nuclear bag fibres. The problem is how far such structural differences are functionally meaningful, particularly from the point of view of the central nervous system.

Variability of rhythm of discharge

Another interesting functional difference between primary and secondary ending lies in the degree of regularity of their discharges. B. H. C. Matthews (1933) originally noticed the extreme regularity with which muscle spindle afferents discharge when the intrafusal fibres are made quiescent by de-efferentation. Twenty years later, Eldred, Granit & Merton (1953) found that in the decerebrate cat the familiar regular rhythm was replaced by a highly irregular one with the 'spike interval often varying discontinuously from spike to spike' even though the length of the muscle was constant and there was no overt muscular contraction. The irregularity can be presumed to be the simple result of the intrafusal fibres being continuously excited at relatively low frequency and so not contracting quite smoothly, and thereby applying an irregular mechanical stimulus to the afferent endings. Such irregularity has since become a familiar sign of fusimotor activity and has been used for its detection.

From the functional point of view any irregularity of discharge may be looked upon as 'noise' limiting the accuracy with which the afferent fibre and its attached ending can signal information about the environment. Figure 4.13 illustrates this idea diagrammatically. The solid line shows the relation between the mean frequency of discharge of a spindle afferent fibre and the length of the muscle,

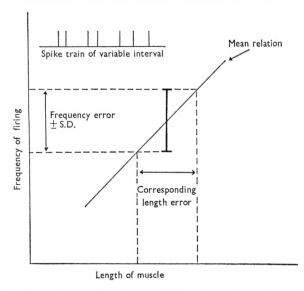

FIG. 4.13. Diagram illustrating how variability in a spike train leads to a decrease in the accuracy with which it can signal information about a steady state. The line shows the presumed mean relation between the frequency of firing of a spindle afferent and the length of the muscle when the length is held constant (cf. Fig. 4.8). The thick vertical bar shows the error which would be found in any experimental measurement of frequency on a variable spike-train, such as that shown at the top. This will produce a corresponding error in an estimate of muscle length based on any particular measurement of spike frequency.

with the muscle held at a series of different lengths. Any experimental measurement of frequency would, however, have to be made over a finite time on a more or less variable train of real spikes, as indicated at the top; as an inevitable result the actual experimental points would have an appreciable standard deviation, as indicated by the vertical bar. Turning the problem round, one can imagine an observer who knows the mean frequency-extension relation on the basis of a pre-existing calibration of the ending and makes a single measurement of the discharge frequency in order to determine the length of the muscle at a particular time, acting on the assumption that the length is constant throughout the period of measurement. Obviously his estimate of the length is liable to be in error by an amount related to the variability of the discharge (Fig. 4.13); the more regular the discharge, the greater the accuracy with which the length can be determined. It is not-able, therefore, that the secondary ending should turn out to have an appreciably more regular discharge than the primary ending, showing that it provides a more accurate signal of the length of the muscle (Pascoe, 1965; Stein & Matthews, 1965; Matthews & Stein, 1969*b*; Eysel & Grüsser, 1970). This is illustrated in Fig. 4.14 which shows the variability of discharge displayed in terms

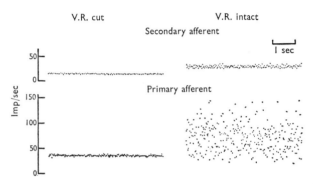

FIG. 4.14. Comparison of the variability of the discharges of a primary and of a secondary ending, both in the presence and absence of fusimotor activity. The records show the 'instantaneous frequency' of discharge of the endings determined spike-by-spike (cf. Fig. 4.4.). The discharge of the two endings were recorded simultaneously. They lay in the soleus muscle of the decerebrate cat and were studied at the same length of the muscle both in the presence of 'spontaneous' fusimotor activity and after its abolition by ventral root section. (Matthews & Stein, 1969*b*, Fig. 4.)

of the instantaneous frequency of discharge, both in the presence and absence of fusimotor activity.

Coefficients of variation. More systematic comparisons of the variability have been made by determining the coefficient of variation of the distribution of interspike intervals (i.e. the stand-ard deviation/mean). For frequencies of discharge around 30/sec the coefficient of variation only changes slightly with changes in the mean frequency. Its mean value in de-efferented preparations is about 0·02 for secondary endings (i.e. the standard deviation is only 2% of the mean) and 0·06 for primary endings. In the decerebrate cat, with its continuous spontaneous fusimotor activity, the coefficient of variation is increased about fourfold for both kinds of ending so that the primary ending remains relatively the more variable; the mean value is then 0·064 for secondary endings and 0·25 for primary endings. (Matthews & Stein, 1969*b*.)

The functional meaning of these values for the coefficient of variation may be further illustrated by a particular arbitrary example. Imagine an observer supplied with a 1 sec period of spindle afferent discharge from a decerebrate cat and asked to deduce the length of the muscle, which on independent evidence he knew to be constant throughout the 1 sec. Because of the variability the observer would clearly only be able to distinguish between lengths differing by an appreciable amount, and this would have the effect of reducing the normally continuous scale of length to the limited number of values which could be distinguished on statistical criteria on the limited sample of the discharge available. On various assumptions the number of lengths of the muscle which the observer could so discriminate in the decerebrate cat turns out to be about 6 on the basis of the information in a 1 sec spike train from a single primary ending, while it is 25 for that from a secondary ending (Matthews & Stein, 1969*b*; this includes an allowance for serial correlations—see later.) The top record of Fig. 4.15 helps illustrate the relative inefficiency with which the primary ending records length, and shows the 'instantaneous' frequency of discharge of this kind of ending in the decerebrate on stretching a muscle by 6 mm. In the body, of course, the signals from a number of similar receptors could be utilised centrally to permit the same accuracy to be achieved in a shorter time or a greater accuracy to be achieved over 1 sec; the information supplied by a number of independent receptors signalling the same event increases with the square root of their number and also with the square root of the observation time (Stein, 1967).

The circumvention of the deleterious effects of the variability of individual discharges provides a teleologically satisfying reason why individual muscles should contain a number of receptors all of which are signalling much the same thing, and why muscles subserving fine movements should be the more densely packed with muscle spindles. Another reason for the occurrence of a number of similar afferents is to overcome the 'granularity' inherent in the signal by virtue of the all-or-none nature of the action potential (i.e. more endings help to improve the high-frequency response). It might be thought that the greater variability in the discharge of the primary ending made it inherently less efficient in signalling all types of message and represented a sacrifice in performance in order to achieve some completely different objective, such as speed of response. This may turn out to be so, for detailed understanding has yet to be achieved of the precise factors underlying the observed variability of spindle discharge and why the variability is so much greater for primary endings. However, on theoretical grounds Stein & French (1970) have suggested that variability may sometimes actually be a good thing and help improve the signalling of events which contain frequencies comparable to the mean frequency of the spike-train signalling the event. This is because an extremely regular spike-train is particularly liable to become 'phase-locked' upon the stimulus, with one spike for each cycle of the stimulus; when this happens any central decoding mechanism reading the message is liable to have difficulty in distinguishing other components of the signal.

One further interesting point about the rhythm of the spindle discharges in the decerebrate cat is that the long interspike intervals tend to be followed by short ones, and vice versa. In other words the values of successive interspike intervals are negatively correlated. The extent of this effect may be assessed by measuring the first serial correlation coefficient which is found to have values down to -0.6 (Matthews & Stein, 1969b). There is no mystery about the origin of this negative correlation for it is what would be expected from the afferent fibres tending to fire on the rising phase of an intrafusal twitch and to be silent on its falling phase, as has been observed experimentally. This, of course, gives rise to a relatively short interspike interval followed by a relatively long one. The negative correlation, however, does have an important consequence from the point of view of information signalling for it means that if the frequency of discharge of an afferent is determined by averaging over an appreciable time then some of the variability will cancel out, and the information content of the signal will be greater than if the frequency were computed spike-by-spike. This is illustrated in Fig. 4.15 in which 'instantaneous frequency' is determined by averaging over a successively greater number of intervals from above downwards. The efficacy of this averaging is shown by the increasing ease with which the eye can pick out the response to the stretch. Analysis confirms that

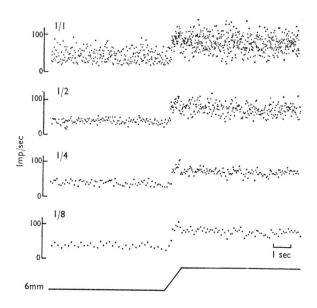

FIG. 4.15. The effect of averaging in reducing the variability of the discharge of a primary ending which was under the influence of spontaneous fusimotor activity in the decerebrate cat. The top record shows the unaveraged display of the instantaneous frequency of discharge of the ending on stretching the soleus muscle by 6 mm at 10 mm/sec. The lower records show the response to the same stretch but with progressive amounts of averaging, so that the frequency was determined over several interspike intervals instead of just one. The averaging was done by feeding the frequency display with every second spike (1/2), every fourth spike (1/4) or every eighth spike (1/8) by means of a series of binary counters fed with a tape recording of the original spike-train. In all records the scale shows the frequency of the original spike-train at approximately the same sensitivity. (Matthews & Stein, 1969*b*, Fig. 9.)

the averaging reduced the variability much more than it would have done for an initial spike train without significant correlations between the values of successive interspike intervals. Likewise, the CNS can be expected to compute some kind of running average, as by summing post-synaptic potentials, and so is probably less affected by the extreme irregularity of discharge seen in the decerebrate than is a physiologist equipped with a display of instantaneous frequency but without an averaging device.

Sensitivity to tendon taps

The greater dynamic sensitivity of the primary ending in relation to that of the secondary ending is further shown in their responses to brief phasic stimuli. This was first noted by Lundberg & Winsbury (1960) who used a mechanical device to briefly stretch the soleus by a controllable distance and immediately release it again so that the whole mechanical stimulus lasted less than 5 msec. With the muscle under slight initial tension the thresholds for activation of 43 Ia afferent fibres, presumed to be supplying primary endings, were all less than 60 μm peak displacement and over half of them were below 20 μm; the brief stimulus evoked a single impulse in each afferent. In contrast, of 12 group II fibres, presumed to be supplying spindle secondary endings, half required the stretch to be over 0·5 mm to produce excitation and a further third had thresholds of between 150 and 200 μm; 2 endings had thresholds of below 100 μm but for only one of these was the threshold as low as that of the primary endings with the highest threshold. These experiments were performed on de-efferented endings in the absence of fusimotor stimulation. Figure 4.16 shows the simultaneously recorded responses to a light

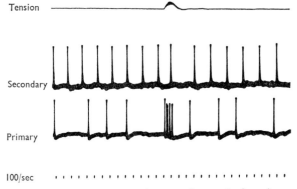

FIG. 4.16. The different responses of a secondary and of a primary ending in the soleus muscle to a tendon tap. The tension record shows the duration of the tap but not its size; it was derived from an isometric myograph. The tap was delivered with a light screw driver. The records were obtained from a decerebrate cat with intact ventral roots and in which the endings were being steadily excited by background fusimotor activity (note variability of resting discharge). (Previously unpublished record from experiments of Jansen & Matthews, 1962a.)

tendon tap of a primary and a secondary ending in the soleus muscle of a decerebrate cat with intact ventral roots. The primary ending was excited to discharge a high-frequency burst of 5 impulses, whereas the secondary ending fired just one impulse. Thus once again the two kinds of ending may be differentiated on their dynamic behaviour. Lundberg & Winsbury (1960) found also that in a non-contracting muscle the Golgi tendon organs were appreciably less sensitive to a brief stimulus than were the primary endings. On this basis they were able to show that a synchronous afferent volley restricted to the Ia fibres from the spindle primary endings produces autogenetic excitation as judged by the intracellular recording of EPSP's. This all fortifies the conventional view that the familiar tendon jerk, elicited by tapping a tendon in the whole animal, is mediated purely by the primary endings for these are the only ones which are appreciably excited by such a stimulus.

A recent repetition of Lundberg & Winsbury's experiments confirmed their findings for the spindle primary endings and the tendon organs. Unfortunately it failed to do so for the secondary endings, 41% of which were found to be excited by a stretch of 60 μm or below (Stuart, Mosher, Gerlack & Reinking, 1970). The more recent experiments need not, however, be taken to invalidate the earlier ones, as there were several differences in points of detail. In particular, the duration of the stretch was 20 msec. in the recent experiments as opposed to 5 msec. in the earlier ones. In addition, it seems possible that the initial tension on the muscle was higher in the more recent experiments and that this led to an enhancement of the sensitivity of the secondary endings. At any rate, Lundberg & Winsbury's finding the secondary endings to have a high threshold for brief taps fits in with the unresponsiveness of secondary endings to high-frequency vibration (see later).

A brief stretch normally has a negligible component of absolute displacement but even so may have an appreciable velocity component; for example a symmetrical triangular stretch and release of 50 μm extent and 5 msec duration briefly stretches the muscle at a velocity of 20 mm/sec. It is thus not unreasonable to attribute the great sensitivity of the primary ending to tendon taps to its high sensitivity to velocity, as also shown by its response to ramp stretches of large extent. A further factor is the sensitivity of the primary ending to the acceleration component of a stimulus, for this will be relatively very large for a brief stimulus.

Acceleration responses. Acceleration sensitivity may be considered to manifest itself also as the 'initial burst' of impulses which sometimes occurs at the beginning of a ramp stretch. This is illustrated in Fig. 4.17 which shows that the frequency of the burst increases

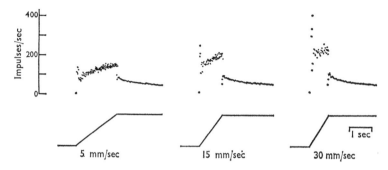

FIG. 4.17. The effect of increasing the velocity of stretching on the peak frequency reached in the 'initial burst' of firing given by a primary ending at the beginning of the stretch. The transient slowing occurring on completion of the stretching also becomes more marked as the velocity increases. These phenomena may be looked upon as 'acceleration' responses. Six mm stretch applied to a de-efferented soleus muscle (Matthews, 1963, Fig. 5, re-arranged.)

with the velocity of stretching and hence also with the initial acceleration (see also Schäfer & Schäfer, 1969). The functional significance of this 'acceleration response', however, is rather hard to assess as its prominence varies greatly under different conditions (Matthews, 1963; Lennerstrand & Thoden, 1968). In particular, as illustrated in Fig. 4.18, it may be almost absent during the physiologically natural state of a steady fusimotor discharge while being markedly present when all intrafusal tone has been abolished by de-efferentation. Moreover, the initial 'acceleration response' may be even further enhanced in the somewhat abnormal condition of fusimotor quiescence immediately following their intense discharge (Brown, Goodwin & Matthews, 1969). The 'acceleration response' of the spindle also appears to be preferentially shown for

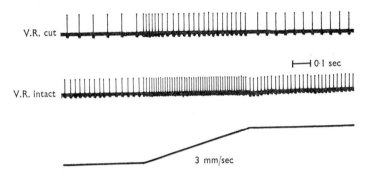

FIG. 4.18. The insignificance of the 'initial burst' occurring during steady fusimotor activity in comparison with that found for the same ending when it was de-efferented. The records show the response of a primary ending to a stretch of about 1·5 mm applied at 3 mm/sec to the soleus muscle of the decerebrate cat both before and after cutting the ventral roots. (Jansen & Matthews, 1962a, Fig. 7, re-arranged.)

movements beginning from rest, as if it depended upon a static frictional force rather than just upon the absolute value of the acceleration irrespective of whether or not movement was already occurring, as would the signal from a true accelerometer. 'Acceleration responsiveness' may also be held to be responsible for the momentary slowing of the discharge of a primary ending, below its final static level, which occurs on completion of a ramp stretch in the de-efferented state; at this point the acceleration momentarily goes negative.

For the present limited purpose of comparing the two kinds of spindle afferent the important finding is that acceleration responses have never been seen to be prominent for secondary endings, as judged by their responses to a ramp stretch, and are usually completely absent (Matthews, 1963). It may be concluded that the greater sensitivity of primary endings to brief taps in comparison with that of secondary endings is yet another expression of their greater 'phasic sensitivity', using this term in its widest sense. In addition, it must also be a consequence of the non-linear behaviour of the primary ending which leads it to have a relatively much greater sensitivity to small than to large stimuli (see later, p. 176); any such behaviour is very much less marked for the secondary ending.

Sensitivity to 'driving' by high-frequency vibration

High frequency vibration may be looked upon as a series of rapidly repeated brief phasic stimuli, and so might be expected to affect the primary ending much more powerfully than the secondary ending. Experiment has shown that this is indeed so. In 1938, Echlin & Fessard applied tuning forks to various tendons and showed, by recording massed activity from nerves, that some or all of the stretch receptors in muscle could be excited to discharge in synchrony with the rhythmic stimulus. Considerably later, Kuffler, Hunt & Quilliam (1951) and Granit & Henatsch (1956) showed by single fibre recording that the spindle primary endings are highly sensitive to vibration. They found, moreover, that vibration did not merely synchronise any pre-existing discharge in time with itself but also had a specific excitatory action so that the mean frequency of firing of the ending was greatly increased. Granit & Henatsch (1956) showed additionally that the vibration sensitivity of primary endings was increased by the fusimotor activity occurring in the decerebrate cat, and in due course this was confirmed by stimulating single fusimotor fibres. This proven high sensitivity of the primary endings subsequently prompted the use of vibration as a tool for the investigation of their central actions in both man and animals (see Chaps. 8 and 10).

Bianconi & van der Meulen (1963) were the first to compare the responses of primary and secondary endings to vibration. They applied the vibration to the muscle with a fine glass stylus which was attached to an electro-mechanical vibrator. When the tip of the stylus was placed on the surface of the muscle immediately over the muscle spindle studied, which was taken to be the point where its threshold was lowest, there was no absolute difference between the responsiveness of primary and secondary endings. All the primary endings and about half the secondary endings could be 'driven' to discharge one impulse per cycle for frequencies of 100 to 300 Hz, though driving of secondary endings was found to require a more crucial location of the vibrator stylus. In contrast, when the vibrator was placed on the tendon so that the stimulus had to be transmitted to the sense endings in a more normal manner Bianconi & van der Meulen found that none of the secondary endings could then be driven with their particular apparatus, though by implication all the primary endings could be so driven.

(This difference between the two kinds of endings is perhaps the most interesting finding in their paper, but it receives only a passing mention and the behaviour of the primary endings on tendon vibration does not appear anywhere to be explicitly stated.)

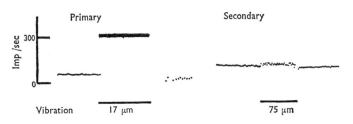

FIG. 4.19. The different effects of vibration on a primary and on a secondary ending in the same de-efferented soleus muscle. Longitudinal vibration at 300 Hz was applied to the muscle during the periods indicated; its peak-to-peak amplitude of movement is given below. (Matthews, 1967, Fig. 6.)

A more exact and reproducible method of applying vibration is to connect a vibrator to the cut end of a tendon and then vibrate the muscle longitudinally; this of course is only possible in the experimental animal. Brown, Engberg & Matthews (1967) systematically studied the thresholds of primary and secondary endings to this mode of application of vibration and found that the threshold of the secondary endings is then always very much the higher. This is shown in Fig. 4.19 which contrasts the response of a primary ending to vibration at 300 Hz of 17 μm peak-to-peak amplitude and which was able to drive the ending at 300/sec, with that of a secondary ending in the same muscle to a five-fold larger vibration of the same frequency and which barely influenced it. Figure 4.20 shows the threshold amplitude required to drive three different primary endings over a range of frequencies. Unit C was one of the most sensitive endings studied, and unit A one of the least. The thresholds of units B and C were approximately constant at different frequencies, but unit A had a rather high threshold for frequencies of 100–200 Hz. This was believed to be due to resonances in the muscle impairing the transmission of the vibration to the spindle rather than to any specific resonances within the spindle itself. Of 25 secondary endings studied by Brown et al. (1967) only a single one could be driven by vibration

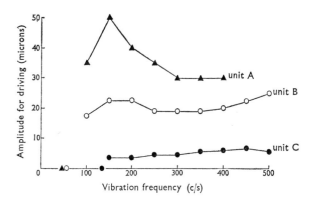

FIG. 4.20. The threshold amplitudes of vibration required to 'drive' three different primary endings to discharge one spike per cycle of vibration at each of a series of frequencies. The 'amplitude' is the peak-to-peak amplitude of the movement. (Brown, Engberg & Matthews, 1967, Fig. 3.)

at all; this was at 100 Hz but not at 150 Hz by a vibration of 250 μm amplitude. None of the others could be driven at 100 Hz or above with any amplitude vibration available, and most of them were not significantly excited by vibration to increase their frequency of firing above the pre-existing rate. Eight secondary endings were also tested with vibration during their simultaneous activation by stimulation of single fusimotor fibres. This did not appreciably increase their vibration sensitivity, though it markedly does so for primary endings. Thus with yet another form of mechanical stimulation a clear difference has again emerged between the responsiveness of primary and secondary spindle endings.

In passing it seems worth emphasising the remarkably high sensitivity of the primary ending to vibration. For example, unit C of Fig. 4.20 was driven over a wide range of frequencies by a peak-to-peak amplitude of movement of the tendon of less than 5 μm, which represents an extension of the muscle of about 1 part in 10,000 (soleus is about 5 cm long). The actual vibration applied to the spindle itself must have been less than 1 μm for it would have been less than a fifth of the length of the muscle. This makes the sensitivity of the ending similar to that of the vibration receptor *par excellence*, the Pacinian corpuscle (Sato, 1961). Most other endings became similarly sensitive during fusimotor stimulation. It should be noted, however, that for primary endings to be able to manifest their high sensitivity the muscle usually had to be moderately stretched before applying the vibration. Both stretching and fusimotor stimulation probably have their favourable effect on vibration sensitivity merely by increasing the stiffness of the poles of the spindle and so ensuring that the vibratory deformation is concentrated in the non-striated sensorially innervated region of the spindle.

Sensitivity to sinusoidal stretching of sufficiently small amplitude to evoke a linear response

The response of the endings to sinusoidal stretching is of particular interest because this form of input is one favoured by engineers in analysing inanimate control systems. In addition, the movements of tremor may be closely sinusoidal. Sinusoidal stretching at around 1 Hz and of appreciable amplitude evokes the different response from primary and secondary endings which would be expected from the well-established differences in their sensitivity to other dynamic stimuli of large amplitude. Thus during the stretching phase of the cycle the primary endings fire more spikes at a higher frequency and earlier in the cycle than do the secondary endings, and during the releasing the primary endings show a greater tendency to silence (Fig. 4.12; Stuart, Ott, Ishikawa & Eldred, 1965; Grüsser & Thiele, 1968; Dabbert & Grüsser, 1968; Eysel & Grüsser, 1970). It is, however, difficult to make a quantitative comparison of the responses of different endings to various frequencies and amplitudes, for it is not at all clear just which facets of the response are best studied and it becomes rather overwhelming to attempt to measure everything. Moreover, when the amplitude of stretching is large the responses appear to be essentially non-linear in the engineering sense, meaning by this that doubling the size of the stimulus at any frequency does not double the resulting spindle response, whatever measure of response is chosen. In a linear system, doubling the input does double the output and as a result measurements of the response to sinusoidal stretching permit the prediction of the response of the system to other input waveforms, for example by means of a Fourier analysis.

Non-linear behaviour seriously upsets the predictive value of any measurements made with sinusoidal stretching and thus negates one of the reasons for taking an interest in them. Fortunately, however, if the amplitude of sinusoidal stretching of a muscle is sufficiently reduced the responses of both primary and secondary endings are found to become linear. This thus permits the determination for an ending of a unique frequency-response curve which is independent of the precise amplitude of stretching. From this curve it should prove possible to predict the response of the ending to other shapes of stimuli, provided that these also are sufficiently small not to transgress the linear range. For these reasons Matthews & Stein (1969a) and Poppele & Bowman (1970) have recently compared the behaviour of primary and secondary endings in their linear ranges and have found certain unexpected similarities between them, which are not apparent from their responses to large-amplitude stimuli. The achievement of linearity by reduction of the input signal is commonplace in engineering practice and often has no firmer basis than the obvious fact that the shorter the segment of a curve the more closely it approximates to a straight line. Even when this is so, the value of a sinusoidal analysis is largely preserved.

Averaging methods. For any except the lowest frequencies the response to sinusoidal stretching can usually only be assessed at all accurately by averaging the response to a number of repeated cycles of stretching. This is because of the variability of the spike-train and because of the limited number of spikes occurring in each individual sinusoidal cycle. One simple way of averaging is to divide each cycle up into a number of bins of constant duration (12 to 72 have been used) and to sum the spikes occurring in equivalent bins on successive repetitions of the cycle. If the amplitude of the sinusoidal stretching is made infinitely small then each bin must on average contain the same number of spikes, since by definition the discharge of the ending must then be unaffected by the stretching. The ending may be assumed to be discharging 'spontaneously' as this is usual for all spindle afferents subject to either moderate stretch or moderate fusimotor excitation. The frequency of discharge will thus be the same at all points in the cycle and will be given simply by the number of spikes in any bin divided by the duration of the bin and the number of repetitions (i.e. if 100 spikes are found in a bin of 100 msec width which has been repeated 10 times then the total recording time for the bin is 1 sec and so the mean frequency of discharge is 100/sec). When the amplitude of stretching is increased to a finite value it will begin to influence the ending and to modulate the otherwise steady 'generator current' which may be presumed to be initiating the resting spike discharge. Naturally, spikes will be initiated most

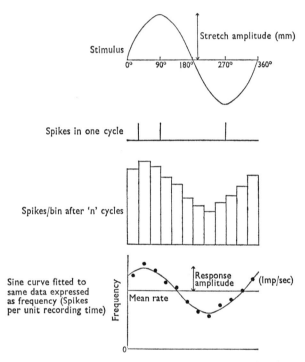

FIG. 4.21. Diagram of method of averaging used to determine the response of spindle afferents to sinusoidal stretching. It is drawn for a frequency of stretching which is comparable to the spontaneous rate of discharge of the afferent, but the procedure is equally applicable when the stretching is at a far higher or a far lower frequency than the discharge. The method simply consists of fitting a sine curve to the 'post stimulus time histogram' or 'cycle histogram' resulting from a large number of repetitions of the cyclic stretching.

readily when the generator current is the greatest and so the number of spikes in successive bins will no longer be constant. Likewise the frequency of discharge of the ending calculated bin by bin will vary rhythmically throughout the cycle. Experiment shows that when the amplitude of stretching is small enough the modulation of frequency throughout the cycle is approximately sinusoidal and this may be taken to express the response of the ending to the sinusoidal stretching. Alternatively, the response curve may be seen simply as the cyclic change in the probability of firing of the ending as a result of the sinusoidal stretching, without bothering to think about it as a frequency. The computation which has just been described is illustrated in Fig. 4.21.

The physiological significance of the above procedure is heightened by the fact that the CNS can obtain rather similar information by simultaneously averaging the discharges in a number of afferent fibres all of which are influenced by the same stretching. Suppose, for example, that a number of similar afferents all synapse with a single neurone then the resulting summed post-synaptic potential would be proportional to the total number of presynaptic spikes arriving per unit time. The CNS, however, cannot perform the averaging over successive cycles because it lacks a set of reference marks timing the stimulus and required to permit the allocation of spikes to pre-determined bins related to the stimulus repeat cycle. Thus the nervous system should not be thought to be capable of examining the afferent discharges in every way that is open to the neurophysiologist.

An alternative averaging procedure, which is particularly useful for frequencies of stretching of below about 1 Hz, is to determine the mean interspike interval for all the various spikes falling into each bin. This is done by summing for each bin, firstly the number of spikes falling into it and, secondly the interval between each one of these spikes and its predecessor. Simple division then gives the mean interspike interval for each bin and taking its reciprocal gives the mean frequency for the bin. When the frequency of stretching is low this second method gives a result identical to that obtained by the probability method, but it has the advantage of obtaining it with greater accuracy. This is because the second method preserves the information contained in the actual frequency of firing of the afferent fibre at any time, instead of simply utilising the time of occurrence of spikes in relation to the phase of the sinusoidal cycle. This is advantageous when the stimulus is varying slowly because the instantaneous frequency of discharge of the afferent, calculated spike-by-spike, then provides a reasonable measure of the instantaneous value of the stimulus.

However, the direct measurement of frequency breaks down when the stimulus is varying rapidly. Each interspike interval then spans an appreciable number of bins and lasts long enough for the stimulus to change appreciably in size. It is then no longer good enough to refer the interval simply to the particular bin into which the spike happens to fall and systematic errors result from doing so. These errors can be compensated for by calculation provided the ending has a reasonably steady 'carrier frequency' in the absence of sinusoidal stretching (Poppele & Bowman, 1970). But such correction becomes somewhat less certain when the discharge has a high spontaneous variability, as occurs in the decerebrate cat, and the first method is probably then to be preferred.

Both methods of determining the response to sinusoidal stretching tend to run into difficulties when the frequency of stretching is near to the frequency of spontaneous discharge of the ending studied. The trouble arises largely because of a tendency of the discharge to become 'phase-locked' to the stimulus so that all of the spikes fall into only a few of the bins and the others are empty. The response can then no longer be analysed in linear terms. Phase-locking is the less likely to occur the more variable is the spontaneous discharge of the afferent, and in simulation studies may be reduced by adding white noise to the system under study (Stein & French, 1970). It is thus less troublesome in the decerebrate cat with its considerable spontaneous variability of afferent discharge than it is for the de-efferented ending. Poppele & Bowman (1970) recognise a further superficially similar disturbing feature for discharges close to the spontaneous frequency. They have called it 'carrier dependence' and consider it to be quite separate from phase-locking. They suggest that phase-locking is shown by the primary ending but not the secondary, whereas carrier dependence is shown by the secondary but not the primary and they believe that this betokens a fundamental difference in the properties of the nerve terminals themselves.

These various technical matters have been dealt with in some detail in order to emphasise that the determination of the response to sinusoidal stretching involves a certain abstraction, particularly when the frequency of stretching approaches or exceeds the spontaneous frequency of firing of the ending studied. The results obtained should none the less throw light on intrafusal mechanisms even if they should prove to have rather little to do with the way the body uses its spindles in life.

The linear range and the measurement of sensitivity. The magnitude of the response of an ending to the sinusoidal stretching may be taken as the modulation, in impulses/sec, of its firing frequency as determined by fitting a sine curve to the experimental points of frequency against bin number. Figure 4.22 shows the magnitude of the response plotted against the size of the stimulus for a primary and for a secondary ending studied in the decerebrate cat on stretching at 1 Hz. The secondary ending behaved linearly throughout the range of amplitudes studied, for its response

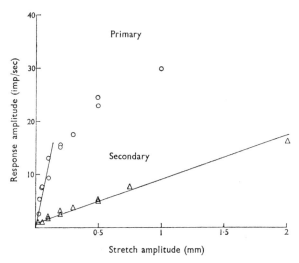

FIG. 4.22. Comparison of the responses of a primary and of a secondary ending to increasing amplitudes of sinusoidal stretching. The change in the frequency of firing produced by sinusoidal stretching at 1 Hz is plotted against the amplitude of stretching (the amplitude is half the peak-to-peak extent of the stretch). The preparation was the soleus muscle of the decerebrate cat with intact ventral roots and spontaneous fusimotor activity. (Matthews & Stein, 1969a, Fig. 4.)

increased in proportion to the stimulus. The response of the primary ending, however, only increased linearly with the stimulus up to amplitudes of 0·1 mm. For larger stretches the response increased less rapidly than the stimulus showing that the ending was then behaving non-linearly.

Thus another difference between the two kinds of ending is in the extent of their linear range, which is uniformly larger for the secondary ending than for the primary. This has been most definitely established in the decerebrate cat with its steady intrafusal tone, but still appears to be true for the de-efferented state though the linear range of both kinds of ending is then often much smaller than in the decerebrate. It might not, however, perhaps be true during steady intensive static fusimotor bias. As will appear in a moment, the extent of the linear range appears to vary inversely with the sensitivity of the ending, and the restricted linear range of the primary is a simple consequence of its greater sensitivity. It may also be noted that as the frequency of stretching is increased so the linear range of both kinds of ending, expressed as a variation of length, becomes progressively smaller. This is because the sensitivity of the endings to a given length change increases with increasing frequency of stretching. However, under all the conditions so far studied stretching to the extremes of the linear range appears to modulate the discharge by about the same amount and approximately by 30% of the pre-existing resting discharge. The 'driving' of spindle afferents by vibration is, of course, a non-linear form of response. There is then a one-to-one relation between each sine wave and the resulting spindle response, and all the spikes occur at the same phase of the cycle and so fall into the same bin. As usual the ending may be brought to behave linearly by further reduction of the amplitude of the stimulus.

The sensitivity of an ending to any particular frequency of sinusoidal stretching may be defined as the amplitude of the response divided by the amplitude of the stimulus. This gives a value expressed in impulses sec^{-1} mm^{-1} (i.e. impulses/sec firing per mm stretching). In Fig. 4.22 the sensitivity is simply the slope for the lines which join the points. It was slightly over 100 impulses sec^{-1} mm^{-1} for the primary ending and about 8 for the secondary ending. Such a tenfold or so greater sensitivity of the primary ending has been the usual finding for all frequencies of stretching from 0·3 to 300 Hz. Figure 4.23 shows a plot of the sensitivity measured within the linear range against the frequency of stretching for such a wide range of frequencies. The sensitivity of both kinds of ending is seen to increase tremendously as the frequency of stretching is increased. The results were obtained in the decerebrate cat with an appreciable amount of spontaneous fusimotor activity. Poppele & Bowman (1970) have obtained broadly similar results for a smaller range of frequencies applied to the de-efferented spindle.

The predominant 'corner frequency'. A remarkable but constant feature of data such as those shown in Fig. 4.23 is that curves of the same form can be fitted over a wide range to the response of both kinds of ending. Those drawn in Fig. 4.23 differ in their vertical displacement, that is in their absolute level of sensitivity, but not in their horizontal displacement, that is in the frequency at which their sensitivity begins to increase. The curve shown is the one which would be given by a system which was responsive

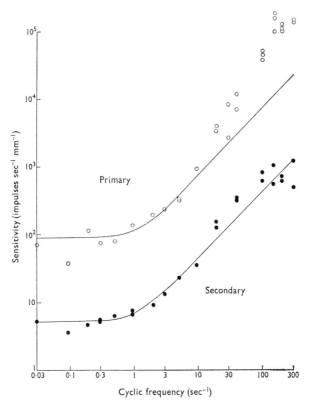

FIG. 4.23. Comparison of the sensitivity to sinusoidal stretching within the linear range of a primary and a secondary ending studied over a wide range of frequencies of stretching. The sensitivity is the amplitude of the response divided by the amplitude of the stretching (cf. Fig. 4.21). The preparation was the soleus muscle of the decerebrate cat with intact ventral roots and spontaneous fusimotor activity. The continuous lines represent the vector sums of a response to the length component (horizontal portion at low frequencies) and of a response to the velocity component (diagonal portion at high frequencies) of the stretching. The same curve transposed vertically approximately fits both endings. This shows that in the linear range they differ in their absolute sensitivities rather than in the ratio of their length to velocity sensitivity. (Matthews & Stein, 1969a, Fig. 5.)

to the vector sum of the length and velocity components of the sinusoidal stimulus. The sensitivity is then given by $S = \sqrt{(1 + f^2/F^2)}$ where S is the sensitivity at low frequencies, f is the frequency in question, and F is the 'corner frequency' at which the responses to the length and velocity components of the stimulus are equal (1·5 Hz for the curves of Fig. 4.23). This relation fits the experimental results quite reasonably over the range 0·3 to 20 Hz, which is perhaps the range of greatest physiological interest.

Measurements of phase angle, however, confirm what is obvious on simple inspection, namely that the equation is only an approximation and that further terms are required, particularly to describe the responses at higher and lower frequencies. Poppele & Bowman (1970) have recently fitted their own experimental data rather accurately by using transfer functions with four variable parameters for the secondary ending (1 for gain and 3 for time constants) and six for the primary (1 for gain, 3 time constants with same values as those for the secondary, plus 2 additional time constants —one for high and one for low frequencies). None the less, the striking feature remains that the responses of primary and of secondary endings can be fitted over an essential part of their range by curves of the same form and with the same corner frequency. In the decerebrate cat the mean value of the corner frequency for 25 primary endings was 1·6 Hz (range 0·9–2·3) and that for 17 secondary endings was 1·4 Hz (range 0·7–2·5) (Matthews & Stein; 1969a). In the de-efferented preparation Poppele & Bowman found the predominant corner frequency to be at 1·8 Hz for both primary and secondary endings (some of the other time constants in their transfer functions approximately cancel each other out).

The corner frequency may be looked upon as a measure of the velocity-sensitivity of an ending relative to its length-sensitivity. This means that for stretches small enough to fall within the linear range of the endings the difference between primary and secondary endings resides primarily in the absolute level of their sensitivity to stretching, rather than in a preferential phasic sensitivity of the primary ending! This might be taken to contradict much that has already been said, but the contradiction arises simply because the behaviour of the primary ending is quite different outside and inside its small linear range, while the linear range of the secondary ending is large enough for most studies to have been performed within it. The corner frequency of 1·5 Hz for the secondary would not appear to imply a greater velocity-sensitivity than has long been apparent from the finite value of the dynamic index found for secondary endings on completing a ramp stretch.

The value of the sensitivity at low frequencies. This brings us back to the value of S, the sensitivity at low frequencies and which as a first approximation may be considered as a measure of length-sensitivity. As was typical, the secondary ending illustrated in Fig. 4.23 had the comparatively modest length-sensitivity of 8 impulses sec^{-1} mm^{-1} and a correspondingly wide linear range. The primary ending of Fig. 4.23, however, had a length-sensitivity of nearly 100 impulses sec^{-1} mm^{-1}, though this was only applicable for stretches of up to about 0·1 mm. Hitherto the 'static' or position-sensitivity of the primary ending has been conventionally determined by stretching the muscle to a series of lengths, allowing a variable time for receptor adaptation, and then measuring the frequency of discharge at each length. As already noted, when this is done the resulting points of frequency against extension can usually be tolerably well fitted by a straight line, the slope of which is often considered as the length-sensitivity of the ending (Fig. 4.8). The value obtained is usually of the order of 5 impulses sec^{-1} mm^{-1} on measuring a few seconds after attaining each new length (Granit, 1958) and a similar value was found for the particular endings studied by Matthews & Stein (1969a) with sinusoidal stretching. Thus the length-sensitivity determined by small sinusoids may be a factor of 20 times greater than determined with large stretches. The unexpectedly high value for the small sinusoids arises partly because the stimulus is restricted to the linear range of the ending, and partly because sinusoidal stretching tests the response of the ending to alternate stretching and releasing; large maintained stretches used in the standard way only test the response of the ending to progressive increases in the degree of stretch.

Thus for the time being the paradox exists that two incompatible statements are required to compare the behaviour of the two kinds of spindle afferent over the whole of their working range. For large stretches it remains appropriate to say that the primary ending differs from the secondary ending in being appreciably the more sensitive to the dynamic components of any stimulus, while the two kinds of ending are approximately equally sensitive to static components of the stimulus. On the other hand, for small stretches with frequency components in the range 0·3–30 Hz this formulation becomes entirely misleading, for the primary ending then differs from the secondary ending in having a greater all-round sensitivity and has no special sensitivity to velocity. However, even for small amplitudes of stretching the primary ending is probably relatively the more dynamically sensitive for frequency components above 20 Hz, for in plots such as those as Fig. 4.23 the points for the primary endings then lie systematically above the simple curve, while those for the secondary endings usually do not do so (Matthews & Stein, 1969a; Poppele & Bowman, 1970). This upwards deviation of the points for the primary ending may be taken to indicate a sensitivity to acceleration over and above that to velocity. Such 'acceleration-sensitivity' of the primary ending along with its high absolute sensitivity at low frequencies helps explain why it is so much more easily driven by high-frequency vibration than is the secondary ending. The mechanism of such actions remains almost entirely unstudied. It may, how-ever, be tentatively suggested that the similarity of the form of a large part of the frequency-response curves for the two kinds of ending reflects similarities in the properties of the nerve terminals themselves. On the other hand, the dissimilarities in the responses of the endings to large stretches may reflect the dissimilarities in their anatomical arrangement with regard to the intrafusal fibres and depend upon mechanical rather than purely nervous factors. Such matters are discussed more fully in Chap. 6.

It should be next emphasised that the value of S in plots such as that of Fig. 4.23 does not provide a completely true measure of length responsiveness and is not applicable to measurements made a minute or so after applying a maintained stretch (Poppele & Bowman, 1970). This is also why at frequencies of stretching as low as 0·1 Hz the afferent response is still appreciably phase-advanced on the stimulus. However, for periods of static stretch of some 1–2 sec the value of static sensitivity determined by observing the response of the primary ending to alternately stretch-ing and releasing the muscle and then maintaining its length constant in between agrees quite well with the value of S deter-mined by sinusoidal stretching. This is illustrated in Fig. 4.24 which compares the effect of sudden stretching with that of sinusoidal stretching of twice the total extent. Working with static stretches or with low-frequency sinusoidal stretches also permits the direct observation of the qualitative features of the response with the now conventional display of 'instantaneous frequency' without the need for elaborate averaging procedures. This helps fortify the belief in the validity of the conclusion that

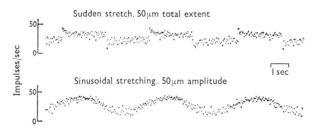

FIG. 4.24. The high sensitivity of a primary ending to small stretches shown directly by means of a display of its instantaneous frequency of discharge. The muscle was either stretched and released sinusoidally (below), or its length was changed suddenly and then maintained (above). The repeat period was 5 sec for a complete cycle of either manœuvre. The total extent of the sinusoidal movement was twice that of the sudden movement (i.e. the 'amplitude' of a sine wave is half its peak-to-peak extent). The preparation was the de-efferented soleus muscle of the cat. (Matthews & Stein, 1969a, Fig. 8.)

the primary ending may have a very high sensitivity for small stretches, even when they are of rather low frequency.

Physiological relevance. It might be suggested that the whole comparison of the responsiveness of the two kinds of ending to sinusoidal stretching is irrelevant for normal function and that the linear range over which it is applicable is too small to have any physiological significance. Even at low frequencies the linear range of the primary is no more than 0·5% of the length of the muscle and it becomes infinitesimal for frequencies of 100 Hz or above (a fraction of a μm). But the linear range is not small when it is judged by the modulation of the primary afferent discharge which at the linear extremes is about $\pm 30\%$ of the pre-existing discharge. At low frequencies this represents a very real change in the gross pattern of spike firing and would seem an adequate signal to be important, at the least in the reflex control of posture. The responses to frequencies of above about 30 Hz, however, are probably only of interest for the study of internal working of the spindle and may have no part to play in normal function, for muscles can but rarely change their length so rapidly.

The importance of the low-frequency responsiveness is further argued by the findings illustrated in Fig. 4.25. This shows the response of two primary endings and a secondary ending in the

GM

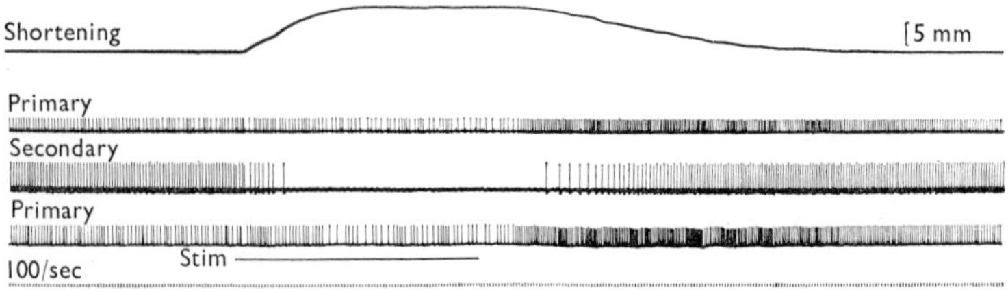

FIG. 4.25. Physiological manifestation of the high sensitivity to small stretches of the primary ending but not of the secondary ending. The remarkable sensitivity of the primary ending is demonstrated by its response to the small irregularities occurring during a reflexly induced contraction which was taking place under nearly isotonic recording conditions. The preparation was the soleus muscle of the decerebrate cat with intact ventral roots, severed dorsal roots, and spontaneous fusimotor activity. The reflex contraction of soleus was induced by repetitive stimulation of the lateral popliteal nerve of the other leg for the period indicated. The muscle then shortened by about 10 mm when its tension rose only by about 120 g. The discharges of the three afferent fibres were recorded simultaneously. The recording was made isotonic by connecting the muscle to an isometric myograph via a weak spring. (Previously unpublished record of experiments of Jansen & Matthews, 1962a.)

soleus muscle of the decerebrate cat when the muscle was reflexly induced to contract by stimulating a contralateral nerve. The recording was under semi-isotonic conditions so that at the height of the contraction the muscle had shortened by nearly 10 mm. This shortening caused both primary endings to discharge less rapidly than before, and the secondary to fall silent. As the reflex contraction waned the secondary discharge picked up smoothly with no irregularity, and in approximate proportion to the increasing re-extension of the muscle by the isotonic recording system. As would be expected the primary endings fired more rapidly during this re-extension phase than they had done before, but in addition their discharge was modulated into periods of higher and lower frequency. These modulations corresponded for the two primary endings, and appear to have depended upon the slight irregularities in the muscle contraction which can just be seen on the myographic trace. The modulation would thus appear to be an expression, under reasonably physiological conditions, of the high sensitivity of the primary ending to small displacements; in this particular case they were below 0·5 mm. Thus sinusoidal analysis has been instrumental in bringing to light an important difference in sensitivity between primary and secondary endings and which is now readily recognisable without the need for computer averaging.

Finally it deserves mention that after a stretch of large amplitude the primary ending can 'reset' itself so that its high sensitivity applies again at the new length, thus avoiding the saturation which might otherwise occur in such a highly sensitive system. Indeed, the non-linear behaviour of the primary ending may perhaps be looked upon as a useful way of extending its working range. Small signals are transmitted with relative fidelity at a high sensitivity, while larger signals are transmitted with a lower sensitivity but without complete saturation. In this respect it is interesting that the frequency–response curve of the secondary ending should be largely similar to that of the primary ending in its linear range. This means that as a stimulus increases in size from nothing upwards it will first be detected by the primary endings and signalled in a manner defined by the standard frequency–response curve. Then, as the linear range of the primary is overshot, the calibration of the primary will change; but the secondary ending with its lower sensitivity will begin to respond appreciably and to transmit information about the stimulus by means of the code that the primary ending is just stopping using. Thus in this sense the two kinds of ending can be thought of as signalling much the same thing rather than different things, though whether the CNS possesses the appropriate internal connections to see things this way is quite another matter.

On the other hand, the importance of the rather different type of response of the primary endings to large stretches should not be minimised. The fact that the ending is then behaving non-linearly in the engineering sense does not mean that its responses become physiologically unimportant. Large movements of muscles are as normal an occurrence as postural fixation, and the spindle primary alters its response to them in a systematic way with variations in their extent and velocity of application. The same holds true for releases of appreciable extent, provided that there is enough steady fusimotor activity to prevent the endings then falling silent. 'Release', of course, is what happens to a muscle spindle when its own muscle contracts and so the behaviour of the spindle on release would appear to be at least as important as its behaviour on stretch.

TABLE 4.1. Summary of the comparison of the two kinds of spindle afferent ending as seen in the cat soleus

Differences	Primary ending	Secondary ending
1. Location	Mid-equatorial Bag and chain fibres	Juxta-equatorial Predominantly chain fibres
2. Afferent fibre	Large, Ia (12–20 μm, 70–120 m/sec)	Medium, group II (4–12 μm, 20–70 m/sec)
3. Efferent control	Both γ_S and γ_D	Solely γ_S
4. Response to ramp stretch of several mm extent	High dynamic sensitivity	Low dynamic sensitivity
(a) at beginning	May have prominent acceleration response, anyhow rapid increase in firing frequency	Progressive increase in firing linearly related to progressive extension
(b) on completion of dynamic stretching	Large dynamic index (40–120 impulses/ sec on 10 mm/sec stretching in de-efferented preparation)	Small dynamic index (5–21 impulses/sec under same conditions)
(c) on release	Abrupt silencing of discharge (provided insignificant γ_S activity)	Progressive decrease in firing to zero
5. Response to tendon tap	Low threshold (<50 μm, may be multiple discharge)	High threshold (>500 μm)
6. Response to vibration applied to tendon	Low threshold (<50 μm for 'driving' at 100–300 Hz)	High threshold (at least 250 μm for 100 Hz)
7. Variability of inter-spike interval	High (mean coefficient of variation; 6% when de-efferented, 25% in decerebrate)	Low (variability, 2% de-efferented, 6% in decerebrate)
8. Sensitivity to small displacements	High (typically 100 impulses sec^{-1} mm^{-1} in decerebrate)	Low (typically 7 impulses sec^{-1} mm^{-1} in decerebrate)

Similarities
1. Ultrastructural appearance of nerve terminals themselves.
2. Static response to large extensions. Sensitivity around 4 impulses sec^{-1} mm^{-1} for both.
3. Main 'corner frequency' determined by small amplitude sinusoidal stretching is around 1·5 Hz for both.

It would be remarkable if the CNS were to ignore any of the information contained in the signals it receives but it seems possible that this may be so. Indeed, the problem of understanding the spindle afferent discharges is rapidly changing its nature. For the last decade the interest has been in establishing functional differences between the primary and secondary endings, in relating these to differences in the structure and location of the endings, and in describing the patterns of firing of the two kinds of ending to a variety of simple stimulus waveforms. Such things are summarised in Table 4.1. They have now been investigated in reasonable detail and the interest is shifting to the use to which the signals are put by the CNS. The present problem is to distinguish between those features of the afferent discharges to which the CNS pays particular attention and those which it ignores. The fact that a physiologist can extract certain information about a stimulus from a particular detail of the spindle response is no guarantee that the CNS bothers to do so, or that the information is preserved on synaptic transmission to higher order neurones. As such problems begin to be tackled more intensively yet further patterns of mechanical stimulation may well be found the most appropriate for their study, and the effect of these on the spindle will have to be determined. New parameters of stimulation may also be found appropriate for developing and testing models of the internal functioning of the spindle. For the moment it is enough that the morphologically distinct primary and secondary afferent endings of the spindle have been established as functionally distinct entities.

Résumé of functional differences between primary and secondary endings

The fact that the primary and secondary endings differ in their anatomical arrangement suggests that they should have different functions and send different messages to the CNS. That this is indeed so has now been established by experiment. The present chapter describes these differences as they are seen in the de-efferented spindle and also in the decerebrate with intact ventral roots. The spindles in the latter preparation possess a continuous intrafusal tone as a result of a spontaneous fusimotor discharge and so may perhaps behave more normally than flaccid ones.

Receptor classification by afferent conduction velocity. The initial problem is to develop a way of recognising whether any particular spindle afferent fibre which is being studied electrophysiologically comes from a primary or from a secondary ending. This can now be decided by measuring the conduction velocity of the fibre in question where it runs in the main nerve. Histological work has long suggested that the large afferent fibres from spindles should supply primary endings and the smaller ones secondary endings, but has not been able to guarantee that this is so in the main nerve trunk itself as well as at the site of termination of the fibres. Electrophysiological work has now verified that the suggestion is correct, and has demonstrated that large and small afferent fibres do supply receptors with quite different functional properties, and that each group is quite reasonably functionally homogeneous within itself. The dividing line between the two kinds of afferents in nerves of the cat's hindlimb is conventionally placed at 72 m/sec. This precise figure, however, represents little more than an inspired guess for it was introduced before the receptor properties had been delimited. Present evidence is against the existence of any such sharp dividing line at this or any other place, for the diameters of the two kinds of afferent fibre would appear to overlap somewhat. None the less, if the dividing line is broadened so as to form a 'no man's land' from 60 to 80 m/sec the classification by afferent conduction velocity works out surprisingly well in terms of receptor properties, and so may be taken as quite reliable on its own.

Response to large stretches applied at constant velocity (ramps). These may be looked upon as comprising a static component, equivalent to the instantaneous value of the applied extension, and a dynamic component, equivalent to the instantaneous value of the velocity of stretching. The spindle endings behave as if they are responding to the sum of these two sub-components of the stimulus. It turns out that the primary and secondary endings are about equally sensitive to the static component of the stimulus, but that the primary ending is very markedly the more sensitive to the dynamic component.

The static component of response may be assessed on its own by measuring the frequency of discharge of an ending when the length of the muscle is held constant. The only difficulty in this procedure is in deciding how long should be allowed for receptor adaptation before taking any measurement, for this inevitably influences the precise figure obtained. The graph of frequency against length is usually a straight line and its slope may be defined as the 'position-sensitivity' of the ending. Values around 5 impulses sec^{-1} mm^{-1} are commonly found for both kinds of ending in the soleus muscle when it is de-efferented; the values are often slightly higher in the decerebrate.

The dynamic component of the response may be most easily assessed by seeing how far the discharge of the ending falls when the dynamic phase of stretching is completed and the final length of the muscle maintained. At this point the velocity falls from a finite value to zero whereas the length remains the same. This gives the so-called 'dynamic index' which is defined as the decrease in frequency occurring in the first 0·5 sec after completing a ramp stretch at constant velocity. The time of 0·5 sec is experimentally convenient but has no theoretical significance, nor has the dynamic index itself. The dynamic index meets the minimum requirement of a velocity measure for it increases progressively with the velocity of stretching. It is found to be systematically larger for primary than for secondary endings; for example, on stretching at 10 mm/sec the values are around 60 and 10 impulses/ sec respectively.

At the very beginning of a stretch primary endings sometimes fire a brief initial burst of impulses. This burst may be formally described as an acceleration response as its peak frequency increases with the initial acceleration; but it is still uncertain how far it represents a true response to acceleration *per se*, for it seems to be preferentially shown for movements starting from rest rather than from a pre-existing movement. On release of a stretch which has been maintained for some time the de-efferented primary ending usually immediately falls silent, whereas the secondary ending may continue to fire for an appreciable proportion of the release. In the decerebrate, however, primary endings may also fire somewhat on release. A release may be thought to combine a positive stimulus of length with a negative stimulus of velocity. Virtually all these differences have been confirmed by observing simultaneously the responses of a pair of endings, one of each kind, both of which lie in the same muscle spindle.

A residual problem is whether endings with afferents conducting

at near the original dividing line of 72 m/sec have intermediate
properties, or whether they fall into one or other of the two main
groups. The present indication is that though they may show somewhat intermediate properties when they are de-efferented, yet
they divide cleanly into the usual two classes when their intrafusal
fibres are made to contract by the injection of suxamethonium.

Variability of discharge. For unknown reasons the primary
ending always fires rather less regularly than does the secondary
ending. In both de-efferented and decerebrate preparations the
co-efficient of variation of the interspike interval distribution is
3–4 times greater for the primary than for the secondary. However,
in the decerebrate the variability of the discharge of both kinds of
ending is increased about fourfold as a result of the lack of smooth-
ness of the intrafusal contraction. In the de-efferented state at
moderate frequencies of discharge the coefficient of variation is
around 0·06 for primary endings and 0·02 for secondary endings.

Sensitivity to brief phasic stimuli. A tendon tap is a highly potent
stimulus for primary endings but barely affects secondary endings.
The threshold displacement required to excite a single spike
from a primary ending is invariably less than 60 μm, whereas
that for the secondary ending is always much higher and often
over 500 μm. Likewise, primary endings can be readily 'driven'
by vibration of 100–500 Hz to discharge one spike per cycle; the
threshold peak-to-peak amplitude of movement is regularly
below 50 μm. In contrast, secondary endings cannot be
driven even at 100 Hz by a vibration of as much as 250 μm
amplitude.

Sensitivity to small amplitude sinusoidal stretching. When the
amplitude of a sinusoidal stretch is sufficiently reduced both kinds
of ending respond in a linear manner. A linear response is one
which is precisely halved when the amplitude of the stimulus is
halved. Sinusoidal stretching within the linear range of an ending
evokes a sinusoidal modulation of its frequency of firing. The
sensitivity of the ending to the stretching may then be defined
as the amplitude of its response modulation (in impulses/sec)
divided by the amplitude of the stretching (in mm). By the use of
computer averaging the sensitivity of an ending may be determined over a wide range of frequencies of stretching. For both

kinds of ending the graph of sensitivity against frequency is usually approximately flat from 0·1 to 1 Hz. It then begins to increase along the curve which describes the behaviour of a system which is sensitive to the vector sum of the length and velocity components of the stretching.

The 'corner frequency' at which the curve begins to rise provides a measure of the relative sensitivity of an ending to length and to velocity. Somewhat unexpectedly, this corner frequency turns out to be the same for the two kinds of ending, about 1·5 Hz, in spite of the fact that the primary ending is so much the more sensitive to velocity when the amplitude of stretching is large. However, at still higher frequencies the primary ending may sometimes show a sensitivity to acceleration which the secondary ending lacks. This general similarity in behaviour of the two kinds of ending in response to small stretches probably reflects a similarity in the properties of the nerve terminals themselves. On the other hand, the dissimilarities seen in their responses to large stretches probably reflect dissimilarities in the anatomical arrangement of the two kinds of ending in relation to the underlying intrafusal fibres.

The responses of the two kinds of ending to small sinusoidal stimuli are, however, far from identical. At all frequencies of stretching the absolute value of the sensitivity of the primary ending is usually an order of magnitude greater than that of the secondary ending. At frequencies around 1 Hz the sensitivity of the primary in the decerebrate cat is usually around 100 impulses sec^{-1} mm^{-1} whereas that for the secondary is below 10 impulses sec^{-1} mm^{-1}. This difference, and the remarkably high value for the primary ending, seem likely to be important in the regulation of posture. The position sensitivity of the primary determined by large stretches falling outside the linear range is only about 5 impulses sec^{-1} mm^{-1}.

Table 4.1 summarises most of the differences that have so far been described between the two kinds of ending. In view of them all there can no longer be any doubt about the functional distinctiveness of the primary and secondary spindle endings. The current question is what all this means to the CNS, and which of the various differences matter for function under physiological conditions. The ingenuity of physiologists has probably enabled them to recognise differences in patterns of discharge which pass quite unnoticed by the central decoding mechanisms normally employed by the CNS.

References

Alnaes, E., Jansen, J. K. S. & Rudjord, T. (1965). Fusimotor activity in the spinal cat. *Acta physiol. scand.* **63**, 197–212. [145, 147, 152, 154]

Bessou, P. & Laporte, Y. (1962). Responses from primary and secondary endings of the same neuromuscular spindle of the tenuissimus muscle of the cat. In *Symposium on Muscle Receptors*, ed. Barker, D. pp. 105–119. Hong Kong: Hong Kong University Press.   [147, 155, 156]

Bianconi, R. & van der Meulen, J. P. (1963). The responses to vibration of the end-organs of mammalian muscle spindles. *J. Neurophysiol.* **26**, 177–190.   [158, 169]

Boyd, I. A. (1962). The structure and innervation of the nuclear bag muscle fibre system and the nuclear chain muscle fibres system in mammalian muscle spindles. *Phil. Trans. R. Soc.* B **245**, 81–136.
[155]

Brown, M. C., Crowe, A. & Matthews, P. B. C. (1965). Observations on the fusimotor fibres of the tibialis posterior muscle of the cat. *J. Physiol.* **177**, 140–159.   [150]

Brown, M. C., Engberg, I. & Matthews, P. B. C. (1967). The relative sensitivity to vibration of muscle receptors of the cat. *J. Physiol.* **192**, 773–800.   [158, 170, 171]

Brown, M. C., Goodwin, G. M. & Matthews, P. B. C. (1969). After-effects of fusimotor stimulation on the response of muscle spindle primary afferent endings. *J. Physiol.* **205**, 677–694.   [167]

Cooper, S. (1959). The secondary endings of muscle spindles. *J. Physiol.* **149**, 27–28P.   [146]

— (1961). The responses of the primary and secondary endings of muscle spindles with intact motor innervation during applied stretch. *J. exp. Physiol.* **46**, 389–398.   [146]

Crowe, A. & Matthews, P. B. C. (1964). The effects of stimulation of static and dynamic fusimotor fibres on the response to stretching of the primary endings of muscle spindles. *J. Physiol.* **174**, 109–131.
[148]

Dabbert, H. & Grüsser, O. J. (1968). Reaktionen primärer und sekundärer Muskelspindelafferenzen auf sinusförmige mechanische Reizung. II. Änderung der statischen Vordehnung. *Pflügers Arch. ges. physiol.* **304**, 258–270.   [172]

Diete-Spiff, K. (1961). The discharge pattern of muscle spindles of the rabbit on activation of intrafusal muscle fibres. *J. Physiol.* **159**, 282–296.   [145]

Echlin, F. & Fessard, A. (1938). Synchronized impulse discharges from receptors in the deep tissues in response to a vibrating stimulus. *J. Physiol.* **93**, 312–334.   [169]

Eldred, E., Granit, R. & Merton, P. A. (1953). Supraspinal control of the muscle spindles and its significance. *J. Physiol.* **122**, 498–523. [153,159]

Eysel, U. Th. & Grüsser, O. J. (1970). The impulses pattern of muscle spindle afferents. A statistical analysis of the response to static and sinusoidal stimulation. *Pflügers Arch. ges. physiol.* **315**, 1–26. [161,172]

Fehr, H. U. (1962). Aktivitat der Muskelspindel-Endigungen der Fasergruppen IA and II als Funktion der Muskelelongation. *Helv. physiol. pharmac. Acta* **20**, 163–172. [145]

Granit, R. (1958). Neuromuscular interaction in postural tone of the cat's isometric soleus muscle. *J. Physiol.* **143**, 387–402. [181]

Granit, R. & Henatsch, H. D. (1956). Gamma control of dynamic properties of muscle spindles. *J. Neurophysiol.* **19**, 355–366. [169]

Granit, R. & van der Meulen, J. P. (1962). The pause during contraction in the discharge of the spindle afferents from primary end organs in cat extensor muscles. *Acta physiol. scand.* **55**, 231–244. [158]

Grüsser, O. J. & Thiele, B. (1968). Reaktionen primärer und sekundärer Muskelspindelafferenzen auf sinusförmige mechanische Reizung. I. Variation der Sinusfrequenz. *Pflügers Arch. ges Physiol.* **300**, 161–184. [172]

Haase, J. & Ortgieze, H.-J. (1966). Die Frequenz-Dehnungbeziehungen von Katzen-Flexorspindeln des fusimotorischen α- und γ-Typs bei dynamischer und konstanter Muskeldehnung. *Pflügers Arch. ges. physiol.* **291**, 28–42. [158]

Harvey, R. J. & Matthews, P. B. C. (1961). The response of de-efferented muscle spindle endings in the cat's soleus to slow extension of the muscle. *J. Physiol.* **157**, 370–392. [147, 149, 154]

Hunt, C. C. (1954). Relation of function to diameter in afferent fibres of muscle nerves. *J. gen. Physiol.* **38**, 117–131. [144, 145]

Jansen, J. K. S. & Matthews, P. B. C. (1962a). The central control of the dynamic response of muscle spindle receptors. *J. Physiol.* **161**, 357–378. [148–152, 165, 168, 184]

— (1962b). The effects of fusimotor activity on the static responsiveness of primary and secondary ending of muscle spindles in the decerebrate cat. *Acta physiol. scand.* **55**, 376–386. [154]

Kuffler, S. W., Hunt, C. C. & Quilliam, J. P. (1951). Function of medullated small-nerve fibres in mammalian ventral roots: efferent muscle spindle innervation. *J. Neurophysiol.* **14**, 29–54. [169]

Lennerstrand, G. (1968). Position and velocity sensitivity of muscle spindles in the cat. I. Primary and secondary endings deprived of fusimotor activation. *Acta physiol. scand.* **73**, 281–299. [154]

Lennerstrand, G. & Thoden, U. (1968). Dynamic analysis of muscle spindle endings in the cat using length changes of different length–time relations. *Acta physiol. scand.* **73**, 234–250. [147, 167]

Lundberg, A. & Winsbury, G. (1960). Selective activation of large afferents from muscle spindles and Golgi tendon organs. *Acta physiol. scand.* **49**, 155–164. [165, 166]

Matthews, B. H. C. (1933). Nerve endings in mammalian muscle. *J. Physiol.* **78**, 1–53. [159]

Matthews, P. B. C. (1963). The response of de-efferented muscle spindle receptors to stretching at different velocities. *J. Physiol.* **168,** 660–678.
                                            [147, 151, 153, 158, 167, 168]
— (1964). Muscle spindles and their motor control. *Physiol. Rev.* **44,** 219–288.   [157]
— (1967). Vibration and the stretch reflex. In *Myotatic, Kinesthetic and Vestibular Mechanisms*, eds. de Reuck, A. V. S. & Knight, J. pp. 40–50. London: Churchill.   [170]
Matthews, P. B. C. & Stein, R. B. (1969a). The sensitivity of muscle spindle afferents to small sinusoidal changes of length. *J. Physiol.* **200,** 723–743.   [173, 177–183]
— (1969b). The regularity of primary and secondary muscle spindle afferent discharges. *J. Physiol.* **202,** 59–82.   [161–164]
Pascoe, J. E. (1965). The effects of ethyl chloride on the muscle spindles of the triceps surae of the rabbit. *J. Physiol.* **180,** 673–683.   [161]
Poppele, R. E. & Bowman, R. J. (1970). Quantitative description of linear behaviour of mammalian muscle spindles. *J. Neurophysiol.* **33,** 59–72.   [173, 176, 178, 180, 182]
Rack, P. M. H. & Westbury, D. R. (1966). The effects of suxamethonium and acetylcholine on the behaviour of cat muscle spindles during dynamic stretching, and during fusimotor stimulation. *J. Physiol.* **186,** 698–713.   [158]
Renkin, B. Z. & Vallbo, Å. B. (1964). Simultaneous responses of groups I and II cat muscle spindle afferents to muscle position and movement. *J. Neurophysiol.* **27,** 429–450.   [147, 154]
Sato, M. (1961). Response of Pacinian corpuscles to sinusoidal vibration. *J. Physiol.* **159,** 391–409.   [171]
Schäfer, S.-S. & Schäfer, S. (1969). Die Eigenschaften einer, primären Muskelspindelafferenz bei rampenförmiger Dehnung und ihre mathematische Beschreibung. *Pflügers Arch. ges. Physiol.* **310,** 206–228.   [167]
Stein, R. B. (1967). The information capacity of nerve cells using a frequency code. *Biophys. J.* **7,** 797–826.   [162]
Stein, R. B. & French, A. S. (1970). Models for the transmission of information by nerve cells. In *Excitatory Synaptic Mechanism*, eds. Andersen, P. & Jansen, J. K. S. pp. 247–257. Oslo: Universitetsforlaget.   [163, 176]
Stein, R. B. & Matthews, P. B. C. (1965). Differences in variability of discharge frequency between primary and secondary muscle spindle afferent endings of the cat. *Nature Lond.* **208,** 1217–1218.   [161]
Stuart, D. G., Mosher, C. G., Gerlack, R. L. & Reinking, R. M. (1970). Selective activation of Ia afferents by transient muscle stretch. *Expl. Brain Res.* **10,** 477–487.   [166]
Stuart, D., Ott, K., Ishikawa, K. & Eldred, E. (1965). Muscle receptor responses to sinusoidal stretch. *Expl. Neurol.* **13,** 82–95.   [172]

5

THE PHYSIOLOGICAL STUDY OF FUSIMOTOR FIBRES

The discovery of the γ efferents

Early work. From the turn of the century it has been accepted
on histological evidence that the muscle spindle is under motor
control. Because of the well-marked striations of the intrafusal
muscle fibres such control of the afferent endings has usually been
thought to be mediated mechanically via the contraction of the
intrafusal muscle fibres. At various times, however, it has been
suggested that part or all of the control might be mediated electrically via changes in the membrane potential of the activated
intrafusal fibres, without particular enquiry as to whether the
change was propagated or non-propagated (Hinsey, 1927; Leksell,
1945; Tower, 1932). Direct study of such matters had to await
upon the development of single unit recording techniques. The
first thing then to engage experimental attention was the anatomical
problem of the origin of the motor fibres seen entering the spindle
and in particular whether they were derived from branches of the
ordinary motor fibres, as long known to occur in reptiles, or
whether from a specialised fusimotor supply. As already described,
B. H. C. Matthews (1933) obtained excitation of some spindle
afferents on increasing the strength of a stimulus to the motor
nerve above that required to cause a maximal contraction of the
muscle (Fig. 3.5). He thought that this occurred because 'the
threshold of the nerve fibres to the intrafusal fibres of the spindle
is higher than that of other motor fibres' and related this to
Ruffini's description of small fibres entering the spindle to supply
the plate endings. In spite of some subsequent criticism (Hunt
& Kuffler, 1951*b*), B. H. C. Matthews' effect does appear to have
been genuinely due to contraction of the intrafusal fibres and was
thus the first demonstration of their excitatory action on the
afferent endings, for similar effects were subsequently obtained
by Harvey & P. B. C. Matthews (1961*a*) and shown to be indubitably due to fusimotor action.

Somewhat surprisingly, B. H. C. Matthews' paper (1933) made
no reference to the prior findings of Eccles & Sherrington (1930)
on the existence of two sizes of motor fibre in the ventral roots and
muscle nerves. Two years later O'Leary, Heinbecker & Bishop
(1935) feeling that such anatomical grouping 'denotes the existence
of discrete functions' and ignorant of the fact that a similar suggestion had been made long before by Langley (p. 72) said that 'it

occurred to us that the smaller group might be motor to the muscle spindles'. They could not devise 'any clear cut method of testing this directly', but as expected on this idea they were able to show that increasing the strength of a simulus to a muscle nerve (medial head of gastrocnemius) above that required to excite all the large fibres failed to produce any increase in the contraction which was detectable with their isotonic myograph, even though the stimulus could then be presumed to be additionally exciting the small fibres. They recorded the compound action potentials set up in the ventral roots by their stimuli and so were able to determine when all the large fibres were excited, but their technique was insufficiently advanced for them to be able to detect the compound potential due to the small fibres. O'Leary *et al.* quite properly felt that their experiment left the story unfinished.

Recording of the γ wave. Ten years later the question of the destination of the small motor fibres was taken up in Granit's laboratory by Leksell (1945) who started by confirming the experiment described above using improved experimental conditions. Leksell used isometric myographic recording instead of isotonic and in the face of various artefacts successfully recorded the compound 'γ wave' due to the small fibres. Figure 5.1 shows Leksell's diagrammatic reconstruction of the α and γ waves portrayed on the same scale to emphasise the relative smallness of the latter. Leksell proved that the small wave really was conducted in the small fibres and was not due to repetitive firing of the large fibres, as may be produced among other things by their ephaptic stimulation by the muscle action potential (Brown & Matthews, 1960). He did this by showing that the γ wave was propagated in fibres with a higher threshold to electrical stimulation and a lower conduction velocity than the large fibres (measured by moving the stimulating electrodes) and that the γ wave could survive collision with the α wave.

Figure 5.2 illustrates the progressive recruitment to the compound action potential of the more slowly conducting γ fibres as the strength of the stimulus is increased. Leksell (1945) found the γ fibres to conduct at velocities between 20 and 40 m/sec, relative to an assumed conduction velocity of the fastest fibres of 100 m/sec. Later studies have given a slightly wider range of conduction velocities for γ fibres (cf. 15–55 m/sec by Kuffler,

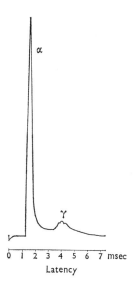

FIG. 5.1. The relative sizes of the α and γ waves shown by Leksell's reconstruction of the compound action potential produced in the S1 ventral root on stimulating the nerve to the medial head of gastrocnemius. The original records were taken at two different amplifications to display in turn each of the two waves to the best effect. (Leksell, 1945, Fig. 11.)

Hunt & Quilliam, 1951). Under his particular conditions (rapidly rising stimulating pulse with an approximately exponential decay of about 0·2 msec) Leksell found the threshold of the most excitable γ fibres to be nearly four times that of the most excitable α fibres, while the threshold of the least excitable γ fibres was about 20 times the α threshold. Figure 5.3 shows the relation between threshold and conduction velocity determined with a square pulse of 100 μsec duration; it is broadly in agreement with Leksell's findings but shows that his precise values of threshold need not be treated as sacrosanct.

The use of a pressure block to permit study of the action of the γ fibres on their own. On the basis of being able to monitor the γ wave Leksell (1945) was able to move on to more ambitious experiments than simply observing the effect on the contraction of increasing the stimulus to the motor nerve. He pointed out that this experiment was inconclusive for deciding on whether or not

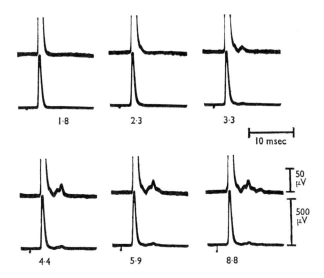

1·8   2·3   3·3

10 msec

50 μV

500 μV

4·4   5·9   8·8

FIG. 5.2. The progressive recruitment of the γ wave with progressive increase of the stimulus strength. The records are placed in pairs, one above the other, showing the same response at two different amplifications. The simulus strength is shown below each pair, and is expressed as a multiple of the threshold of the most excitable α fibres. The records were taken from L7 ventral root on stimulating the nerve to the soleus. (Harvey & Matthews, 1961a, Fig. 4.)

the γ fibres supplied extrafusal muscle fibres. This was, firstly, because the addition of a small extra contraction to a large pre-existing contraction might escape detection, and secondly because if individual muscle fibres were to be innervated by both α fibres and γ fibres then the latter need not produce any effect at all when the two fibres are excited simultaneously, since the muscle might already be maximally activated by the large fibres. Investigation of the effect of the small fibres requires that they should be activated on their own; but because of their higher threshold this cannot be done simply by adjustment of the stimulus strength.

Leksell got round this problem by exciting both groups of fibres with a strong stimulus and then preventing the large fibres from influencing the muscle by selectively blocking their conduction at a point between the stimulating electrodes and the muscle. After some trials he abandoned the then usual polarisation block

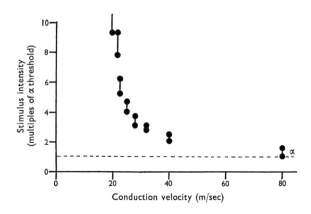

FIG. 5.3. The strength of stimulus required to excite γ motor fibres of different conduction velocities. The stimuli were applied to the soleus nerve and the resulting compound action potential recorded from the ventral root as in Fig. 5.2. The two points at each velocity correspond to the stimulus required to excite the least detectable γ wave and that required to excite a maximal γ wave of that velocity. The most right-hand pair of points refer to the α fibres; those to soleus are smaller than those to many other muscles and so conduct at only 80 m/sec. The stimuli were square pulses of 100 μsec duration. (Harvey & Matthews, 1961a, Fig. 5.)

produced by the passage of a direct current; although it produced a satisfactorily selective paralysis of large fibres the polarising current itself was liable to set up spontaneous discharges. Pressure block was free of this disadvantage and produced a reasonably selective paralysis of the large fibres in which he found that the α wave could be nearly completely abolished without any marked effect on the gamma wave. The pressure was applied either by a clamp lined with rubber or more simply by squeezing the sciatic nerve 'for some 15–20 minutes between the thumb and the fore-finger' (Leksell, 1945, p. 19).

When the block was at its best the contraction produced by supramaximal stimulation was reduced to 1–2% of its original value though most if not all the γ fibres were still conducting. This small residual contraction was felt most likely to have been due to the few α fibres remaining unblocked, though this does not seem to have been systematically tested by varying the strength of the stimulus. Leksell therefore concluded that 'no definite motor function can be demonstrated for the gamma fibres'

(p. 78), meaning by this the control of 'muscular contraction regarded as a process for conversion of energy into movement and tension' (p. 52); he admitted quite properly that the precision of this statement was limited by the sensitivity of his recording and, more significantly, by the incomplete selectivity of the block. His work effectively disproved the view which was then current in some quarters that the small motor fibres were part of a 'tonus' system directly responsible for producing contraction in certain spastic states (Häggqvist, 1940). A few years later Kuffler, Hunt & Quilliam (1951) extended the precision of Leksell's conclusion by observing the effects of stimulating functionally single gamma motor fibres which had been isolated apart from α fibres in ventral root filaments. Simultaneous stimulation of 6 such γ fibres then produced no detectable tension under isometric conditions and using a myograph sufficiently sensitive to record about 50 mg.

Leksell (1945) also investigated the effect of selective activation of the gamma fibres on the massed afferent discharge from the gastrocnemius muscle, which he recorded diphasically from the intact nerve to its medial head. Figure 5.4 shows the particular

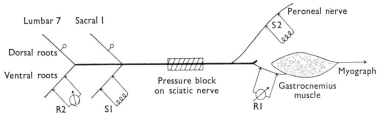

FIG. 5.4. Diagram of Leksell's preparation for studying the action of the γ motor fibres by exciting both α and γ fibres and then selectively blocking the nerve so that only the γ impulses reach the muscle. S1: Electrodes for applying supramaximal stimulus to ventral root to activate both α and γ fibres. R1: Electrodes on intact muscle nerve for diphasic recording of afferent action potentials. S2, R2: Stimulating and recording electrodes for monitoring the progress of the nerve block; note that the fibres monitored are not the self-same ones whose action is being studied. (After Fig. 33, Leksell, 1945.)

arrangement of electrodes that he used. Before applying the block, stimulation of the ventral root produced an unanalysably complex increase in the afferent discharge and he could not find any effect of progressively increasing the stimulus strength so as to excite

γ fibres as well as α fibres. However, when the contraction had been virtually eliminated by the pressure block, Leskell found that the afferent discharge was still increased on both twitch and tetanic stimulation, provided that the muscle was initially subjected to a certain amount of stretch. A single experiment seems to have confirmed that this effect was only obtained when the stimulus was made supramaximal for the residual contraction. He rightfully concluded that the 'gamma fibres serve as regulators of sensory activity originating in the muscle'. On the basis of B. H. C. Matthews' (1933) work he suggested that the observed excitatory effect was likely to be upon the primary endings of the muscle spindles (i.e. the A2 endings). In view of the importance of Leksell's work and the repeated confirmation of his main conclusion it is perhaps not unreasonable to note that his published records do not appear adequate to have closed the matter for all time; for one thing, on recent findings, even a small residual contraction would be expected to be adequate to give some excitation of Golgi tendon organs (see Chap. 3). The common short summaries of his work tend to skip over the difficulties associated with the employment of selective nerve blocks and multi-unit recording, and may thus produce a misleading optimism about the cogency of the results which may be obtained thereby.

Stimulation of single γ fibres. Ample confirmation of Leksell's conclusions was provided five years later by Kuffler, Hunt & Quilliam (1951) who used a preparation which was 'single-fibre' on both the motor and the sensory side, as illustrated in Fig. 5.5. The functional singleness of the fibres could be determined by observing their all-or-nothing response on stimulation of the muscle nerve. Anatomically, of course, the fine filaments which were placed on the electrodes contained an appreciable number of fibres but only one of these supplied the muscle studied; the actions of other fibres in the filaments were eliminated by widespread denervation. This elegant preparation demonstrates once again the clarity and decisiveness of the answers that can be obtained to appropriate questions by developing suitable single-unit techniques. Kuffler *et al.* found that stimulation of single gamma motor fibres, which they actually called small-nerve efferent fibres, increased the discharge from single spindle afferent endings, recognised by their behaviour during muscle contraction; tendon

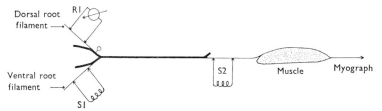

FIG. 5.5. Diagram of preparation for studying the action of a single gamma efferent fibre on a single spindle afferent fibre. Most of the results described in the present chapter were obtained using such a preparation. R1: Electrodes for recording discharge of single afferent. S1: Electrodes for stimulating single efferent. S2: Electrodes for eliciting muscle contraction in order to characterise the ending as a spindle or tendon organ. These electrodes may also be used to determine the conduction velocities of both the single fibres studied; in this case electrodes S1 must be used for recording. Alternatively, the velocities may be determined by applying the stimuli to the spinal root filaments and recording the single fibre potentials diphasically from the muscle nerve; this was done by Kuffler, Hunt & Quilliam (1951) in their original study on the small efferent fibres.

organs were not affected. Figure 5.6 shows examples of the effect of small-nerve excitation on a spindle afferent and demonstrates their greater effectiveness when the initial tension is not too low. The conduction velocities of the motor fibres which produced this effect ranged from 15 to 55 m/sec for the soleus and the tenuissimus muscles, which corresponded to a fibre diameter of 3–9 μm and thus the whole of the group of smaller fibres seen in the fibre spectrum. None of these fibres evoked a detectable contraction in the muscle or a propagated action potential.

Subsequently, Hunt & Kuffler (1951a; Kuffler & Hunt, 1952) found that every spindle afferent which was closely studied could be shown to be influenced by small motor fibres and often individual endings could be excited by three to five different small motor fibres; conversely, a single γ motor fibre might influence several afferents. Judging by their conduction velocity most of the afferent fibres they studied supplied primary endings. Since every spindle contains a primary ending their results show that in the muscles studied (soleus, tenuissimus of cat) every spindle is supplied by γ motor fibres. Subsequent work has generally confirmed that this may be taken as the usual arrangement (for example in the tibialis posterior; Brown, Crowe & Matthews,

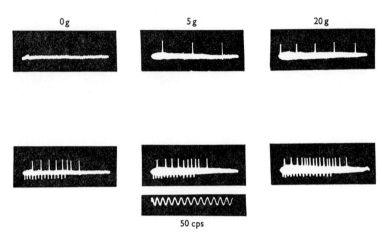

FIG. 5.6. Excitation of a spindle afferent by repetitive stimulation of a single fusimotor fibre using the preparation of Fig. 5.5. The upper records show the afferent discharge in the absence of fusimotor stimulation and with the muscle (soleus) stretched so as to produce the tensions shown above. The lower records show the effect of about 15 stimuli at 100/sec on the afferent with the muscle at the same three tensions; note downward-going stimulus artefacts. (Kuffler, Hunt & Quilliam, 1951, Fig. 7.)

1965). Hunt & Kuffler's results can also be reasonably taken to show that in the ordinary limb muscles of the cat all the small motor fibres are exclusively fusimotor and this view has found no contradiction in much subsequent work. This leaves open the question, which will be discussed later in this chapter, as to how frequently spindles may be additionally supplied by branches of ordinary α motor fibres.

Thus by 1951 the small motor fibres of Eccles & Sherrington (1930) had been established as exclusively supplying the muscle spindles. This is essentially an anatomical conclusion but one which required delicate and ingenious physiological work for its achievement. The chief importance of the conclusion lies not in the fact that the fusimotor fibres are of small diameter and are therefore relatively slow at propagating an impulse from spinal cord to spindle. Rather it is simply that there are specific motor fibres to the muscle spindles which are quite separate from the motor fibres to ordinary muscle fibres, and which thus lend themselves to independent control by the central nervous system; such independence is not found in many lower animals such as the frog.

The subdivision of γ efferents into static and dynamic fusimotor
fibres by their action on the dynamic responsiveness of the
primary ending to ramp stretches

Ten years ago, with the histological demonstration of two kinds
of intrafusal muscle fibres, it became natural to enquire whether
the motor supply to the spindle was also double, and to speculate
on the nature of the different effects which each kind of intrafusal
fibre might be presumed to produce. Jansen & Matthews (1962*a*)

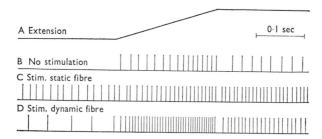

FIG. 5.7. The different effects of stimulation of static and dynamic
fusimotor fibres. The response of a primary ending to stretching is
shown in the classical manner, namely with spikes on a linear time scale,
both in the presence and absence of stimulation of a single fusimotor
fibre of either kind at 70/sec. The fusimotor stimulation was started
before the beginning of the portions of record illustrated and continued
throughout their course. The spindle studied lay in the soleus muscle
which was stretched 6 mm at 30 mm/sec. The diagram has been constructed from records of 'instantaneous frequency' as in Fig. 5.8.
(Crowe & Matthews, 1964*a*, Fig. 1.)

suggested that they might provide a way for the central nervous
system to control somewhat independently of each other the two
facets of the response of the primary ending to large amplitude
stretches, namely its response to length and its response to velocity.
This suggestion was based on structural arguments and the
observation that in the decerebrate cat the length and velocity
responses of a spindle primary might vary independently in size
with variations in fusimotor activity.

The suggestion was followed up by investigating the effect of
stimulating single γ motor fibres, isolated in ventral root filaments
as in Fig. 5.5, on the response of primary endings to stretching at

various velocities. This immediately showed that fusimotor fibres could be differentiated into two functionally distinct kinds (Matthews, 1962). They were given the name of static and dynamic fusimotor fibres on the basis of their effects on the responsiveness of the primary ending to a 'ramp' stretch (Matthews, 1962). The validity and widespread applicability of the classification have since come to be generally accepted.

Figures 5.7 and 5.8 illustrate the basis of the classification,

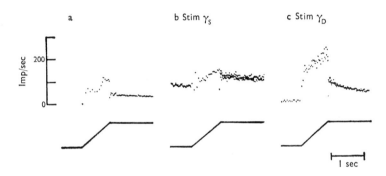

FIG. 5.8. The contrasting effects of the two kinds of fusimotor fibre on the response of a primary ending to stretching shown by records of 'instantaneous frequency'. The ending lay in the soleus muscle which was stretched 6 mm at 30 mm/sec, (a) in the absence of fusimotor stimulation, (b) during continuous stimulation of a single static fibre at 70/sec, and (c) during continuous stimulation of a single dynamic fibre at 70/sec. The time scale is expanded during the dynamic phase of stretching and the time bar applies only when the muscle length is constant. (Brown & Matthews, 1966, Fig. 1.)

firstly, diagrammatically in classical type records showing spikes and secondly, with the more convenient recent type of display showing the instantaneous frequency of discharge. Stimulation of either kind of fusimotor fibre excited the primary ending when the muscle was at a constant length, and the difference between their action can be seen only at the beginning and the end of the dynamic phase of stretching. The dynamic fibre can then be seen to have caused an increase in the normal dynamic responsiveness of the primary ending; in contrast, the static fusimotor fibre caused a decrease in the dynamic responsiveness of the ending even though the static fibre had a powerful excitatory action upon it.

As before (Chap. 4) the dynamic responsiveness of the primary ending may be assessed by measuring the dynamic index, namely the fall in frequency of firing which occurs in the first 0·5 sec after completing the dynamic phase of a ramp stretch. Figure 5.9

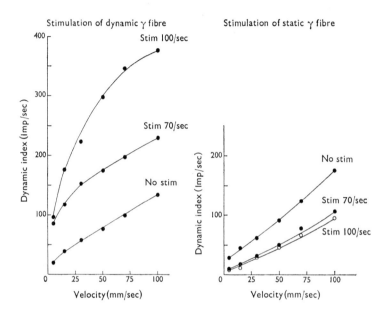

FIG. 5.9. The different effects of static and of dynamic fusimotor stimulation shown by their action on the relation between the dynamic index of a primary ending and the velocity of stretching. The dynamic index is the difference between the frequency of discharge just before the end of the dynamic phase of a ramp stretch and that occurring 0·5 sec later with the muscle at the final length. Results from a spindle in the soleus muscle which was stretched by 6 mm. (Crowe & Matthews, 1964a, Fig. 3.)

shows a plot of the dynamic index against velocity of stretching during stimulation of a dynamic fibre and a static fibre both of which influenced the same primary ending. For any particular velocity of stretching the enhancement of the dynamic index on dynamic fusimotor stimulation increased with the frequency of stimulation, while static fusimotor stimulation reduced the index to an approximately constant value which did not then change appreciably with the frequency (Crowe & Matthews, 1964*b*).

Measurement of the dynamic index allows virtually all fusimotor fibres to be classified without difficulty as either static or dynamic in their action. This is shown in Fig. 5.10 where for 100 more or less randomly selected fusimotor fibres the change in the dynamic index produced by fusimotor stimulation is plotted against the increase in afferent firing produced by the stimulation when the muscle was at the initial length. Some fusimotor fibres elicited large increases in static firing while having little action on the dynamic index; these may be classified as static fibres (●). Other fusimotor fibres elicited an increase in the dynamic index which increased *pari passu* with their action on the static firing of the ending; these may be classified as dynamic fibres (o). All fibres with significant excitatory action are readily classifiable as either static or dynamic, and fibres with intermediate effects are absent. Fibres with a weak action are perhaps classifiable with rather less certainty and though they conform to the classification provide rather less cogent evidence for its validity. Thus systematic measurement of the dynamic index confirms the qualitative impression of the different actions of the two kinds of fusimotor fibre. It has also helped establish that a wide variety of muscles receive both static and dynamic fusimotor fibres which are typical of those originally described for the soleus of the cat. (For example: cat tibialis posterior—Brown, Crowe & Matthews, 1965; cat tenuissimus—Appelberg, Bessou & Laporte, 1966; cat lumbrical—Bessou, Emonet-Dénand & Laporte, 1965; rabbit tenuissimus—Emonet-Dénand, Laporte & Pagès, 1966.)

The distinctiveness of the two kinds of fusimotor fibre is perhaps shown even more cogently by experiments in which the action of a single fusimotor fibre has been studied upon more than one primary ending. Every ending affected by any particular fusimotor fibre is then found to be influenced in the same way, whether static or dynamic (Crowe & Matthews, 1964*b*; Brown, Crowe & Matthews, 1965; Bessou, Laporte & Pagès, 1966). As there is only one primary ending in any muscle spindle this provides the most crucial evidence available that the classification is physiologically meaningful, for it shows that any particular fusimotor fibre has a static or dynamic specificity in its own right, rather than by virtue of some chance relation it enters into with one particular muscle spindle.

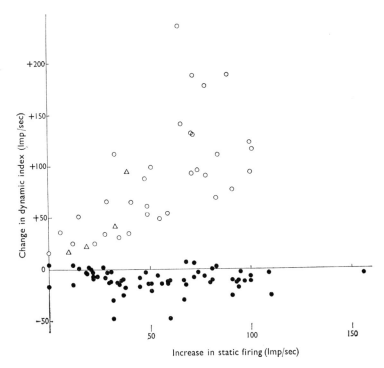

FIG. 5.10. Scatter diagram relating the effect of stimulating single fusimotor fibres on the dynamic index of a number of primary endings to
their effect in exciting the same endings under static conditions. Each
point shows the effect of a particular motor fibre upon a particular
primary ending. Open symbols, effect of dynamic fibres; closed symbols,
effect of static fibres. The spindles were in the tibialis posterior muscle of
the cat which was stretched 3 mm at 5 mm/sec; the frequency of fusimotor stimulation was 100/sec; the increase in static firing was measured
at the initial length. (Brown, Crowe & Matthews, 1965, Fig. 6.)

*Restriction of the fusimotor excitation of the secondary ending
to the static fibres*

Another crucial point of differentiation between static and
dynamic fibres lies in their action on the secondary ending. This
was investigated by Laporte and his colleagues (Appelberg,
Bessou & Laporte, 1966) who, by using the tenuissimus preparation
already described, were able to record simultaneously the responses
of a secondary and a primary ending lying in the same muscle

spindle (see Chap. 4 and Fig. 4.10). The fusimotor fibres were initially identified as static or dynamic by their action on the primary ending and their action on the secondary ending was then tested. Every one of 19 static fusimotor fibres so tested proved to have an excitatory action on the secondary ending studied. The action on the secondary ending was like that on the primary ending and consisted of excitation but without the development of any dynamic sensitivity, as may be seen in Fig. 5.11. More significantly,

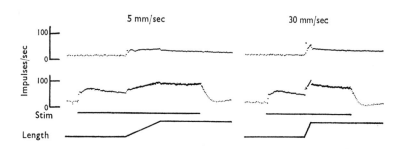

FIG. 5.11. Typical effect of static fusimotor stimulation on the response of a spindle secondary ending to ramp stretches. As with the primary ending, the secondary ending is strongly excited without becoming dynamically sensitive. The response of the ending to stretching at 5 and 30 mm/sec was recorded both during stimulation of a single fusimotor fibre at 100/sec (below) and in the absence of stimulation (above). Results from a soleus muscle stretched by 5 mm; the time scale is given by the rising phase of the left-hand stretch which was 1 sec. (Brown, Engberg & Matthews, 1967, Fig. 1.)

7 out of the 8 dynamic fibres studied were found to have no observable action on the secondary ending tested, even though the action on the primary ending proved that the dynamic fibre did supply the spindle containing the secondary ending which was being studied.

The eighth dynamic fibre, however, quite definitely influenced the secondary ending studied, and in a somewhat dynamic manner. This secondary ending was somewhat atypical in certain other respects also, for in the absence of fusimotor stimulation it displayed slightly more phasic sensitivity than usual and it was supplied by a relatively fast group II afferent fibre (55 m/sec). This exception should not be forgotten, but the general conclusion is that the action of dynamic fibres is virtually restricted to primary endings. This is important both for attempting to elucidate the mode of action of the fusimotor fibres inside the spindle and for understanding the functional roles of the two kinds of fusimotor fibre considered as servants of the central nervous system.

Further points of comparison between static and dynamic actions on the primary ending

The two kinds of fusimotor fibre were originally characterised by virtue of their different actions on the response of the primary ending to ramp stretches, and this probably still provides the most convenient way of distinguishing between them in the course of an electrophysiological experiment. But a number of other differences between their actions have now been recognised. These seem just as potentially interesting as the originally described effects, for it remains to be established just which of them all are important from the point of view of the use made of the spindle by the central nervous system. Reaching a decision on such matters is tied up with the unresolved problem discussed in Chap. 4, namely as to which facet of the spindle afferent discharges is the most important to the CNS. These additional effects of fusimotor stimulation will be described next and will also be found summarised in Table 5.1 on p. 224.

Fusimotor actions during release of large amplitude stretch

The release of a pre-existing stretch may be considered as the application of a negative rather than a positive velocity of stretching. Hence the difference in dynamic sensitising action of the two kinds of fusimotor fibre might be expected to lead to a greater 'depressing' effect of the release during dynamic than during static stimulation. Figure 5.12 illustrates that this is so, but no systematic measurements comparable to that on the dynamic index have as yet been performed. Lennerstand & Thoden (1968c) carried the matter further in an important respect by showing that under their particular conditions an increase in the frequency of dynamic fusimotor stimulation was unable to overcome the depressing effect of the release and make the ending fire faster than before, though an increase in static fusimotor stimulation could do so. This is important because fusimotor action must be able to increase afferent firing during muscle shortening if a fusimotor discharge is to act via the γ loop as a 'command' for movement (see Chap. 10).

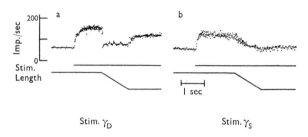

FIG. 5.12. Typical responses of primary endings seen on releasing a stretched muscle during fusimotor stimulation. (*a*) response of one ending during stimulation of a dynamic fibre at 70/sec during bar; (*b*) response of another ending during stimulation of a static fibre at 70/sec. In the absence of stimulation both endings stopped firing abruptly at the beginning of the release (cf. Fig. 4.3). Results from the soleus muscle which was released 6 mm at 5 mm/sec; time bar, 1 sec. (Crowe & Matthews, 1964*b*, Fig. 5.)

Fusimotor actions on responses to sinusoidal stretching

Sinusoidal stretching provides a direct contrast of the effects of stretching and of releasing a muscle. When the stretching is of large amplitude it evokes very similar responses to those seen on the stretching and releasing phases of large ramp stretches, and which have just been described. Thus dynamic fusimotor stimulation enhances the response of the primary ending on the stretching phase of the cycle while leaving it silent on the releasing phase. Static stimulation produces an increase in the mean frequency of firing of the ending but there is then comparatively little difference in the frequency of its discharge between the stretching and releasing phases of the cycle. This is illustrated in Fig. 5.13 which shows the effect of stretching with a medium sized peak-to-peak amplitude (1 mm). As before, the actions of the two kinds of fusimotor fibre may be summarised by saying that the dynamic fibre increases the dynamic sensitivity of the ending while the static fibre excites it without doing so, and in fact appears to decrease its sensitivity to the stimulus of velocity *per se*.

Things look slightly different when the amplitude of the stretching is made sufficiently small for the ending to respond 'linearly',

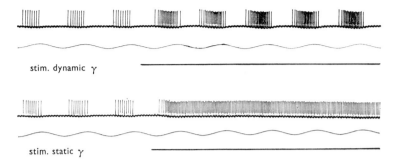

FIG. 5.13. The effect of fusimotor stimulation on the response of a primary ending to sinusoidal stretching of medium extent (1 mm peak-to-peak movement at 3 Hz). Results from a soleus muscle during fusimotor stimulation at 100/sec; the sinusoidal records show the length change imposed on the muscle. (Crowe & Matthews, 1964*b*, Fig. 6.)

for as already noted (p. 176) the primary ending then shows rather a different side of its character. In the linear range, the response of an ending to sinusoidal stretching may be conveniently assessed by measuring its sensitivity, in impulses sec^{-1} mm^{-1}, for each frequency of stretching. The sensitivity, it will be remembered, is simply the amplitude of the sinusoidal modulation of the firing of the ending in impulses/sec divided by the amplitude of the sinusoidal stretching in millimetres. Analysis of the effect of fusimotor stimulation on the relation between the sensitivity of an ending and the frequency of stretching is currently in progress, and the preliminary results warrant brief description (Goodwin & Matthews, 1971). The findings fortunately confirm what had already been suspected on the basis of more qualitative studies.

Figure 5.14 shows the response of a primary ending to low-frequency sinusoidal stretching which had been sufficiently reduced in amplitude to fall within the linear range of the ending during stimulation of either kind of fusimotor fibre; the stimulus, however, still fell outside the linear range of the ending when the intrafusal fibres were not contracting. Once more there is an obvious difference in the action of the two kinds of fusimotor fibre. During stimulation of the dynamic fibre the ending now fired throughout the whole of the cycle and not just on its rising phase; but the frequency of discharge varied markedly with the phase of the stretching, thus showing that the ending then had rather a high

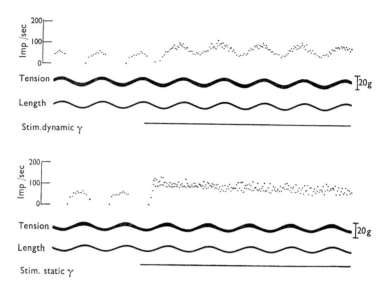

FIG. 5.14. The effect of fusimotor stimulation on the response of a primary ending to small amplitude sinusoidal stretching (0·1 mm peak-to-peak at 2 Hz). Results from a soleus muscle; the frequency of stimulation was 50/sec for the static fibre and 100/sec for the dynamic one. (Crowe & Matthews, 1964*b*, Fig. 7.)

sensitivity. The actual value in Fig. 5.14 is around 500 impulses sec^{-1} mm^{-1} for a frequency of stretching of 2 Hz. In contrast, during static stimulation the primary ending was virtually unaffected by such a small amplitude of stretching and fired at approximately the same frequency at all phases of the sinusoidal cycle, thus showing that it must then have had a rather low sensitivity. As already illustrated in Fig. 5.13 a much larger amplitude of stretching is required to produce appreciable modulation of the firing of the primary ending during static fusimotor stimulation, thus confirming the low sensitivity of the ending under these conditions.

These early results (Crowe & Matthews, 1964*b*) have proved to be quite typical of the response of the primary ending to low-frequency sinusoidal stretching applied during powerful fusimotor stimulation. During static stimulation the primary ending has a low sensitivity to stretching at 0·5–5 Hz. During dynamic stimulation it has a high sensitivity and, moreover, one which is maintained at a high value over a wide range of muscle lengths. The value of the sensitivity during dynamic stimulation, however, is often no more than that found for the same ending in the complete absence of intrafusal contraction; but a high value is then usually only found when the muscle is stretched comfortably taut, and not over the wide range of physiologically important lengths as occurs during dynamic stimulation.

When the frequency of sinusoidal stretching is increased above 1–2 Hz the sensitivity of the primary ending has been found to increase with the frequency under all conditions so far investigated. The interesting new feature is that for frequencies above about 5 Hz the sensitivity of the primary ending increases much more rapidly with frequency during stimulation of a static fibre than it does during stimulation of a dynamic fibre. The curve obtained during dynamic stimulation mirrors that found in the absence of intrafusal contraction, whereas that obtained during static stimulation rises more rapidly than either of the other two. However, the exact position of the additional 'corner frequency' required to characterise the response of the primary ending during static stimulation remains to be properly determined. This is partly because the phase angle of its response to various frequencies of stimulation has yet to be studied in detail. Inevitably, the more rapid rise of sensitivity with cyclic frequency found during static stimulation leads the initial low value of sensitivity to be overcome, and as the cyclic frequency increases the sensitivity during static stimulation progressively approaches the high values found during dynamic stimulation and in the well-stretched passive spindle. At frequencies of stretching of around 100 Hz there is no longer any difference between the values of sensitivity obtained during static and dynamic stimulation. This is just what would be expected from the earlier known equivalence of their effects on the responsiveness of the primary ending to being 'driven' by high-frequency vibration, of an amplitude falling outside the linear range, and which will be described next.

Before doing this, however, and in order to remove any apparent mystery, it is perhaps helpful to note that the finding of a similar sensitivity of the primary ending to high-frequency stretching during stimulation of either kind of fusimotor fibre probably simply reflects the tremendous sensitivity of the afferent terminals themselves, and has nothing special to do with the nature of the fusimotor effects. When the speed of movement occurring during

HM

the stretching becomes much greater than the maximum speed of contractile shortening of both kinds of intrafusal fibre, then the striated regions of the intrafusal fibres must largely fail to yield in the face of the vibratory force. Thus the full amount of the vibratory deformation applied to the spindle as a whole would be concentrated in the poorly striated regions of intrafusal fibre, which is where the primary ending lies. At medium frequencies of stretching, however, the intrafusal fibres supplied by the static fibres would appear to be able to move fast enough to take up much of the applied deformation in their contractile regions so that the primary ending would no longer receive such a large mechanical stimulus. On the other hand, the intrafusal fibres supplied by the dynamic fusimotor fibres would appear to contract too slowly for this to happen until a much lower frequency of stretching. At medium frequencies of stretching the full deformation would therefore still be applied to the sensorially innervated region of intrafusal fibre. This would make the sensitivity of the ending higher during dynamic than during static fusimotor stimulation. These matters are further discussed in Chap. 6.

Fusimotor actions on the sensitivity of the endings to being 'driven' by high-frequency vibration

Classically, high-frequency vibration has been considered as a stimulus in its own right rather than being seen as an extension to the high-frequency range of an engineering-type linear analysis using sinusoidal stimuli. Thus Granit & Henatsch (1956) showed early on that fusimotor activity increased the frequency at which a primary ending could be 'driven' to follow vibration of any particular amplitude and give one spike per cycle of the vibration. In their experiments the fusimotor activity was that occurring naturally in the decerebrate cat with intact ventral roots. If vibration is considered merely to be testing the 'dynamic sensitivity' of an ending it might perhaps be expected that dynamic but not static fusimotor stimulation would increase the vibratory responsiveness of an ending. Indeed, in line with such an idea secondary endings which are normally largely insensitive to vibration, as judged by their failure to be 'driven' by vibration applied to the tendon, do not become appreciably more so during static fusimotor stimulation (Brown, Engberg & Matthews, 1968). However, for the primary ending it has been found that stimulation of static

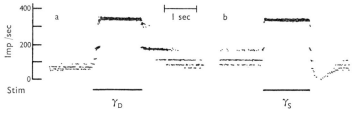

FIG. 5.15. The sensitisation of the primary ending to vibration produced by stimulating either kind of fusimotor fibre. Throughout the whole of both records the muscle tendon was vibrated longitudinally at 350 Hz with a peak-to-peak amplitude of movement of about 10 μm. The fusimotor stimulation enabled the vibration to drive the ending to discharge one impulse on each cycle of vibration so that it then fired at 350/sec. In the absence of fusimotor stimulation the vibration had a relatively weak excitatory action, but it influenced the precise moment of firing of the afferent so that it discharged at certain preferred frequencies corresponding to subharmonics of the vibration frequency; it is this which leads to the banded appearance of the records. Results from two different soleus muscles during fusimotor stimulation at 70/sec of either a dynamic fibre (left) or a static fibre (right). Crowe & Matthews, 1964b, Fig. 9.

fibres as well as dynamic fibres increases the ease with which it can be driven by vibration. This is illustrated in Fig. 5.15. Moreover, no difference between the actions of the two kinds of fusimotor fibre has been discoverable in this respect (Crowe & Matthews, 1964b; Brown, Engberg & Matthews, 1968). This is unimportant for considering the role of the two kinds of fusimotor fibre in the body since vibration frequencies ($>$100 Hz) are probably never encountered in life. But the absence of a difference is interesting both from the point of view of the internal mechanisms of the spindle and also for using vibration as a tool to selectively activate the Ia fibres and so to study their central actions.

Fusimotor actions on the 'position-sensitivity' of the endings assessed by large stretches

As already noted (Fig. 4.8) the relation between the frequency of discharge of a spindle afferent and the applied extension is approximately linear when determined with stretches of appreciable size. The slope of the relation gives a measure of the 'position-sensitivity' of the ending over the whole of its working range, though the precise value obtained will depend upon the time of

measurement with regard to the preceding stretch. *A priori*, fusimotor stimulation might have been expected to have had some
consistent effect on this position-sensitivity but so far no clear
picture has emerged although early studies encouraged the belief
that there should be one (Whitteridge, 1959; Harvey & Matthews,
1961*b*).

Unrelated to any other obvious actions, stimulation of single
static fusimotor fibres sometimes does and sometimes does not
increase the position-sensitivity of either primary or secondary
endings; increases are commoner for secondary than for primary
endings (Crowe & Matthews, 1964*a*; Lennerstrand & Thoden,
1968*b*; Brown, Lawrence & Matthews, 1969). The simultaneous
stimulation of several static fibres, particularly at the relatively
high frequency of 150/sec, may increase the position-sensitivity
quite markedly; values of 10 impulses sec^{-1} mm^{-1} are then common for primary endings and 15–20 for secondary endings. Such
high frequencies of stimulation are, however, probably unphysiological, and rather smaller effects were observed with reflexly
evoked fusimotor activity in the decerebrate cat (Jansen &
Matthews, 1962*b*). Lennerstrand & Thoden (1968*b*) subdivided
the actions of static fibres on the position sensitivity of an ending
into two classes which they called type I and II effects. In type II
effects the value of the position-sensitivity was increased on
stimulation, whereas in type I effects the value was unaltered or
slightly decreased. In re-investigating the matter Brown, Lawrence
& Matthews (1969) failed to confirm that the effects of different
fusimotor fibres were sharply separable on this basis, and thus felt
that it did not provide a useful way of sub-classifying static fusimotor fibres even though the effects themselves are of interest.

The effect of dynamic fusimotor stimulation is more consistent
and more interesting. When the muscle is stretched up to a certain
length and a single dynamic fibre then stimulated, the position-
sensitivity during the stimulation is unaltered or slightly reduced;
this is illustrated in the bottom half of Fig. 5.16 (i.e. at both
lengths the fusimotor stimulation produces the same increase in
afferent firing). In contrast, the position-sensitivity is uniformly
increased by dynamic stimulation when it is determined under
dynamic conditions by applying a slowly increasing stretch at a
constant velocity. This is illustrated in the top part of Fig. 5.16,
which shows the response of a primary ending to a stretch at

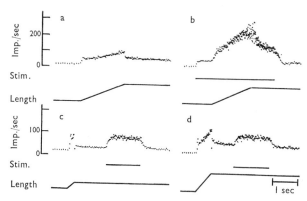

FIG. 5.16. The contrasting effects of dynamic fusimotor stimulation on the position-sensitivity of a primary ending assessed under static and under dynamic conditions; i.e. firstly, by stimulating the fusimotor fibre with the muscle already stretched by different amounts, and secondly, by observing the afferent response during a single slow stretch applied while the fusimotor fibre was being stimulated. (*a*) response to 6 mm stretch at 5 mm/sec in absence of stimulation; (*b*) response to similar stretching during repetitive stimulation of a dynamic fibre at 90/sec during bar; (*c*, *d*) responses to same frequency of fusimotor stimulation when the muscle had already been stretched by 2 or by 6 mm respectively. (Crowe & Matthews, 1964*a*, Fig. 8.)

5 mm/sec both in the presence and absence of fusimotor stimulation. After an initial rapid increase the frequency of the response increases linearly with time and hence also with the extension. In the absence of stimulation this dynamically determined 'position-sensitivity' was 10 impulses sec^{-1} mm^{-1} and it increased to 30 impulses sec^{-1} mm^{-1} on stimulation; similar values of position-sensitivity were found during different velocities of stretching. The different effects shown in Fig. 5.16 for stimulation under static and dynamic conditions were typical. In some ways the dynamically obtained value would appear the more physiologically significant. Lennerstrand & Thoden (1968*a*) have since obtained broadly similar results during 'triangular stretching' instead of ramp stretching, but have used rather a different terminology to describe them.

Figure 5.16 shows another related point of interest, namely the slow decay of the frequency of firing on completion of the dynamic phase of stretching. This probably represented, at least in part, the decay of the dynamically determined 'position response'. Higher velocities of stretch elicited a response in which there was a separate component of rapid decay of the velocity response (see Fig. 5.8), and the size of this fast component increased with the velocity of stretching. In contrast, the initial amplitude of the slow component of decay was approximately constant for increases in the velocity of stretching above 5 mm/sec; though presumably it would have decreased for slower velocities. The value of the 'dynamic index' measured at 0·5 sec during dynamic fusimotor stimulation is dominated by the slow fall rather than the rapid fall; this increases the difficulty of attaching a precise meaning, in control theory terminology, to the value of the dynamic index and it cannot be treated as though it were derived from a linear system. (i.e. the dynamic index cannot be simply divided by the velocity to give a unique figure for 'velocity-sensitivity' for stretching applied during fusimotor stimulation. The behaviour of the endings has not so far yielded to simple analytical treatment though various attacks have been made upon the problem; cf. Lennerstrand & Thoden, 1968a,b,c; Crowe, 1968).

Overlap of conduction velocity of the two kinds of fusimotor fibre

From the point of view of the central nervous control of the spindle a few milliseconds more or less conduction delay from spinal cord to spindle may perhaps be immaterial. However, from the point of view of the identification of single efferent fibres in the course of an electrophysiological experiment, knowledge of the range of velocities of different kinds of fibres is of crucial value. Experiments of all kinds would have been greatly facilitated if the static and dynamic fusimotor fibres had proved to have different velocities and, in particular, this would greatly have assisted the correlation of experimental and histological findings. Unfortunately, as Fig. 5.17 illustrates, there is no absolute separation between the two kinds of fibre in this respect. A limited degree of separation, however, occurs for the tibialis posterior muscle of the cat where all the slower γ fibres, below 25 m/sec, have so far proved to be static fibres, but a fusimotor fibre conducting at between 25 and 50 m/sec may be either a static or a dynamic one (Brown, Crowe & Matthews, 1965). For the rabbit tenuissimus the slowest fusimotor fibres also appear to be exclusively static in function (Emonet-Dénand, Laporte & Pagès, 1966).

Numbers and strength of action of the two kinds of fibre

When isolating single γ fibres in ventral root filaments it is usual to find two to three times as many static as dynamic fibres,

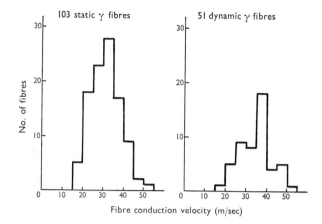

FIG. 5.17. The distribution of the conduction velocities of the two kinds of fusimotor fibres. The histograms include the pooled data from several series of experiments; one series was on the tibialis posterior muscle and the resulting histogram is already published (Brown, Crowe & Matthews, 1965, Fig. 7); the rest of the data was obtained from the soleus muscle by the author and his colleagues and has mostly not been previously published. The relative numbers of the two kinds of fusimotor fibres probably underestimates the greater abundance of static fibres.

and this may reasonably be taken to reflect their relative frequency of occurrence in the body (cf. Fig. 5.17). This difference in their frequency of occurrence has been observed both when the fibres are detected by virtue of their excitatory action on an afferent ending and when they are detected by measurement of their conduction velocity.

It is interesting to compare the strengths of action of the two kinds of fusimotor fibre when the length of a muscle is constant, and to see by how much each increases the frequency of firing of the afferent endings. When this is done the effect of a static fibre on a particular primary ending is sometimes found to be much greater than that of a dynamic fibre acting on the same ending, even though the dynamic fibre dramatically enhances the responsiveness of the ending to dynamic stimuli. Perhaps because of such observations it is sometimes implied that under static conditions the effect of dynamic fibres is always so weak as to be insignificant. Unfortunately things are not quite so simple. Recourse to Fig. 5.10 shows that with the muscle held at a constant length the two kinds of fusimotor fibres may have a similar range of action on the primary ending. Moreover, in the particular experiments illustrated in Fig. 5.10, stimulation of static fibres at 100/sec produced on average no greater increase in primary firing than did stimulation of dynamic fibres at the same frequency; these findings were for the tibialis posterior muscle which was held a few millimetres below its maximum physiological length. Crowe & Matthews (1964b) working under similar conditions on the soleus muscle also found that static and dynamic fibres had equally powerful actions on the primary ending. However, when the length of the muscle is held constant in the whole animal then the static fibres, by virtue of their greater numbers, should be capable of exerting a greater overall excitatory effect than do the dynamic fibres. Whether they do so will depend upon the relative frequencies of discharge of the two kinds of fibre.

In addition, it should be noted that the equality of action of individual fusimotor fibres, which has just been described, may have depended upon the particular experimental conditions employed and possibly also upon the sampling of the fusimotor fibres selected for study. Andersson, Lennerstrand & Thoden (1968) studied the effect of increasing the frequency of stimulation from 60 to 180/sec rather than from 0 to 100/sec. They then found that the static fibres had on average about twice as much effect on the primary ending as did the dynamic fibres (124 and 73 impulses/sec respectively); the measurements were again made when the length of the muscle was constant. Under the same conditions they compared the action of static fibres on secondary endings with that on primary endings. The effect, expressed in impulses/sec increase in firing, was about half as large for the secondary endings as for primary endings (74 and 124 impulses/sec respectively). In this case, however, the results were in agreement with those obtained on increasing the frequency of stimulation from 0 to 100/sec which also had about half as much effect on secondary as on primary endings (Brown, Engberg & Matthews, 1967). The effect on secondary endings might, however, be relatively greater if the endings were to be studied with the muscle more fully extended, since the position-sensitivity of secondary endings is more commonly increased by static fusimotor stimulation than is that of primary endings. Thus no particular stress should be paid to the precise value of the figures just given, for slightly different ones would clearly be obtained with comparatively minor alterations in the experimental conditions.

Further quantitative description of the input–output relations of the spindle would be helpful for assessing the role of the fusimotor fibres in the servo-assistance of movement. What is also currently missing for such a purpose is any proper knowledge of the natural frequencies of firing of various fusimotor fibres and also of the way their effects on the spindle interact. The suspicion is that most of the experiments investigating the action of fusimotor stimulation have employed unphysiologically high frequencies of stimulation. High frequencies of stimulation are necessary to produce appreciable effects on the afferent endings when individual fusimotor fibres are stimulated on their own. Much lower frequencies might well be adequate when several fusimotor fibres are acting co-operatively. The experiments so far described are more than adequate to establish that the static and dynamic fusimotor fibres are functionally distinct entities. But they may perhaps not have sufficiently emphasised the difference between them, whatever it may be, that is of most importance for normal function. Table 5.1 on p. 224 summarises the present state of affairs.

Speed of intrafusal contraction as judged by time-course of response to fusimotor stimulation

'Driving'. Crowe & Matthews (1964b), in studying the fusimotor control of the primary ending, had the impression 'that in general the effects of stimulation of static fusimotor fibres started and stopped more abruptly than those of stimulation of dynamic fusimotor fibres', and partly on this basis suggested that the contraction of the nuclear bag fibres might be slower than that of the nuclear chain fibres. In addition, it early became apparent that repetitive static fusimotor stimulation at 50–150/sec fairly frequently produces 'driving' of the primary ending, in which each efferent spike evokes one afferent spike, while dynamic fusimotor stimulation has never yet been observed to do so. For example, driving was observed in 20 out of 62 occasions in which static fibres were tested on primary endings of the tibialis posterior muscle, but on none of the 34 occasions in which a dynamic fibre was tested (Brown, Crowe & Matthews, 1965). As 'driving' seems likely to be due to a mechanical vibratory excitation of the

TABLE 5.1. Summary of the effects of stimulating the two kinds of fusi-motor fibre

	Dynamic stimulation	Static stimulation
On the static firing of the primary ending	Increase	Slightly larger increase
On the static firing of the secondary ending	No action	Increase
On the dynamic responsiveness of the primary to a ramp stretch	Increase	Decrease
On the dynamic responsiveness of the secondary	No action	Remains small
On the sensitivity of the primary to low-frequency sinusoidal stretching	Remains high	Decrease
On the responsiveness of the primary to being 'driven' by vibration	Increase	Increase
Frequency of stimulation required to produce a maximal effect	Over 150/sec	Over 150/sec
Speed of intrafusal contraction judged by persistence of stimulus rhythm in the frequencygram	Slow ('fusion frequency' well below 100/sec)	Fast ('fusion frequency' somewhat over 100/sec)
Driving of afferent in time with fusimotor stimulus	Never	Fairly frequently
Intrafusal potentials	Non-propagated	May be all-or-none spike with overshoot and partial propagation (? not always)
Conduction velocity of fusimotor fibres	15–50 m/sec	The same, but relatively more slow fibres
Approximate frequency of occurrence	One quarter of gamma motor fibres	Three quarters of gamma motor fibres
Intrafusal fibre type responsible for action (see Chap. 6)	Nuclear bag	Nuclear chain

primary ending, consequent on an 'unfused' intrafusal contraction, this further favours the idea that the static fibres supply faster intrafusal muscle fibres than do the dynamic fibres. This does not mean, however, that on increasing the frequency of stimulation the mean effect of dynamic activation saturates before that of static activation; as illustrated in Fig. 5.18 the action of either

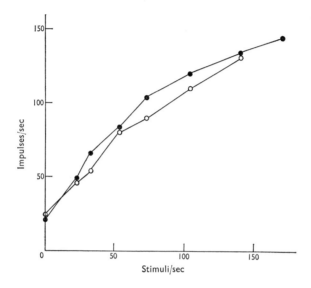

FIG. 5.18. The similar effect on the discharge of a primary ending of increasing the frequency of stimulation of the two kinds of fusimotor fibre when the muscle is at a constant length. ●, stimulation of a static fibre; o, stimulation of a dynamic fibre. Results from a soleus muscle. (Matthews, 1962, Fig. 5.)

kind of fibre may increase for frequencies of stimulation at up to at least 150/sec. In this respect the dynamic fusimotor fibres in particular behave rather differently from the more familiar twitch extrafusal muscle fibres. 'Driving' of the secondary endings on high-frequency static fusimotor stimulation would appear to be rare if it occurs at all, for it has yet to be observed by the author and his colleagues. However, Appelberg, Bessou & Laporte (1965, Fig. 5) have illustrated its occurrence on stimulating at the low frequency of 22/sec.

The frequencygram. The matter of the speed of intrafusal contraction was taken up more thoroughly by Bessou, Laporte &
Pagès (1968) who developed a graphic method of averaging the
response of the afferent ending to which they gave the name of
'frequencygram'. This consists simply of superimposing successive
sweeps of a display of instantaneous frequency on a storage
oscilloscope while keeping the stimulus at the same point on the
sweep. The spikes, however, occur at different points on successive
sweeps so that the display gradually comes to have spikes all
along its length thereby providing a continuous curve of 'frequency' against time. Such 'frequencygrams' thus provide one
way of attempting to estimate the size and time-course of the
presumed continuous processes which underly the generation of
spikes, and which cannot be determined from the small number
of all-or-nothing action potentials occurring on a single sweep. It
should be noted, however, that when the underlying sensory events
are changing rapidly such averaging of the instantaneous frequency
of discharge of an ending will give a rather different and probably
less informative result than that obtained by constructing a post-
stimulus time histogram (cf. discussion on p. 176).

Figure 5.19 shows the typical type of frequencygram recorded
for a primary ending on stimulating a single static fusimotor fibre.
On stimulation at 22/sec the response is analogous to myographic
records of a series of twitch contractions. As the frequency of
stimulation is increased, the records progressively pass through
stages like those of a more fused tetanic contraction, though with
the fusion still not quite complete on stimulation at 180/sec.
Such changes in the frequencygram, occurring in phase with the
stimulus, suggest that there is a rhythmic variation in the underlying receptor potential and can be presumed to indicate a
rhythmic mechanical deformation of the afferent terminals. It
seems reasonable to conclude, therefore, that static fusimotor fibres
must act via a quick contractile system. In the present connotation
'quickness' means the ability of the myofibrils to shorten and
relax rapidly, which is presumably linked with a brief duration of
their 'active state', and has nothing to do with whether the contraction is initiated by a propagated action potential or by a localised
junction potential. In contrast, the effect of dynamic fusimotor
stimulation on the frequencygram of the primary ending is
illustrated in Fig. 5.20 and looks as if it might be mediated by a

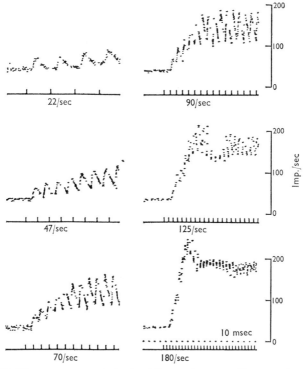

FIG. 5.19. 'Frequencygrams' obtained for a primary ending on stimulating a static fusimotor fibre at various frequencies. The short vertical marks rising from the horizontal lines show the timing of the stimuli; their frequency is indicated below each record. The dotted lines result from superimposing 30 traces of the instantaneous frequency of firing of the afferent on stimulating the fusimotor fibre at the same times on each sweep; this gives what is called a frequencygram. Results from the tenuissimus muscle. (Bessou, Laporte & Pagès, 1968, Fig. 3.)

slow contractile system, though this cannot be guaranteed. Here 'fusion' occurs at a frequency somewhere below 47/sec, though the mean response continues to increase with further increases in the frequency of stimulation. Essentially similar results have been obtained in the rabbit (Emonet-Dénand & Laporte, 1969). Thus the findings are entirely in line with the idea that the dynamic fibres act via a slower contractile system than do the static fibres. Most probably the fast and slow contractile systems are simply the nuclear chain and nuclear bag fibres respectively (see Chap. 6).

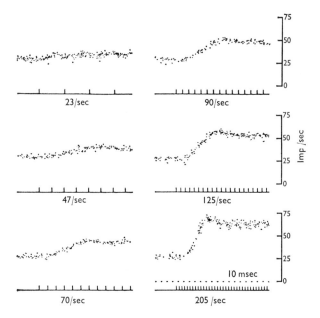

FIG. 5.20. Frequencygrams obtained for a primary ending on stimulating a dynamic fusimotor fibre. Display as in Fig. 5.19. Results from the tenuissimus. (Bessou, Laporte & Pagès, 1968, Fig. 11.)

However, it would be improper to conceal the fact that frequency-grams obtained on static fusimotor stimulation occasionally have a far lower 'fusion frequency' than that illustrated in Fig. 5.19. For example, in the rabbit Emonet-Dénand & Laporte (1969) illustrated one with fusion apparently complete on stimulation at 62/sec. On the other hand, stimulation of a dynamic fibre appears never to have elicited a frequencygram with a high fusion frequency.

The familiarly simple appearance of frequencygrams should not be allowed to obscure the complex factors underlying their generation and which prevent them from being interpreted simply as the direct record of intrafusal contraction provided by a particularly well-sited transducer. For one thing, the ability of the ending to reflect high-frequency contractile changes will depend upon the ability with which it is able to follow high-frequency stimulation of any kind. The secondary ending is well known to be worse at this than the primary ending, very possibly because it lies on a more viscous region of intrafusal fibre (see Chap. 6). If so, its frequencygram may perhaps indicate a spuriously low value for the 'fusion frequency' of the intrafusal fibres operating upon it (i.e. presumed to be chain fibres). Experimentally, the simultaneous recording of the frequencygrams of a primary and a secondary ending in the same spindle on stimulation of single static fibres has shown that in general 'the stimulation rate causing fusion of secondary responses was lower' (Bessou & Pagès, 1969a, p. 579); stimulation at only 90/sec was found to give well-fused frequency-grams for secondary endings whereas much higher frequencies of static stimulation are almost always required to produce fused frequencygrams for primary endings. However, it seems unlikely that the low 'fusion frequency' found for primary endings on dynamic fusimotor stimulation can be due to an insensitivity of the primary terminals to high frequencies, since such stimulation increases the sensitivity of the ending to an externally applied vibration (see Fig. 5.15.)

Another major complication in the interpretation of frequency-grams is the fidelity with which any shortening of a contracted region of intrafusal fibre is transmitted along the spindle so as to produce deformation of the sensorially innervated region of the fibre. If a local contraction occurs some distance from the ending then it may largely expend itself in taking up the slack in the intervening region of intrafusal fibre; the magnitude of this effect will depend upon the elasticity of the inactive region of the fibre and upon its length. This may be the reason for the very different effect of a single fusimotor impulse on different endings. Usually this elicits no detectable response at all, irrespective of whether the impulse is in a static or a dynamic fibre; sometimes, however, either kind of efferent may elicit a well-marked 'twitch-like' response in the frequencygram of a primary ending. The same is true for the action of static fibres on secondary endings.

Figure 5.21 shows a range of responses elicited on single-shock static stimulation from the secondary and the primary endings of three different spindles; together these show that even within a single spindle there is no correlation between the effects on the two kinds of ending, as would have been expected if the presence or absence of a response had depended solely upon the 'strength' of contraction of individual intrafusal fibres and upon how many of them had been activated. Repetitive stimulation of

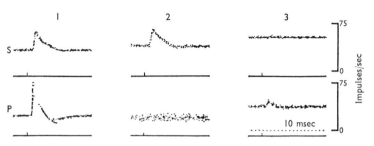

FIG. 5.21. Comparison of the frequencygrams of primary (P) and secondary (S) endings elicited on single shock stimulation of a static fusimotor fibre. The records show the responses of three pairs of endings (1, 2, 3); each pair consisted of a primary and a secondary ending which lay in the same muscle spindle and the responses of which were recorded simultaneously on stimulating a single static fibre, different for each pair. The lowest trace shows the stimulus. Results from the tenuissimus. (Bessou & Pagès, 1969a, Fig. 7.)

fibres which failed to produce responses on single shock stimulation could give large responses in the frequencygrams; these did not differ in any systematic manner from those elicited by stimulating fibres which could produce twitch-like effects on single-shock stimulation except that 'driving' was never found for fibres incapable of eliciting 'twitch responses'. The greater efficacy of repetitive stimulation seems likely sometimes to be due to an enhancement with repetitive stimulation of the effectiveness of the junctional transmission from the γ efferent to the intrafusal muscle fibres. Bessou, Laporte & Pagès (1970) have recently observed that this may occur on occasion by stimulating individual static fusimotor fibres and recording the electrical activity of the intrafusal muscle fibres both intracellularly and extracellularly. However, in addition it seems probable that the contraction elicited by repetitive activation of the contractile machinery is the more effective at taking in slack than is the contraction elicited by a single intrafusal potential, for Eyzaguirre (1960b) noted marked facilitation of the spindle afferent discharge with repetitive stimulation at a time when the intrafusal potentials remained the same size.

Thus the results obtained with repetitive activation seem likely to give a better idea of the speed of intrafusal contraction than those obtained on stimulation with a single shock. None the less it is interesting that when a primary and secondary ending are excited within the same spindle, a single static fusimotor impulse 'evoked approximately a similar duration of increased discharge' from the two kinds of afferent, though in general 'the rising phase of the secondary response was more gradual' (Bessou & Pagès, 1969a). When a single dynamic impulse produces an action on a primary ending the effect is usually slightly more prolonged than that of single static activation, though this does not seem to have been compared in the self-same spindle. Thus, the rising phase of static stimulation lasts 5–8 msec and the falling phase 15–30 msec, while on dynamic stimulation the rising phase lasts 15–25 msec and the falling phase 40–60 msec (Bessou, Laporte & Pagès, 1968). This is again entirely compatible with a slower contraction of the dynamically-innervated intrafusal fibres (presumed bag fibres), but provides somewhat less cogent evidence for it than the effects of repetitive stimulation.

Electrical activity of intrafusal fibres

An obvious question to ask about the activation of intrafusal contraction is whether it is achieved by propagated or by non-propagated muscle action potentials or whether even by some combination of the two methods. Because of the technical difficulties, this matter is still not entirely resolved. In their original study Kuffler, Hunt & Quilliam (1951) succeeded in recording a localised spindle potential extracellularly from the surface of the tenuissimus muscle on stimulating single γ efferents; they thought that it was most likely to be non-propagated. Ten years later, Eyzaguirre (1960a,b) recorded polyphasic potentials under similar circumstances and concluded that they were probably propagated along the intrafusal fibres. The best evidence for propagation of some at least of the potentials was then obtained by progressively curarising the preparation, when the potentials sometimes failed in an all-or-none manner. The polyphasic form of the potential alone is inadequate evidence for propagation along the intrafusal muscle fibre. In a system as complex as the spindle, polyphasicity might arise merely from the activation of one or more intrafusal fibres at one or more different points along the length of the spindle by a single slowly-conducting γ motor nerve fibre and its branches.

Five years later, Bessou & Laporte (1965) performed essentially the same experiment but now with single γ motor fibres which had been categorised as either static or dynamic by their action on the primary ending of the spindle in question. Their only published results are shown in Fig. 5.22. The dynamic fibre produced a

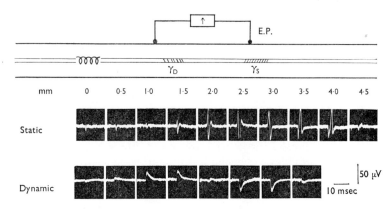

FIG. 5.22. The potentials set up by intrafusal muscle fibres and recorded extracellularly on stimulating a static and a dynamic fusimotor fibre. Above, the experimental arrangement showing a diagrammatic spindle with a single intrafusal fibre embedded in the tenuissimus muscle. The millimetre scale shows the position of the right-hand electrode (E.P.) for the various insets below, and is zero when the electrode is over the spindle equator. The electrodes were moved as a pair with constant inter-electrode separation. The shaded areas show the presumed locations of the end-plates supplied by each fusimotor fibre, as judged by the reversal of the potentials with movement of the electrodes. The fusimotor fibres were isolated in ventral root filaments and were characterised as static or dynamic by their action on a primary ending. The location of the spindle equator was deduced from the point of maximum responsiveness of the primary ending. The actual length of the spindle was unknown. The fusi-motor fibres were stimulated at 50/sec and each trace consists of 20 super-imposed traces. (From Bessou & Laporte, 1965, whose Figs. 1 and 2 showing results from two separate spindles have been combined.)

potential which was indubitably non-propagated, both because of its simple monophasic form and because of a reversal of its polarity on moving the stimulating electrodes. The static fibre produced a polyphasic potential whose form changed in a complex way on moving the electrodes, and so could not easily be ascribed to a single focal depolarisation. The potential was therefore suspected to be basically a propagated one, though it was clear that it failed to propagate itself across the equator of the spindle.

Further support for some degree of propagation was obtained quite recently by Bessou & Pagès (1969b) who managed to insert a micro-electrode into certain intrafusal fibres, though it was not resolved whether these were bag or chain fibres. On stimulating a single static fusimotor fibre they recorded an all-or-none spike which overshot the resting potential, and which blocked in an all-or-nothing manner with progressive neuromuscular paralysis with gallamine; in their illustrated example the resting potential of the intrafusal fibre was 66 mV and the spike was 80 mV. The effect of a static fibre on a secondary ending has also been shown on occasion to be blocked in an all-or-none manner by progressive curarisation (Bessou & Pagès, 1969a). Thus on present evidence static fibres appear to be able to set up intrafusal spikes which are propagated along at least part of the length of the fibre. But it cannot be considered settled that static fibres invariably act via propagated intrafusal spikes and can never do so by means of non-propagated potentials directly activating the contractile machinery. Dynamic fibres, on present evidence, would appear to act solely via local potentials.

It has been suggested (Bessou & Laporte, 1966) that a static and a dynamic fibre may evoke respectively a propagated and a non-propagated potential in the same intrafusal fibre and so lead to their different actions on the afferent endings (see Chap. 6). For the moment it is sufficient to note that this has yet to be established experimentally, whether by recording from a single intrafusal fibre on stimulating each kind of fusimotor fibre, or by studying the mode of summation of the extracellularly recorded potentials that they evoke. In the latter case, algebraic summation of the potentials would be anticipated if the fusimotor fibres supplied different intrafusal fibres whereas some degree of occlusion should occur if they supplied the same ones.

The physiological demonstration of the existence of skeleto-fusimotor (β) fibres

Having dealt with the new features of the physiology of the fusimotor fibres, the next section of this chapter will return to a classical anatomical problem, namely whether muscle spindles in the mammal are at all regularly supplied by branches of the ordinary motor fibres. This is, of course, the usual arrangement in amphibia and reptiles. Because of the indefinite nature of much of the evidence, discussion of this topic unfortunately consumes rather more space than the intrinsic intellectual interest of the problem would appear to warrant.

Definitive experiments. Fortunately, there now exists incontrovertible evidence that on occasion the mammalian spindle may be supplied by branches of ordinary motor fibres to the extrafusal fibres; this occurs in addition to their being supplied by specialised fusimotor fibres. The first definite demonstration of such an arrangement was provided by Bessou, Emonet-Dénand & Laporte (1965) using physiological methods. They were immediately confirmed by Adal & Barker (1965a) using anatomical methods. Bessou *et al.* studied the 1st deep lumbrical muscle of the hindlimb of the cat using the standard method of recording from dorsal root filaments and stimulating ventral root filaments. This little muscle contains 3–6 muscle spindles and is supplied by around 10 motor fibres, about half of which are large and half small. The small fibres are perfectly typical fusimotor fibres which produce no overt contraction of the muscle, but which produce spindle excitation of either static or dynamic type. The large fibres produce the usual contraction of the main muscle, but in addition a few of them may have an excitatory action on spindle primary endings.

Two methods were used to determine whether these excitatory effects should be attributed to a genuine motor innervation of the spindle eliciting an intrafusal contraction, or whether they were merely due to excitation of the spindle by an external mechanical stimulus arising from the contraction of nearby extrafusal muscle fibres. First, the frequency of stimulation to the single fibre was varied to see whether a maximal activation of the spindle was produced by the same frequency as that required to elicit a maximal extrafusal contraction. Second, a progressive neuromuscular block was produced by the intravenous injection of gallamine in order to see whether the excitatory action on the spindle was paralysed at the same time as the extrafusal contraction. These tests were used because it was already known that the intrafusal contraction elicited on γ efferent stimulation is only maximally developed for frequencies of stimulation well above that required to produce a maximal contraction of extrafusal muscle fibres, and also that on paralysis with curarising agents the intrafusal contrac-

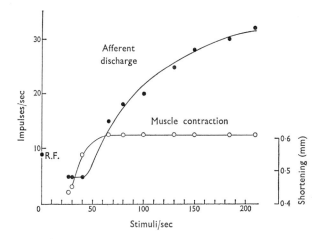

FIG. 5.23. The dual destination of a skeleto-fusimotor (β) fibre demonstrated by comparing the effects of varying its frequency of stimulation on the discharge of a spindle afferent (●) and on the overt muscular contraction recorded simultaneously with an isotonic myograph (o). The point labelled R.F. gives the resting frequency of discharge of the ending in the absence of contraction. On low-frequency stimulation the unloading of the spindle by the extrafusal contraction predominated, while on high-frequency stimulation the intrafusal contraction had the more powerful action on the afferent. The results were obtained from the 1st deep lumbrical muscle of the hindlimb of the cat using the preparation of Fig. 5.5. The conduction velocity of the β fibre was only 31 m/sec; other β fibres to the same muscle conducted at up to 56 m/sec. (Bessou, Emonet-Dénand & Laporte, 1965, Fig. 3.)

tion, elicited by γ efferent stimulation, outlasts the extrafusal contraction produced on α motor stimulation. As illustrated in Figs. 5.23 and 5.24 the same was found to be true for the spindle excitation elicited on stimulating some single large motor fibres, thus showing that the motor fibres in question must have directly innervated muscle spindles. Such fibres are now called mixed or skeleto-fusimotor fibres, or sometimes β fibres. Although this last term is the most convenient it is hard to defend on logical grounds for mixed fibres may overlap in size with purely skeleto-motor or purely fusimotor fibres.

It should be immediately emphasised that in these experiments excitation of spindles by large fibres did not always prove to be due to a specific innervation of the spindle. Quite often the effect on

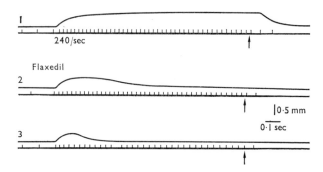

240/sec

Flaxedil

|0·5 mm

0·1 sec

FIG. 5.24. The differential effect of curarisation on the muscle contraction and the spindle afferent discharge elicited on stimulation of a β fibre. 1, myographic and afferent responses elicited by repetitive stimulation of a single motor fibre at 240/sec terminating at arrow. 2, 3 the responses elicited by similar stimulation after the intravenous injection of two successive doses of Flaxedil (gallamine triethiodide). Same experiment as Fig. 5.23. (Bessou, Emonet-Dénand & Laporte, 1965, Fig. 4 reversed in contrast.)

the spindle and the extrafusal fibres were not separable by the means employed and so the effect on the spindle was thought to be mediated non-specifically by extrafusal fibres. Such a excitation via extrafusal contraction seems unlikely to be physiologically important, and may well assume undue prominence under the artificial conditions of expriments involving high-frequency activation of just a single one of the several motor units to a muscle.

The genuine β intrafusal action was only demonstrable for a minority of the lumbrical spindles studied. The failure to detect it regularly was thought to be physiologically meaningful because it was usually possible to isolate most of the small number of motor fibres to the muscle. Thus at least for the cat lumbrical, β innervation was felt to be a facultative rather than an obligatory condition, though it seems possible that some further weak β actions may then have passed unnoticed because they were masked by the concomitant extrafusal contraction. Adal & Barker (1695a) traced individual motor fibres under the microscope to their destination in teased preparations of the same muscle and confirmed that mixed skeleto-fusimotor fibres do indeed occur, but again they found that not every spindle is so supplied. The receipt of a mixed motor fibre by any particular muscle spindle does not prevent it receiving purely fusimotor fibres of both static and dynamic kinds; thus mixed fibres seem to be in addition to, rather than instead of, a normal fusimotor innervation and appear therefore to be something of an 'optional extra'. In the cat lumbrical all mixed fibres proved to have a dynamic action, which was indistinguishable from that of a dynamic fusimotor fibre; the same was found for 4 mixed fibres supplying the tibialis posterior muscle (Brown, Crowe & Matthews, 1965). Mixed fibres have also been found in muscles of the rat's tail though here the fibres were not tested appropriately to distinguish between a static and a dynamic action (Kidd, 1964).

Quite recently, Emonet-Dénand, Jankowska & Laporte (1970) studied the mixed fibres supplying spindles in the lumbrical muscle of the rabbit hindlimb. Of 12 β fibres isolated, 8 had the dynamic action known from the cat but 4 had a typical static action. Thus in this species at any rate a mixed fibre may have either a static or dynamic action thereby raising interesting questions about the site and morphological nature of their terminations. In addition, these experiments raised the question, without providing a final answer, as to whether the rabbit lumbrical is supplied by any purely fusimotor fibres or whether its spindles have to rely entirely upon β fibres. In the limited number of experiments which were then performed no purely fusimotor fibres were isolated. Whether they exist should be readily resolvable by further study with present techniques. On anatomical grounds, Adal & Barker (1965b) have also suggested that some rabbit lumbrical muscles may be without purely fusimotor fibres. Other muscles in the rabbit, however, may possess static and dynamic fibres which are purely fusimotor and of γ conduction velocity, and which are typical of those found in the cat (Emonet-Dénand, Laporte & Pagès, 1966).

The dubious significance of the early discharge. This leads on to the controversial question as to whether the presence of a skeletomotor innervation of any particular spindle can be reliably established by methods less painstaking than those employed by Bessou, Emonet-Dénand & Laporte (1965). The particular question is whether the occurrence of afferent spikes at the foot, or during the rising phase, of a twitch contraction elicited on weak stimulation of a muscle nerve can be taken to indicate the presence of a mixed innervation. On the classical picture the spindle should then be silent, and so the presence of spikes might be taken to be due to an intrafusal contraction; and with an appropriately weak stimulus this would have had to have been elicited by mixed fibres rather than by γ efferents. It is the present author's opinion that the existence of plausible alternative explanations for spindle firing during a twitch contraction makes its detection largely irrelevant for attempting to decide whether or not any particular spindle is influenced by a mixed fibre.

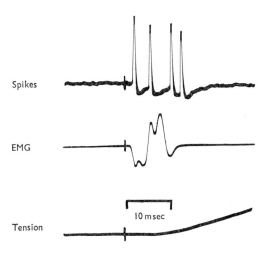

FIG. 5.25. The 'early discharge' shown by a spindle primary ending just before and at the foot of a twitch contraction. The afferent discharge was recorded from a dorsal root filament. The muscle was made to twitch by stimulating its nerve; this also directly excited the spindle afferent to give the first spike in the record. The ensuing 3 spikes constitute the 'early discharge'; its origin is still in question. Experiment on the soleus muscle of the anaesthetised cat. The tension was recorded with an iso-metric myograph. The electromyogram was recorded with leads placed about 2 cm apart on the surface of the muscle.

The problem was first taken up by Hunt & Kuffler (1951b). They distinguished between spikes occurring during much of the rising phase of a twitch contraction and those occurring at the very beginning or even just before the overtly recorded contraction. This brief burst of 2–4 spikes occurring with a very short latency was named the 'early discharge'. It has since become widely familiar because it obtrudes itself on those attempting to measure the conduction velocity of single afferent fibres by stimulating an intact muscle nerve while recording from a dorsal root filament. Figure 5.25 shows the 'early discharge' of a primary ending in relation to the contraction and the electromyogram; the recordings were made from a dorsal root filament so the spikes must have been actually initiated about 2 msec earlier. The 'early discharge' may be readily elicited by stimuli which are too weak to have excited γ efferents and so may be confidently attributed to α motor fibres. The early discharge may or may not be followed by a certain number of spikes on the rising phase of the twitch, and these latter may also be found in the absence of an early discharge.

Hunt & Kuffler (1951b) attributed both the early discharge and any subsequent spikes to a mechanical stimulation of the spindle by the contraction of nearby extrafusal muscle fibres. They suggested that the early discharge appeared to precede the contraction merely because of 'tension changes which arise within the muscle before they are recorded myographically' (1951b, p. 310). Granit, Pompeiano & Waltman (1959b) subsequently disputed this interpretation and suggested that the early discharge was really a compound event due to two separate causes. They attributed its first spike to an ephaptic excitation of the afferent fibre by the large flow of current produced by the synchronous occurrence of action potentials in a number of extrafusal muscle fibres. Any later spikes of the early discharge were suggested to be due to a functionally specific influence on the spindle mediated by certain particular α motor fibres, though they did not confirm this by stimulating single α motor fibres on their own. They left the question open as to whether their suggested specific influence was due to the α fibres themselves eliciting an intrafusal contraction, which they clearly felt to be the most likely, or to the contraction of 'nearly extrafusal fibres to which the spindles are inserted' (1959b, p. 416). The supposedly different components of the early discharge were dissociated by varying the strength of the stimulus to the muscle nerve, the initial length of the muscle, and the frequency of stimulation.

There are, however, certain difficulties in accepting all this. Ordinary α motor fibres may sometimes be excited ephaptically by the muscle action potential (Leksell, 1945; Brown & Matthews, 1960), and so it would be surprising if the afferent fibres were not also sometimes so excited. But once such ephaptic excitation is admitted to play a part in the generation of the first part of the early discharge, then it becomes very difficult to refuse that the whole of the early discharge might not be so initiated. The early discharge rarely outlasts the muscle action potential and the limited dissociation of it into separate components which has been observed is somewhat unconvincing as evidence that it must be due to more than one cause. In the present author's opinion it seems most likely that the early discharge is usually wholly due to ephaptic excitation. Even if it is not entirely so caused, the remainder might be due to the accidental effects of the extrafusal contraction and so again of no particular physiological significance. In the face of these two possible but essentially trivial causes for the early discharge (ephaptic excitation, early tension changes) it becomes almost impossible to decide whether or not a third factor, namely specific innervation, is also playing a part. Because of its importance, mixed innervation requires more secure evidence for its acceptance, and conclusions about its existence based on the study of the early discharge must be considered invalid. For example, it seems premature to conclude that mixed innervation is relatively common in flexor muscles of the cat hindlimb, as has been suggested (cf. Haase, & Schlegel, 1966). Likewise, taken alone the observation of the presence or absence of spikes on the rising phase of the twitch also appears insufficient to decide for or against the existence of a mixed motor innervation in a particular case. Spikes on the falling phase of a twitch have even less significance for this purpose as they can be attributed to the re-extension of the spindle after it has been allowed to shorten slightly on being unloaded by the contraction.

Granit, Pompeiano & Waltman's belief in a specific α control of the spindle rested also on experiments in which the latency of the spindle afferent discharge was determined on stimulating various structures within the central nervous system and also certain peripheral nerves (Granit, Pompeiano & Waltman, 1959a; Rutledge & Haase, 1961). It was then felt that the afferent spikes were sometimes found slightly too early to have been due to a spindle activation via the γ efferents. However, for various reasons such precise comparisons of timing tend to be unreliable and so judgement on the existence of an α innervation may again reasonably be suspended (Matthews, 1964). There is a further difficulty in accepting either the early discharge, or any spikes on the rising phase of contraction, as a sign of mixed innervation. This is that the proven mixed fibres studied by Laporte and his colleagues do not appear to have produced any appreciable spindle excitation on single shock stimulation. Repetitive stimulation was required to demonstrate the action of proven β fibres, as is also usually required to demonstrate the action of specific fusimotor fibres of small diameter (cf. Figs. 5.18, 5.19 and 5.20).

None of this discussion is meant to deny the possibility of the existence of mixed fibres for the usual large limb muscles, as well as for small muscles with a restricted motor innervation; rather it is a plea for the study of the matter with suitably discriminating methods and the avoidance of premature conclusions. On present evidence it remains unknown whether or not mixed innervation is widespread. This is simply because the currently reliable experimental methods are not easily applied to muscles with a large number of motor fibres. Mixed fibres with a weak action will particularly easily escape detection because, even on repetitive stimulation, their action will tend to be masked by unloading of the spindle by the inevitable concomitant extrafusal contraction (Emonet-Dénand, Jankowska & Laporte, 1970). Barker (see p. 42) has suggested that the type of motor ending which he calls the p_1 plate is derived from mixed fibres. If so, their distribution is remarkably widespread.

On the other hand, it can be stated fairly confidently that large motor fibres of α diameter are probably never purely fusimotor and restricted to supplying spindles without sending branches to extrafusal fibres. Emonet-Dénand, Joffroy & Laporte (1971) recently isolated some 1100 single α fibres each of which was selected on the basis of having a conduction velocity of over 50 m/sec. When stimulated on its own all but 3, which were suspected to be damaged, elicited an obvious twitch contraction of the main muscle. The muscles studied were the tibialis anterior and the extensor digitorum longus both of which, on the basis of the sort of indirect evidence discussed above, have been suspected to have their spindles supplied by α motor fibres.

For the time being it is simplest to believe that any muscle which histological observation shows to be supplied by both large and small motor fibres is likely to be predominantly controlled by specific fusimotor fibres. The extraocular muscles, however, may provide an exception. The significance of the partial persistence in the mammal of the more primitive amphibian and reptilian arrangement is unknown. Certainly it provides for an economy of motor fibres, but at the cost of an independent control of the spindle. In so far as the intrafusal and extrafusal fibres are often required to contract at the same time a partial such economy may perhaps be achievable with little loss, provided that an independent fusimotor pathway is also available for use on occasions when a measure of independent fusimotor control is required. A mixed fibre, by virtue of usually being of large size, will also provide for a slight saving in conduction time from motor centre to the spindle. But in view of the slowness of contraction of the nuclear bag fibres (see Chap. 6) little would seem to be gained by saving a few milliseconds in conduction time from the spinal cord; bag fibres are the ones which seem the more likely to receive a mixed innervation, for they more commonly have p_1 plates upon them. Pending the more exact determination of the frequency of occurrence of such mixed fibres and the power of their action, attention may reasonably be concentrated on the control of the spindle by specific fusimotor fibres. These appear to be the more usual and the more advanced method of fusimotor control in the mammal.

The use of drugs for investigating fusimotor function

Full discussion of the pharmacology of the muscle spindle can be found in several comparatively recent reviews and will not be attempted here (Smith, C. M., 1963; Matthews, 1964; Paintal, 1964). It does, however, seem worth briefly describing the action of some of the drugs which have been used as tools for investigating fusimotor function as well as being of interest in their own right.

Suxamethonium. The histochemical demonstration of cholinesterase at both the plate and trail types of intrafusal motor ending indicates that they both act cholinergically, and all the experimental evidence fits in with this view. This opens the way for the use of the standard armoury of drugs for mimicking or antagonising the action of acetylcholine in order to study fusimotor action. The most striking effect in this respect is that suxamethonium (succinylcholine or SCh) produces a powerful dynamic action on the primary ending. As discussed later (p. 294) it probably does this by causing a prolonged contracture of the nuclear bag fibres. As earlier observed by Granit, Skoglund & Thesleff (1953) SCh also produces a powerful excitation of spindle endings when the length of a muscle is held constant, whereas Golgi tendon organs are not excited. The excited endings were presumed to be primary endings and thus the injection of SCh came to be widely used to investigate the central effects of spindle afferent activity. However, it gradually became clear that secondary endings were usually excited as well as primary endings, though not nearly so powerfully (see for example, Fehr, 1965, who gives earlier references). Thus the problem of disentangling the central action of Ia and II fibres remains untouched and as yet the reflex effects elicited by SCh have mostly been explained by invoking previously known synaptic connections rather than leading to the discovery of anything novel (for example, Henatsch, 1962; Voorhoeve & Verhey, 1963). It does appear, however, that in contrast to its powerful reflex effects on the firing of α motoneurones, SCh has little effect on that of γ motoneurones. This supports the idea that the latter function largely independently of feedback from the effects of their activity on the spindle.

Recently, the necessity of controlling the dose of SCh used to obtain spindle afferent excitation has been emphasised by the finding that in the rat an increase of the dose to 10 times that just required to excite spindle afferents also excites other kinds of afferent ending, though whether by a direct action on the nerve terminals or by the contraction of smooth muscle remains un-decided (Kidd & Kučera, 1969). This finding would seem to reduce drastically the value of SCh as a tool for the investigation of the central action of spindle activity for it no longer appears to be an entirely specific stimulus. It also keeps alive the problem of how far SCh has a direct excitatory action on spindle endings, as well as an indirect one mediated by the contraction of intrafusal fibres; such contraction has now been observed microscopically (Smith, R.S., 1966).

Curare and gallamine. Curare and other neuromuscular blocking agents prevent transmission at the intrafusal motor endings just as they do at the end-plates on extrafusal muscle fibres. However, as first shown in the frog, intrafusal neuromuscular transmission often persists after that to the extrafusal fibres has been blocked, and this happens even when an intrafusal and an extrafusal motor ending are both supplied by branches from the same single β fibre (Bessou, Emonet-Dénand & Laporte, 1965). The greater resistance of the intrafusal endings in the cat was first noted in passing by Granit, Homma & Matthews (1959) who found that an increase of spindle afferent discharge could still be produced by the simultaneous stimulation of a and γ fibres after the extrafusal contraction had been eliminated by curarisation. This has since been used as a tool in a variety of circumstances to demonstrate that an excitatory effect on a spindle afferent is indeed dependent upon an intrafusal rather than an extrafusal contraction (for example, to produce 'excitation across the γ loop', Chap. 10; also Fig. 5.24).

There appears, however, to have been no definite study of the time-course, and the critical concentrations, of drug required to curarise intrafusal and extrafusal motor endings in the whole animal. Eyzaguirre (1960a) found relatively little difference between them when he studied the matter in the tenuissimus muscle which had been isolated and placed in an organ bath; he recorded the potential set up by the activity of the intrafusal fibres rather than their action on the afferent ending. On the basis of the effects of vestibulo-spinal stimulation in exciting spindle afferents in the whole animal, Carli, Diete-Spiff & Pompeiano (1967) considered that the intrafusal motor endings did become blocked appreciably after the extrafusal ones but that they also took longer to recover. This thus suggests that the usual delayed block of the fusimotor action in the whole animal depends upon the fusimotor endings being less accessible to the drug than the extrafusal ones, as well as to any differences in their absolute sensitivity. Emonet-Dénand & Houk (1968) furthered this view when they compared the ease of blocking of the motor endings supplied by static and by dynamic fusimotor fibres. They eliminated many chance factors by simultaneously studying the action on a single primary ending of a fusimotor fibre of each kind, thus ensuring that they were studying the progress of the block within a single spindle. As Fig. 5.26 illustrates the action of the dynamic fibre was regularly found to be paralysed before that of the static fibre; but equally regularly it recovered the first. This could well be due to the dynamic fusimotor endings being more accessible to the drug than are the static ones. This would fit in with the idea of the dynamic fibres

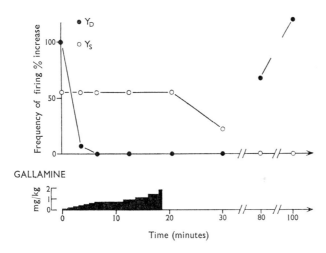

FIG. 5.26. The different patterns of the neuromuscular blockade of the intrafusal actions of static and dynamic fusimotor fibres. The graphs show the effect of stimulating a single fusimotor fibre of each kind on the discharge of a primary ending when the dose of the curarising agent was progressively increased. The spindle lay in the tenuissimus muscle of the anaesthetised cat. Subdivided spinal root filaments were used for both stimulating and recording. The measurements were made with the muscle at a constant length. The gallamine was given intravenously. (Emonet-Dénand & Houk, 1968, Fig. 2.)

supplying plate endings, mostly lying towards the spindle pole, and the static fibres supplying trail endings lying predominantly inside the spindle capsule and surrounded by fluid.

It thus remains an open question as to whether there is any absolute difference in sensitivity between the two kinds of fusimotor ending, and between either of them and the ordinary extrafusal motor end-plates. Fortunately, this uncertainty is immaterial to the use of neuromuscular block as tool for the investigation of fusimotor function, though it certainly restricts its precision; the differential blockade of the transmission from static and dynamic fibres has yet to be exploited, though this might not be easy. However, absolute differences in sensitivity between all the kinds of ending have certainly not yet been excluded. Most obviously, differences in sensitivity might arise from differences in the affinity of the acetylcholine receptors on different kinds of muscle fibre.

Differences in sensitivity might also be expected between motor endings which elicit a propagated action potential from a muscle fibre and those which act via junctional potentials capable by themselves of activating the contractile machinery. When the concentration of a curarising agent is progressively increased then a system relying on a propagated muscle potential would be expected to fail abruptly after having initially shown no diminution of its action, whereas one relying on local potentials might be expected to show a more gradual failure.

Adrenergic mechanisms and asphyxia (including sympathetic stimulation). Sympathetic stimulation and the injection of sympathomimetic drugs produce a mixture of excitatory and depressing effects upon the discharge of spindle afferent endings. In his detailed review, Paintal (1964) suggested that only a slight initial excitation could be attributed with confidence to a genuine action of the drug upon the sensory ending, and that all other effects so far described could equally well have been due to asphyxia which has powerful effects on its own. These were first described by B. H. C. Matthews (1933) and are illustrated in Fig. 5.27. Here depression was followed by a powerful excitation and then a period of complete inexcitability of the ending; rapid recovery ensued on re-establishing the circulation. The whole cycle of events usually occurred with asphyxia produced simply by circulatory occlusion but was speeded up and intensified if the muscle was also made to contract so as to increase its metabolic requirements; without stimulation, however, the spontaneous discharge only rarely rose above 50/sec. A more recent study has shown that in simple anoxia the partial pressure of oxygen has to be reduced to 20 mm of Hg to produce any obvious effect in the anaesthetised animal (Zimmerman & Grossie, 1969).

The high-frequency asphyxial discharge is particularly interesting for several reasons. First, it is found only in preparations which are unanaesthetised (spinal or decerebrate); in anaesthetised preparations asphyxia produces merely a depression of firing (urethane, ether and chloroform tested). This provides an unusual example of the action of general anaesthetic on the peripheral nervous system and means that the effects of adrenaline might be different in anaesthetised and non-anaesthetised animals. More recently, Pagès & Proske (1970) found that halothane may occasion-

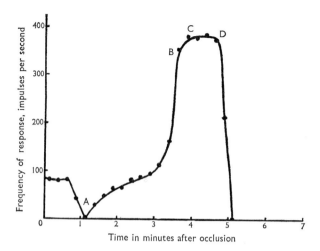

FIG. 5.27. The response of a muscle spindle afferent in an unanaesthe-tised preparation to occlusion of the circulation to its muscle. The asphyxial response was accentuated, and its onset accelerated, by tetanis-ing the muscle at 20/sec for 5 sec in every 15 sec. In between, the muscle was kept at a moderate resting tension thus ensuring a steady afferent response. After an early depression of the discharge (A) there was a tremendous increase in firing (BCD) which was followed by a complete inexcitability of the ending. Unloading the muscle at any time before C decreased the discharge of the ending, but after C it became quite un-responsive to mechanical stimulation. The same sequence of events occurred about ten times more slowly when the muscle was not tetanised, though the late period of increased discharge was then usually much less intense. The ending may be presumed to have been a primary ending. (Matthews, B. H. C., 1933, Fig. 21.)

ally have a dynamic type of action upon the spindle and this would seem most likely to be due to an action on the intrafusal fibres rather than upon the nerve terminals themselves. Second, such high-frequency asphyxial discharges do not appear to be shown by receptors lying outside muscle. Paintal (1964) suggested that they might be due to the accumulation of potassium, particu-larly in the intracapsular fluid of the spindle, though whether this would act on the nerve terminals or on the intrafusal fibres remains to be established. B. H. C. Matthews, however, implied that ten-don organs might also show a similar type of response suggesting an action on the terminals. Third, these high-frequency explosive

IM

discharges were originally suggested to have a part to play in the development of the intense pain which arises from muscles with an inadequate circulation. This, however, now seems unlikely as the high-frequency Ia discharges which may be set up by vibrating a muscle produce no pain at all.

Returning to the action of adrenergic drugs, it can be seen to be virtually impossible to decide whether their late actions on the spindle are due to a specific effect upon it or merely an indirect action as a result of local asphyxia. In most experiments in which sympathetic effects have been studied the circulation to the muscle involved must inevitably have been interfered with and in some of them this was actually demonstrated to be so. Thus it seems inevitable that large injections of adrenaline and high-frequency stimulation of the sympathetic must produce some of their effects secondarily by their action on the local circulation. But there is probably also a direct action on the spindle afferent endings themselves though it has not yet proved possible to explore this in any detail. Nor has the action of the sympathetic on the strength, speed and fatigueability of intrafusal contraction been studied, though an action on intrafusal muscle would seem as likely as one on the afferent endings. The physiological significance of any direct intrafusal sympathetic action remains quite uncertain, and it should be remembered that the sympathetic fibres to the spindle probably end largely on blood vessels rather than the intrafusal fibres or the sensory endings. In man, adrenaline has been suggested to 'sensitise' spindles thereby increasing the degree of spontaneous tremor and their sensitivity to vibration (Hodgson, Marsden & Meadows, 1969). In any case, the long latency of the effects of sympathetic stimulation so far described shows that the sympathetic can take no part in the moment-to-moment regulation of the spindle afferent discharge and so it cannot subserve functions similar to those of the normal fusimotor fibres.

Selective paralysis of small nerve fibres by local anaesthetics. Gasser & Erlanger showed long ago (1929) by recording compound action potentials that small nerve fibres are rather more susceptible to local anaesthetics than large nerve fibres. They did not, however, find an absolute separation of sensitivity with fibre size and this has been the experience of many since. Leksell (1945) later demonstrated that, as might be expected, the γ fibres are somewhat more sensitive than the α motor fibres to ethocaine applied to a peripheral nerve, for in the few cases tested 'the effect upon the gamma wave was greater than the effect upon the alpha wave'. This was confirmed by Matthews & Rushworth (1957, 1958) who showed further that their particular method of applying procaine to a nerve to a single muscle produced a reasonably complete differential action. For an appreciable time, as the nerve was slowly narcotised, virtually all the γ fibres were blocked before any significant number of α motor or group I afferent fibres were affected. They then used this selectivity to study the role of the γ efferents in the development of the enhanced stretch reflex of the decerebrate cat, and the method has been employed again more recently to try to elucidate the contribution provided by the group II spindle afferents (see Fig. 8.12). By careful adjustment of the concentration of procaine applied to a severed ventral root Nathan & Sears (1961) were also able to produce a stable and complete block of γ efferent fibres without interfering with the conduction of the α motor fibres; this was achieved with concentrations of procaine around 0·05%. A fairly high degree of selectivity in the acute paralysis of γ fibres has also been described on applying phenol or sodium deficient solutions to ventral roots (Iggo & Walsh, 1960; Nathan & Sears, 1960, 1962). Phenol and ethyl alcohol both also produce a chronic damage to nerve fibres which again affects γ fibres more than α fibres, thereby offering scope for their therapeutic use to relieve spasticity, etc. (Nathan, Sears & Smith, 1965; Tardieu, Tardieu, Hariga, Gagnard & Joly, 1962; Hariga, 1966).

Thus there seems little doubt that with appropriate attention to experimental detail γ fibres can be blocked largely independently of α fibres and Group I afferents, thereby providing yet another pharmacological method for investigating fusimotor function. Unfortunately, however, the diameters of the static and dynamic fusimotor fibres overlap too greatly for them to be expected to be differentially affected. The most straightforward use of anaesthetic blocks is to help distinguish between α and γ spikes in a mixed recording taken simultaneously from a number of active units in a nerve filament (see p. 511). It has also been used to help attribute increases in spindle firing, that occur during contraction of a muscle, to a genuine increase in fusimotor discharge, for example during breathing (Fig. 10.9). In addition, on studying the more intact animal it offers a way of attempting to assess the role of the

γ fibres in mediating a movement or in the genesis of some pathological symptom, such as the increased tone of the decerebrate
cat and many human patients.

A difficulty in using local anaesthetics for some of these purposes,
however, is that when the γ fibres are blocked then almost inevitably a number of other small fibres of quite different function
must also be blocked. A particular difficulty is provided by the
spindle Group II fibres. Thus additional evidence is required
before any particular effect can be confidently attributed to fusimotor paralysis. Moreover, there is no reason to believe that the
indiscriminate application of narcotising agents to nerves, in
any concentration and in any manner, will automatically ensure a
period of selective paralysis of the γ efferents along with other
small fibres. What happens in any particular type of experiment
requires to be established by suitably direct experiment. Among
other things, the more rapid is a block the less likely it is to be
selective. A slow block of a thin nerve probably exposes all its
fibres to a uniform slow increase in the concentration of anaesthetic,
as the drug slowly diffuses across the nerve sheath. This should
help allow slight differences in the absolute sensitivities of different
fibres to manifest themselves. A rapid block of a large nerve trunk
with internal diffusion barriers is likely to expose nerve fibres in
different places to different concentrations of anaesthetic, with a
corresponding loss of any selectivity based on fibre size and absolute
sensitivity. Other factors are probably also important, such as the
length of nerve narcotised. In man, Gassel & Diamantopoulos
(1964) obtained indirect evidence that the injection of 1% procaine with adrenaline into the sciatic nerve blocked Group I
afferents before the α motor fibres, although they would be expected to be if anything the larger. In the cat, the relative sensitivity
to blocking by cold of α motor fibres and Group I afferents may
vary from preparation to preparation, the former sometimes being
appreciably the more sensitive (Douglas & Malcolm, 1955).
Cooling also has often been considered to produce a selective block
of smaller medullated fibres, including the γ efferents, but Paintal
(1965) has attributed this merely to the difficulty in detecting
their compound action potential when it has been dispersed
as a result of a slowing of conduction produced by the
cooling.

Another difficulty with the use of blocking methods of any kind is that they interfere with the transmission of high-frequency trains of impulses before they prevent the transmission of single impulses or those discharged at a low frequency (i.e. Wedensky inhibition). This means that when a block is employed to interfere with natural discharges those fibres which normally fire at a high frequency, such as the Ia fibres, may be paralysed for all practical purposes before smaller and intrinsically more susceptible fibres which happen to be discharging slowly. Thus the use of local anaesthetics to paralyse γ efferents provides a unique tool for investigating fusimotor function, but one which requires to be used with caution.

Résumé of fusimotor actions

The establishment of the γ efferents as fusimotor. The first major step in achieving physiological understanding was the use of experimental methods to establish that the small motor fibres in somatic nerves are devoted to supplying the muscle spindles. In modern jargon this is expressed by saying that the γ efferents are exclusively fusimotor. This may be demonstrated by exciting γ motor fibres without α motor fibres and showing firstly, that this produces no detectable contraction of the muscle as a whole, and secondly that it does produce an increase in the spindle afferent discharge. The only really reliable way of doing this is to isolate single γ motor fibres by splitting down ventral root filaments and to record the discharge of single spindle afferent fibres from dorsal root filaments. Such experiments have amply demonstrated that the γ efferents are indeed purely fusimotor. However, as is usual in the advance of science, the same conclusion was initially reached on the basis of evidence that was slightly less cogent. In the earlier experiments the large and small motor fibres were excited together by stimulating the whole of a ventral root, and the large fibres were then prevented from influencing the muscle by applying a selective pressure block to the muscle nerve. Small nerve fibres have a higher electrical threshold than large ones and so cannot be directly excited on their own, but fortunately they are the less susceptible to pressure. Such selective activation of the γ efferents in the mass produced no significant contraction of the muscle studied, but it did increase its afferent discharge as was shown by the diphasic recording of multi-unit discharges via electrodes placed on the intact muscle nerve.

The subdivision of the γ efferents into static and dynamic fusimotor fibres. With the histological recognition of two kinds of intrafusal muscle fibre it became natural to enquire whether they were separately innervated and thus whether the fusimotor fibres could be subdivided into two kinds. This led to the discovery of the so-called static and dynamic fusimotor fibres. These have long been generally accepted to be reliably separable on functional criteria, even though there has been a continuing controversy as to precisely how they operate within the spindle to achieve their separate actions. As discussed in Chap. 6 it seems likely that they do this simply by supplying one or other of the two kinds of intrafusal fibre, just as was originally suggested on their discovery. But whether or not this is so is immaterial for the description of their rather different actions which comprises most of the present chapter.

The two kinds of fibre were first separated by means of their different actions on the response of a primary ending to a ramp stretch of large extent. This entailed the usual stimulation of a single γ efferent fibre while recording from a single Ia afferent fibre. The primary ending normally shows a pattern of firing at the beginning and end of the dynamic phase of the stretch which may be attributed to its being sensitive to the instantaneous value of the velocity of stretching as well as to the instantaneous value of the length. The dynamic fibres enhance this dynamic responsiveness of the primary ending, whereas the static fibres depress it. More specifically, the stimulation of a dynamic fibre increases the dynamic index of a primary ending for any particular velocity of stretching while stimulation of a static fibre decreases the dynamic index (the dynamic index is the fall in the discharge frequency which occurs in the first 0·5 sec on reaching the final extension). However, under static conditions the two kinds of fusimotor fibre have very similar excitatory actions on the primary ending. A given fusimotor fibre always produces an action of the same type irrespective of the frequency of stimulation, the length of the muscle, or the velocity of stretching. Only rarely is there any difficulty about allocating an individual fusimotor fibre to one or other subgroup.

It is especially important that when several primary endings can be studied which are all excited by any one particular fusimotor fibre then they are all found to be influenced in the same way, whether static or dynamic. As there is only one primary ending in any particular muscle spindle this provides one of the most cogent arguments available that the classification is physiologically significant, for it proves that a given fusimotor fibre has a static or dynamic specificity by virtue of its own right, rather than by virtue of some chance relation that it enters into with one particular spindle. This functional specificity is not, however, matched by any gross anatomical difference between the two kinds of nerve fibre where they run in the main nerve trunk. The conduction velocities of the two kinds of fibre overlap to a very high degree, though for some muscles the majority of the slow γ fibres have a static action.

Further differences between the actions of static and dynamic fibres. A good many other differences have now been established between the actions of the two kinds of fusimotor fibre and are important both for thinking about their mode of action within the spindle and also for understanding their physiological role in the body. These differences are summarised in Table 5.1 on p. 224 and will also be briefly reiterated here.

The secondary afferent ending is found to be exclusively influenced by static fibres. Stimulation of static fibres has regularly been found to have an action on the secondary ending rather like their action on the primary ending, namely to excite an increased afferent discharge while leaving the ending largely unresponsive to dynamic stimuli. Stimulation of dynamic fibres does not excite the secondary ending even when the particular dynamic fibre stimulated can be shown to be causing an intrafusal contraction in the very muscle spindle in which the secondary studied happens to lie.

In the absence of fusimotor activity the primary ending normally falls silent at the very beginning of the release of a ramp stretch of large extent. Static fusimotor stimulation has been found to counteract such silence very much more effectively than does dynamic stimulation.

Sinusoidal stretching of large amplitude applied during fusimotor stimulation evokes the responses from the primary ending which would be expected on the basis of its response to ramp stretches. Thus dynamic fusimotor stimulation enhances the response of the primary ending on the stretching phase of the cycle while leaving it silent on the releasing phase. Static fusimotor stimulation produces an increase in the mean frequency of firing of the ending but there is then comparatively little modulation of its discharge by the rhythmic stretching.

The response of the primary ending to sinusoidal stretching of small amplitude may be assessed by measuring its sensitivity, expressable in impulses sec^{-1} mm^{-1}, for each frequency of stretching. The stretching, however, must be of small enough amplitude for the ending to be behaving 'linearly'. During static fusimotor stimulation the sensitivity of the primary ending is rather low for frequencies of stretching between 0·5 and 5 Hz, and appreciably lower than for the same ending in the absence of fusimotor activity and with the muscle stretched taut. During dynamic fusimotor stimulation the primary ending manifests a high sensitivity over the same range of frequencies and over a wide range or muscle lengths; but, the sensitivity need then be no greater than that found in the passive spindle with the muscle well-stretched. Under all conditions the sensitivity of the primary ending increases progressively as the frequency of cyclic stretching is increased above 1–2 Hz. However, above about 5 Hz the increase is much more rapid during static than during dynamic fusimotor stimulation. As a result, at frequencies of 100 Hz and above the sensitivity of the primary ending is similarly high during stimulation of either kind of fusimotor fibre. In line with this it has been found that stimulation of either kind of fusimotor fibre lowers the threshold amplitude required for high-frequency vibration to 'drive' the ending, and elicit one spike on each cycle of vibration.

The 'position-sensitivity' of an ending may be defined as the slope of the relation between its frequency of firing and the applied extension when the measurements are made under static conditions. For no apparent rhyme or reason stimulation of static fusimotor fibres sometimes does, and sometimes does not, increase the value for primary endings. The value for secondary endings, however, is usually increased. Dynamic fusimotor stimulation never appreciably increases the true position-sensitivity measured under static conditions, but it regularly increases the value of the similar measure made during slow stretching of a muscle.

Speed of intrafusal actions of static and dynamic fibres. This may be indirectly judged from the time-course of the change in afferent discharge produced by fusimotor stimulation. The system supplied by the static fibres then appears to be appreciably faster in its action than is that supplied by the dynamic fibres. This is indicated in the first place by the finding that stimulation of static fibres not infrequently evokes 'driving' of the primary ending so that it discharges an afferent spike for each fusimotor impulse. Driving has never yet been observed on stimulation of a dynamic fusimotor fibre. A rapid intrafusal contraction would appear to be a pre-requisite for driving to occur, as driving probably depends upon a slightly oscillatory intrafusal contraction. In the absence of driving, the primary afferent response to a period of fusimotor stimulation starts and stops more abruptly on stimulating a static fibre than it does on stimulating a dynamic fibre. This is clearly shown in the method of graphic averaging which passes under the name of a 'frequencygram'. A frequencygram is produced by superimposing successive responses to the same stimulus on a storage oscilloscope while using it to display 'instantaneous frequency'. In addition, it is then found that the 'fusion frequency' at which the responses lose their fluctuations in time with the stimulus is usually appreci-ably higher on static than on dynamic fusimotor stimulation. Even so, similarly high frequencies of stimulation of the two kinds of fusimotor fibre are required to produce a maximal excitatory effect on the primary ending and these frequencies are far above the 'fusion frequency' of the dynamic fibres.

In line with the relative slowness of their action the dynamic fibres have been found to act by means of local potentials which do not propagate along the intrafusal fibres concerned. This is shown by the simple monophasic form of the intrafusal potentials set up by stimulating a single dynamic fibre and recorded with extracellular electrodes. In contrast, on occasion static fibres have been shown to elicit all-or-none potentials which then propagate along part of the length of the intrafusal fibre. This has been demonstrated using both intracellular and extracellular recording. Whether static fibres are always incapable of influencing the con-tractile machinery by local potentials is another matter, and would not presently appear to admit of a definite answer.

Skeleto-fusimotor or β fibres. That these may exist in the mammal as well as in amphibia and reptiles has now been established by physiological as well as by anatomical methods. The only currently reliable physiological way of proving their existence is to isolate single motor fibres and show that their stimulation produces both an extrafusal contraction and an excitatory action on a spindle afferent ending. And, moreover, the excitatory action requires to be established as genuinely due to an intrafusal contraction rather than to an adventitious effect of the extrafusal contraction. This can be done either by demonstrating that the action on the spindle is more resistant to curare-like drugs than is the extrafusal contraction, or by demonstrating that the maximal effect on the ending is produced by an appreciably higher frequency of stimulation than that required to produce a maximal extrafusal contraction. All this has been achieved for the lumbrical muscles of the cat and of the rabbit. In the cat lumbrical, all the β fibres have proved to have a dynamic action and to be additional to perfectly normal static and dynamic fusimotor fibres of γ conduction velocity supplying the same spindles; moreover, the β fibres are not invariably present. In the rabbit lumbrical, some β fibres have a static action and some have a dynamic action, and as yet no purely fusimotor fibres have been isolated. Thus it has been tentatively suggested that the rabbit lumbrical may have dispensed with specialised fusimotor fibres. Other muscles of the rabbit, however, possess static and dynamic fibres which are purely fusimotor and which are quite typical of those found in the cat.

It remains undecided whether the large limb muscles are significantly supplied by β fibres as well as by pure fusimotor fibres of γ velocity. The present uncertainty arises largely because the methods which have just been described are not nearly as easy to apply to large muscles as they are to small ones. The existence of pure fusimotor fibres of α velocity does, however, appear to have been largely excluded. There has been a good deal of work attempting to establish the presence of a β innervation of large muscles by analysing the 'early discharge' or by looking for spindle afferent firing on the rising phase of a twitch contraction. The early discharge is a brief burst of impulses which sometimes occurs at the foot of the twitch contraction of a muscle elicited by stimulating its nerve. On classical ideas the spindle should be silent both before and during the rising phase of an extrafusal contraction, since it lies 'in parallel' with the main muscle fibres and so should be unloaded by their contraction. There is thus a tendency to attribute any spindle firing during and just before a twitch to the occurrence of a concomitant intrafusal contraction which overcomes the unloading. Unfortunately, however, things are not so simple in practice and such findings would appear to be inconclusive in the attempt to decide either for or against the existence of a β innervation in any particular case.

Drugs. The action of certain drugs provides a useful tool for analysing various aspects of fusimotor function. Suxamethonium has a powerful excitatory action on primary endings and a weaker one on secondary endings. It probably does this by causing an intrafusal contraction, particularly of the nuclear bag fibres.

The injection of curarising agents into the whole animal blocks the end-plates of both the static and the dynamic fusimotor fibres somewhat after it blocks the ordinary end-plates on extrafusal fibres; the static end-plates tend to be blocked slightly after the dynamic ones. These apparent differences in sensitivity to curarising agents may perhaps result from the differing ease of access of the drug to the various motor endings. After all the endings have been completely blocked they tend to recover in the same order as that in which they were originally paralysed (i.e. the last to block is also the last to recover).

Asphyxia has a mixture of excitatory and depressing effects on the primary ending. The most notable of these is that in the un-anaesthetised preparation the primary endings may discharge 'spontaneously' at several hundred impulses/sec just before they fail altogether; such discharges are not seen in the anaesthetised animal. Adrenaline and sympathetic stimulation also produce a mixture of excitatory and depressing effects. As yet it is unresolved as to how far these effects represent a secondary action of asphyxia resulting from an interference with the local circulation, and how far a genuine action of catecholamines on the sense endings or on the intrafusal muscle fibres.

Local anaesthetic applied to a muscle nerve in an appropriate manner will paralyse the γ efferent fibres at a time when the α motor fibres and the group I afferent fibres are still conducting normally. Such selectivity, however, does not apparently necessarily result from the application of local anaesthetic to a nerve in any manner and in any concentration.

References

Adal, M. N. & Barker, D. (1965a). Intramuscular branching of fusimotor fibres. *J. Physiol.* **177**, 288–299.   [234, 236]

— (1965b). Motor supply to hindlimb muscles of the cat and rabbit. *J. Anat.* **99**, 918–919.   [237]

Andersson, B. F., Lennerstrand, G. & Thoden, U. (1968). Response characteristics of muscle spindle endings at constant length to variations in fusimotor activation. *Acta physiol. scand.* **74**, 301–318.   [222]

Appelberg, B., Bessou, P. & Laporte, Y. (1966). Action of static and dynamic fusimotor fibres on secondary endings of cat's spindles. *J. Physiol.* **185**, 160–171.   [208, 209, 225]

Bessou, P., Emonet-Dénand, F. & Laporte, Y. (1965). Motor fibres innervating extrafusal and intrafusal muscle fibres in the cat. *J. Physiol.* **180**, 649–672.   [208, 234–237, 244]

Bessou, P. & Laporte, Y. (1965). Potentials fusoriaux provoqués par la stimulation de fibres fusimotorices chez le chat. *C.r. Séanc. Acad. Sci., Paris* **260**, 4827–4830.   [231, 232]

— (1966). Observations on static fusimotor fibres. In *Muscular Afferents and Motor Control*, ed. Granit, R. pp. 81–89. Stockholm: Almqvist & Wiksell.   [233]

Bessou, P., Laporte, Y. & Pagès, B. (1966). Similitude des effets (statiques ou dynamiques) exercés par des fibres fusimotrices uniques sur les terminaisons primaires de plusieurs fuseaux chez le chat. *J. Physiol.* (*Paris*) **58**, 31–39.   [208]

— (1968). Frequencygrams of spindle primary endings elicited by stimulation of static and dynamic fusimotor fibres. *J. Physiol.* **196**, 47–63.   [226–231]

— (1970). Phénomènes de facilitation temporelle observés au niveau des synapses des fibres fusimotrices statiques, chez le chat. *C.r. hebd. Séanc. Acad. Sci., Paris* **271D**, 2145–2148.   [230]

Bessou, P. & Pagès, B. (1969a). Spindle secondary ending responses elicited by stimulation of static fusimotor axons. *J. Physiol.* **202**, 569–584.   [229–233]

— (1969b). Intracellular recording from spindle muscle fibres of potentials elicited by static fusimotor axons in the cat. *Life Sci., Oxford* **8**, 417–419.   [233]

Brown, M. C., Crowe, A. & Matthews, P. B. C. (1965). Observations on the fusimotor fibres of the tibialis posterior muscle of the cat. *J. Physiol.* **177**, 140–159.   [203, 208, 209, 220–223, 237]

Brown, M. C., Engberg, I. & Matthews, P. B. C. (1967). Fusimotor stimulation and the dynamic sensitivity of the secondary ending of the muscle spindle. *J. Physiol.* **189**, 545–550.   [210, 222]

— (1968). The relative sensitivity to vibration of muscle receptors in the cat. *J. Physiol.* **192**, 773–800.   [216, 217]

Brown, M. C., Lawrence, D. G. & Matthews, P. B. C. (1969). Static fusimotor fibres and the position-sensitivity of muscle spindle receptors. *Brain. Res.* **14**, 173–187. [218]

Brown, M. C. & Matthews, P. B. C. (1960). The effect on a muscle twitch of the back-response of its motor fibres. *J. Physiol.* **150**, 332–346. [197, 239]

— (1966). On the subdivision of the efferent fibres to muscle spindles into static and dynamic fusimotor fibres. In *Control and Innervation of Skeletal Muscle*, ed. Andrew, B. L. pp. 18–31. Dundee: Thomson. [206]

Carli, G., Diete-Spiff, K. & Pompeiano, O. (1967). Mechanisms of muscle spindle excitation. *Archs ital. Biol.* **105**, 273–289. [244]

Crowe, A. (1968). A mechanical model of the mammalian muscle spindle. *J. theor. Biol.* **21**, 21–41. [220]

Crowe, A. & Matthews, P. B. C. (1964a). The effects of stimulation of static and dynamic fusimotor fibres on the response to stretching of the primary endings of muscle spindles. *J. Physiol.* **174**, 109–131. [205, 207, 213–219]

— (1964b). Further studies of static and dynamic fusimotor fibres. *J. Physiol.* **175**, 132–151. [208, 212, 217] 222, 223]

Douglas, W. W. & Malcolm, J. L. (1955). The effect of localised cooling on conduction in cat nerves. *J. Physiol.* **130**, 53–71. [250]

Eccles, J. C. & Sherrington, C. S. (1930). Numbers and contraction-values of individual motor units examined in some muscles of the limb. *Proc. R. Soc.* B **106**, 326–357. [196, 204]

Emonet-Dénand, F. & Houk, J. (1968). Étude comparative de la curarisation des synapses neuromusculaires des fibres fusimotrices γ dynamiques et statiques, chez le chat. *J. Physiol., Paris* **60**, 367–372. [244, 245]

Emonet-Dénand, F., Jankowska, E. & Laporte, Y. (1970). Skeleto-fusimotor fibres in the rabbit. *J. Physiol.* **210**, 669–680. [237, 241]

Emonet-Dénand, F., Joffroy, M. & Laporte, Y. (1971). Absence d'axones α exclusivement fusimoteurs dans les muscles prétibiaux du chat. *J. Physiol., Paris.* **63**, 46A. [241]

Emonet-Dénand, F. & Laporte, Y. (1969). Frequencygrams of rabbit spindle primary endings elicited by stimulation of fusimotor fibres. *J. Physiol.* **201**, 673–684. [227, 228]

Emonet-Dénand, F., Laporte, Y. & Pagès, B. (1966). Fibres fusimotrices statiques et fibres fusimotrices dynamiques chez le lapin. *Archs ital. Biol.* **104**, 195–213. [208, 220, 237]

Eyzaguirre, C. (1960a). The electrical activity of mammalian intrafusal fibres. *J. Physiol.* **150**, 169–185. [231, 244]

— (1960b). The motor regulation of mammalian spindle discharges. *J. Physiol.* **150**, 186–200. [230, 231]

Fehr, H. U. (1965). Activation by suxamethonium of primary and secondary endings of the same de-efferented muscle spindle during static stretch. *J. Physiol.* **178**, 98–110. [243]

Gassel, M. M. & Diamantopoulos, E. (1964). The effect of procaine nerve block on neuromuscular reflex regulation in man. *Brain* **87,** 729–742.
[250]

Gasser, H. S. & Erlanger, J. (1929). The role of fibre size in the establishment of a nerve block by pressure or cocaine. *Am. J. Physiol.* **88,** 581–591.
[248]

Goodwin, G. M. & Matthews, P. B. C. (1971). Effects of fusimotor stimulation on the sensitivity of muscle spindle endings to small-amplitude sinusoidal stretching. *J. Physiol.* **218,** 56–58P.
[213]

Granit, R. & Henatsch, H. D. (1956). Gamma control of dynamic properties of muscle spindles. *J. Neurophysiol.* **19,** 356–366.
[216]

Granit, R., Homma, S. & Matthews, P. B. C. (1959). Prolonged changes in the discharge of mammalian muscle spindles following tendon taps or muscle twitches. *Acta physiol. scand.* **46,** 185–193.
[244]

Granit, R., Pompeiano, O. & Waltman, B. (1959a). Fast supraspinal control of mammalian muscle spindles: extra- and intrafusal co-activation. *J. Physiol.* **147,** 385–398.
[240]

— (1959b). The early discharge of mammalian muscle spindles at onset of contraction. *J. Physiol.* **147,** 399–418.
[239]

Granit, R., Skoglund, S. & Thesleff, S. (1953). Activation of muscle spindles by succinylcholine and decamethonium. The effect of curare. *Acta physiol. scand.* **28,** 134–151.
[243]

Haase, J. & Schlegel, H. J. (1966). Einige funktionelle Merkmale von α-innervierten Extensor- und Flexor-Spindeln der Katze. *Pflügers Arch. ges. Physiol.* **287,** 163–175.
[240]

Häggqvist, G. (1940). A contribution to the question of nervous and muscular substratum of the muscle tone. *Acta med. scand.* **104,** 8–20.
[201]

Hariga, J. (1966). Influences sur la motricité de la suppression des effecteurs gamma par alcoolisation des nerfs peripheriques. Thesis. Brussels: Acta Medica Belgica.
[249]

Harvey, R. J. & Matthews, P B. C. (1961a). Some effects of stimulation of the muscle nerve on afferent endings of muscle spindles, and the classification of their responses into types A1 and A2. *J. Physiol.* **156,** 470–497.
[196, 199, 200]

— (1961b). The response of de-efferented muscle spindles endings in the cat's soleus to slow extension of the muscle. *J. Physiol.* **157,** 370–392.
[218]

Henatsch, H. D. (1962). Effects of chemically excited muscle spindles on spinal motoneurones in cats. In *Symposium on Muscle Receptors*, ed. Barker, D. pp. 67–80. Hong Kong: Hong Kong University Press.
[243]

Hinsey, J. C. (1927). Some observations on the innervation of skeletal muscle of cat. *J. comp. Neurol.* **44,** 87–195.
[196]

Hodgson, H. J. F., Marsden, C. D. & Meadows, J. C. (1969). The effect of adrenaline on the response to muscle vibration in man. *J. Physiol.* **202,** 98P.
[248]

Hunt, C. C. & Kuffler, S. W. (1951a). Further study of efferent small-nerve fibres to mammalian muscle spindles. Multiple spindle innervation and activity during contraction. *J. Physiol.* **113**, 283–297. [203]

— (1951b). Stretch receptor discharges during muscle contraction. *J. Physiol.* **113**, 298–315. [196, 238, 239]

Iggo, A. & Walsh, E. G. (1960). Selective block of small fibres in the spinal roots by phenol. *Brain* **83**, 701–708. [249]

Jansen, J. K. S. & Matthews, P. B. C. (1962a). The central control of the dynamic response of muscle spindle receptors. *J. Physiol.* **161**, 357–378. [205]

— (1962b). The effects of fusimotor activity on the static responsiveness of primary and secondary endings of muscle spindles in the decerebrate cat. *Acta physiol. scand.* **55**, 376–386. [218]

Kidd, G. L. (1964). Excitation of primary muscle spindle endings by β-axon stimulation. *Nature, Lond.* **203**, 1248–1251. [237]

Kidd, G. L. & Kučera, J. (1969). The excitation by suxamethonium of non-proprioceptive afferents from caudal muscles of the rat. *Experientia* **25**, 158–160. [243]

Kuffler, S. W. & Hunt, C. C. (1952). The mammalian small-nerve fibres; a system for efferent nervous regulation of muscle spindle discharge. *Res. Publs Ass. Res. nerv. ment. Dis.* **30**, 24–37. [203]

Kuffler, S. W., Hunt, C. C. & Quilliam, J. P. (1951). Function of medullated small-nerve fibres in mammalian ventral roots: efferent muscle spindle innervation. *J. Neurophysiol.* **14**, 29–54. [198, 201–204, 231]

Leksell, L. (1945). The action potential and excitatory effects of the small ventral root fibres to skeletal muscle. *Acta physiol. scand.* **10**, Suppl. 31, 1–84. [196–201, 239, 248]

Lennerstrand, G. & Thoden, U. (1968a). Position and velocity sensitivity of muscle spindles in the cat. II. Dynamic fusimotor single-fibre activation of primary endings. *Acta physiol. scand.* **74**, 16–29. [219–222]

— (1968b). Position and velocity sensitivity of muscle spindles in the cat. III. Static fusimotor single-fibre activation of primary and secondary endings. *Acta physiol. scand.* **74**, 30–49. [218–220]

— (1968c). Muscle spindle responses to concomitant variations in length and in fusimotor activation. *Acta physiol. scand.* **74**, 153–165. [211, 220]

Matthews, B. H. C. (1933). Nerve endings in mammalian muscle. *J. Physiol.* **78**, 1–53. [196, 202, 246, 247]

Matthews, P. B. C. (1962). The differentiation of two types of fusimotor fibre by their effects on the dynamic response of muscle spindle primary endings. *Q. Jl. exp. Physiol.* **47**, 324–333. [206, 225]

— (1964). Muscle spindles and their motor control. *Physiol. Rev.* **44**, 219–288. [240, 242]

Matthews, P. B. C. & Rushworth, G. (1957). The relative sensitivity of muscle nerve fibres to procaine. *J. Physiol.* **135**, 263–269. [249]

— (1958). The discharge from muscle spindles as an indicator of γ efferent paralysis by procaine. *J. Physiol.* **140**, 421–426. [249]

Nathan, P. W. & Sears, T. A. (1960). Effects of phenol on nervous conduction. *J. Physiol.* **150**, 565–580. [249]

Nathan, P. W. and Sears, T. A. (1961). Some factors concerned in differential nerve block by local anaesthetics. *J. Physiol.* **157**, 565–580.
[249]

— (1962). Differential nerve block by sodium-free and sodium-deficient solutions. *J. Physiol.* **164**, 375–394.   [249]

Nathan, P. W., Sears, T. A. & Smith, M. C. (1965). Effects of phenol solutions on the nerve roots of the cat: an electrophysiological study. *J. neurol. Sci.* **2**, 7–29.   [249]

O'Leary, J., Heinbecker, P. & Bishop, G. H. (1935). Analysis of function of a nerve to a muscle. *Am. J. Physiol.* **110**, 636–658.   [196]

Pagès, B. & Proske, U. (1970). Effect of halothane anaesthesia on responses from primary endings of muscle spindles in the cat. *Expl. Neurol.* **28**, 393–402.   [246]

Paintal, A. S. (1964). Effects of drugs on vertebrate mechanoreceptors. *Pharmac. Rev.* **16**, 341–380.   [242, 246, 247]

— (1965). Block of conduction in mammalian myelinated nerve fibres by low temperatures. *J. Physiol.* **180**, 1–19.   [250]

Rutledge, L. T. & Haase, J. (1961). Flexor muscle spindles and reflex firing of early discharging units. *J. Neurophysiol.* **24**, 182–192. [240]

Smith, C. M. (1963). Neuromuscular pharmacology: Drugs and muscle spindles. *Annu. Rev. Pharmacol.* **3**, 223–242.   [242]

Smith, R. S. (1966). Properties of intrafusal muscle fibres. In *Muscular Afferents and Motor Control*, ed. Granit, R. pp. 69–80. Stockholm: Almqvist & Wiksell.   [243]

Tardieu, G., Tardieu, C., Hariga, J., Gagnard, L. & Joly, C. (1962). Action des infiltrations nerveuses d'alcool dilué sur diverses raideurs d'origine cérébrale. *Bull. Mém. Soc. med. Hôp. Paris* **113**, 7–12.   [249]

Tower, S. H. (1932). Atrophy and degeneration in the muscle-spindle. *Brain* **55**, 77–90.   [196]

Voorhoeve, P. E. & Verhey, B. A. (1963). Pre- and post-synaptic effects on fusimotor and alpha motoneurones of the cat upon activation of muscle spindle afferents by succinylcholine. *Acta physiol. pharmacol. néerl.* **12**, 12–22.   [243]

Whitteridge, D. (1959). The effect of stimulation of intrafusal muscle fibres on sensitivity to stretch of extraocular muscle spindles. *Q. Jl. exp. Physiol.* **55**, 385–393.   [218]

Zimmerman, G. W. & Grossie, J. (1969). Sensitivity and behaviour of muscle spindles to systemic arterial hypoxia. *Proc. Soc. exp. Biol. Med.* **132**, 1114–1118.   [246]

6

POSSIBLE MODES OF THE INTERNAL FUNCTIONING OF THE MUSCLE SPINDLE

SPECULATION on the internal working of the spindle might appear to have become a sterile exercise now that methods are to hand for the direct study of the isolated spindle and the work has begun. As yet, however, the experimental results obtained on the isolated spindle are insufficient to provide a full understanding and so need to be supplemented by indirect evidence and somewhat hypothetical arguments. It is to be hoped that such discussion will lead to an elucidation of the problems in principle and help to direct attention to the things which demand direct measurement, some of which might otherwise have tended to be overlooked in the complexity of experimentation. But the immediate future belongs to the experimentalist rather than the theoretician and much that follows may shortly be expected to be replaced by more exact knowledge.

The problem of the origin of the different types of behaviour shown by primary and secondary spindle endings

As already described in some detail (Chap. 4) the same stimuli lead to quite different patterns of firing of the primary and secondary endings of the spindle. It is natural to enquire how this comes about, and whether the differences can be attributed to any particular one of the links lying between the mechanical stimulus and the resulting afferent response. According to current ideas these links are as follows: extension applied to whole muscle—extension applied to whole spindle—stretching of those parts of the intrafusal fibres on which the sensory endings lie—deformation of the sensory terminals—membrane 'mechano-electric' transduction producing a generator current leading to a receptor potential—initiation of action potentials at one or more pacemaker regions, possibly after electrotonic spread of the potential from the transducer region to the pacemaker region (location unknown)—propagation of impulses into the main afferent fibre. Further subdivisions can be suggested but become progressively less amenable to experimental analysis. Figure 6.1 summarises a slightly simplified version of the present scheme.

For many stimuli the waveform of the neural output from the secondary ending is reasonably close to that of the mechanical input. In this case, therefore, each link in the chain may be presumed to transmit the stimulus waveform relatively unchanged

A. The problem - the patterns of afferent response

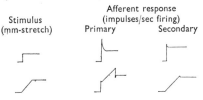

B. Possible solutions - sites at which 'adaptation' might occur

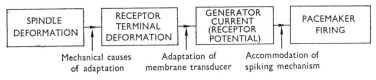

FIG. 6.1. Some of the intrafusal sites at which adaptation and hence velocity sensitivity might arise.

to the next element downstream. In amplifier terminology, each link must have a frequency–response curve that is relatively flat from d.c. (0 Hz) up to all frequencies of reasonable power contained in the Fourier expansion of the stimulus waveform. Alternatively, a distortion introduced by one link might be compensated by an inverse distortion produced by another link. The output of the primary ending is, however, strikingly different from that of the input for a wide range of stimuli. This is described physiologically by saying that the ending is highly dynamically sensitive, as well as responding to steady length changes. The same idea can be put slightly more formally by saying that under many circumstances and for large stimuli the primary ending responds to a combination of the instantaneous values of the length and the velocity components of a stimulus, and possibly also to any acceleration components. For an ending to behave in this way one or more of the causal linking mechanisms must act on the stimulus waveform to perform a first order differentiation, and perhaps also a second order one, and add the result to the undistorted waveform. In amplifier terminology, one of the links must have a 'corner frequency' above which the gain increases with frequency while remaining constant below this so as to retain a static response for the ending. Most physical systems for producing such a transformation of the transmitted signal introduce some delay, so that any velocity or acceleration response superimposed on the basic length response will rise and fall smoothly rather than instantaneously.

Any dynamically sensitive system when presented with a step input (sudden stretch) will give a response which rises rapidly to a peak and then decays more or less slowly to a pleateau level, as does the primary ending. Such slow decay observed physiologically is usually called 'adaptation' which may be seen simply as a way of referring to the behaviour of a dynamically sensitive ending when presented with one particular kind of input. Thus the search for the origin of dynamic sensitivity is the same as the search for the causes of receptor adaptation. Put in these terms it can be seen that dynamic sensitivity may have more than one cause, for some degree of adaptation might be expected to occur at each of the links of the chain shown in Fig. 6.1. The question thus becomes whether one or other of the links is of predominant importance for the transformation of the range of stimuli of physiological interest. There is no final answer to this question, but it will be presently argued that variations in the viscoelastic properties of the intrafusal muscle fibres along their length play an important part in determining the difference in velocity sensitivity shown to large stimuli by the primary and secondary endings of the mammalian spindle. Moreover, it seems likely that the static and dynamic fusimotor fibres produce their physiologically important effects as much by altering the mechanical properties of the intrafusal fibres as by causing a frank intrafusal shortening.

Methods of investigation illustrated by the study of the Pacinian corpuscle

Experiments on the Pacinian corpuscle have established the principle that the adaptation of a mechanoreceptor may be partly determined by the mechanical properties of the tissues immediately related to the afferent nerve terminal, as well as by the properties of the nerve terminal itself. The body may thus reasonably be suspected to possess yet other sense endings embodying the same principle. The mechanical properties of the onion-like capsule of the corpuscle lead it to act as a high-pass filter and so to transmit mechanical transients but not steady states, and thus help to produce the notably rapid adaptation of the corpuscle as a whole. This was the first demonstrated by Hubbard (1958) who charted the position of the various capsular layers by flash photographs taken at a series of times after applying a sudden displacement to the outside of the corpuscle. Loewenstein & Mendelson (1965) later showed that after removal of virtually all the capsular lamellae a steady displacement elicited a receptor potential which lasted for some 70 msec instead of the normal 6 msec or so. This effect of removing the lamellae is illustrated in Fig. 6.2 and

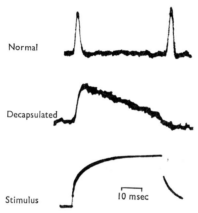

Normal

Decapsulated

Stimulus   10 msec

FIG. 6.2. The prolongation of the receptor potential of the Pacinian corpuscle produced by removing the majority of the concentric lamellae surrounding the nerve terminal (decapsulation). Decapsulation also abolishes the normal 'off response'. The potentials were recorded extracellulary and had a peak amplitude of about 100 μV. (Loewenstein & Mendelson, 1965, Fig. 2 re-arranged.)

proves that the possession of its capsule would force the Pacinian corpuscle to be rapidly adapting, whatever the properties of its transducer and pacemaker regions. This view was further substantiated by enclosing the desheathed corpuscle in an artificial capsule made of layers of frog mesentery separated by fluid when the normal rapid adaptation of the receptor potential was largely restored (for practical reasons the ending was enclosed between plates of mesentery rather than in a cylindrical spiral). In addition, Loewenstein & Skalak (1966) were able to develop an analytical model of the capsule by treating each lamella as an elastic element (spring) which was connected to the next lamella by a largely viscous element (dash-pot) which was presumed to correspond to the viscous forces developed by movement of the fluid between the layers on compressing the corpuscle. This model gave results which quite reasonably mimicked the behaviour of the ending.

However, the Pacinian corpuscle seems to be 'designed' in all respects as a rapidly adapting ending and removal of its capsule does not make it behave like a genuine slowly adapting receptor, such as the spindle secondary ending. In the first place, the desheathed receptor does not produce a really prolonged receptor potential on receipt of a steady stimulus, but one lasting only about 0·1 sec (Fig. 6.2). Possibly this residual adaptation is due to the action of any few remaining lamellae, but it seems more likely to depend upon adaptation in the transducer mechanism itself. In the second place, the somewhat prolonged receptor potential of the desheathed ending excites no more spikes than the one or two set up by the normal short receptor potential, thus suggesting that there is rapid accommodation of the pacemaker region to excitation by the generator potential. This was confirmed by stimulating the presumed pacemaker region with a steady current which again failed to elicit a significant number of impulses. Thus Loewenstein & Mendelson (1965) were led to conclude that the rapid adaptation of the Pacinian corpuscle had more than one cause.

All this leaves the matter open for the spindle, though *a priori* it would be surprising if its complicated mechanical structure had no part to play in determining its dynamic properties. It should be noted also that the velocity-sensitivity of the primary ending is not easily explained by accommodation of a pacemaker, because the ending would not then be expected to discharge steadily in response to a steady stimulus. However, description of the work on the Pacinian corpuscle has served to introduce the limited number of methods presently available for attempting to track down the sites of adaptation. These methods are: the optical study of the deformation actually applied to the terminals themselves and of the movements occurring at various points along the intrafusal bundle in response to various waveforms of stretching, the electrical recording of the receptor potential, and the direct stimulation of the pacemaker region by an extrinsically originating current. Together these should be sufficient to decide upon the origin of the velocity-sensitivity of the primary ending in terms of the scheme shown in Fig. 6.1. These methods with the supplementary recording of intrafusal tension have, however, yet to be systematically applied in the comparison of spindle primary and secondary endings.

Comparison of the response of spindle afferents to electrical and to mechanical stimulation

B. H. C. Matthews suggested long ago (1933, p. 14) that the high-frequency discharge of the spindle afferent endings which occurs during a rapid stretch might arise through 'the terminal portions of the structure on which the nerve ending was situated being more viscous than the centre' (i.e. that the poles of the intra-fusal fibres are more viscous than their nucleated equator), though other possibilities were also envisaged. Currently there is no doubt that, as with the Pacinian corpuscle, mechanical models could be developed which would be capable of explaining the entire range of behaviour of both kinds of spindle afferent ending. Such success in descriptive modelling would not, however, prove the validity of the model in terms of its working parts. This requires direct quantitative study of at least the various inter-mediate stages shown in Fig. 6.1, preferably combined with the simultaneous recording of the afferent discharge.

The first attempt to study the stimulus transformations occur-ring inside the mammalian spindle was made by Lippold, Nicholls & Redfearn (1960). They compared the adaptation of spindle afferents on exciting them with a sudden stretch, with that occurring on the sudden application of a steady current through electrodes lying over the supposed position of the spindle; the endings lay in the isolated tenuissimus muscle and were pre-sumably mostly primary endings though no attempt appears to have been made to identify them as such. The two modes of stimulation appeared to initiate spikes at the same pacemaker region, for when applied at the same time their effects summated. Lippold *et al.*'s most important finding, which is illustrated in Fig. 6.3, was that there was no sign of the usual initial rapid adaptation when the pacemaker was excited electrically though it occurred in the normal way when the spindle was excited mech-anically. The electrical current was presumed to activate the pace-maker directly, and so their results suggested that accommodation of the pacemaker region is unlikely to contribute to the initial adaptation occurring within the first second or so after the application of a stretch.

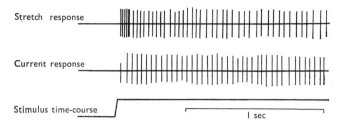

Stretch response

Current response

Stimulus time-course

1 sec

FIG. 6.3. The difference in adaptation shown by a muscle spindle afferent on exciting it mechanically by steady stretch and electrically by steady current. The spindle lay in the tenuissimus muscle of the cat which had been isolated from the body. (Lippold, Nichols & Redfearn, 1960, Fig. 4, traced. The unequal sizes of the different spikes has been preserved in the tracing, but not the gross thickening of the base line to which it was related.)

Unfortunately, the direct repetition of the above experiment on spindles in the same muscle, but *in situ* in the intact cat and with proven primary afferents, failed to give quite the same result. As illustrated in Fig. 6.4, Emonet-Dénand & Houk (1969) found that

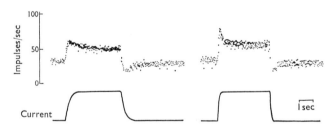

FIG. 6.4. Responses of a primary ending which showed some adaptation on excitation by a polarising current. The ending lay in the tenuissimus muscle which was *in situ* with an intact circulation. (Emonet-Dénand & Houk, 1969, Fig. 1, traced. This ending showed the most adaptation of all those that they studied.)

in their hands the afferent response elicited by a steady current might show some initial adaptation, though unfortunately they did not compare this with the adaptation produced by a mechanical stimulus of similar waveform. They also raised the question, to which there is so far no conclusive answer, as to whether excitation by current might not be partly mediated by an un-

observed intrafusal contraction instead of just by a direct activation of the pacemaker. In these circumstances it is perhaps best
to emphasise that Emonet-Dénand & Houk usually found relatively little adaptation to current and that 'for two receptors no
significant amount of adaptation was seen'.

Until more detailed experiments have been performed it may
thus reasonably be concluded that the typical dynamic sensitivity
of the primary ending is not essentially dependent upon pacemaker accommodation (which should manifest itself even if the
current acted partly on intrafusal fibres), though if any such
accommodation occurs it must presumably contribute to the
overall adaptation shown by the ending. At any rate, both the
studies with excitation by current have shown that it does produce
steady firing from the pacemaker regions of spindle afferents; this
contrasts with the behaviour of the Pacinian corpuscle afferent
and is a pre-requisite for a slowly adapting receptor. Lippold,
Nicholls & Redfearn (1960) also made extracellular recordings
of the receptor potential transmitted electrotonically into the
afferent fibre on mechanical stimulation of the spindle. They
found that it had an initial dynamic phase during the application
of the stretch, thereby confirming that mechanisms leading to
adaptation must exist at an earlier stage than the pacemaker. Thus,
on current evidence, any accommodation of the spindle afferent
pacemaker is unlikely to play a major part in producing the
adaptation shown by the whole ending in response to sudden
stretches.

Microscopic observation of the living spindle in the absence of intrafusal contraction

Direct microscopic observations of the displacements occurring
within the spindle on stretching were initiated by Smith (1966)
and have also been performed in some detail by Boyd (1966;
1971a) who has produced a commercially available film of his
preparation (1970). The method awaits yet further exploitation
to answer the present questions; this is simply because of the
technical difficulties involved. None the less, the present findings
have already shown that the viscoelastic properties of intrafusal
muscle fibres may differ at different points along their length in
the manner required to play a part in adaptation.

Smith (1966) isolated spindles from the rat lumbrical muscle so that they were free of the extrafusal muscle fibres along most of their length; but they were presumed to be in a relatively normal state because the intrafusal fibres remained contractile. He photographed the spindle under the microscope and was able to distinguish large from small intrafusal fibres, which he presumed to correspond to nuclear bag and nuclear chain intrafusal fibres respectively. Figure 6.5 shows the movement of a point on each

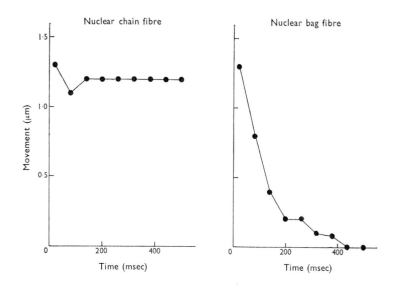

FIG. 6.5. A difference between the mechanical properties of non-contracting nuclear bag and nuclear chain fibres shown by their behaviour after applying a sudden stretch. The position of a point on each of the fibres was recorded by micro-cinephotography to allow its movement to be followed after completion of a step stretch which initially displaced the points by 40 μm. Both fibres lay in the same isolated rat lumbrical spindle. (Smith, 1966, Fig. 4, redrawn.)

kind of intrafusal fibre immediately after applying a sudden stretch to the muscle which moved the points under observation by 40 μm. The point on the nuclear chain fibre then almost at once became still; this shows that there was no further continuing movement within the intrafusal fibre due to a delayed redistribution of the degree of stretch of its different parts. In contrast, the point on the nuclear bag fibre moved by about 1 μm in the first

500 msec after completing the stretch. The movement was towards the centre of the spindle showing that the equatorial region of the nuclear bag fibre must have been shortening at the expense of the polar region (this follows by implication in Smith's paper but does not appear to have been explicitly stated). Smith pointed out that the time course of the creep was similar to the adaptation found by Lippold, Nicholls & Redfearn (1960) on stimulating cat spindles mechanically and suggested that the two might be related. The smallness of the creep in relation to the size of the sudden displacement (only 3%) somewhat reduces the force of the argument but does not entirely militate against it. What one really wants to know is the extent and time-course of the deformation of the innervated equatorial region of the intrafusal fibres.

Boyd & Ward (1969) subsequently performed essentially similar experiments on single spindles isolated from the cat tenuissimus muscle but with the addition of simultaneous recording of the afferent discharge. In their preliminary communication they stated that 'when the stretching ceased the polar regions of the nuclear bag fibres continued to extend slowly, with consequent shortening of the equatorial zone'. In addition they said that the time-course of this creep 'was similar to the adaptation of the sensory discharge'; but unlike its normal behaviour the primary ending of their isolated spindles showed no static response and ceased firing the moment the dynamic phase of stretching ceased; so their statement appears to have been based on a comparison of the creep in the bag fibres with the adaptation of secondary endings. Boyd (1971a) later made this point more explicitly and also stated that any slow component of adaptation of the primary ending could be associated with a slow yielding of the bag fibres. At any rate, it may be concluded that the nuclear bag fibres, though apparently not the nuclear chain fibres, have the different mechanical properties along their length of the kind required to contribute to adaptation and velocity sensitivity. But the direct experimental evidence is as yet too slight to decide whether or not this provides a complete explanation of adaptation. Further exact study of the problem is to be welcomed and particularly the extension of the work to spindles whose intrafusal fibres are contracting tonically at the time of application of the stretch.

In the rather different case of the amphibian spindle it has recently been suggested that the rapid decay of the receptor potential which occurs on suddenly stretching the isolated spindle to a new length does not depend upon a concomitant yielding of the innervated central region of the spindle. In two recent attempts to observe it no such yielding could be seen (Ottoson & Shepherd, 1970; Smith, 1971). This conclusion, however, could perhaps usefully be fortified by measurements of the sarcomere spacing of both the kinds of amphibian intrafusal fibre for it presently rests on rather grosser measurements. Anyhow, there is no justification for transferring the conclusion *in toto* to the mammalian spindle. For this there is already a variety of evidence suggesting that mechanical factors play an important though not an exclusive part in its adaptive behaviour, particularly when the intrafusal fibres are contracting. The isolated frog spindle has usually been studied after being mutilated by cutting off 'the greater part of the extracapsular portions of the intrafusal muscle fibres' (Husmark & Ottoson, 1971, p. 588) and thereby eliminating the opportunity for these portions of the fibres to contribute mechanically to the overall behaviour of the sense ending; the behaviour of what remains is very interesting but should not be extrapolated entirely to the normal.

Linear mechanical modelling of the spindle

It seems of interest to give an elementary outline of the way in which differences in the viscoelastic properties of the intrafusal fibres along their length might lead to the observed velocity sensitivity of the primary ending. This is illustrated diagrammatically in Fig. 6.6, but it should immediately be emphasised that more complicated models are required to reproduce fully the behaviour of the spindle (Angers, 1965; Gottlieb, Agarwal & Stark, 1970; Rudjord, 1970a,b). The receptor terminal is assumed to lie on a purely elastic region of the intrafusal fibre (i.e. force generated proportional to displacement and independent of velocity, mass ignored) and to give a response which mirrors the deformation of this region and hence the force applied to it (i.e. no transducer or pacemaker adaptation). If the rest of the intrafusal fibre were supposed to be purely elastic, as in Fig. 6.6B, then the deformation of the innervated region would always be a constant proportion of an applied stretch and the ending would give a pure static response showing neither adaptation nor dynamic sensitivity. If,

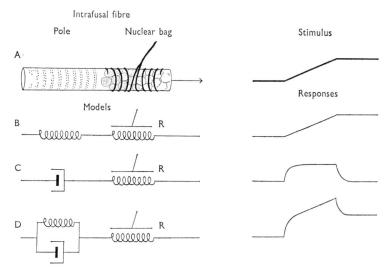

FIG. 6.6. Simple mechanical models illustrating how a sensitivity to velocity might arise from differences in the regional viscoelastic properties of an intrafusal fibre. A: an intrafusal fibre which is stretched by the waveform on the right. B, C, D: on the left, three models of the fibre composed of springs (elastic elements) and of dashpots (viscous elements); on the right, their responses to the stimulus. The responses may be considered as the generator potential of the receptor R, and are assumed to mirror the extension of the innervated region of the intrafusal fibre. The response of model D somewhat resembles that of a primary ending, as judged by its afferent firing. (Matthews, 1964, Fig. 3.)

as in C, the receptor region were to be in series with a purely viscous region (force generated proportional simply to the velocity of stretching) then the ramp stretching of the spindle would give an afferent response proportional to the velocity of stretching, but without any static response at all so that the ending adapted completely to a constant stretch. The velocity response occurring during the stretching would rise and fall exponentially at the beginning and end of the dynamic phase of stretching with a time constant equal to the product of the compliance of the central region and the viscosity of the polar region.

If these two forms of response (pure static and pure dynamic) are mixed, the overall response becomes not unlike that of a primary ending (Fig. 6.6D). For there is then a length-response and a superimposed velocity-response blending smoothly into each other, albeit with slight time lags. Such mixing might occur in either of two ways. First by having a nerve fibre which divides to send one branch to an intrafusal fibre like that in B and the other to a fibre like that in C, and by having a single pacemaker region to allow the summation of the receptor potentials from the two different branches. Second and more probably by having an intrafusal fibre with the more realistic properties shown on the left in D, where the polar region possesses both elasticity and viscosity. The quantitative details of the responses obtained with the two methods of mixing would be slightly different depending upon the precise parameters chosen for modelling. The model in D will behave in much the same way if the central region is somewhat viscous as well as elastic, provided that its viscosity is less than that of the polar region. Thus velocity-sensitivity could be conferred on the primary ending by a surprisingly simple mechanical arrangement.

The equations describing the behaviour of the above models allow rapid and complete determination of their responses to a variety of different inputs. But such analysis is so elementary from the engineering point of view that it does not merit present description, especially as it does not provide an exact description of the behaviour of the real muscle spindle. From a qualitative point of view, however, it is perhaps helpful to describe what happens inside model D on stretching it with a ramp. Initially the viscosity almost totally resists the movement and so the receptor region is extended giving an immediate increase in the afferent response. But as the receptor region is progressively extended so it develops a progressively greater force and this causes the viscous element to yield ever more rapidly. Whatever the velocity of stretching, an equilibrium will soon be reached in which the innervated and non-innervated intrafusal regions are being extended at rates dependent upon their relative elasticities. The extra force required to overcome the viscous resistance on the polar region will then have produced a constant over-extension of the innervated region relative to the value expected from the ratio of the elasticities alone; this over-extension will be proportional to the velocity in each particular case. On completion of the dynamic phase of stretching the innervated region will immediately stop being extended and will start shortening down to the final static length determined by the ratio of the elasticities. A record of intrafusal tension would throughout mirror the response shown on the bottom right. In the present case this equivalence of tension and equatorial extension is an inevitable consequence of the assumption of perfect elasticity of the innervated region. But the equivalence would only be approximate if the centre were also somewhat viscous, as seems likely in real life.

Tension and length clamping of the crustacean slow stretch receptor

Mechanical factors have also been suggested to play an important part in the adaptation of the crustacean abdominal stretch receptor which, like the spindle, consists of a sense ending lying on a muscle fibre. The crustacean receptor, however, has the advantage for the experimentalist since it is the more readily isolated for detailed study and since the cell body of the afferent fibre lies directly on the muscle fibres and so permits intracellular recording of the receptor potential; the transducer action is believed to take place in the dendrites. There are actually two kinds of crustacean stretch receptor which lie side by side and which are called slow and fast on the basis of their rate of adaptation to a steady stimulus, and also on the speed of contraction of their associated muscle fibres. On intracellular injection of current the discharge of the fast fibre accommodates rather rapidly (Nakajima & Onodera, 1969), and so pacemaker accommodation probably plays a large part in making it rapidly adapting, though this has been disputed.

The slow receptor accommodates rather slowly on excitation by steady current and most of its adaptation after a rapid stretch seems to be due to a decay of its receptor potential. The causes of this behaviour of the slow receptor have been studied in some detail as follows. Recording of the tension in the muscle bundle of the slow receptor shows that the tension in it falls along a similar time-course to the adaptation, as occurs in the simple model of Fig. 6.6D. In addition, it has been shown that if the fall in tension is counteracted, then the adaptation of the receptor potential is largely annulled as would also be expected on the model of Fig. 6.6 (Wendler & Burkhardt, 1961; Nakajima & Onodera, 1969). This is illustrated in Fig. 6.7 which contrasts the form of the receptor potential observed on stretching the muscle bundle to a constant final length, when the adaptation is marked, and on stretching the muscle to a constant final tension, which is then maintained by a feedback device, when adaptation is almost absent. In other slow cells studied in the same experiments there was a slight decline of the generator potential elicited by constant tension stretches, but on average about 80% of the adaptation of the receptor potential occurring with the usual constant length

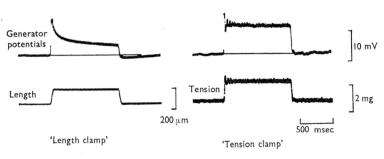

FIG. 6.7. The difference in adaptation of the generator potential of the isolated crustacean stretch receptor seen between applying a stretch to a constant final length (left) and to a constant final tension (right). Above, the responses; below, the stimuli. Intracellular records from a slowly adapting receptor neurone. (Nakajima & Onodera, 1969, Fig. 7.)

stretches was felt to be attributable to mechanical causes (Nakajima & Onodera, 1969). Comparison of the adaptation of the spike-train set up by constant-length stretches and by intracellular constant currents suggested that about 70% of the adaptation of the mechanically elicited afferent response was due to adaptation of the generator potential rather than of the pacemaker. So at least half of the adaptation of the spike-train initiated by mechanical stimulation of the receptor could plausibly be attributed to mechanical causes (these figures have been slightly rounded off from the original).

It should, however, be emphasised that experiments like the above can only be securely interpreted when they are accompanied by observation of the internal displacements occurring within the receptor bundle or muscle spindle. This is because, even if the receptor muscle bundle were to be mechanically uniform all along its length including its innervated region, a fall in tension on completion of dynamic stretching would probably still be expected to occur; such 'stress relaxation' is a common property of biological tissues. But the fall in tension would then be unrelated to receptor adaptation. Moreover, the counteracting of any such stress relaxation by applying a constant-tension rather than a constant-length stretch would still also counteract adaptation. However, the tension clamp would now produce a progressive elongation of the central region as well as the poles instead of merely holding the equatorial length constant as the poles yielded. Thus there would be a progressively increasing stimulus to the receptor terminals which would tend to anul any adaptation due to non-mechanical causes.

The tendon organ. Slightly earlier, Houk (1967) performed a rather similar experiment on the mammalian tendon organ. He found that its adaptation became somewhat less marked when the non-contracting soleus muscle was stretched to a constant final tension rather than to the more usual constant final length. This was to be anticipated since the tendon organ responds to the tension in the tendon rather than the length of the muscle, and as the tension produced by a sudden extension of fixed size decays with time. Houk analysed the matter further by fitting the adaptive decay of the afferent discharge with the sum of three exponentials. This showed that stress relaxation of the muscle could be held responsible for only the slowest of these components of adaptation (time constant 3 sec, initial size 9 impulses/sec firing per kg load) for only this component was mirrored in the decay of muscular tension. The size of the adapted static response of the ending was 27 impulses sec^{-1} kg^{-1}. The two faster components of receptor adaptation (time constants 0·6 sec and 50 msec, sizes 9 and 75 impulses sec^{-1} kg^{-1}) had no counterpart in the records of muscular tension and so were presumed to be 'more intimately associated with the receptor mechanism' (cf. Fig. 6.1.). Slightly oddly, however, one component of decay of muscular tension was not reflected in the adaptation of the receptor (time constant 220 msec, size same as that of the portion of the tension response which was thought to be responsible for the slow component of adaptation). No comparable analysis has as yet been applied to the isolated spindle and until then any tendency to direct transfer of the conclusion of the relative unimportance of mechanical factors may be resisted on two grounds. Firstly, the primary endings show a much more marked sensitivity to the velocity of stretching than do the tendon organs, which in this respect are comparable to the secondary endings. Secondly, the mechanical properties of intrafusal fibres, particularly the bag fibres, can be expected to differ from those of extrafusal fibres.

Attempts to deduce the mechanical properties of different regions of intrafusal fibre from their histological appearance

Perhaps the chief value of the model of Fig. 6.6 is to concentrate

KM

attention on the importance of the observation which has been described earlier, namely that after the application of a sudden or a ramp stretch to an isolated spindle its equatorial regions shorten slightly after the initial forcible elongation. This must inevitably cause some of the observed adaptation of the primary ending and it really only remains for suitably quantitative studies to show what proportion of its adaptation can be accounted for in this way.

It would be interesting to have the actual mechanical properties of mammalian intrafusal fibres studied directly. The central region of the nuclear bag fibre is so grossly deficient in myofibrils compared with the rest of the fibre that it seems inevitable that the mechanical properties of this region must also differ from those of the rest of the fibre. The microscopic observations already described show that it must be less viscous than the rest of the fibre, as has long been supposed. The regions deficient in myofibrils require to possess some structure with equivalent strength, as otherwise the fibre might rupture itself when it contracts; but what provides the requisite strength and how far it is purely elastic are unknown. The equatorial concatenation of nuclei seems un-likely to provide much strength but possibly there may be suffi-cient elastic fibres to do so. Histology shows that the nuclear chain fibres have a more uniform structure along their length than do the nuclear bag fibres, and relatively more myofibrils run through their equatorial region. This greater homogeneity pre-sumably provides the basis for the apparent absence of any slow creep within them after a sudden stretch (Fig. 6.5); likewise, the generator potential of the primary afferent spirals lying upon chain fibres would not be expected to show adaptation for mechanical reasons.

It is, however, a little odd that the very real histological differences along the length of the chain fibre should be unaccompanied by any mechanical counterpart. An alternative possibility for the absence of any slow creep on microscopic observation of chain fibres is that their contractile regions may show far less stress relaxation than do the bag fibres and that in spite of its content of myofibrils the central region of the chain fibre behaves in a predominantly 'elastic' manner. An elastic be-haviour of the centre of the chain fibre is suggested by the finding that static fusimotor stimulation increases the sensitivity of the primary ending to high-frequency vibration, which it may be assumed to do by causing a contraction of the nuclear chain fibres. A prerequisite for such an increase in vibration-sensitivity would appear to be that the equatorial region of the chain fibre should be relatively more compliant for the frequency in question than the rest of the fibre. This would concentrate the deformation applied to the spindle as a whole into the region where it could have most effect on the afferent terminal thus making a less exacting demand on the sensitivity of the transducer. For example, during fusimotor stimulation a sensitive primary ending may be driven at frequencies of several hundred per second by vibration of only about 1 μm applied to the spindle itself, and this would correspond to a deformation of the central region of only about 0·04 μm if the deformation were to be uniformly distributed throughout the length of the spindle (Brown, Engberg & Matthews, 1967). An elastic central chain region in series with a contractile pole would have the required effect, for at high frequencies the movement would be too fast for the contraction to follow and the contracting region would consequently appear very stiff. Such behaviour on the part of the bag fibres on their contraction would provide an entirely acceptable explanation for the increase in vibration sensitivity of the primary ending which occurs on dynamic fusimotor stimulation, since the bag equator may reasonably be presumed to be relatively elastic in its behaviour. On the other hand, an equatorial concentration of vibratory deformation in the chain fibre might perhaps occur merely as a result of a deficiency of myofibrils weakening this sensorially innervated region of the chain fibres even though it could well fail to behave as a simple elastic element; in addition, by its action on the contractile process any partial concentration of the vibratory deformation might serve to yet further weaken the contraction of the centre of the chain fibre.

A further reason for believing that the equatorial region of the chain fibre may be relatively elastic is provided by the action of a large ramp release of the muscle in abruptly silencing the primary ending at the very beginning. This suggests that the equatorial regions of both the bag and the chain fibres are relatively elastic in relation to their polar regions, for only then would release produce an abrupt decrease in the length of the equatorial regions of both kinds of fibre.

A further and perhaps more cogent argument for mechanical factors playing a crucial role in the adaptation of the primary ending is provided by the effect of fusimotor stimulation on its velocity-sensitivity. Dynamic stimulation increases this while static stimulation reduces it. Fusimotor activity seems likely to be able to influence the ending by mechanical means alone and to be unable to interfere with any adaptation either in the transducer or at the pacemaker. In the face of all the foregoing, mechanical factors may be provisionally concluded to have an important role to play in determining the velocity-sensitivity and adaptation shown by the primary ending; but this is not to say that their role need be an exclusive one. In particular, the velocity-sensitivity manifested by both primary and secondary endings in response to sinusoidal stretching of high frequency and small amplitude may well depend upon neural rather than upon mechanical factors.

The secondary ending. The lack of adaptation of the secondary ending is readily explained in terms of intrafusal structure. The secondary lies predominantly on nuclear chain fibres, and on regions where they are well striated and so where their mechanical properties would be expected to be much the same as those of the poles of the fibre. This is equivalent to the model of Fig. 6.6B, or to a related model with two similar viscoelastic elements in series and the receptor placed upon one of them. Both of these give a response without adaptation, for whatever the waveform of the stimulus it will at all times be distributed in the same proportions between the innervated and non-innervated intrafusal regions. (The precise condition is that the mechanical time constants, defined as viscosity × compliance, of the different regions should be the same.) Any branches of the secondary ending on the nuclear bag fibres also lie on obviously striated regions, the properties of which would be expected to be more like those of the poles than of the equatorial regions of these fibres. These bag branches would not therefore be expected to provide a generator potential which contained a particularly marked dynamic component. However, the mechanical properties of the region of the bag fibres immediately next to the equator may well be somewhat like those of the equator itself for the change in structure is relatively gradual. Hence, for the usual mechanical reasons, any juxta-equatorial branches of the secondary ending lying on the bag fibres might acquire a moderate dynamic sensitivity, and appreciably more than that of secondary endings lying more polarly. The experimental fact is that some secondary endings are certainly more dynamically sensitive than others, and this is particularly so for those with relatively large afferents which are the ones more commonly supplying the immediate juxta-equatorial region (see p. 84).

Non-linear behaviour and its possible partial mechanical origin in terms of the sliding filament hypothesis of muscle

The model of Fig. 6.6 lends itself to simple and complete analytical formulation, but no adjustment of its few parameters will enable it to fit all types of spindle responses which have been observed. In particular, it will not cover the so-called acceleration responses, as has recently been emphasised (Schäfer & Schäfer, 1969; Rudjord, 1970a). This may be partly overcome by introducing further springs and dash-pots, and one published model contained five elements of each kind (Angers, 1965). This is by no means an excessive number in view of the proven anatomical complexity of the spindle, but it introduces the possibility of so many arbitrary constants that such modelling becomes little more than an exercise in curve fitting unless the mechanical parameters can be confirmed by direct measurement rather than being simply chosen to fit the observed afferent responses. Gottlieb, Agarwal & Stark (1970) in recently presenting an equally complicated model emphasised that the chief virtue of such complexity is that it allows each one of the anatomically recognisable longitudinal subdivisions of the intrafusal fibres to be represented by an individual set of physical components employed in the model. But they felt that equally good agreement with the experimental results could be obtained with much simpler models. A more serious objection is that it seems unlikely that the spindle can be successfully modelled by using any combination of purely linear elements, particularly when the intrafusal fibres are contracting. The failure of the primary ending to behave linearly with stretches of increasing amplitude has already been illustrated (Fig. 4.22) and is probably due at least partly to a non-linear behaviour of the intrafusal fibres (see later), though a saturation of the transducer mechanism has also been suggested (Rudjord, 1970a). In addition, the pacemaker might also be expected to behave non-linearly when the pre-existing spike-train is deeply modulated by any stimulus.

Acceleration response as shown by the initial burst. A further example of what is probably non-linear behaviour is seen after a period of fusimotor stimulation when the primary ending behaves in the way which would be expected if the polar regions of the intrafusal fibres were manifesting static friction. This is shown in Fig. 6.8. When the muscle was stretched in the absence of any preceding motor stimulation (upper records) the firing of the primary ending rose smoothly during the progressive stretch. When the same stretch was applied some seconds after the end of a short period of repetitive stimulation of a single fusimotor

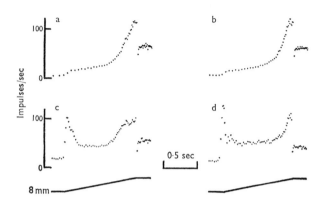

FIG. 6.8. The change in the responsiveness of a primary ending following a period of repetitive fusimotor stimulation. (*a, b*) 'normal' responses to stretch; (*c, d*) responses of same afferent to similar stretches applied 15 sec after a 1·5 sec period of stimulation at 150/sec of a single dynamic fusimotor fibre (*c*) or of a single static fibre (*d*). This leads to the appearance of a prominent 'initial burst' in the response which is probably attributable to a non-linear static friction type of resistance to stretching of the previously contracted intrafusal regions. (Brown, Goodwin & Matthews, 1969, Fig. 1.)

fibre, either static or dynamic, then the ending showed a pronounced initial burst or 'acceleration response' at the beginning of the stretch. Further stretches applied without an intervening period of fusimotor stimulation led to responses without initial bursts, showing that the prolonged process set up by the original fusimotor stimulation had been destroyed by the stretching which elicited the enhanced initial burst. This and related findings (Brown, Goodwin & Matthews, 1969) are simply explained by postulating that after a period of fusimotor stimulation a number of rather stable bonds may persist between the actin and myosin filaments in the previously activated regions of the intrafusal fibres. A few such stable bonds are believed to exist in ordinary resting striated muscle (frog sartorius) and to there give rise to a 'short-range' elastic resistance which gives way on stretching the muscle through any distance (Hill, 1968). If such bonds were present in the poles but not the central regions of the intrafusal fibres, then, on slowly extending the whole spindle, there would be an initial over-extension of the central region, followed by a partial shortening; this would happen as first the polar bonds were stressed without yielding and second they were ruptured by the continuing extension so that the actin and myosin filaments could slide past each other and the poles yield. Such a static friction type of effect would appear to provide a better explanation for the acceleration response shown in response to large stimuli than the suggestion that the spindle performs two successive stages of linear differentiation by operating upon the stimulus waveform with appropriate combinations of linear springs and dash-pots (Schäfer & Schäfer, 1969; Rudjord, 1970a). The static friction responses, however, no longer lend themselves to such simple modelling for the different sarcomeres along a single intrafusal fibre can be expected to have different numbers of 'stuck bonds' and so to differ in the force required to start them moving. An accurate model probably requires to have parameters which are 'distributed' and not simply lumped together as if they applied to a single thing at a single place.

However, as noted earlier (p. 182 and 215) the relation between the 'sensitivity' of the primary ending and the frequency of small amplitude sinusoidal stretching rises steeply for frequencies above about 10 Hz, thus betokening an acceleration-sensitivity in the linear as well as in the non-linear range of response of the ending. This facet of the acceleration-response may well depend upon the transducer properties of the nerve terminals rather than just upon mechanical properties of the intrafusal fibres, but the position is far from clear. A partial role for mechanical factors being important under some conditions is suggested by the finding that the acceleration sensitivity is appreciably more marked during static than during dynamic fusimotor stimulation (p. 215). In addition, it is interesting in this respect that Poppele & Bowman (1970) found that decreasing the temperature of the de-efferented spindle decreased the value of the frequency at which the 'acceleration-sensitivity' began to manifest itself while having no effect on the other parameters describing the response of the ending (i.e. a decrease from 37 to 26°C decreased the value of their uppermost corner frequency from 7 to 2 Hz). This change in the responsiveness of the primary ending was not shown by the secondary ending and so perhaps seems more likely to have been due to a change in the mechanical properties of the intrafusal fibres than in the properties of the receptor terminals.

Non-linearity of response with increasing amplitude of stretching. The non-linear behaviour of the primary ending shown by its response to sinusoidal stretches of increasing extent may well also depend partly upon the presence of relatively stable bonds between actin and myosin filaments, for these will influence the way in which movement occurs in the individual sarcomeres of the intrafusal muscle fibres. Large stretches will rupture any such bonds so that the filaments can slide past each other relatively easily. Thus the tension developed in the intrafusal fibres and the consequent deformation of the equatorial region will then vary relatively slowly with extension. If, however, the stretch is sufficiently small the bonds will be strained but will not give way. Individual sarcomeres will then resist movement relatively more forcibly than for large stretches and the deformation of the spindle equator will be relatively greater. In other words, the stiffness of the striated regions of the intrafusal fibres will be larger for small stretches than it is for large ones, and consequently relatively more of the small stretch will be consumed in the poorly striated equatorial intrafusal region, at any rate for the bag fibres. This will lead to a relatively greater response of the primary ending to small stretches than to large ones, as observed experimentally.

The linear range of 100 μm applied to the whole soleus of the cat corresponds to a displacement of only about 25 Å per half sarcomere of the intrafusal fibres; this is a perfectly possible distance for cross-bridges to be deformed rather than ruptured (Huxley, 1957). Within this small range, linear modelling should once again become possible but it is no longer clear how far mechanical factors have a significant part to play in producing the velocity-sensitivity manifest by the increasing sensitivity with increasing frequency to sinusoidal stretching starting at about 1 Hz. As already emphasised (Table 4.1 on p. 186) the prominent difference in the velocity-sensitivity shown by the two kinds of spindle afferent endings (primary and secondary) in response to large stretches is barely present for stretches small enough to be restricted to the linear range of the primary ending; differences in the form of the frequency–response curves of the two kinds of ending appear chiefly for frequencies above 10 Hz. The prominent 'corner frequency' seen for both kinds of afferent around 1·5 Hz seems more likely to reflect the behaviour of the transducer rather than the viscoelastic properties of the intrafusal fibres, but the matter awaits investigation. Moreover, transducer or pace-maker properties are probably also responsible for the progressive restriction of the linear range, expressed as a length, with increase of the frequency of stretching. Expressed as a modulation of firing, the linear range remains approximately constant with increasing frequency.

Effects of intrafusal contraction

It is generally agreed that the fusimotor fibres produce their effects on the sense endings by eliciting a contraction of the intra-fusal muscle fibres. Such contraction has now been observed microscopically by several workers and the resulting contractile tension has been recorded myographically by Diete-Spiff (1967). On direct repetitive electrical stimulation of single spindles isolated from the lumbrical of the cat Diete-Spiff found that the spindle as a whole developed 1–5 mg tension when the contraction appeared 'fused'. It is not, however, clear whether all the intrafusal fibres were then contracting nor whether those which were doing so were behaving normally. The most obvious effect of the intrafusal contraction on the endings is to excite them to discharge more rapidly. This presumably arises by mechanical stimulation of the endings and simply because of an extension of the region of intra-fusal fibre upon which they lie. It may be assumed that transversely the myofibrils are firmly bound to each other and to the sarco-lemma, so that each short segment of intrafusal fibre can be treated as a single mechanical element. This assumption would not be allowable if the myofibrils could shorten freely without taking the sarcolemma with them and it would then become important to know precisely how the myofilaments terminated as they neared the equatorial regions of intrafusal fibre.

Excitation of the primary ending. Stretching of the equatorial region of both bag and chain fibres, which is where the primary ending lies, has been actually seen by Boyd (1966) on stimulating one or more fusimotor fibres in the intact tenuissimus nerve. Such local yielding would be expected because the equatorial regions of either kind of intrafusal fibre contain relatively few myofibrils and so should be weaker than the rest of the fibre, even if the fibre were to be uniformly activated along its length. In fact, fusimotor stimulation may elicit contractions which are localised to only a portion of the length of the spindle, presumably because the con-traction is elicited by local rather than by propagated potential changes. There are no motor endings along the central 300 μm of the spindle where the primary ending lies, and so this region would always be expected to be less strongly activated than regions depolarised directly by a chemical transmitter liberated from the motor endings.

In the above respect it would be of considerable interest to determine how rapidly the local potentials set up at intrafusal motor endings decrement along the intrafusal fibres, for this will greatly influence the efficacy with which non-propagated potentials can elicit contraction. The length constant of a fibre is defined as the distance in which the potential set up by a local stimulus would decay to $1/e$ of its original value if the fibre were of infinite length. Its value is about 2 mm for frog fast fibres and 10 mm for frog slow fibres (Stefani & Steinbach, 1969). Except in the occasional tandem spindle individual intrafusal fibres are rarely more than 7 mm long, so that if the value of their length constant were to be similar to that of frog slow fibres a potential which was not actively propagated could none the less spread far enough to activate an appreciable proportion of the fibre; this is especially so as spread is more effective in a short closed cable (such as an intrafusal fibre) than in a nearly infinitely long cable (such as a nerve fibre) so that in the closed cable the potential is still appreciably greater than $1/e$ of its initial value at a distance of one length constant from its source. Longitudinal spread of a local potential would also be assisted by any small increase in sodium permeability consequent on the depolarisation, even though it was inadequate to lead to a full-sized spike.

Excitation of the secondary ending. The secondary afferent endings are also regularly excited on intrafusal contraction but it is not quite so obvious why this should be so, for unlike the primary endings they lie on regions of intrafusal fibre which are well filled with myofibrils. Excitation of the secondary endings is produced by the spontaneous fusimotor activity of the decerebrate cat as well as by stimulating single fusimotor fibres. This makes it less likely that the excitation is solely due to a local contraction of one pole of the spindle stretching the whole of the other end of the spindle where the particular secondary ending studied lies. One simple answer to the problem is to suggest that the density of myofibrils under the secondary ending is still not as great as elsewhere in the fibre and so the contraction is not so strong. Alternatively, as secondary endings only occasionally lie on the same intrafusal regions as motor endings, the contraction under the secondary ending may be weaker than elsewhere because the membrane does not become so fully depolarised; this presupposes activation of the fibre by a local rather than a propagated potential which may not be fully justified for chain fibres. If the region of intrafusal fibre beneath the secondary ending contracted as strongly as the rest of the fibre then excitation of the ending would not be expected to occur, but rather a slight slowing of discharge because of a yielding of the central region of the fibre or its far pole. Such slowing has been reported in only a single instance (Bessou & Laporte, 1962) and so seems unlikely to be a fundamental feature in the behaviour of the spindle.

Effects of contraction on the mechanical properties of the intrafusal fibres. The second and sometimes more neglected effect of intrafusal contraction is to change the mechanical properties of the activated regions of intrafusal fibre and thereby control the sensitivity of the spindle afferents to mechanical stimuli. Most simply, for example, an increase in the stiffness of the intrafusal poles on their contraction would lead to a higher proportion of a deformation applied to the whole spindle being concentrated in the poorly contractile equatorial regions of the fibres and thus increase the positional sensitivity of the primary ending (assuming that the equatorial region obeys Hooke's law). In addition, the production of different types of change in intrafusal 'viscosity' would provide a ready explanation for the different effects of the static and dynamic fusimotor fibres. Figure 6.9 in conjunction with the models of Fig. 6.6 illustrates diagrammatically how a change in velocity-sensitivity might be brought about. A contraction causing an increase of intrafusal 'viscosity' would increase the velocity-responsiveness assessed by large-amplitude stretches, while a contraction occurring without such a viscosity increase would leave the velocity-responsiveness unchanged or even decrease it (see later discussion on sites of pacemakers).

Whether or not a fibre behaves 'viscously' during its contraction probably depends very much upon its speed of contraction. If the fibre is fast, meaning by this that it has a high maximal rate of shortening and an associated rapid rate of turnover of the bonds between its actin and myosin filaments, then the tension it produces would be expected to be relatively little affected by whether

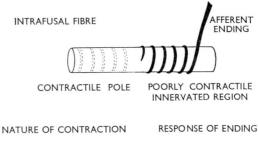

FIG. 6.9. One possible way in which differences in the contractile proper-ties of different intrafusal fibres might lead to their having either a static or a dynamic action. (Brown & Matthews, 1966, Fig. 6.)

the fibre was shortening or being lengthened. On the other hand, if the fibre is slow it will not be able to contract fast enough to keep up with shortening so the tension it develops will fall abruptly during release; and conversely it will not be able to re-arrange itself during stretching by rapidly breaking and remaking its bonds so the tension in it will then rise steeply. Thus an afferent ending connected in series with a slowly contracting muscle fibre would be expected to be rather more dynamically sensitive than one connected in series with a rapidly contracting intrafusal fibre. Of course, slow and fast as presently used are relative terms so the different actions of different speeds of intra-fusal contraction would be manifest only for a certain range of velocities of stretching; it remains to be seen whether mechanical differences, other than that of simple speed, exist between slow and fast contractions.

In considering the effects of intrafusal contraction there is also the recurring problem of whether or not the intrafusal fibres contract with uniform strength throughout their polar regions. All the present evidence suggests that the dynamic fibres act via a local contraction of the bag fibres and this might lead to the typical dynamic action by a rather different mechanism from the one just discussed above; this was first suggested to me by Dr. J. Houk in a conversation in 1969. If the local contraction were sufficiently 'slow' then the contracted region would appear completely rigid for the short time (<1 sec) that it takes to apply the usual ramp stretch of large amplitude. The remaining non-contracted regions of the intrafusal fibre would then inevitably be extended more rapidly than normal because they would have to absorb the whole of the deformation applied to the spindle instead of just part of it; they would thus therefore develop a greater viscous force than normal. This greater viscous force would produce a larger than normal deformation of the central equatorial region of the bag fibre with a corresponding enhancement of the velocity-sensitivity of the primary ending. This sensitisation arises now, however, not from the particular value of the viscosity of the contracted region but from the normal viscosity of the non-contracted region being effectively enhanced by an augmentation of the stimulus. Likewise, though the non-contracting region will be no stiffer than before it will have to absorb a greater part of the extension than normal and so will show a correspondingly enhanced increase in its tension. This will produce an increase in the positional sensitivity of the primary ending, as measured during the dynamic phase of stretching, just as occurs in practice (p. 219). The initial rapid drop in the firing of the primary ending which occurs on reaching the final length would correspond in the usual way to the continued yielding of the non-contracted polar region allowing the less viscous equatorial region to shorten somewhat from its initial over-extension. The subsequent slow decay of firing which is characteristic during dynamic fusimotor stimulation would correspond to the gradual yielding of the contracted regions, which could reasonably take some seconds to complete.

On this view the sensitivity of the primary ending during dynamic fusimotor stimulation would largely reflect the normal properties of the non-contracted intrafusal region, rather than the particular new properties of the contracted region. The spindle acquires its greater sensitivity, so to speak, by being made shorter; quite obviously, if a spindle were to suddenly be deprived of the whole of one pole while retaining a normal equator the position- and velocity-sensitivity of its primary ending would be approximately doubled. This appears at least as plausible a possibility for the action of the dynamic fusimotor fibres as the suggestion that they produce a graded uniform increase in viscosity along the whole length of the relevant intrafusal fibres. The position is further complicated, however, by the probability that there might be quite large transitional regions near the edge of the local potentials which are neither fully contracted nor fully relaxed, and whose precise mechanical properties might well be important for the way the spindle behaves.

Small-amplitude responsiveness. The speed of intrafusal contraction, whether of the whole or part of the fibre, probably also influences the effect fusimotor activity has on the degree of sensitivity displayed by the primary ending in response to stretches of small amplitude. If the rate of turnover of bonds is rapid then they will quickly re-arrange themselves at each new length, and any individual bonds will not be strained for an appreciable time; in consequence the sensitivity will not be particularly high when the amplitude of stretching is restricted. This would appear to be the case during static fusimotor stimulation. If, however, the rate of bond turnover is low then on applying a sufficiently small stretch the bonds will be strained rather than broken, and will remain so for an appreciable time before they re-arrange themselves spontaneously; as discussed earlier this would cause a high sensitivity of the primary ending. Large stretches, however, would forcibly rupture the bonds, as occurs in the de-efferented spindle (Fig. 6.8), and so the sensitivity of the ending would be lower for large than for small stretches. This may be presumed to be the mode of action of the dynamic fusimotor fibres.

Figure 6.10 illustrates these contrasting effects of different speeds of muscle contraction more fully for the frog, which has recently been studied by Brown (1970, 1971). The bottom records show the tension changes produced in extrafusal fibres by small-amplitude stretches applied either during a contraction of slow extrafusal fibres (left), when the tension changes are prominent, or during contraction of fast fibres (right), when the maintained tension changes are insignificant. The upper records show the firing of an afferent fibre from a spindle in the same muscle recorded at the same time as the extrafusal tension changes. The frog spindle has two kinds of intrafusal fibre, which are probably fast and slowly contracting in much the same way as the fast and

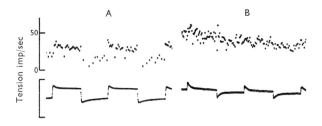

FIG. 6.10. The parallel effects of small-amplitude stretching in the frog on the extrafusal tension and on the spindle firing. Above, the afferent discharge of a spindle in the iliofibularis muscle in response to square stretches and releases of 100 μm alternating at 1 sec intervals and applied during stimulation either of slow motor fibres (left, A) or of fast motor fibres (right, B). Below, the tension changes simultaneously evoked in the extrafusal fibres. The pattern of afferent firing suggests that the intrafusal fibres behaved similarly to the extrafusal ones. Tension calibration 40 mN for A and 20 mN for B. (Brown, 1970, Fig. 1.)

slow extrafusal muscle fibres, and which are supplied by branches of their respective motor nerve fibres. The spindle responses obtained during contraction of presumed slow and fast intrafusal contractions (left and right respectively) are seen to mirror the respective extrafusal tension changes, as might be expected.

Thus the speed of intrafusal contraction would appear to be of crucial importance in determining the afferent responsiveness of the mammalian primary ending whatever kind of stimulus is under consideration. When the stimulus is of large amplitude, the velocity-sensitivity of the ending appears to be the parameter of its response which is chiefly controlled by the effect of the speed of contraction on intrafusal 'viscosity'. When the stimulus is of small amplitude, the parameter of apparent importance is the absolute value of the sensitivity of the ending to low-frequency stretches which is controlled by the effect of the speed of contraction in permitting or otherwise the rapid re-arrangement of the cross-bridges between the actin and myosin filaments.

The mammalian secondary ending usually becomes both somewhat less velocity-sensitive during intrafusal contraction and also somewhat less sensitive to stimuli of small amplitude. Both these effects probably result from contraction of the region of intrafusal fibre beneath the ending making its mechanical properties yet more like those of the rest of the intrafusal fibre. When a region of intrafusal fibre is contracting the mechanical properties conferred upon it by the activity of the myofilaments probably override the passive properties conferred by other elements (such as parallel elasticity by the sarcolemma and connective tissue). From this point of view it probably would not matter if the contraction of the secondary innervated intrafusal region were to be weaker than that of much of the rest of the fibres, since contraction could none the less have the physiologically significant action of making the viscoelastic behaviour of the region the same as the rest of the fibre (i.e. equalise their mechanical time constants, etc.). Indeed this may be the chief physiological significance of the fact that the secondary lies on a contractile rather than a non-contractile intrafusal region.

Evidence that the static and dynamic fusimotor fibres achieve their separate actions by respectively supplying the nuclear chain and nuclear bag intrafusal muscle fibres

At the time of their discovery the static and dynamic fusimotor fibres were felt to achieve their different action by each supplying one or other of the two different kinds of intrafusal muscle fibre. More specifically, the static fibres were suggested to supply the nuclear chain fibres and the dynamic fibres the nuclear bag fibres (Matthews, 1962). This hypothesis was based on the deductions from the histological structure of the spindle which had just been advanced by Jansen & Matthews (1962) and which included certain unproven assumptions about intrafusal mechanics. Largely because of uncertainties about the histological details of the motor innervation these suggestions failed to win general favour among other workers in the field, as shown for example by the discussion at the First Nobel Symposium (Granit, 1966). In particular, up to and including 1969 the active Toulouse School of experimentalists apparently felt that their results could be equally well explained by the supposition that the self-same intrafusal muscle might produce either a static or a dynamic action, depending upon the kind of nerve fibre which activated it and where along its length (cf. Bessou & Laporte, 1966; Bessou & Pagès, 1969). This view was based partly on Barker's contention (see Chap. 1) that the nuclear bag and nuclear chain fibres were commonly supplied by branches of the same fusimotor fibre, and partly on evidence from the rabbit. In this species, as already noted, all the intrafusal fibres often appear to be of the nuclear bag type when examined with the conventional stains for light microscopy, yet functionally separable static and dynamic fibres proved to be regularly detectable. It was therefore argued that the static and dynamic fibres could not achieve their separate actions by supplying different kinds of intrafusal fibre. This objection always rested precariously on the assumption that intrafusal fibres of the same gross appearance must have the same contractile properties, and the assumption has now been invalidated by the demonstration of histochemical and ultrastructural differences between different intrafusal fibres in the rabbit as in other species. After the removal of this objection and in the light of a variety of other evidence there is at last a widespread feeling that static and dynamic fusimotor fibres produce their different actions by supplying predominantly one or other of the two kinds of intrafusal fibre, and that these differ in their contractile properties, most notably in their speed of contraction. Moreover, there is no longer a serious contender to the original suggestion that the static fibres supply predominantly the nuclear chain fibres and the dynamic fibres the nuclear bag fibres. It seems important to review the arguments in favour of this view as its acceptance entails certain complications; and there are some who still withhold judgement. The arguments are summarised diagrammatically in Fig. 6.11.

FUSIMOTOR FIBRE		INTRAFUSAL FIBRE	
γ_D	Slow intrafusal system. Excites primary alone. Mimicked by S. Ch.	N bag	Slow contraction. Primary innervation alone. More strongly excited by S.Ch.
γ_S	Fast intrafusal system. Excites primary & secondary.	N chain	Fast contraction. Primary & secondary innervation.

Ergo: $\gamma_D \longrightarrow$ NB and $\gamma_S \longrightarrow$ NC.

FIG. 6.11. Summary of the arguments for the dynamic and static fusimotor fibres innervating predominantly the nuclear bag and nuclear chain fibres respectively. (Matthews, 1971, Fig. 13.)

1. *Physiological evidence for the independence of the motor innervation of the bag and chain fibres.* The histological evidence for and

against this has already been discussed (Chap. 1) and suggested to be as yet inconclusive for deciding on the frequency of occurrence of cross-innervation of the two kinds of intrafusal fibre by individual motor fibres. More recently, Boyd's (1971a,b) cinephotographs of spindles isolated from the tenuissimus muscle have shown that the nuclear bag and the nuclear chain fibres often appear to contract independently on stimulation of different nerve fibres in the intact tenuissimus nerve, thus favouring the belief that they are commonly independently innervated. Of the 139 fusimotor fibres which have so far been studied (Boyd, 1971b) 123 proved to have a physiologically specific action, for their stimulation elicited an obvious contraction of one or other kind of intrafusal fibre, but not of both; about half of these supplied bag fibres and about half supplied chain fibres. Stimulation of the remaining 16 fibres (11% of total), however, elicited some degree of contraction of both kinds of fibre confirming the belief that cross-innervation does occur on occasion. Thus there would appear to be a sufficiently high degree of independence of the motor innervation of the two kinds of intrafusal fibre for this to be a matter of crucial functional significance. On the other hand, cross-innervation would appear to take place sufficiently often to explain its regular detection by histological methods and to suggest that it too may perhaps be of definite though minor functional significance. It may be noted also that the reliability of simple visual observation still remains to be established as a method for detecting the occurrence of a weak contraction in one intrafusal fibre when another one lying 'in parallel' beside it is contracting strongly.

A quite different kind of physiological observation suggests that static and dynamic fusimotor fibres normally supply different intrafusal muscle fibres. When each kind of fusimotor fibre is used to set up a post-excitatory facilitation of the primary ending (cf. Fig. 6.8) then this is found to be independent of that set up in the same spindle by the other. This independence of action would not be expected if they both supplied the self-same intrafusal fibres (Brown, Goodwin & Matthews, 1969).

2. *Speed of intrafusal contraction.* Microscopic observation shows additionally that the bag fibres contract more slowly than the chain fibres. This has been seen both on exciting them by direct

electrical stimulation (Smith, 1966) and on activating them through their motor nerves (Boyd, 1966). So far this is based more on naked-eye observation than on measurement of intrafusal movement or sarcomere spacing, and is readily confirmed by any observer of Boyd's film of isolated spindles. Figure 6.12 shows

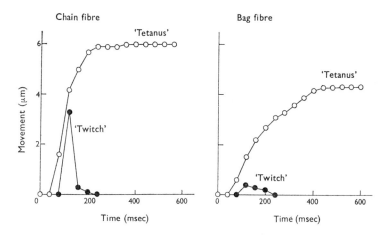

FIG. 6.12. The time-course of the intrafusal movement occurring on contraction of nuclear bag and nuclear chain fibres. The position of a point on each of the fibres was recorded by micro-cinephotography during direct electrical stimulation of the fibres. The curves labelled 'twitch' show the responses elicited by a single stimulus and those labelled 'tetanus' the responses elicited by stimulation at 50/sec. The zero of the time scale is placed arbitrarily with regard to the beginning of the stimulation. The responses of the two kinds of fibre to each type of stimulus were recorded simultaneously, but the original paper does not indicate whether the twitch and tetanic records were derived from the same preparations. (Smith, 1966, Figs. 2 and 3, redrawn.)

some of the few results published so far of the 'speed' of the contractions of the two kinds of intrafusal fibre and demonstrates marked differences in the duration of the rising phases of the 'tetanic' contractions elicited by repetitive stimulation. The differences for the 'twitch' responses on single shock stimulation are not particularly impressive, but might become more so if studied on a more rapid time scale. It should be noted, however, that such 'twitch' responses must be influenced by the value of the 'series elastic component' of the respective intrafusal fibres, and whether these differ is unknown; in this context any non-contracting intra-fusal regions will contribute to the series elastic component. As already described the time-course of afferent firing on fusimotor stimulation, particularly as observed in the 'frequencygram' (Chap. 5), suggests that the static fibres act via a contractile system which is faster than that through which the dynamic fibres act. Thus on the basis of speed of action a correspondence may be made between static and chain fibres, and between dynamic and bag fibres respectively.

3. *Suxamethonium.* The effects of suxamethonium (succinyl-choline, SCh) further strengthen the correlation of dynamic action with contraction of nuclear bag fibres. Smith (1966) applied suxamethonium to isolated spindles and observed that the presumed nuclear bag fibres exhibited 'a strong prolonged contracture, as evidence by a shortening of the sarcomere length'. He was unable to observe the sarcomere spacing of the nuclear chain fibres well enough to detect any slow contraction, and assessed the action of Sch upon them by whether or not he could still activate them by direct electrical stimulation; the nuclear bag fibres could not be activated by direct stimulation when they had contracted in response to SCh. On this slightly indirect evidence it appeared

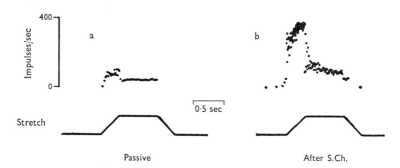

FIG. 6.13. The effect of suxamethonium in increasing the dynamic responsiveness of the primary ending. The ending lay in the soleus muscle of the cat which was stretched 5·5 mm before and after the intravenous injection of SCh. (Rack & Westbury, 1966, Fig. 1.)

that the Sch had an appreciably weaker action on the chain fibres than it did on the bag fibres. Rack & Westbury (1966) gave SCh intravenously to the whole cat and found by afferent recording that it produced a powerful dynamic action on the primary ending, which closely resembled that produced on the same ending by dynamic fusimotor stimulation. This is illustrated in Fig. 6.13. The close arterial injection of acetylcholine produced a similar dynamic action.

4. *Action on secondary.* The static and dynamic fibres produce the different effects on the secondary ending which would be anticipated on the basis of spindle structure. Figure 1.11 has already illustrated the histological finding that the secondary ending lies predominantly, and sometimes entirely, upon the nuclear chain fibres. This suggests that contraction of the chain fibres should excite the secondary ending while contraction of the bag fibres should not, because there are no secondary terminals upon them. Experiment shows that static fibres do excite the secondary endings but that dynamic fibres do not, even though they are producing an intrafusal contraction in the very spindles in which the secondary endings studied lie (see Chap. 5, Appelberg, Bessou & Laporte, 1966).

On the basis of these various independent pieces of evidence it may be concluded that the dynamic and static fibres achieve their effect by predominantly innervating the nuclear bag and nuclear chain fibres respectively. This view would not appear to be disturbed by the occurrence of a small amount of cross-innervation of the two kinds of intrafusal fibres by individual motor fibres. Such cross-innervation might well not manifest itself in many types of physiological experiments. If a fusimotor fibre which predominantly supplied bag fibres were also to have a slight action on chain fibres then this would probably merely have the effect of increasing the amount of static firing produced by its stimulation without abolishing the usual increase in dynamic sensitivity. Conversely, if a fibre which predominantly supplied chain fibres were to have a single ending on a bag fibre then this latter termination might have no detectable action at all, since the effect of a weak dynamic fibre may be almost entirely occluded when the fibre is stimulated at the same time as a powerful static fibre (Lennerstrand, 1968). On the other hand, in the cat soleus and tibialis posterior muscles the action of static and dynamic fibres is remarkably readily separated, arguing against an appreciable amount of functionally effective cross-innervation. Further, the dynamic effects of a population of dynamic fusimotor fibres increase *pari passu* with their static effects (cf. Fig. 5.10) suggesting that both the static and the dynamic actions of individual dynamic fusimotor fibres result from the contraction of a single kind of intrafusal fibre which is activated to a different degree in different spindles. If the static and dynamic effects of dynamic fibres depended respectively upon their activating two different kinds of intrafusal fibre then the relative balance of static and dynamic action might be expected to vary for different dynamic fibres, depending upon the relative numbers of intrafusal fibre of each kind supplied by each particular dynamic fusimotor fibre.

Residual problems

It would be unwise to suppose, however, that all is now solved with regard to the destination of the various fusimotor fibres. The spindle is sufficiently complicated for it to be quite possible that some new feature will be disclosed with the development of some new method of study. A slightly disquieting aspect of the present picture is that the slow bag fibres with their non-propagated potential should be the ones that are largely innervated by plate endings, which are classically associated with 'twitch' fibres, while the faster chain fibres should be the ones that are supplied predominantly with trail endings, which are more usually associated with slow fibres. In addition, there remains the question whether morphologically different endings (i.e. p_1, p_2 and trail) occurring on the same fibre can activate it to a different degree, perhaps in one case leading only to a small local potential and another to a large junctional potential followed by a spike. Moreover, motor endings of even the same type might have different effects on the afferent endings depending upon just how far away from them they lie; this would be particularly so if the endings were to act via local potentials and the intrafusal length constant is small. It is also intriguing that the mixed fibres can be presumed to elicit a propagated muscle action from their endings on the relatively fast extrafusal fibres while presumably eliciting only a non-propagated potential from their morphologically similar endings on the slow bag intrafusal fibres. This goes against the view that a motor fibre is able to determine the nature and speed of contraction of any muscle fibre that it innervates, though of course in the case of the intrafusal fibres the mixed motor fibre would have to meet the competition of pure fusimotor fibres innervating the same intra-fusal fibre.

It is, however, probably wisest to build up a view of the working of the spindle from evidence obtained on the spindle itself irres-pective of any contradictions with possibly premature generalisa-tions derived from the study of a limited number of types of extra-fusal fibre, especially those of the frog. It is to be hoped that the spindle evidence can be made progressively more direct by the measurement of the behaviour and mechanical properties of isolated spindles. Such work on isolated spindles, however, has its dangers for on its own it is debarred from showing whether or not the procedures of microdissection have led to some more or less subtle change in function, such as the failure of a potential to propagate or of a fibre to contract at its normal strength through-out its length. For example, the primary ending of Boyd & Ward's (1969) original isolated spindles failed to give the normal main-tained discharge in response to a maintained stretch, and the significance of this difference has yet to be fully established. Boyd & Ward were inclined to relate it to a change in the pressure in the fluid inside the spindle capsule which is reminiscent of Bridgman & Eldred's (1965) earlier abortive suggestion that the presence of the intracapsular fluid allows the muscle spindle to function as a transducer of intramuscular pressure. In this latter case, however, for no very convincing reason the secondary rather than the primary ending was suggested to be the one which was influenced by the intracapsular pressure. This illustrates that all conclusions based on findings on the isolated spindle need to be supported by the less direct evidence obtainable about the functioning of the spindle in its normal environment of the circulated muscle.

Possible types of interaction between the effects of the contraction of the bag and chain fibres

The elucidation of the internal working of the spindle is further complicated by the need to assess the ways in which its different parts interact. Figures 6.14 and 6.15 illustrate the two kinds of intrafusal interaction which would be expected, namely mechanical interactions arising from the 'in-parallel' arrangement of the two kinds of intrafusal fibre and electrical interactions arising from the setting up of receptor potentials at different transducer regions

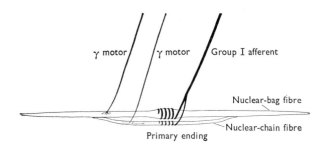

FIG. 6.14. Simplified diagram of spindle structure to illustrate the compound origin of the primary afferent ending from branches on both kinds of intrafusal fibre. (Crowe & Matthews, 1964, Fig. 10.)

of the same afferent fibre. The primary ending is notably compound, and its terminals on the two kinds of intrafusal fibre may be anticipated to provide functionally different contributions to the overall response which is transmitted by one and the same afferent fibre to the CNS. As yet rather little is known about such intrafusal interactions but the matter seems too important for its discussion to be shirked.

Mechanical interactions arising from the 'in-parallel' arrangement of the two types of fibre

Because of their 'in-parallel' arrangement, a local contraction anywhere in the central half of the bag fibre would be expected to unload the chain fibre, and a contraction of any part of the chain fibre would be expected to unload the centre of the bag fibre. In both cases the yielding required to produce the unloading would occur at the pole of the bag fibre. Boyd (1966) has actually observed such unloading of non-contracting bag fibres on contraction of chain fibres. Unloading would lead intrafusal contraction to have mixed excitatory and depressing effects on the endings; excitation would arise from direct stretching of the afferent terminals on the contracting intrafusal fibre; depression could arise from unloading relieving the terminals on the non-contracting fibre of any pre-existing strain. To complicate matters further, a bag fibre contraction which was limited to its poles would stretch the nuclear chain fibres rather than unloading them, and so tend to excite the chain branches of the primary as well as its bag branches. Under static conditions the slow contractions of the bag fibres might be relatively unimportant in producing unloading, but under dynamic conditions their greater 'viscosity' would perhaps become important and lead to significant mechanical interaction. At present it seems quite impossible to predict

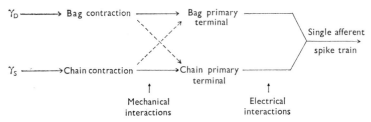

FIG. 6.15. The sites at which interaction may be 'expected between the effects of contraction of the two kinds of intrafusal fibre. Mechanical interactions may arise because of the 'in-parallel' arrangement of the two kinds of fibre. Electrical interactions may arise because the different sensory terminals feed their signals into a single afferent fibre for transmission to the CNS.

what will happen under physiological conditions, when both kinds of intrafusal fibre will commonly be contracting to some degree; prediction requires a knowledge of the relative strengths of contraction of different intrafusal regions, which is currently more than can be reasonably asked for. On the experimental side there is only a single finding which necessitates unloading as its explanation. This was the observation by Bessou & Laporte (1962, Fig. 10) that on a unique occasion the stimulation of a particular fusimotor fibre caused slowing of a secondary ending though it excited the primary ending in the same spindle. This could conceivably have resulted from the contraction of the central region of a bag fibre unloading a chain fibre.

There is one fact which suggests that mechanical intrafusal interactions may not provide an essential feature for the working of the spindle. This is that spindles from some muscles, such as the cat's interosseus, have bag and chain fibres which are of equal length (cf. Fig. 1.7). In these, contraction of the bag fibre poles would not stretch the chain fibres. In addition, the 'in-parallel' arrangement of the two kinds of fibre loses much of its significance if the spindle is attached at either end to structures which are relatively rigid. The spindle usually inserts on to the perimysium of adjoining muscle bundles and this seems likely to be pretty rigid in relation to the strength of intrafusal contraction. If so, the contraction of either kind of intrafusal fibre will not lead to appreciable unloading of the other kind, for the contraction would be effectively isometric. Thus the 'in-parallel' arrangement of the two kinds of intrafusal fibre may not be 'designed' primarily for any unloading that it may produce, and such unloading seems more likely to manifest itself in the experimental situation when single fusimotor fibres are activated at high frequency, than in the probably rather more physiological circumstance of low-frequency activation of a number of different fusimotor fibres. None the less, it is difficult to believe that mechanical interactions have no part to play in normal function. In particular, in those spindles with bag and chain fibres of unequal length any contraction localised to the pole of a bag fibre must almost inevitably influence the response to stretching of the afferent terminals on the chain fibre, whether primary or secondary, as well as those on the bag fibre itself. There is clearly scope for further study. Such studies, however, may be complicated by any cross-innervation of the two kinds of intrafusal fibre by individual fusimotor fibres. Indeed, in so far as it occurs such cross-innervation might even provide an automatic way of adjusting the relative strengths of contraction of bag and chain fibres and thus counteracting unwanted mechanical interactions and particularly unloading. Now it is accepted that the independent innervation of the bag and chain fibres is an essential feature in the design of spindle it would be pleasing to find a functional role for cross-innervation rather than simply writing it off as an accident of development.

Electrical interactions

1. *Arising from the electrotonic spread of receptor potentials.* Interaction between the effects of contraction of bag and chain intrafusal fibres will also occur in the course of the generation of nerve impulses in the primary afferent fibre. The primary ending is a compound ending with quite separate spirals on the nuclear bag and on the nuclear chain fibres, and in line with much that has already been discussed these may well be responsible for signalling different facets of the mechanical state of the muscle. The bag branches may perhaps provide much of the high sensitivity to stimuli of small amplitude and the sensitivity to the velocity of

large stimuli, while the chain branches may provide a static signal of low sensitivity indicating the length of the muscle. Both signals require to be transmitted to the CNS down the self-same afferent fibre and so the question immediately arises as to how they are mixed for compression into a single channel. The details are as yet so incompletely explored that either of two rather different operations might be involved, with rather different results on the input/ output transformations carried out within the spindle. Firstly, the signal in the afferent fibre might simply reflect the sum of two independent input signals, one arising from the terminals on each of the two kinds of intrafusal fibre. Secondly, the output signal might reflect the value of only one of the input signals at any one time, and simply be the instantaneous value of whichever happened to be the greatest. Intermediate operations may also be suggested but for clarity in description it is simplest to concentrate on the extremes.

Perhaps the most straightforward mechanism for the summation of signals is that it should occur by the summation of receptor potentials acting at a unique pacemaker site at which impulses are initiated irrespective of the precise origin of the generator current. On this view the generator potentials set up at the bag and chain primary afferent terminals would be transmitted electrotonically to the pacemaker and their combined action would determine the frequency of firing. Such a mechanism is that which is usually envisaged for the motoneurone where the uniqueness of the pacemaker is guaranteed by its having a lower threshold for spike initiation than does anywhere else in the cell. If this occurs for the spindle, precise analysis of the contributions provided by the different terminals will be far from easy because of the relatively complex geometrical arrangement and because of the uncertainty about the precise site of the transducer action (Rudjord & Rommetvedt, 1970).

2. *Switching of the site of the pacemaker*. The other extreme mechanism is that the primary afferent terminals on the two kinds of intrafusal fibre should each have their own pacemaker. The signals from the bag and chain terminals would then interact by the collision of streams of fully formed impulses at a branching point in the afferent fibre, rather that by the summation of subthreshold potentials. The discharge in the main afferent fibre at any time

would then simply be the same as that of the pacemaker with the highest instantaneous frequency, and signals from the other pacemaker would not have any effect at all on the final discharge. This presupposes that the impulses set up by the more rapidly discharging pacemaker propagate back from the point of branching so that they reach the potentially more slowly discharging pacemaker and reset its rhythm so that it never actually fires. If the slower pacemaker continued to discharge out of phase with the faster pacemaker, without being reset, it would be able to interject impulses into the main afferent fibre at times when it was not refractory, and the overall discharge would reflect the sum of the actions at the separate pacemakers; this might well manifest itself by affecting the form of the interval histogram.

'Pacemaker switching' can certainly occur when the pacemakers and their associated transducers are far apart as in the touch corpuscles of the toad (cf. Lindblom, 1958); but the small scale of the spindle makes it unlikely that different pacemakers could be situated sufficiently far apart to be completely uninfluenced by receptor potentials set up in even the most distant transducer regions. None the less, some results in the cat are most simply explained by the suggestion of pacemaker switching. These are illustrated in Fig. 6.16 which shows the response of a spindle primary ending to a stretch which was repeated during progressively greater amounts of static fusimotor activity. The notable

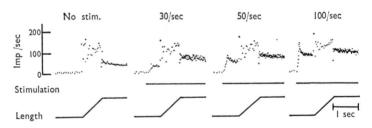

FIG. 6.16. The constancy of the discharge of a primary ending during the dynamic phase of stretching occurring in spite of an increasing discharge elicited at the initial and final lengths by static fusimotor stimulation. This is most easily explained by 'pacemaker switching'. During the stimulus bars a single static fibre was stimulated repetitively at the frequency given above. Six millimetre stretch at 30 mm/sec of soleus muscle of cat; time scale expanded during dynamic phase of stretching. (Crowe & Matthews, 1964, Fig. 6.)

point is that the absolute frequency of discharge during the dynamic phase of stretching remained practically the same, in spite of a progressively increasing discharge at both the initial and final lengths of the muscle. This is what would be expected if switching occurred during the stretching from a static pacemaker to a dynamic one and then back again on reaching the final length. If the spikes had been initiated at a single pacemaker throughout then with increasing fusimotor stimulation the discharge during the dynamic phase of stretching would have been expected to increase *pari passu* with that at the initial length through the summation of an increasing static receptor potential (presumed from chain fibres) with a constant dynamic receptor potential (presumed from bag fibres). Mechanical interactions between bag and chain fibres cannot readily be used to provide a coherent explanation for the observation, as the unloading of the dynamic terminals would have to proceed at just the right rate to keep the sum of the static and dynamic receptor potentials equal throughout the dynamic phase of stretching, and this seems implausible. Lennerstrand (1968) has reported that simultaneous stimulation of a static fibre and a dynamic fusimotor fibre with the muscle at a constant length may evoke an afferent response that is no larger than that evoked by stimulating the strongest of them alone (always the static) and attributed this to pacemaker switching, though it could perhaps be equally explained by unloading.

The acceptance that pacemaker switching provides a plausible explanation for certain experimental findings does not demonstrate, however, that at any one time the primary afferent fibre can only signal the behaviour of one or other of its terminals and that it never signals some combination of bag and chain actions. In other experiments (Crowe & Matthews, 1964) simultaneous stimulation of a static and of a dynamic fibre evoked an afferent discharge which was larger than that evoked by either alone, suggesting that contraction of both kinds of intrafusal fibre is able to influence the same pacemaker. An interesting possibility, which is intermediate between the two deliberately extreme positions so far outlined, is that the pacemaker may shift so as to alter the relative weight given to different signals. For example, if there were two pacemakers of equal threshold but the one closer to the bag primary terminals and the other to the chain terminals then at any time the pacemaker closest to the most depolarised terminals would automatically become the active one, but it would none the less receive some excitatory contribution from the more distant receptor terminals. The receptor potential set up by transduction at any particular terminal would, however, have rather less action on a distant pacemaker than an adjacent one because then it would have to be electrotonically transmitted through a greater distance. The same principle will hold if there are several potential pacemakers and not just two. In the frog, Katz (1951) has shown by local recording that there is certainly more than one potential pacemaker, for he found several sizes of abortive but all-or-nothing spikes which failed to propagate into the main nerve. Katz attributed these potentials to spikes which were full-sized in the fine terminals of the afferent fibre but which, because of a low safety factor at points of branching, failed to propagate into the main fibre. These abortive spikes, however, were only seen when there was little stretch and the afferent fibre was firing at low frequency (<10/sec), possibly because large stretches evoked a receptor potential which was large enough to facilitate propagation across the point of blockage. In the cat, the variability of the discharge of the primary afferent may conceivably be related to a wandering of the pacemaker.

It would certainly be interesting to know more about the site of initiation of spikes in a sense ending as complicated as the primary ending of the mammalian spindle. Meanwhile, uncertainty over this and other matters makes it difficult to establish just what the primary ending signals in terms of intrafusal events. From the point of view of central nervous function such elucidation of internal intrafusal mechanisms is largely immaterial. It is enough to determine the input/output relations and the patterns of firing of the 'black box' of the spindle under a suitably wide range of physiological conditions. Given this, it is fortunately possible to proceed to the study of the higher levels of the nervous machinery for the control of movement even though in certain respects the working of the lower levels remains mysterious.

Résumé of intrafusal mechanisms

The detailed working of the microcosm of the muscle spindle will only be finally unravelled by experimenting directly upon isolated spindles using suitable micro-techniques. Such work is only just getting under way and meanwhile when attempting to understand the internal functioning of the spindle one must be content with less direct evidence and arguments based on structure. Such discussion may help to highlight the real problems and hence encourage the design of the appropriate experiments to sort things out.

Role of mechanical factors in adaptation and velocity sensitivity. As described earlier the primary ending is markedly more sensitive to the dynamic component of a large mechanical stimulus than is the secondary ending. Similarly, when the muscle is suddenly stretched to a new length the primary ending adapts more rapidly to a new level of firing than does the secondary ending. Dynamic sensitivity and rapid adaptation are two manifestations of the same basic property of the receptor, namely a sensitivity to the rate of change of the stimulus as well as to its absolute value. The present question is as to just how this differentiation (in the mathematical sense) of the stimulus waveform is brought about. *A priori*, it might be suspected to take place at any or all of the links lying between the receipt of a mechanical stimulus by the spindle as a whole and the despatch of trains of all-or-nothing action potentials up its afferent nerve fibres. The three main sites at which adaptation might occur are as follows: in the transmission of the mechanical stimulus to the receptor nerve terminals; in the mechano-electric transduction of the deformation of the nerve terminals into a generator potential across the nerve membrane; and in the excitation by the generator potential of all-or-none spikes at some pacemaker region which may or may not be coterminous with the transducer region. In the rather different case of the Pacinian corpuscle, which has been the more thoroughly investigated, adaptation would appear to be occurring to some degree at all three sites, though with mechanical factors predominating. The question for the spindle thus becomes whether, for it also, one or other of the links predominates in importance for the type of stimuli which are of relevance for normal function. There is now a good deal of indirect evidence that a variation in the viscoelastic properties of the intrafusal muscle fibres along their length plays an important part in determining the major functional differences between the primary and secondary endings. The first point in favour of this view is that the chief site of adaptation of the primary ending undoubtedly lies upstream of the pacemaker. This is known because excitation of the pacemaker by an extrinsically applied current elicits a maintained afferent discharge with little or no sign of adaptation. In addition, limited recordings of receptor potentials show that they also show adaptation to a maintained stimulus.

The next point is that the intrafusal muscle fibres show marked histological differences between their equatorial and their polar regions that can be expected to be accompanied by regional differences in their mechanical properties. If the nucleated equatorial regions were to behave as predominantly elastic elements and the striated poles to behave as predominantly viscous elements then this would lead to the sort of difference in dynamic sensitivity which is observed between the primary and secondary endings. This would happen roughly as follows. On applying a stretch the viscous poles would initially resist deformation relatively strongly, with a force proportional to the velocity of their extension, while the elastic equator would resist with a force proportional only to its extension and independent of the velocity. The equator would thus initially yield relatively more than the poles. On full application of the stretch and termination of its dynamic phase the viscous poles would continue to yield somewhat, for they would be pulled upon by the elastic tension of the extended equator. This would allow the equator to shorten slightly thus reducing the mechanical stimulus to the primary ending and explaining its adaptation. The secondary ending, however, lies on an intrafusal region which may be assumed to have mechanical properties like those of the poles and so would not show this effect and would adapt slowly.

Microscopic observation of isolated spindles has shown the sort of yielding required to account for adaptation of the primary ending in mechanical terms; the yielding, however, occurs only for the nuclear bag fibres and not for the nuclear chain fibres. A quantitative correspondence has yet to be established between the movements occurring within the spindle and the adaptation of its endings; this is essential for establishing just how far adaptation can be entirely ascribed to mechanical factors. The similarity of the sensitivity of primary and secondary endings to an increase in the frequency of small-amplitude sinusoidal stretching suggests that under some conditions non-mechanical factors may be predominant in determining adaptation and velocity-sensitivity. This similarity in their behaviour encourages the view that when differences do appear they are due to the different arrangement of the nerve terminals with regard to the intrafusal fibres.

A third reason for believing in the importance of mechanical factors in producing adaptation under many important physiological conditions is the great change in the velocity-sensitivity of the primary ending which may be produced by fusimotor stimulation. The fusimotor fibres seem likely to act solely by producing an intrafusal contraction and to be incapable of directly influencing the transducer mechanism or the pacemaker.

Possible explanation of non-linear behaviour of primary ending in terms of the sliding filament hypothesis of muscle contraction. The general pattern of adaptation of the primary and secondary endings is easily mimicked in outline by an elementary mechanical model consisting of two springs and one dash-pot (viscous resistance). Such a simple model is, however, unable to reproduce the full range of behaviour of the spindle endings and in particular it will not give an acceleration response. This limitation is readily overcome by suitable reduplication of springs and dash-pots in an appropriate arrangement and such complexity is entirely appropriate in view of the number of separate working parts of the spindle itself. But it introduces the possibility of so many arbitrary constants that such modelling becomes little more than an exercise in curve fitting until the mechanical parameters can be determined by direct measurement upon the spindle itself, rather than simply being chosen to fit the observed afferent responses.

A more serious objection is that it seems unlikely that the spindle can ever be successfully modelled by combinations of passive and purely linear elements. Nobody would now try to model an extrafusal muscle fibre in this way, particularly when it is contracting. From this point of view it is important that contraction is now known to occur by the repeated re-arrangement of the cross-bridges which link the actin and myosin filaments. When it is attached at both ends each cross-bridge has only a very limited range of movement, but during contraction it repeatedly engages and disengages one end from the actin filament thus allowing the two kinds of myofilament to slide past each other and so produce a gross movement. It has been suggested that even in 'resting' muscle there are a certain number of cross-bridges more or less

LM

permanently connected at both ends. A similar occurrence in intra-fusal muscle fibres would provide a ready explanation for two particular properties of the primary ending, namely its acceleration-sensitivity as manifested in the appearance of an initial burst of impulses at the beginning of a large ramp stretch, and the non-linearity of its response seen on progressively increasing the amplitude of sinusoidal stretching. Both of these follow immediately if it be accepted that an intrafusal fibre will become very much less stiff once a stretch is made large enough to rupture the pre-existing cross-bridges. Thus at the beginning of a large ramp stretch the polar tension will rise to an initial peak just before the cross-bridges rupture. This initial surge of tension will lead to an initial over-extension of the equatorial region of the spindle (supposed purely elastic), and so elicit an initial high-frequency burst of firing from the primary ending. This mechanism would also provide a ready explanation for the increase in the acceleration response which is found for the first of a series of stretches applied after a period of repetitive fusimotor stimulation. Likewise, when the amplitude of sinusoidal stretching is kept deliberately small then the stable bonds should remain unbroken and so the poles able to manifest a high stiffness. In consequence, a large proportion of any deformation applied to the spindle as a whole will be concentrated in its innervated equatorial region and so the primary ending will manifest a high sensitivity, expressed in impulses/sec firing per unit extension applied to the whole spindle. A large sinusoidal stretch, however, will rupture the resting bridges in some or all sarcomeres thus allowing the myofilaments to move relatively freely so leading the primary ending to manifest a lower sensitivity than that shown to small stretches which do not rupture the bridges.

Effects of contraction on the mechanical properties of the intrafusal muscle fibres. The contraction of an intrafusal fibre has long been held to lead to a stretching of its equatorial region. This is because the equatorial region is deficient in myofibrils and so may be presumed to contract less strongly than the rest of the fibre; and this argument is applicable to both the bag and the chain fibres. Such equatorial yielding has now been observed microscopically in the living spindle and provides an immediate explanation for the increased firing of the primary ending produced on fusimotor stimulation. In this respect stretch and fusimotor stimulation provide equivalent stimuli.

The secondary ending is also excited by fusimotor stimulation but it is not so immediately obvious why this should be so. Possibly the intrafusal region beneath the secondary ending is also sufficiently deficient in myofibrils to yield somewhat on contraction of the fibre as a whole. Alternatively it is possible that the fibre does not contract fully in the region underneath the secondary ending because it has been activated by a local potential set up at a distant motor ending.

The more interesting and sometimes more neglected effect of intrafusal contraction is to change the mechanical properties of the intrafusal fibres themselves and hence change the response of the endings to stimuli applied to the spindle as a whole. Thus changes in polar stiffness might change the position-sensitivity of the primary ending and changes in polar viscosity might change its velocity-sensitivity. In particular, the dynamic fusimotor fibres may perhaps produce their characteristic velocity-sensitising action by increasing the viscosity of the spindle poles and the static fibres may perhaps produce the opposite action by lowering the polar viscosity. This is most easily envisaged if the static and dynamic fibres act upon separate kinds of intrafusal fibre, as is currently believed. Over the range of velocities most commonly studied experimentally (5–50 mm/sec for a muscle some few centimetres long) 'viscosity' may perhaps be inversely equated with the speed of intrafusal contraction. The dynamic fibres appear to supply a slow contractile system which may be suggested to behave more 'viscously' than the fast contractile system supplied by the static fibres. Experiments on the frog fast and slow extrafusal muscle fibres support this view.

The speed of intrafusal contraction is probably also important for determining the sensitivity of the primary endings to small sinusoidal stretches of low frequency. If the contraction is fast the cross-bridges will be able to re-arrange themselves continuously during the slow change of length the polar stiffness will be fairly low and with it the sensitivity of the primary ending. If the contraction is slow the bridges will not have time to alter their position and so will behave like the stable bonds of the de-efferented spindle, and so lead the primary ending to manifest a high sensitivity towards stretches applied to the whole spindle.

Evidence that the static and dynamic fusimotor fibres achieve their separate effects by respectively supplying the nuclear chain and the nuclear bag fibres. All that has just been said shows that the two kinds of fusimotor fibres could perfectly well produce their various effects by virtue of each providing the motor supply to just one of the two types of intrafusal muscle fibre. This indeed is what was suggested on the discovery of the static and dynamic fibres. By-passing the histological controversies, direct experiment now suggests that individual fusimotor fibres supply predominantly one or other of the two kinds of intrafusal fibre. On observing the living spindle while stimulating individual fusimotor fibres it is usually possible to detect contraction of only one kind of intrafusal fibre.

The following three pieces of evidence all argue that the dynamic fibres supply the bag fibres and the static fibres the chain fibres, rather than the other way round. First, the dynamic fibres act through a slow system and the static fibres through a fast one, while the bag fibres are slow and the chain fibres are fast. Second, suxamethonium predominantly excites the bag fibres and has a powerful action on the primary ending resembling that of the dynamic fibres. Third, the secondary endings lie predominantly on the chain fibres and are excited solely by the static fibres. This correlation of static with chain, and dynamic with bag now seems to have won widespread acceptance. But up and until 1970 several influential workers preferred the idea that the two kinds of fusimotor fibre induced different kinds of contraction in one and the same intrafusal fibre. There was never any direct evidence for this view which was based largely on the belief that the rabbit had the usual two kinds of fusimotor fibre but only one of the kinds of intrafusal muscle fibre. This view was abandoned rather abruptly when histochemical and ultrastructural observations showed that the rabbit also had two kinds of intrafusal fibre.

Possible interactions between the effects of contraction of bag and chain fibres. The understanding of the internal functioning of the spindle is further complicated by the likelihood of interaction between its various working parts. Two kinds of interaction appear probable. Firstly, mechanical interactions arising from the 'in-parallel' arrangement of the bag and chain fibres. Secondly, electrical interactions arising from the need for the quite separate afferent terminals on the bag and on the chain fibres to compress their signals into a single train of all-or-none impulses carried in their common afferent fibre of origin.

Mechanical interactions, with the contraction of one kind of intrafusal fibre unloading the other kind, have yet to be demonstrated to play a significant physiological role and it is possible that they never do. Some spindles have bag and chain fibres which are of equal length and which appear unlikely to be able to significantly unload each other because the extrafusal fibres upon which they both insert may be assumed to be relatively rigid.

Electrical interactions might take place in either of two quite different ways with rather different consequences for the mixing of the information transmitted by the terminals on the two kinds of intrafusal fibre. On the one hand, the receptor potentials from the different terminals might sum more or less arithmetically after electrotonic transmission to a unique pacemaker at which impulses are initiated irrespective of the site of transducer action. On the other hand, there might be separate pacemakers for each kind of terminal. The pacemaker with the highest instantaneous frequency of firing would then take command of the main afferent fibre and send its own signal up this channel uncontaminated by that from the other terminals. For this to happen the rhythm of the currently slower pacemaker would have to be regularly reset by antidromic invasion by the spikes initiated at the more rapidly discharging pacemaker. There is some indirect evidence that there may be more than one pacemaker, but some degree of summation of the receptor potentials set up by the different terminals also seems likely to occur.

All these various problems are ripe for solution by a direct attack upon the isolated spindle. However, even before this has been achieved it is fortunately possible to proceed to the study of the functional role of the spindle in the body. Such hurrying on is possible because the CNS is concerned with the input/output relations of the spindle rather than with precisely how it manages to do its job.

References

Angers, D. (1965). Modèle mécanique de fuseau neuromusculaire dé-éfferenté: terminaisons primaires et secondaires. *C.r. hebd. Séanc. Sci., Paris*, **261**, 2255–2258. [274, 283]

Appelberg, B., Bessou, P. & Laporte, Y. (1966). Action of static and dynamic fusimotor fibres on secondary endings of cat's spindles. *J. Physiol.* **185,** 160–171.   [299]

Bessou, P. & Laporte, Y. (1962). Responses from primary and secondary endings of the same neuromuscular spindle of the tenuissimus muscle of the cat. In *Symposium on Muscle Receptors,* ed. Barker, D. pp. 105–119. Hong Kong: Hong Kong University Press.   [289, 303]

— (1966). Observations on static fusimotor fibres. In *Muscular Afferents and Motor Control,* ed. Granit, R. pp. 81–89. Stockholm: Almqvist & Wiksell.   [294]

Bessou, P. & Pagès, B. (1969). Spindle secondary responses elicited by stimulation of static fusimotor axons. *J. Physiol.* **202,** 569–584. [294]

Boyd, I. A. (1966). The behaviour of isolated mammalian muscle spindles with intact innervation. *J. Physiol.* **186,** 109–110P.
        [271, 287, 297, 302]

— (1970). *The Muscle Spindle* (film), distributed by J. Wiley & Sons, Chichester, England.   [271]

— (1971a). The mammalian muscle spindle—an advanced study (film). *J. Physiol.* **214,** 1P.   [271, 273, 296]

— (1971b). Specific fusimotor control of nuclear bag and nuclear chain fibres in cat muscle spindles. *J. Physiol.* **214,** 30–31P.   [296]

Boyd, I. A. & Ward, J. (1969). The response of isolated cat muscle spindles to passive stretch. *J. Physiol.* **200,** 104–105P.   [273, 301]

Bridgman, C. F. & Eldred, E. (1965). Intramuscular pressure changes during contraction in relation to muscle spindles. *Am. J. Physiol.* **209,** 891–899.   [301]

Brown, M. C. (1970). Small amplitude displacement sensitivity of frog spindles during fast and slow muscle contraction. *J. Physiol.* **206,** 27–28P.   [292, 293]

— (1971). The responses of frog muscle spindles and fast and slow muscle fibres to a variety of mechanical inputs. *J. Physiol.* 218, 1–17.   [292]

Brown, M. C. Engberg, I. & Matthews, P. B. C. (1967). The relative sensitivity to vibration of muscle receptors of the cat. *J. Physiol.* **192,** 773–800.   [281]

Brown, M. C., Goodwin, G. M. & Matthews, P. B. C. (1969). After-effects of fusimotor stimulation on the response of muscle spindle primary afferent endings. *J. Physiol.* **205,** 677–694.   [284, 296]

Brown, M. C. & Matthews, P. B. C. (1966). On the subdivision of the efferent fibres to muscle spindles into static and dynamic fusimotor fibres. In *Control and Innervation of Skeletal Muscle,* ed. Andrew, B. L. pp. 18–31. Dundee: Thomson.   [290]

Crowe, A. & Matthews, P. B. C. (1964). The effects of stimulation of static and dynamic fusimotor fibres on the response to stretching of the primary endings of muscle spindles. *J. Physiol.* **174,** 109–131.
        [302, 306, 307]

Diete-Spiff, K. (1967). Tension development by isolated muscle spindles of the cat. *J. Physiol.* **193,** 31–43.   [287]

Emonet-Dénand, F. & Houk, J. (1969). Some effects of polarising current on discharges from muscle spindle receptors. *Am. J. Physiol.* **216**, 404–406. [270]

Gottlieb, G. L., Agarwal, G. C. & Stark, L. (1970). Studies in postural control systems. Part III: A muscle spindle model. *I.E.E.E. Trans. on Systems Science and Cybernetics*, Vol. SSC-6, pp. 127–132. New York: Institute of Electrical Electriconic Engineers. [274, 283]

Granit, R. (ed.) (1966). *Muscular Afferents and Motor Control.* Stockholm: Almqvist & Wiksell. [294]

Hill, D. K. (1968). Tension due to interaction between the sliding filaments in resting striated muscle. The effects of stimulation. *J. Physiol.* **199**, 637–684. [284]

Houk, J. (1967). A viscoelastic interaction which produces one component of adaptation in responses of Golgi tendon organs. *J. Neurophysiol.* **30**, 1482–1493. [279]

Hubbard, S. J. (1958). A study of rapid mechanical events in a mechanoreceptor. *J. Physiol.* **141**, 198–218. [267]

Husmark, I. & Ottoson, D. (1971). The contribution of mechanical factors to the early adaptation of the spindle response. *J. Physiol.* **212**, 577–592. [274]

Huxley, A. F. (1957). Muscle structure and theories of contraction. *Prog. Biophys. biophys. Chem.* **7**, 255–319. [286]

Jansen, J. K. S. & Matthews, P. B. C. (1962). The central control of the dynamic response of muscle spindle receptors. *J. Physiol.* **161**, 357–378. [294]

Katz, B. (1951). Action potentials from a sensory nerve ending. *J. Physiol.* **111**, 248–260. [308]

Lennerstrand, G. (1968). Position and velocity sensitivity of muscle spindles in the cat IV. Interaction between two fusimotor fibres converging on the same spindle ending. *Acta physiol. scand.* **74**, 257–273. [299, 307]

Lindblom, U. F. (1958). Excitability and functional organisation within a peripheral tactile unit. *Acta physiol. scand.* **44**, Suppl. 153, 1–84. [306]

Lippold, O. C. J., Nicholls, J. G. & Redfearn, J. W. T. (1960). Electrical and mechanical factors in the adaptation of a mammalian muscle spindle. *J. Physiol.* **153**, 209–217. [269, 271, 273]

Loewenstein, W. R. & Mendelson, M. (1965). Components of receptor adaptation in a Pacinian corpuscle. *J. Physiol.* **177**, 377–397. [267, 268]

Loewenstein, W. R. & Skalak, R. (1966). Mechanical transmission in a Pacinian corpuscle. An analysis and a theory. *J. Physiol.* **182**, 346–378. [267]

Matthews, B. H. C. (1933). Nerve endings in mammalian muscle. *J. Physiol.* **78**, 1–53. [269]

Matthews, P. B. C. (1962). The differentiation of two types of fusimotor fibre by their effects on the dynamic response of muscle spindle primary endings. *Q. Jl. exp. Physiol.* **47**, 324–333. [294]

Matthews, P. B. C. (1964). Muscle spindles and their motor control. *Physiol. Rev.* **44**, 219–288. [275]

— (1971). Recent advances in the understanding of the muscle spindle. In *The Scientific Basis of Medicine Annual Reviews*, 1971, eds. Gilliland, I. & Francis, J. pp. 99-128. London: Athlone Press. [295]

Nakajima, S. & Onodera, K. (1969). Adaptation of the generator potential in the crayfish stretch receptors under constant length and constant tension. *J. Physiol.* **200**, 187–204. [277, 278]

Ottoson, D. & Shepherd, G. M. (1970). Length changes within isolated frog muscle spindle during and after stretching. *J. Physiol.* **207**, 747–759. [274]

Poppele, R. E. & Bowman, R. J. (1970). Quantitative description of linear behaviour of mammalian muscle spindles. *J. Neurophysiol.* **33**, 59–72. [285]

Rack, P. M. H. & Westbury, D. R. (1966). The effects of suxamethonium and acetylcholine on the behaviour of cat muscle spindles during dynamic stretching and during fusimotor stimulation. *J. Physiol.* **186**, 698–713. [298]

Rudjord, T. (1970a). A second order mechanical model of muscle spindle primary endings. *Kybernetik*, **6**, 205–213. [274, 283, 285]

— (1970b). A mechanical model of the secondary endings of mammalian muscle spindles. *Kybernetik*, **7**, 122–128. [274]

Rudjord, T. & Rommetvedt, H. J. (1970). Muscle spindle receptors. Effects of geometrical structure on passive current spread in group Ia terminals. *Kybernetik*, **7**, 72–77. [305]

Schäfer, S. -S. & Schäfer, S. (1969). Die Eigenschaften einer primären Muskelspindelafferenz bei rampenförmiger Dehnung und ihre mathematische Beschreibung. *Pflügers Arch. ges. Physiol.* **310**, 206–228. [283, 285]

Smith, R. S. (1966). Properties of intrafusal muscle fibres. In *Muscular Afferents and Motor Control*, ed. Granit, R. pp. 69–80. Stockholm: Almqvist & Wiksell. [271, 272, 297, 298]

— (1971). Sensory transduction in the frog muscle spindle: the role of the intrafusal muscle fibres. In *Research on Muscle Development and the Muscle Spindle*. Cleveland: Muscular Dystrophy Association of America. In the press. [274]

Stefani, E. & Steinbach, A. B. (1969). Resting potential and electrical properties of frog slow muscle fibres. Effect of different external solutions. *J. Physiol.* **203**, 383–401. [288]

Wendler, L. & Burkhardt, D. (1961). Zeitlich abklingende Vorgänge in der Wirkungskette zwischen Riez und Erregung (Versuche an abdominalen Streckreceptoren dekapoder Krebse). *Z. Naturf.* **16b**, 464–469. [277]

7

THE REFLEX ACTIONS OF THE MUSCLE RECEPTORS

THE muscle receptors clearly exist in order to feed back information to the central nervous system about the mechanical state of muscle. Such feedback would be unhesitatingly provided by a human engineer faced with the problem of designing a control system to make muscle carry out the wide variety of tasks that it does in the body. For several reasons the various 'computations' required to exert effective motor control may be expected to be carried out at a heirarchy of levels in the nervous system and, correspondingly, the central projection of the information carried by the muscle afferents may be expected to be widespread. The receipt of such an afferent projection is not, however, an essential for any and every centre concerned with motor control. A sufficiently high-level controller might be unconcerned with mundane mechanical details, and be left free to issue rather general instructions for detailed implementation by a lower level controller which acted in the light of the moment-to-moment situation, as shown in part by signals from the muscle afferents. In particular, suitable spinal reflex connections might enable the muscle afferents to be used to produce rapid automatic corrections to the motor outflow, leaving it to the higher centres to take slower action on the basis of information garnered from a wider field. The uniquely high speed of conduction of the Ia and Ib fibres (from spindle primaries and tendon organs respectively) shows that the body is indeed interested in receiving their signals with a minimum of delay; nor are the spindle group II afferents so much slower for their information to be considered non-urgent.

A priori, the initial central evaluation of, and response to, all this information would seem likely to be the prerogative of the spinal cord for this would avoid any further delay in simple conduction. Particular interest therefore attaches to the study of the direct reflex actions of the three main mechanoreceptors of muscle. Such work has been encouraged by the progressive discovery of autonomous spinal mechanisms which are readily seen to be meaningful in themselves from the point of view of muscular control. Of course, in most mammals the spinal cord is equally the servant of the higher centres and the study of its intrinsic mechanisms in isolation can in the long term be expected to achieve only a limited success. The higher centres themselves are, however, currently rather less amenable to experimental study, and the results which have so far been obtained often provide little more than a description of what is connected to what, rather than showing in control terms what different parts of the motor system do and how they do it. Thus up to the present attention has perforce been concentrated upon the role of the muscle afferents in reflex control, rather than upon their action at higher levels of the nervous system and most tantalisingly in the cerebellum.

The classical approach to the study of reflexes stems from Sherrington's work and is to accurately observe the reflex response of a fully innervated limb to various natural stimuli. From the turn of the century simple observation was progressively supplemented by myographic recording of the contraction of individual muscles, and then later by electromyographic observation of their electrical activity. The development of the isometric myograph and the general improvement in high-speed recording led to a peak of activity based on these methods in the mid to late 1920's. In the early 1940's the recording of efferent activity shifted to the ventral root, and subthreshold effects on the motoneurone became detectable by means of the testing of the excitability of the motoneurones by activating them monosynaptically and seeing whether the number driven to discharge changed. The introduction of the intracellular microelectrode in the early 1950's opened the way for the direct study of the changes in membrane potential and conductivity underlying these changes in motoneuronal excitability. All this work with electrical recording methods usually depended also upon the electrical stimulation of a range of nerves and to begin with showed a natural but undue pre-occupation with the responses occurring within the first few milliseconds of the entry of a single synchronous afferent volley into the spinal cord. The methods were also employed in parallel for the productive analysis of the mechanisms of synaptic transmission and thereby led on to the study of the properties of the motoneurone itself; all this yielded important understanding of how the motoneurone integrates the information it receives from different sources.

By the early 1960's the new electrical techniques had exhausted their easy triumphs and the field became relatively static as it settled down to the more patient and thorough study of the details of synaptic organisation. This was particularly so because by then it was becoming clear that the 'wiring diagram' which many seek is not an invariant pattern of straight-through synaptic connections between afferent input and reflex output. Rather, the responsiveness of various interneurones may be preset by the tonic discharge from higher centres so that the spinal cord is, so to speak, pre-programmed to respond appropriately under the prevailing conditions and so at different times may vary its response to any particular afferent input. This adds a new dimension of complexity to experimental analysis. The present account can do no more than chart the halting progress to our present somewhat limited understanding. In doing so, two inter-linked questions may be kept in mind. First, what are the mechanisms underlying the reflex responses that may be elicited by physiologically natural stimuli applied to an intact muscle or limb? Second, what are the reflex actions of each of the known types of muscle receptor?

The tendon jerk

The establishment of its reflex mediation. The brevity and simplicity of the tendon jerk have made it an ideal object for physiological study and this has led on to an understanding of several important aspects of the reflex control of muscle. The tendon jerk has also a special interest from the point of view of control theory for it is the response of the motor control system to one of the basic types of input used for engineering analysis, namely the unit impulse or δ function. According to Liddell (1960) 'the knee-jerk had been introduced to the notice of scientists by Erb and Westphal, working independently, in 1875', though it had presumably been noticed casually before then. For the next generation a grumbling controversy continued as to whether it was a genuine reflex or whether it was simply a direct response of muscle to mechanical stimulation. On the basis of clinical observation and Tschirjew's (1878) repeatedly confirmed experimental findings it was generally recognised that a jerk could only be elicited when the reflex arc was intact from the muscle back to itself, and that the size of the jerk could vary with changes in spinal excitability. But those who believed that the jerk was a direct muscular response attributed these awkward findings to a 'reflex muscular tonus' influencing the excitability of muscle to a 'particular form of mechanical stimulation'. This was how Sherrington saw the matter when he wrote a textbook account in 1900 and he summarised it by stating 'the phenomenon, though not a reflex act, is therefore dependent on a reflex spinal arc'. A few years later (1906, p. 87) he more cautiously said 'it is customary to regard the knee-jerk not as a reflex action . . .; hence it is termed "knee phenomenon", "knee-jerk", etc.' but he then proceeded to elaborate various objections to this view suggesting that he had had a change of heart.

The basis for what now appears to have been a remarkably head-strong persistence in error in spite of simple evidence to the contrary was an understandable but misplaced trust in the earliest experiments in which the latency of the tendon jerk was measured. Such timing was done with some care with the methods currently available by Waller in 1881 and 1890 and by Gotch in 1896. In man, Waller found that the latency of the knee-jerk was about 30 msec and that the latency on direct stimulation of the muscle was about 20 msec, thus leaving only some ten msec for transmission round the reflex arc. He believed that in man 'any reflex movement of a limb occurs at least 1/10 sec after the stimulus' and therefore considered reflex action to be excluded. In the rabbit, he found the latency of the tendon jerk to be within a millisecond of the contraction elicited from the same muscle by its direct electrical stimulation. Gotch (1896) subsequently repeated Waller's experiments on the rabbit and in spite of an initial bias against him was forced to agree that there was insufficient time for there to be any reasonable possibility of the jerk being mediated reflexly. Gotch improved on Waller by recording the contraction of the muscle itself with a 'light lever' rather than just recording the movement of the limb. He found the latency of the knee-jerk to be about 5 msec and again approximately the same as the latency on direct stimulation of the muscle; but most curiously he found the latency of the response of the muscle on stimulating its nerve to be ten msec, that is twice as long as the other two. Thus Gotch also concluded that the jerk could not be reflex, and at this distance it is hard to see where his error lay. Perhaps the moral may be drawn that success is not guaranteed by the newest and apparently most precise techniques, which is what both Waller and Gotch felt they were using, for their deficiencies may remain to be fully appreciated.

Some 15 years later with the introduction of yet newer methods the latency of the jerk was re-measured by Jolly (1911) who was able to conclude that though it was short it was quite long enough to permit reflex action. Although Jolly's excellent work is rarely quoted his now obvious conclusion does not seem to have been seriously questioned since. Jolly achieved greater precision than his predecessors by recording the electrical response of the muscle rather than its mechanical response. He did this with the newly developed string galvanometer which he had previously made use of in collaboration with its originator, Einthoven, to study the electroretinogram. This enabled Jolly to circumvent the uncertain delay introduced by crude mechanical recording methods and also to record, albeit imperfectly, the afferent volley set up in the muscle nerve by the mechanical stimulus. In the spinal cat, he found that the minimal latency from the tap to the beginning of the electrical response of the muscle was usually between 5 and 10 msec, whereas the delay between a stimulus to the motor nerve and the resulting muscle action potential was only 1–3 msec. Thus ample time was left for mediation of the jerk phenomenon via a reflex arc. Unlike modern practice and for no very obvious reason Jolly excited the nerve mechanically by the same hammer used to elicit the jerk, but this appears immaterial for the argument.

The elucidation of the monosynaptic transmission of the jerk. Jolly also took the next natural step forward and estimated the time consumed in the various peripheral parts of the reflex so that by elimination he could gauge its central delay. He was able to measure directly two of the peripheral latencies, namely that of the muscle to stimulation of its nerve and that of the afferent volley set up in the nerve by the tap. The residual peripheral latencies were calculated by measuring the lengths of the remaining parts of the afferent and efferent limbs of the reflex arc and assuming that the conduction velocity of both the motor and the afferent fibres was 120 m/sec. The use of such a happily appropriate figure for the conduction velocity appears to have been fortuitous for it was based on measurements by others in man which may now be presumed to have been in error and which in any case could not safely have been held applicable to the cat. On the basis of such calculation the minimum central latency came out at between 1·8 and 2·3 msec. Similar procedures applied to the reflex contractions of the hamstring or adductor muscles on eliciting a presumed 'flexor reflex' response from them by stimulating the dorsum of the foot gave a central delay of around 4 msec. This led Jolly to conclude that 'the relation between the synapse times suggests that the knee-jerk mechanism involves one spinal synapse or set of synapses, while the flexion reflex involves two' (p. 87). Thus though the details are open to question Jolly would appear to have produced the first firm suggestion that the tendon jerk might be transmitted monosynaptically. About the same time Snyder (1910) re-measured the latency of the human knee-jerk using the string galvanometer and confirmed that its latency was sufficiently great to allow for reflex transmission, provided the central delay was not more than about 3 msec. The whole idea became more firmly established some ten years later on the basis of Hoffmann's (1922) extensive studies in man.

Yet another generation elapsed, however, before the mono-synaptic central transmission of the tendon reflex became firmly established by irrefutable experimental evidence. The first need was to establish the delay involved in transmission across the particular synapse involved, since without such knowledge any figure for the central delay of the jerk could be given no precise meaning. The early work would appear to have been based on the implicit assumption that the reflex of shortest delay must have been monosynaptic, for monosynaptic connections were known to exist from unspecified primary afferents to the motoneurones. Eccles & Pritchard (1937) recorded the response in the ventral root on stimulating the dorsal spinal root of the same segment and found that there was a central delay of 0·7–1 msec. This was approximately the same as the figure found by Lorente de Nó for synaptic delay at the occulomotor neurones, and so they suggested that they had observed monosynaptic transmission from the primary afferent fibres to the motoneurones.

Renshaw (1940) applied Lorente de Nó's method to spinal motoneurones and showed that the earliest spike recordable from a ventral root on stimulating a dorsal root must indeed be mono-synaptically transmitted. He did this by inserting a pair of 'small bipolar needle electrodes' (apparently of steel) directly into the grey matter of the spinal cord near the motoneurones and used them to stimulate the surrounding structures. Figure 7.1 illustrates the double response he then obtained by monophasic recording from the ventral root. The two waves appeared to be due to excitation of a single population of motoneurones via two separate routes, for on progressive increase of the stimulus strength the later wave had the lowest threshold but was then progressively occluded with the appearance of the earlier wave. Because of its short latency the earlier *m* wave could only be attributed to direct excitation of the motoneurones. This left the later *s* or synaptic wave to be attributed to the synaptic excitation of the moto-neurons as a result of the stimulus exciting their presynaptic fibres. The interval between the waves of 0·6 to 1·0 msec thus gives the value of the synaptic delay. The lower record of Fig. 7.1 shows the

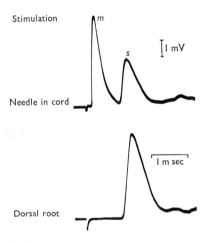

FIG. 7.1. Renshaw's demonstration of the monosynaptic transmission of the reflex response evoked in the ventral root on stimulating the dorsal root of the same segment. The records are monophasic recordings of the motor discharge set up in a ventral root either on maximal stimulation of the corresponding dorsal root (below), or on stimulating with a needle electrode in the 'intermediate gray matter' of the corresponding segment of the cord (above). The *m* wave is attributable to direct excitation of the motoneurones and the *s* wave to their synaptic excitation following stimulation of their presynaptic fibres. Thus the interval between the *m* and *s* waves gives the value of the synaptic delay. (From Figs. 1 & 2, Renshaw, 1940.)

motor discharge which is reflexly evoked in the ventral root on stimulating the dorsal root in the same preparation. The reflex response is seen to occur at such a time that it must have been mediated via a single synapse only. A mass of subsequent studies with intracellular recording leave no doubt that the conclusion is correct, though the actual delay at the synapse may be somewhat shorter than that found by Renshaw (Eccles, 1964*a*); this is largely because the foot of an EPSP (excitatory post-synaptic potential), which can now be taken as the earliest indicator of synaptic action, inevitably occurs somewhat before the spike which it elicits and which was all that Renshaw had access to.

On the basis of Renshaw's work and with the use of oscillographic recording from ventral roots, Lloyd (1943c) was finally able to close the old debate and prove that the reflex response to a brief stretch was indeed 'transmitted through arcs of two neurons'. He did this by showing that it occurred with the same central delay as the monosynaptic reflex elicited by stimulating the dorsal root in the same preparation. Figure 7.2 reproduces Lloyd's

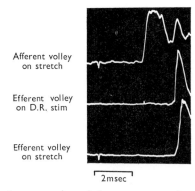

Afferent volley
on stretch

Efferent volley
on D.R. stim

Efferent volley
on stretch

2msec

FIG. 7.2. Lloyd's demonstration of the monosynaptic transmission of the tendon jerk reflex. Top, the afferent volley recorded from the peripheral end of the severed S1 dorsal root on applying a brief stretch to the gastrocnemius muscle (beginning of stretch marked by artefact). Middle, the efferent discharge recorded from the S1 ventral root on stimulating the central end of the S1 dorsal root. Bottom, the efferent volley recorded from S1 ventral root on stretching gastrocnemius. This was done earlier in the experiment before S1 dorsal root had been cut. (Lloyd, 1943c, Fig. 4.)

classical figure illustrating this finding; the middle record has been aligned so that the stimulus to the dorsal root shall occur at the point corresponding to the arrival of the afferent volley at the dorsal root in the upper record. Lloyd's preparation was the acute spinal cat in which he stretched the gastrocnemius muscle by a solenoid device; this delivered a stretch which lasted only a few milliseconds and which was therefore directly comparable to the stimulus for eliciting a normal tendon jerk. Lloyd, however, was unable to show whether or not the tendon jerk was exclusively mediated by a monosynaptic arc. The efferent responses which he observed on stretching usually consisted of several waves of increasing latency, while his measurements demonstrating mono-synaptic transmission were restricted to the earliest component. He argued convincingly that the later waves of the reflex response were most likely to have been due to his mechanical stimulus eliciting an afferent barrage which also lasted several milliseconds, probably because of repetitive firing in individual afferents. The first part of the afferent discharge would depolarise many motoneurones insufficiently to make them discharge an impulse, but would facilitate them so that they could discharge in response to the later impulses. Thus after an initial false start half a century earlier the use of progressively improved methods of physio-logical recording finally allowed the nervous signals responsible for the 'jerk phenomenon' to be traced throughout their course, and thus establish and give precision to the original clinical thesis that it was a reflex. It should be recognised, however, that this tardy success was primarily a technical achievement and had been accompanied by very little new thinking.

The receptor of origin of the tendon jerk. Once it is accepted to be reflex an immediate question about the tendon jerk is from which of the various muscle receptors does it arise? As is now well known the answer is the primary ending of the muscle spindle with its large Ia fibre, and this has been the majority view for at least the last 20 years. But again, understanding was not achieved easily and arose out of intermediate stages of error. Moreover, the correct answer has often been held on the basis of evidence which was of fairly limited cogency, but which it would now be churlish to criticise in detail as it did in fact lead to truth. The choice of the responsible receptor has long appeared to be limited to the three main types of proprioceptor, namely the primary and secon-dary endings of the spindle and the tendon organ; this limitation has been progressively confirmed as the afferents from yet other kinds of receptor have been studied electrophysiologically and shown to be insensitive to stretching. The implicit assumption usually also seems to have been made that only one out of the three kinds of receptor could be chosen.

Before about 1925 most workers deemed it appropriate to

remain silent on the issue, for there was a complete dearth of evidence on which to base a view; if anything the muscle spindle was preferred as the responsible receptor (cf. Snyder, 1910). The matter became momentarily controversial in 1928 with the recognition that when a tendon jerk was elicited in the quadriceps muscle of a decerebrate preparation the pre-existing electrical activity of the muscle ceased during the jerk contraction. Such a silent period had already been demonstrated in man during a voluntary contraction (Fig. 7.3). Fulton & Pi-Suñer (1928) attributed this silent

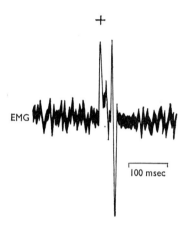

FIG. 7.3. The silent period as originally demonstrated in man. The record shows the electrical activity of the ankle extensors recorded with surface electrodes while the subject is standing on tiptoe. The achilles tendon was tapped at the +. The immediate upwards deflexion is merely an artefact due to the direct effect of the tap on the recording system. The subsequent large diphasic wave is the monosynaptically evoked reflex response of the muscle. It is followed by a period of decreased activity or 'silence'. (Hoffmann, 1920, Fig. 7.)

period to the withdrawal of pre-existing excitation of the moto-neurones as a result of a slowing of the tonic firing of a receptor which, like the muscle spindle, was placed 'in parallel' with the main muscle fibres and which would therefore be relieved of stress when the muscle contracted. The tendon jerk was seen as the central response to stimulating the same endings by a sudden stretch. Thus they suggested that both the tendon jerk and its accompanying silent period were attributable to the behaviour of the muscle spindle, which on this basis they held to produce auto-genetic excitation.

Denny-Brown (1928), however, felt unable to accept this view for in his own experiments he had been impressed by finding a silent period in synergistic muscles as well as in the one which was actually tapped. He claimed that this indicated that the silence was due to a widespread central inhibition rather than simply to the withdrawal of excitation, which on the earlier description of the strict localisation of the tonic stretch reflex (Liddell & Sherrington, 1924) might have been expected to have produced a rather localised disfacilitation. For no very good reason except the existence of the striations on the intrafusal fibres, Denny-Brown believed that the muscle spindle was a contraction receptor and so would increase its discharge during the contraction occurring in the tendon jerk. He thus suggested that the spindles produced autogenetic inhibition, leaving the tendon organs to play the role of the receptor responsible for eliciting the tendon jerk. This view collapsed abruptly with the first single fibre recordings from spindle afferents (1931–1933, Chap. 4) which showed that their discharge decreased during twitch contractions in precisely the manner suggested by Fulton & Pi-Suñer to explain the silent period. From then on it has been generally believed that spindle afferents are responsible for the tendon jerk and, as a corollary, also for the tonic stretch reflex (see later).

The question then arose as to whether the tendon jerk and with it the tonic stretch reflex should be attributed to the primary or to the secondary endings of the spindle. Again some of the evidence led down a false trail. One of the notable features of the tendon jerk is the smallness of its adequate stimulus and about that time it had been found that tap of only 8 μm extent was capable of eliciting a jerk from the supraspinatus muscle of the decerebrate cat (Denny-Brown & Liddell, 1927); the tonic stretch reflex was also known to be elicitable by a stretch of less than one mm. On recording from their afferent fibres, B. H. C. Matthews had found the tendon organ to have a relatively high threshold for the passive stretches that he used, thus helping to exclude it from being an originator of the tendon jerk. Unfortunately, he mistakenly concluded that the spindle secondary ending had a lower mechanical threshold than the primary ending (see Chap. 3) so that for the next ten years it was logical to believe that the secondary rather than the primary ending was responsible for the tendon jerk and the tonic stretch reflex.

The situation was reversed in 1943 by Lloyd's experiments on the monosynaptic transmission of the jerk reflex. In the course of these he measured the conduction velocity of the responsible afferent fibres and found the average value from a number of preparations to be 116 m/sec. This corresponded to that of the very largest fibres in the nerves to muscle and thus made the spindle primary the receptor responsible for the tendon jerk. This then became the conventional view, though it may be noted that it still depended upon a somewhat restricted interpretation of the origin of the silent period and upon measurements of the thresholds of the various kinds of receptor to rapidly applied stretches of large amplitude, rather than to the brief taps which are adequate to elicit a jerk. The conventional view was supported by McIntyre (1951) who found that the tonic stretch reflex of the masseter persisted after cutting the sensory root of the Vth nerve which was believed to contain all the afferents from its tendon organs while its spindle afferents run in the motor root of the Vth nerve; as was then usual, the tonic stretch reflex and the tendon jerk were implicitly equated.

It was not until 1960, however, that the straightforward experiment was performed of directly comparing the afferent volley elicited by the physiological stimulus of a tap and the resulting reflex action. This was done by Lundberg & Winsbury (1960) who applied a brief graded stretch to the soleus muscle and by single fibre recording showed that when below 60 μm in extent it excited solely the primary endings (see Chap. 4). They next confirmed that in their preparations such a stimulus did produce monosynaptic excitation of the motoneurones of the stretched muscle, as judged by the intracellular recording of an EPSP. By then, however, the acceptance of the Ia fibres as the origin of monosynaptic excitation was so widespread and had been in consistent harmony with such a variety of experimental results that this finally conclusive experiment had no significant effect on the development of thought. This was particularly so because just beforehand the belief in such a role for the Ia fibres had been greatly strengthened by experiments in which it had been found possible to selectively excite the Ia fibres to hip muscles by suitably weak electrical stimuli and thereby show an autogenetic monosynaptic excitatory action (see later). In addition, there had been a good deal of work which suggested that tendon organs mediated autogenetic inhibition, and were therefore excluded from mediating the tendon jerk (cf. Granit, 1955).

Thus as long believed it may now be considered fully proven that the Ia fibres can produce the tendon jerk unaided by other afferent inputs. Indeed, as far as can now be seen there is really very little opportunity for any other receptor to contribute to the initial phase of excitation leading to the actual contraction of the jerk. No other receptor is significantly excited by a brief tap of a previously non-contracting muscle, and even if it were the resulting afferent discharge would probably arrive too late to be able to influence the motoneurones before they fired in response to the Ia volley with its rapid conduction and monosynaptic transmission. Moreover, the silent period indicates a period of depressed motoneuronal excitability during which any weak excitatory effect would be precluded from manifesting itself. Other afferents, however, should be presumed to be influencing the depth of depression in the silent period and the time-course of the subsequent recovery of central excitability.

The use of electrical stimulation to study the reflex roles of the various sizes of afferent fibre

The elucidation of the receptor responsible for initiating the tendon jerk is of course only a first step in endeavouring to understand the reflex control of muscle, and in particular does nothing to unravel the central actions of the other two main classes of mechanoreceptor, namely the spindle secondaries and the tendon organs. For this it would be invaluable to possess techniques which would permit each of the three major types of afferent fibre (Ia, Ib and II) to be excited independently of the others and also in any combination with each other. Almost every physiologically natural stimulus, such as muscle stretch or muscle contraction, practically automatically simultaneously influences the discharge in all three kinds of afferent to give a compound reflex response from which their individual contributions cannot usually be convincingly disentangled. Recourse has therefore been natural to the apparent simplicity of the direct electrical stimulation of muscle nerves, with all its advantages in the precise control of the timing and size of the stimulus. The practice has been greatly encouraged by its success in studying the central mediation of the simplest processes, such as monosynaptic excitation and its accompanying disynaptic inhibition of antagonists. Moreover, no other tool is available to attempt to solve questions which are easy in the asking and for which it often appears there should be simple direct answers, such as whether a particular kind of afferent fibre produces excitation or inhibition on a particular kind of neurone and via how many intermediary synaptic connections. Thus there has been a mass of valuable work, and more can be expected, in which electrical stimulation has been used as a tool for evoking afferent volleys of approximately known functional composition and thereby used to study the reflex actions of the different kinds of receptor.

It should be remembered throughout, however, that as Sherrington said (1906, p. 12) electricity 'is always an artificial form of stimulus' and is liable to set up patterns of impulses which could never occur naturally. There is the risk therefore of evoking a correspondingly bizarre reflex response, and unlike any occurring normally. Moreover, any pattern recognition system might refuse to respond at all to such unnatural inputs. Essential features of patterning might lie in the temporal relations of the activity in different nerves, or on mixed spatio-temporal patterns, all of which as yet await artificial reproduction. The scratch reflex is notable for apparently never having been elicited by direct electrical stimulation of an isolated nerve trunk though it can be elicited by appropriate faradic stimulation of the skin with a fine needle. However, to some extent the spinal centres appear to be duly organised so that they can only emit 'sensible answers' even though the mixture of afferent inputs elicited by electrical stimulation presents them with a 'stupid question', for the central integrative processes which lead to the pre-potence of some reflexes over others usually manage to ensure that only one kind of response is emitted at any one time. In any case, almost any experimental approach however 'unphysiological' it appears at first sight should be capable of throwing some light on the way in which the central mechanisms work, though in the face of all the potential complexities experimental findings need to be interpreted with suitable caution and humility. Thus in spite of certain deficiencies electrical stimulation of nerve trunks has been one of the chief tools hitherto available for the investigation of reflex function and has yielded a rich harvest which will be considered next.

As long appreciated, the threshold of a nerve fibre to electrical stimulation varies inversely with its diameter. A sufficiently strong shock applied to a muscle nerve will thus excite every fibre in it and give a complex overall reflex response which will be governed by a variety of factors including the initial state of the reflex centres, the staggered times of arrival of the impulses in the different sizes of fibre, and how far their central effects interact. In the early days, Sherrington (1909, p. 145) succeeded in producing only an inhibition of extensor tone on stimulating nerves to muscle, although he was convinced that they contained fibres which were responsible for maintaining such tone reflexly by producing autogenetic excitation. The practice of using carefully graded stimuli so as to excite fibres of only a limited range of sizes was introduced by Lloyd (1943b, 1946a,b) and was linked to his classification of afferent fibres into four groups. The weakest stimuli excite only the largest afferent fibres so the reflex effects of these can be studied in isolation from those of all other afferents. Stronger stimuli additionally excite smaller fibres and so any new reflex effect elicited by the stronger shocks may be attributed to the recruitment of smaller fibres, and so on progressively; though it should not be forgotten that under these circumstances the smaller fibres can only manifest their action on reflex centres that have been conditioned by the slightly earlier arrival of impulses in the larger and faster fibres. Furthermore it has perhaps influenced progress that the practice of graded electrical stimulation lends itself more readily to excitation with single shocks than with repetitive trains of stimuli; this is because high-frequency firing of a nerve fibre leads to an increase in its electrical threshold so that it becomes more difficult than usual to ensure the complete activation of a group of large fibres without also exciting some smaller fibres. Repetitive stimulation, however, may be essential in some circumstances to allow a polysynaptic pathway to be sufficiently facilitated to transmit activity throughout its course.

The classical studies using ventral root recording as the indicator of reflex action. Lloyd (1943) pioneered the study of reflex action by graded electrical stimulation combined with the recording of massed motor discharges in the whole of a ventral root or a large portion of it. The recording from ventral roots greatly simplifies the investigation of autogenetic muscle reflexes since the motor fibres may be stimulated along with the afferent fibres in a severed muscle nerve without producing muscle contraction and without producing antidromic effects on the motoneurones; hitherto the muscle nerve had had to be left intact in order to preserve muscle contraction as the indicator of the reflex action.

Lloyd (1943b) gave an early summary of his findings which passed into many textbooks and is largely as follows for the reflex effects of muscle afferents: Group I, consisting of 20–12 μm diameter fibres arising from both extensor and flexor muscles, produced autogenetic excitation via a two-neurone arc, that is monosynaptic excitation of the motoneurones from which the excited afferent fibres arose. This action was equated with the tendon jerk of extensors or the similar 'pluck' responses of flexors. Group II fibres (12–6 μm, as then defined, see p. 79) were thought to arise only sparsely from muscle, but like the more numerous cutaneous group II fibres were believed to produce excitation of flexor motoneurones. This flexor action of the muscle group II fibres was thought to occur whatever the muscle of origin of the excited afferents, and whether it was itself a flexor or an extensor. The actions of all these group II fibres were equated with the flexor reflex known classically to be associated with stimulation of nociceptors and was held to be mediated polysynaptically via two or more synapses. Group III fibres from muscle again produced a flexor reflex but more powerful and with a slightly longer central latency than that evoked by group II fibres. Figure 7.4 illustrates the increasingly prolonged discharge excited in the ventral root on increasing the strength of a stimulus to the dorsal root and which has long been accepted as showing that afferent fibres of different sizes do indeed have different reflex actions. Shortly afterwards, Lloyd (1946a,b) extended the picture by systematic monosynaptic testing of the excitability of various motoneurone pools. He found that the group I input also facilitates the motoneurones of muscles which are synergistic to those whose afferent fibres have been stimulated and inhibits the motoneurones of their antagonists. On the basis of a somewhat hasty interpretation of the latency measurements which has since been disputed (see later) both the excitatory and the inhibitory actions were at that time supposed to be mediated monosynaptically.

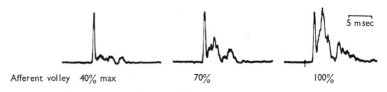

FIG. 7.4. The increase in the segmental reflex discharge observed on increasing the strength of the stimulus. The recordings were taken from the central end of the cut S1 ventral root on stimulating S1 dorsal root with shocks exciting the proportion of A fibres shown below each tracing. The fibres with a higher threshold, and which may thus be presumed to be smaller, produce no appreciable further monosynaptic excitation of motoneurones but greatly increase the polysynaptically evoked discharge. (Lloyd, 1943a, Fig. 2 re-arranged.)

During the initial phase of his work, Lloyd appears to have paid rather little attention to the receptors of origin of the various afferent fibres which he stimulated. A few years later, following Hunt & Kuffler's demonstration that group I fibres could be derived either from spindles or from tendon organs, Laporte & Lloyd (1952) attacked the problem of whether the group I reflex effects were simple or compound. By systematic monosynaptic testing of the time-course of the excitability changes occurring after various conditioning volleys they succeeded, so they believed, in fractionating the effects of group I fibres into two components. The weakest stimuli were held to produce a pure autogenetic facilitation of motoneurones with an accompanying inhibition of antagonists, as had previously been believed to be the prerogative of the whole array of group I fibres. Laporte & Lloyd believed that following a single very weak volley the degree of both the facilitation and the inhibition should properly decay in a strictly exponential manner as assessed by the size of a subsequent testing monosynaptic reflex; and this was certainly sometimes observed experimentally. A slight increase in the stimulus strength caused a sudden departure from this simple time-course from just under 1 msec after the stimulus; the curve of autogenetic facilitation then deviated in the inhibitory direction from its original course and conversely the curve for the inhibition of antagonists deviated in the direction of excitation. This is illustrated in Figs. 7.5 and 7.6. (It may be noted that for experimental reasons strictly autogenetic effects were not studied but merely those to synergists.)

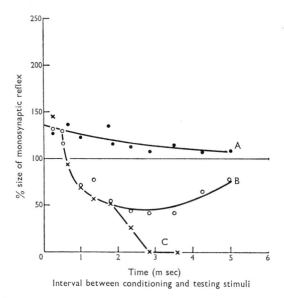

FIG. 7.5. Laporte & Lloyd's demonstration, by monosynaptic testing of motoneuronal excitability, of the appearance of inhibition on increasing the strength of the stimulus applied to a synergistic nerve. The graphs show the size of the monosynaptic reflex recorded in the ventral root in response to a stimulus to the nerve to plantaris when it was preceded at various intervals by a conditioning stimulus to the nerve to its synergist, flexor longus digitorum. Curve A was obtained with the weakest conditioning volley which was presumed to give pure monosynaptic facilitation. Curve B was obtained with a slightly stronger stimulus which was presumed to have excited also the afferent fibres from tendon organs to give a disynaptically mediated inhibition. Curve C was obtained with a yet stronger stimulus which was presumed to have additionally excited group II fibres to give a polysynaptically mediated extensor inhibition. (Laporte & Lloyd, 1952, Fig. 3.)

Further increase in the stimulus strength produced a further delayed effect which was inhibitory for extensor motoneurones and excitatory for flexor ones; this was attributed to a universal flexor action of muscle group II fibres. Yet further flexor effects were described on increasing the stimulus so as to excite group III muscle afferents. The autogenetic excitation and its associated effects produced by group I stimulation had earlier been equated with the stretch or myotatic reflex, and thus Laporte & Lloyd (1952) coined the phrase 'the inverse myotatic reflex' to describe

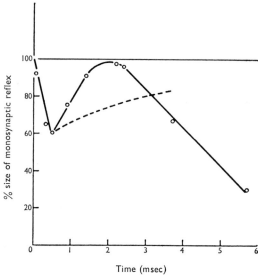

FIG. 7.6. Example of Laporte & Lloyd's disynaptic facilitatory linkage between antagonists. The solid line shows the size of the monosynaptic reflex evoked by a moderately strong stimulus to the nerve to the flexor brevis digitorum when it was preceded by a stimulus to the nerve to its antagonist, extensor longus digitorum. The dotted line shows the exponential decay of inhibition which Laporte & Lloyd believed would have occurred if the conditioning stimulus had excited solely what we now call Ia fibres to produce a pure 'direct' inhibition. Thus the deviation at 0·5 msec from this theoretical curve was attributed to the group I component of the conditioning volley producing excitation as well as inhibition, and which was thought to be due to afferents from tendon organs (Ib fibres). This argument is now recognised to be somewhat insecure though the conclusion may well be correct. The re-appearance of inhibition at an interval of 2 msec was attributed to the delayed polysynaptic action of group II fibres. (N.B. flexor brevis functions physiologically as an extensor muscle. Laporte & Lloyd, 1952, Fig. 11.)

the largely opposite effects introduced by increasing the stimulus just above the minimum for group I activation. They suggested that this pattern of response might be due to stimulating the afferents from the tendon organs.

A remarkable feature of Lloyd's important work in opening up a new field of reflex study was that he never seems to have made any personal observations on the conduction velocities and hence the sizes of the various fibres which were actually being excited by the different strengths of stimuli that he used, nor were there any very convincing measurements available to him in the literature. This deficiency was forcibly pointed out by Brock, Eccles & Rall (1951) who made such measurements in order to see for themselves the reflex effects of volleys in different kinds of afferent. They recorded the compound action potentials set up in the dorsal root on stimulating various muscle nerves, and also the potentials set up in the nerves on stimulating the dorsal root; the results were generally similar, though for any fibre that branches a slightly different response would be anticipated for the two arrangements (i.e. on recording from the root a fibre with a thick and a thin peripheral branch will behave as if it were connected solely to the thick one, while on recording from the muscle nerve each branch will contribute its own spike to the compound potential at its own time, but the threshold will be that of the parent fibre). One difference which was noted between the two situations was that the thresholds of the different sized fibres seemed to be more widely separated on stimulating the muscle nerve than the dorsal root; the same seems to be true for γ motor fibres stimulated at the corresponding sites (Boyd & Davey, 1968) and may be related to whether or not the nerve fibres are enclosed in a connective tissue sheath.

However, in spite of their extra precision Brock, Eccles & Rall (1951) added little of present significance to Lloyd's original account. They agreed with him in finding the by then well known monosynaptic facilitation on exciting group I fibres; but they did not notice any fractionation of the reflex effects of group I into more than one component, even though they felt that group I contained two functionally distinct kinds of afferent (N.B. this work slightly preceded that of Laporte & Lloyd which has just been cited). They agreed also with Lloyd in considering that for extensor muscles 'group II impulses either have no detectable actions or are weak autogenetic inhibitors' whereas for flexors group II gave 'effective' autogenetic excitation. Perhaps the chief current interest of Brock, Eccles & Rall's work lies in the thresholds they found for the different sizes of afferent fibre. Under their particular conditions, which may well also have been employed by others, they found far from perfect separation of the different groups. On using 'cathodal break shocks' the stimulus strength had to be 'increased to about twice threshold in order to set up a maximum group I spike, but a group II spike is usually detectable when the stimulus is increased to 1·3 to 1·4 times group I threshold' (their summary). Thus this work gave no support to the simple idea that the central effects of the different groups of afferent fibre could be cleanly and completely separated on the basis of their thresholds.

Further progress in the separation of Ia and Ib effects. The next stage in understanding came with the study of nerves to muscles acting at the hip rather than the previously employed muscles to the leg. This led to the tolerably successful fractionation of group I fibres into two groups on the basis of their thresholds and conduction velocities and which were thus demonstrable also to have separate central actions. The work began with Bradley & Eccles (1953) who studied the group I compound potential recorded *en passant* from an intact dorsal root with a single electrode; by chance this potential had slightly earlier been noticed often to be double. Such triphasic recording, that is with a single 'active' electrode flanked by an earth electrode on either side provided by the body of the animal, gives a record approximating to the second differential of the spike which would have been obtained with monophasic recording. Triphasic recording thus particularly emphasises small inflections on the monophasic record, such as would arise from slight differences in the times of arrival of the spikes in different fibres. Figure 7.7 shows the bifid spike recorded triphasically from the intact dorsal root on stimulating the nerve to quadriceps and is accompanied by the unimpressively inflected spike obtained with conventional monophasic recording after subsequent section of the nerve. Bradley & Eccles proceeded to show that group I autogenetic excitatory effects, as judged by monosynaptic testing, were mediated almost entirely by the first component of the spike thus demonstrating that the two groups of fibres were indeed functionally distinct. Following all contemporary thought they suggested that the fast and slow fibres arose from the spindle primaries and from the tendon organs respectively.

Definition of Ia and Ib. Bradley & Eccles' paper has the additional interest of containing the first use of the now widely

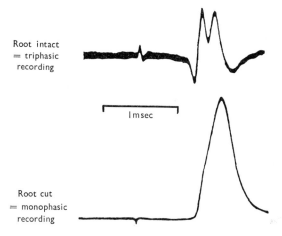

Root intact
= triphasic
recording

1 msec

Root cut
= monophasic
recording

FIG. 7.7. The bifid spike observed with triphasic recording from an intact dorsal root on stimulating the quadriceps nerve compared with the simpler spike subsequently found with monophasic recording from the same root after cutting it centrally. The two components of the bifid spike are often attributed to the Ia and Ib fibres respectively, but the separation would not now appear to be absolute. (Bradley & Eccles, 1953, Figs. 2 and 5 rearranged.)

employed terms Ia and Ib which were introduced as follows: 'Since the fast afferent fibres of muscle (group I) are known to have two major components of quite different reflex function, which respectively may be designated group I*a* from the annulospiral endings and group I*b* from the Golgi tendon organs . . . it was of interest to determine whether the double negative spike was attributable to this dual composition.' It should be specially noted that this definition of Ia and Ib fibres depends upon their receptors of origin rather than upon any distinguishable properties of the nerve fibres themselves, though the implicit assumption has been introduced that all fibres from these receptors fall into group I. The subscripts *a* and *b* appear to have been adopted on the basis of B. H. C. Matthews' original subdivision of muscle receptors into types A and B and which had long been accepted as corresponding to spindle and tendon organ endings respectively. The paper is slightly curious in that it does not state that the new terms are being introduced for the first time and the short piece omitted from the quotation given above contained reference to 11 separate papers to justify the preceding statement. All of these papers contained evidence for functionally subdividing group I, but none of them used the abbreviated terms Ia and Ib though Hunt & Kuffler (1951) came close to it in showing that both type A and B receptors contributed to group I.

A year later Hunt (1954) used the same terms without reference to Bradley & Eccles but with the subscripts written in capitals rather than in small letters, that is IA and IB rather than Ia and Ib. For many years the two virtually identical terminologies co-existed and the particular one employed by any particular author provided a guide to his scientific parentage. But gradually Ia and Ib have come to be the preferred forms with the a and b written in ordinary small letters rather than in italics, even though Eccles & Bradley had originally written them in the latter way. As much as anything the present acceptance of Ia and Ib seems to have been due to Eccles' continuing influence, and it was he himself who dropped the italic notation rather early on in favour of the now standard Ia and Ib (for example at least as early as 1957, see Eccles, Eccles & Lundberg, 1957a).

Bradley, Easton & Eccles (1953) immediately used the newly discovered slight difference in threshold of the Ia and Ib fibres to study by monosynaptic testing the time course of the inhibition produced by an afferent volley which was restricted to Ia fibres. They could not confirm that this decayed in the strictly exponential way previously described by Lloyd (1946a), but as illustrated in Fig. 7.8 found an initial decrease which was far too fast in relation to the later decay. This work thus undermined Laporte & Lloyd's interpretation that any such deviation from the simple curve could be attributed to an excitatory action of Ib fibres on antagonists and thereby upset part of the argument for the existence of an 'inverse myotatic reflex'. Subsequent intracellular studies (cf. Eccles, 1957) have led to a separation of the action of a completely pure inhibitory volley into two phases and suggest that simple exponential recovery of excitability should be rare. There is an initial change in conductance of the post-synaptic membrane which lasts for the duration of action of the transmitter and which may or may not lead to a change of membrane potential, though there typically is one in the hyperpolarising direction. After transmitter action terminates any change in membrane potential decays away in a reasonably exponential

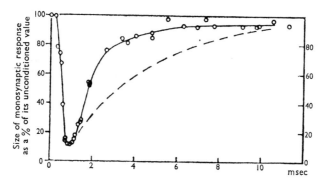

Interval between conditioning and testing stimuli

FIG. 7.8. The time-course of the inhibition of an antagonist produced by a supposedly pure group Ia volley. The solid line shows the size of the monosynaptic reflex evoked by stimulation of the nerve to biceps-semitendinosus when it was preceded by a weak stimulus to the nerve to its antagonist, quadriceps. The dotted line shows a simple exponential with a half-time of decay of 2·8 msec as originally described by Lloyd (1946a) and which clearly cannot be made to fit the experimental points. (Bradley, Easton & Eccles, 1953, Fig. 2.)

manner. However, many of Laporte & Lloyd's conclusions rested equally on a difference in threshold for the fibres producing excitation of antagonists from those producing inhibition (cf. Fig. 7.5) and in which it is still respectable to believe. At the present distance it seems impossible to disentangle the relative reliance Laporte & Lloyd placed on their two criteria and thus to decide how far they were justified in adumbrating the concept of an 'inverse myotatic reflex'.

Ib action assessed by intracellular recording. The matter was re-examined a few years later by Eccles, Eccles & Lundberg (1957a, c) using the newly introduced intracellular recording from moto-neurones and taking depolarising potentials as a sign of excitation and hyperpolarising ones to indicate inhibition. As a preliminary they confirmed that, as expected, the monosynaptically induced autogenetic EPSP depended upon the first component of the double spike set up in the dorsal root on stimulating nerves to muscles of the hip. They found, furthermore, that though stimulation of many other nerves did not lead to such a double spike,

MM

none the less a nearly maximal monosynaptic EPSP was often elicited by stimuli which excited a far from maximal group I volley. They attributed this to the Ia fibres having a lower threshold to electrical stimulation than the Ib fibres even though they did not fall cleanly into two groups separable on their conduction velocity.

Eccles, Eccles & Lundberg (1957c) then employed fine gradations of stimulus strength to investigate the reflex effects of the Ib fibres. They recognised that there must be a certain overlap in the diameter of the two kinds of afferent fibre and reached the conclusion that an effect was attributable to Ib fibres 'by watching the evolution of changes in the synaptic potential as a progressively larger stimulus was applied to the afferent nerve' (p. 230) and relating this to the range of stimuli required to excite fibres of different sizes. The threshold of the Ib fibres was determined by a standard double volley technique which improves on single volley techniques in the detection of the first appearance of the slow component of the bifid compound action potential obtained with triphasic recording. In addition, in order to assist in the recognition of inhibitory effects superimposed on excitatory effects, they sometimes hyperpolarised the motoneurone membrane by passing current from the microelectrode. This transmutes the inhibitory potential from a hyperpolarising to a depolarising direction, as a result of elevating the membrane potential above the reversal potential for the IPSP. As illustrated in Fig. 7.9 a delayed inhibitory action was then more readily detected as a second wave of depolarisation rather than, as normally, by an unduly rapid decay of the initial monosynaptically evoked EPSP. But this did nothing to improve the differentiation of the effects of Ib and II fibres which was often far from easy.

Eccles, Eccles & Lundberg (1957c) found that the Ib effects elicited by stimulating nerves to extensor muscles were not unlike those described by Laporte & Lloyd, that is inhibition of extensors with an accompanying excitation of flexor motoneurones. On the basis of latency measurements, both effects were thought to be usually mediated disynaptically but trisynaptic pathways were also considered to be available. However, both the excitatory and the inhibitory Ib actions seemed to be more widely distributed than those originally described by Laporte & Lloyd and there was no particular tendency to purely autogenetic inhibitory effects. Thus

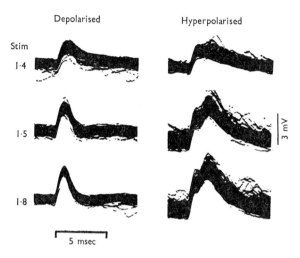

Depolarised   Hyperpolarised

Stim
1·4

1·5

3 mV

1·8

5 msec

FIG. 7.9. Ib autogenetic inhibitory effects shown by the appearance of a definite IPSP with increase of the stimulus strength. Intracellular recordings taken from a gastrocnemius motoneurone on stimulating the nerve to gastrocnemius with the ventral roots cut. The figures on the very left show the strength of the stimulus relative to the group I threshold; a stimulus of 1·8 was just sufficient to excite all the group I fibres. The records on the left were taken with the cell somewhat depolarised when the IPSP manifests itself as an unduly rapid return of the initial EPSP to the baseline. The records on the right were taken with the cell hyperpolarised by the passage of a steady current from the microelectrode so that its membrane potential was then greater than the reversal value for the IPSP. The IPSP then manifests itself as a second wavelet of depolarisation superimposed on the EPSP. (Eccles, Eccles & Lundberg, 1957c, Fig. 1.)

the 'inverse myotatic reflex' no longer appeared to be the simple inverse of the monosynaptic reflex in its distribution and so was possibly misnamed. Nor were these Ib effects found in every motoneurone of a given kind. On stimulating nerves to flexor muscles, Eccles, Eccles & Lundberg observed a remarkable poverty of Ib reflex effects of any kind. Thus on 173 occasions on which they stimulated the combined nerves to the pretibial flexor muscles while recording intracellularly from one or other of a variety of motoneurones they saw Ib effects in only 7 of them. Eccles, Eccles & Lundberg seemed to feel that this reflected on Laporte & Lloyd's findings and it had certainly failed to confirm them, but at this distance in time the whole complex problem would appear to have been dealt with somewhat too cursorily by all parties concerned. A particular point of difference between the two groups of workers was that Laporte & Lloyd worked on acute high-spinal cats in the absence of anaesthesia, whereas Eccles, Eccles & Lundberg used low-spinal cats anaesthetised with barbiturate. There is now no particular reason to think that the two preparations need give identical responses, since there is the possibility of different 'biasses' on the relevant interneurones.

Quite recently, Hongo, Jankowska & Lundberg (1969) performed experiments essentially similar to those of Eccles, Eccles & Lundberg, but with the addition of short bursts of conditioning stimulation to the red nucleus. This greatly facilitated the previously described Ib effects from extensor nerves and also allowed previously unobserved Ib effects from flexor nerves to show themselves clearly. The typical pattern was the inhibition of flexors with excitation of extensors expected from Laporte & Lloyd's work, but as with the corresponding Ib effects from extensor nerves the distribution of the effects was too widespread to be accommodated in the concept of an 'inverse myotatic reflex' operating solely at a single joint; for example stimulation of nerves to hip muscles, whether flexor or extensor, frequently evoked effects in motoneurones of muscles acting at the knee. Moreover, on some occasions completely discordant findings were obtained, with flexor Ib fibres giving extensor excitation and flexor inhibition, instead of the usual opposites. Not unreasonably Hongo, Jankowska & Lundberg (1969) left the matter at that, stating 'clearly the Ib pathways are much more complex in their organisation than has hitherto been supposed'. Much thus remains for future investigation.

Testing of the efficacy of Ia/Ib separation by single afferent fibre recording. It was a curious feature of the work of the early to mid 1950's that none of the workers using electrical stimulation as a tool for investigating reflex function got round to performing the control recordings from single afferent fibres which were needed to allow unequivocal interpretation of their findings. Laporte & Bessou filled this deficiency in 1957 and fortunately were able to confirm that the Ia fibres to hip muscles may indeed have a lower threshold than the Ib fibres, but in so doing they

showed that the matter was not invariably as clear-cut as it sometimes appeared to be made out to be. In the first place, they only
succeeded in finding a double spike on stimulating hip nerves in
about half their preparations so its occurrence would not appear
to be universal. In those cats which did show an obviously bifid
group I spike they isolated 100 group I fibres as functionally single
units in dorsal root filaments. These were then classified as
originating from spindle endings and tendon endings on the usual
criterion of their behaviour during a muscle twitch. Sixty-three
fibres fell into the fast subdivision of group I, and of these 60
came from spindles and only 3 from tendon organs. Thus the
belief that the fast subgroup came exclusively from spindles was
substantiated for all practical purposes. In view of their rapid
conduction these spindle afferents were then, and still may be,
attributed to primary endings. Thirty-seven fibres fell into the
slower subdivision of group I. Of these, 27 came from tendon
organs demonstrating that a volley in the slow group of fibres
does contain a very significant Ib component. However, the
remaining 10 slower fibres came from spindle endings. At that
time there were no methods available, save measurement of conduction velocity, for distinguishing between the afferents from
spindle primaries and secondaries and so Bessou & Laporte left it
open as to the kind of endings in which these relatively slow
group I fibres terminated. From the point of view of reflex
function, however, this still incompletely resolved problem is a
matter of some importance. At any rate, Laporte & Bessou's work
showed that it was impossible to recruit a pure Ib input, uncontaminated by spindle afferents, by simple increase of stimulus
strength. Moreover, they also noted that in their hands it was
exceptional to be able to recruit the whole of the fast subgroup
without also exciting some of the slow subgroup, that is to say
that under their particular stimulating arrangements fibres were
not recruited strictly in order of their size. Slightly later the same
point was made by Kuno & Perl (1960) in relation to the recruitment of higher threshold group II fibres which was always accompanied by 'varying amounts of activity conducted at group III
velocity' (their p. 108).

The situation for the more commonly used triceps surae nerves
was later put to the test by Sumner (1961) who determined the
electrical thresholds for a number of single fibres classified

according to their receptor of origin. This enabled him to synthe-
sise the response curve for the nerve shown in Fig. 7.10. Here the

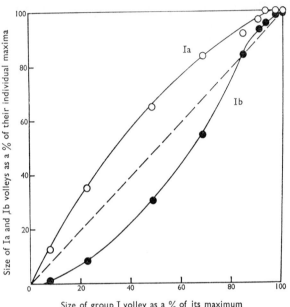

FIG. 7.10. Synthetic curve showing the percentage recruitment of Ia
and Ib fibres with growth of the group I volley elicited by increasing the
strength of a stimulus to the medial gastrocnemius nerve. The dotted
line shows what would have happened if the distribution of the thresholds
of the Ia and Ib fibres had been the same; in fact the very smallest group
I volleys were restricted to Ia fibres, but appreciable further increase in
the group I volley depended upon the recruitment of both kinds of fibre.
The results were obtained by measuring the electrical thresholds of about
200 single afferents which had been classified by receptor of origin.
(Sumner, 1961.)

proportion of the Ia and of the Ib fibres which are excited by each
of a range of stimuli are plotted against the total size of the group I
volley excited by the same stimuli. Again, a very weak stimulus
could excite a virtually pure Ia input but by the time the Ia
volley is half maximal there is appreciable Ib excitation (16% of
maximum); also, as with the hip muscles, at no point could Ib
fibres be recruited without Ia fibres. This is all just what was

expected from the earlier measurement of the conduction velocities of Ia and Ib fibres (Hunt & Kuffler, 1951; Hunt, 1954, see
Chap. 4). Figure 7.11 shows roughly similar types of curves from

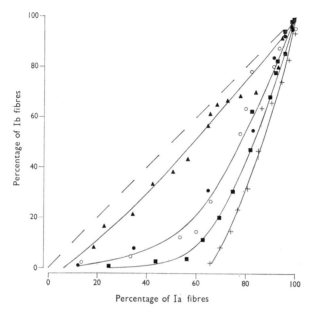

FIG. 7.11. Recent data for several muscle nerves showing the differing
extent to which Ia fibres can be excited without Ib fibres. Notice that the
plotting differs slightly from that of Fig. 7.10. The abscissa is now the
percentage of Ia fibres excited by stimuli of each of a number of strengths.
The ordinate is the percentage of Ib fibres excited by the same stimuli.
Thus each point compares the effect of the same stimulus on the two
kinds of afferent. ▲, peroneus longus for which the Ia and Ib excitabilities
are almost identical; ●, o, medial gastrocnemius (●, same data as that
plotted in Fig. 7.10; o, more recent data); ■, soleus; +, semitendinosus
for which over 60% of the Ia fibres could be excited without Ib fibres.
(Hitherto unpublished data from work of Coppin, Jack & McIntyre,
1969, and Jack & MacLennan, 1971.)

recent work on several different muscle nerves and emphasises
that there is no consistency about whether or not Ia and Ib fibres
can be separately excited by grading the strength of the stimulus
(Coppin, Jack & McIntyre, 1969; Jack & MacLennan, 1971). So
far the two extremes are provided by the nerve to the semitendinosus (+, far right) for which over 60% of the Ia fibres can

be excited without Ib fibres, and by the nerve to peroneus longus (▲, to the left) for which it is virtually impossible to excite Ia fibres without Ib fibres. Where they occur, the differences in excitability of Ia and Ib fibres seem likely to reflect differences in the sizes of the relevant afferent fibres themselves. This is argued by results such as those shown in Fig. 7.12 where there is an approximately linear relation between excitability and conduction velocity when they are studied for a number of fibres in a single preparation. However, Fig. 7.12 also shows that there is enough scatter in the relation for the recruitment of fibres with increase of stimulus strength not to be absolutely strictly in order of fibre size, and this also produces a definite blurring of the boundary between group I and II. Less strict attention to experimental detail might well produce more scatter in the results, with a corresponding loss in the precision of electrical stimulation as a tool for exciting fibres of different kinds; for example, any kind of trauma to the nerve might well have a greater effect on some fibres than others even though they are all the same size.

In view of all this, interest attaches to a new way of electrically exciting Ib afferents on their own. This was introduced by Coppin, Jack & MacLennan (1970) who used a prolonged period of high-frequency vibration to selectively activate intact Ia fibres (see Chap. 4) and thereby raise their threshold to electrical stimulation. After some 20 minutes vibration at 200 Hz the threshold of the Ia fibres has risen above that of the Ib fibres, which have not been activated by the vibration, and remains so for some 5–15 min. During this period it should prove possible to produce a pure Ib volley simply by weak electrical stimulation and thereby to investigate the central action of Ib fibres, but this has yet to be exploited in reflex studies.

In closing this section on electrical stimulation it should be mentioned that physiological methods of activating the afferent fibres via their receptors are probably at least as good for achieving selectivity of activation within the group I range. High-frequency vibration or a brief tap applied to a non-contracting muscle both produce a virtually pure excitation of Ia fibres. Muscle contraction elicited by weak low-frequency repetitive stimulation of ventral root filaments produces a powerful Ib excitation with relatively little spindle contamination. (The first of the train of stimuli will commonly elicit an 'early discharge' from some of the Ia fibres,

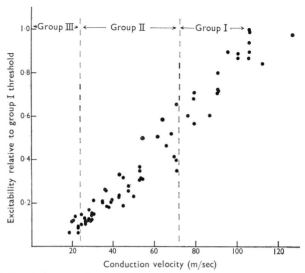

FIG. 7.12. A recent determination of the relation between excitability and fibre conduction velocity for fibres of groups I and II. Each point shows the excitability of a single afferent fibre relative to that of the most excitable group I fibres of the same preparation and measured at the same time (excitability = 1/threshold). All the data was obtained in a single experiment in which the semitendinosus nerve was stimulated with square pulses of 50 μsec duration. The action potentials were recorded from dorsal root filaments. No attempt was made to determine the receptors of origin of the various fibres. The boundaries between groups I, II and III have been drawn in their conventional positions. (Coppin, C.M.L., 1970, hitherto unpublished data.)

but the later stimuli are unlikely to do so. Fusimotor excitation of the spindle afferent endings, whether by γ or by β fibres, will be minimal when the frequency of stimulation is made just, but no more than, adequate to elicit a fused contraction of the extra-fusal muscle fibres.) The particular advantages of electrical stimulation are its experimental convenience, including the fact that each of a number of different muscles may be studied at the same time, and the accuracy with which it allows the effects of a single volley of impulses to be traced round a simple neural pathway and most notably the monosynaptic one. Physiological methods of activation, including simple stretching, may perhaps prove to be the more appropriate for investigating the more com-plicated neural mechanisms which are presumably normally in operation continuously balancing the effects of a number of different kinds of input from a variety of sources. A difficulty in studying these more complicated mechanisms, however, is that they are likely to be integrating the signals from a number of different muscles so that stretch of a single muscle still produces an unduly restricted type of afferent input. The presentation of a suitably physiological type of stimulus, however, becomes a somewhat formidable technical problem. It is all becoming very difficult and it may be doubted whether any of the methods presently available are adequate to sort out the full complexity of spinal reflex action. For example, a pattern recognition system might well fail to respond at all to a single synchronous afferent volley, for this represents an unnatural spatial and temporal combination of impulses in different kinds of fibre. For the time being, however, electrical stimulation remains one of the better methods available and in spite of its obvious deficiencies its continued use has led to an appreciable accumulation of knowledge.

Further description of Ia actions

Pattern of distribution of excitation. One objective in the study of reflexes is to identify the pattern of connections underlying any particular form of behaviour. Among other things this entails tracing the effects of a given input to see how widely it is disseminated to produce either excitation or inhibition of different neurones. The classical example of such a study was provided by Sherrington who enumerated the various muscles which took part in the flexor reflex whether by contracting or relaxing (Sherrington, 1910); indeed the recognition of which muscles then contract probably remains the most meaningful way of classifying a muscle, or part of one, as a physiological flexor. Because of their relative simplicity the reflex effects of the group Ia fibres have lent themselves to a more detailed study in such a respect than has any other group of afferent fibres. In particular, their monosynaptic excitatory action on motoneurones occurs without any complicating interneurone, so all that need be sought is the simple wiring diagram of which motoneurones are supplied by the Ia fibres of each individual muscle, and how powerfully; in doing this, however, it should not be forgotten that the synaptic potency of any particular Ia fibre can vary with the state of its initial membrane polarisation as determined by preceding activity (e.g. for example, by post-tetanic potentiation) and by synapses ending on the afferent itself (presynaptic inhibition).

Lloyd (1943b) opened the study by finding that in the acute spinal cat 'the two-neuron-arc discharge reflects into the stimulated muscle nerve' but not into others; he did this by stimulating group I fibres and looking to see whether or not action potentials were discharged down each of several nerves. Shortly afterwards (1946b), he used monosynaptic testing of excitability to show that group I fibres produced also a subthreshold facilitation of motoneurones of muscles which were synergistic and acted at the same joint as the one whose afferents were stimulated, but under his conditions these synergistic motoneurones did not actually fire. No action at all was thought to be produced on motoneurones of muscles acting at neighbouring joints. Muscles such as the gastrocnemius, which can act at two joints (powerful ankle extensor, weak knee flexor), were thought to be connected reflexly to only one system of Ia fibres though by their peripheral mechanical arrangement were considered to act as 'bridges between adjacent myotatic units'. The myotatic unit consisted of all the major muscles acting at a single joint and these were supposed to be welded into a functional unit by the monosynaptic Ia excitation of synergists with an accompanying inhibition of antagonists.

Ten years later the advent of intracellular recording allowed the matter to be taken up in more detail; the distribution of monosynaptic excitation could then be more expeditiously assessed than before by recording the sizes of the EPSPs evoked in a motoneurone on stimulating a number of different nerves. This was done for a range of leg, hip and forearm muscles (Eccles, Eccles & Lundberg, 1957b; Eccles, R. M. & Lundberg, 1958a; Schmidt & Willis, 1963). The results in the main confirmed what was already believed and, in particular, fortified the conclusion that monosynaptic excitation always reflected back on to motoneurones whose afferents had been excited and also to their close synergists. However, some more distant Ia excitatory connections were also observed, such as from vasto-crureus (a knee extensor) to soleus (an ankle extensor) and to adductor femoris (a hip extensor); in return vasto-crureus received excitatory connection from adductor femoris but not from soleus. Other examples of monosynaptic excitation occurring between functionally related muscles acting at different joints were also quoted. Eccles, R. M. & Lundberg

(1958*a*) particularly emphasised that the distribution of Ia inhibitory actions was often more widespread than originally suggested by Lloyd and stated that the connections of the Ia fibres 'are much more complex than those postulated by the hypothesis of the myotatic unit' which had achieved its simplicity by relying exclusively upon a study of muscles acting at the knee and ankle. They felt that in future attention should be directed to groups of muscles which commonly function together even though they may act at different joints. Indeed, the argument may now reasonably be reversed and the finding of a monosynaptic connection between one muscle and another taken to show that they are closely related in function, even if this had not been previously deduced from their anatomical relationship. In the baboon hand, the distribution of Ia excitation has also been shown to be rather widespread (Clough, Kernell & Phillips, 1968). Thus there is no longer any question of the monosynaptic pathway providing a purely private line from a muscle back to itself as at one time tended to be believed.

Strength of Ia excitatory action on individual motoneurones

The strength of action of the Ia fibres in any particular nerve on the motoneurones in any particular motor nucleus is readily assessed by measuring the size of the EPSP set up on maximal group I stimulation. Table 7.1 shows figures for the three com-

TABLE 7.1. The average sizes in mV of the EPSP's evoked in motoneurones of the three components of the triceps surae on stimulating the Ia fibres of a number of nerves.

	Motoneurone recorded from		
Nerve stimulated	Medial Gastroc. (mV)	Lat. Gastroc. (mV)	Soleus (mV)
Medial Gastroc.	**6·2**	3·0	2·3
Lat. Gastroc.	1·05	**3·0**	1·85
Soleus	2·3	1·7	**5·6**
Plantaris	0·05	1·1	1·3
Quadriceps	0	0·05	0·95
Total EPSP	9·6	8·85	12·0

The bold print emphasizes the values for homonymous responses (i.e. found on recording from motoneurones belonging to the stimulated nerve. From Table 3, p. 36, Eccles, Eccles & Lundberg, 1957*b*; each figure is based on recordings from 6 to 20 neurones).

ponents of the triceps surae. It may be seen that a large EPSP is always set up on stimulating the Ia fibres of the same muscle as the motoneurone (bold print). In addition, however, appreciable potentials may be set up by nerves to synergists, and it is notable that lateral gastrocnemius motoneurones received as much excitation from medial gastrocnemius Ia fibres as from their own; this may be partly related to the greater number of spindles in the medial muscle (about 60 as opposed to 35). Within any particular motor nucleus it seems likely that every motoneurone is supplied by almost every Ia fibres belonging to the same muscle. The evidence for this generalisation is Mendell & Henneman's (1968, 1971) finding that on stimulating single Ia fibres from the medial gastrocnemius they could record an EPSP from virtually every medial gastrocnemius motoneurone penetrated on stimulating any particular single Ia fibre (i.e. in 74 out of 77 motoneurones studied in 1968 on stimulating one or other of 12 single Ia fibres); conversely this shows that individual Ia fibres branch widely, for the medial gastrocnemius is supplied by about 300 motoneurones. In broadly similar later experiments stimulation of one or a few Ia fibres from a synergistic muscle was found to produce an EPSP in just under half the motoneurones studied, in comparison with 90% of them on stimulating strictly homonymous fibres, though the average amplitude of the potentials was nearly the same in the two cases (Jack, Miller, Porter & Redman, 1970; Mendell & Henneman, 1971). Thus the variation in the size of the EPSP's found for different types of motoneurone on stimulating any particular nerve (Table 7.1) is probably determined largely by the number of Ia fibres supplying the individual motoneurones of different motor nuclei, rather than by a differing potency of action of individual Ia fibres on different motoneurones. On the other hand, the EPSP's elicited from different cells on stimulating any particular Ia fibre may vary at least tenfold in size (20–200 μV, Mendell & Henneman, 1968) suggesting that individual Ia fibres may have a variable number of branches on to individual motoneurones; the number would appear to increase with the size of the afferent fibre.

A further factor influencing the size of the EPSP was investigated by Burke (1968) who studied the distribution of monosynaptic effects to motoneurones of different sizes, as judged by their 'input resistance' which varies inversely with size. He found that among those of the triceps surae the smaller ones tended to have larger EPSP's; this difference was best seen on maximal stimulation of the homonymous nerve (i.e. that from the same muscle as the motoneurone studied). Thus the smaller cells would be expected to be the more readily brought to discharge by Ia monosynaptic action. This is particularly interesting because the smaller cells supply the more slowly contracting muscle fibres which are the ones that are most readily excited in the course of the tonic stretch reflex. The correlation between the size of the Ia-evoked EPSP and the speed of contraction was confirmed by recording the contractions of single motor units elicited by the intracellular stimulation of the very same single motoneurones in which EPSP's were recorded. Burke concluded that the smaller motoneurones had a higher density of Ia terminals per unit of surface area than did the larger ones, but he could not decide whether or not the absolute number of Ia terminations also varied with the size of the cell. The higher input resistance of the smaller cells means that the same absolute amount of transmitter liberated by a fixed number of terminals would produce a larger depolarisation in a smaller cell, for the resulting change in membrane conductance would be relatively greater. Thus Kuno & Miyahara (1969) estimated the size of the 'unit EPSP' (considered to be due to the release of a 'quantum' of transmitter) and found it to increase with the input resistance of the motoneurone studied. On the basis of a slower time-course of the EPSP in the smaller cells, Burke suspected that in comparison with the large cells the small cells had a relatively higher proportion of their Ia fibres terminating fairly distally on the dendrites; more recent studies, however, have not really confirmed this view (Jack, Miller, Porter & Redman, 1970; Mendell & Henneman, 1971). In the baboon's forearm, those motoneurones which have large EPSPs on Ia stimulation also tend to have large potentials evoked monosynaptically on stimulating the motor cortex (Clough, Kernell & Phillips, 1968). These results on the primate also furnish an example of the wide variation in the total Ia receptivity of the motoneurones of different muscles, that is to say in the wide differences in the size of the maximum EPSP which may be evoked by simultaneously stimulating all available nerves. Thus even such an apparently simple matter as the description of the 'wiring diagram' of the direct connections from Ia fibres to motoneurones has turned out to be moderately complex.

Possible existence of polysynaptic Ia autogenetic excitatory pathways. The demonstration of the important monosynaptic connection from the Ia fibres to motoneurones does not of itself exclude the possibility of the same Ia fibres further exciting the same motoneurones via polysynaptic pathways. Indeed, unless they can act polysynaptically the Ia fibres would appear to have a somewhat restricted route available to them for influencing the motoneurones. Szentágothai (1958), on the basis of light microscopy, and Conradi (1970), on the basis of electro microscopy, have suggested that the Ia fibres provide only about 0.5% of the synaptic terminals to be found on the soma and proximal dendrites of the motoneurone; the Ia terminals were recognised by their showing degenerative changes following section of the dorsal roots.

The bulk of the electrophysiological work investigating the monosynaptic pathway has been limited to experiments with single shocks applied in the anaesthetised or acute spinal cat. If significant polysynaptic activity occurred under these conditions it would be expected to have been recognised long ago for it should manifest itself as a prolonged motoneuronal depolarisation with a related prolonged increase in their excitability. The problem then becomes one of identifying the duration of the 'transmitter action' underlying the generation of the EPSP evoked by stimulation; if it is suitably short, polysynaptic action is excluded. If it is long, further experimentation is required to distinguish between the delayed arrival of presynaptic impulses via polysynaptic pathways and a slow destruction, with resulting persistence of action, of a transmitter liberated by monosynaptic Ia action. In the early 1950's this seemed a simple question, for in respect of its passive electrical behaviour the motoneurone then tended to be thought of as simply consisting of just one resistor and one capacitor arranged 'in parallel'. A single measurement of 'the membrane time constant' was thus thought to permit unequivocal determination of the time-course of transmitter action, which was equated with the time-course of the current injection required to reproduce the form of the EPSP in the simple model. Arguing along these lines such transmitter action was thus found to be too short (1–2 msec) to indicate the existence of any polysynaptic action, nor were there any of the bumps on the falling phase of the EPSP which might have been expected with any delayed arrival of presynaptic impulses. There was, it is true, a prolonged 'tail' of transmitter action lasting for about 10 msec which was found on Ia activation of the motoneurone but which did not occur for the Ia inhibition of antagonists. This tail, however, was not considered to indicate any polysynaptic action because it could be selectively abolished by hyperpolarising the motoneuronal membrane and this should not have interfered with polysynaptic transmission (Eccles, 1957, Fig. 23).

More recently, the early simple model of the motoneurone has been abandoned in favour of ones which recognise the complexities introduced by the distribution of resistance and capacitance in the dendrites, and that synaptic action need not be uniformly distributed over the entire surface of the neurone. The determination of the duration of transmitter action is then no longer so straightforward and the 'tail' of transmitter action is seen to have probably been an artefact arising from an unduly simple analysis. But equally with this improved understanding the ordinary EPSP evoked by Ia action is still generally thought of as attributable purely to the monosynaptic excitation of the motoneurone. It may be noted, however, that much recent work has attained analytical precision by working with the minimal EPSPs evoked by stimulating single Ia fibres; such experiments would be unlikely to be able to show whether polysynaptic pathways exist, for these would then be unlikely to be adequately facilitated to respond to such a limited input. None the less, it appears improbable that in spinal or in anaesthetised cats appreciable Ia excitation of motoneurones occurs via polysynaptic pathways. This leaves the matter open for other types of preparation since the relevant interneurones, if they exist, may require facilitation from other sources, notably supraspinal ones, in order to be able to transmit Ia activity.

Particular interest therefore attaches to various experiments on the decerebrate cat which would all be most simply explained by postulating the existence of a polysynaptic pathway for Ia autogenetic excitation, though probably none of them would be taken as firmly establishing its existence. The earliest experiments were those of Alvord & Fuortes (1953) who recorded the reflex response of single motor units in ventral root filaments on stimulating the gastrocnemius nerves at 100–200/sec. This led the units studied to discharge rhythmically at 10–20/sec. When the stimulus was strong and excited all the group I fibres the individual responses occurred with a fixed latency after the individual stimuli and appeared attributable simply to monosynaptic excitation. But when the stimulus was weak and excited a markedly submaximal group I volley (as judged by their published records) the spikes became 'less strictly linked or randomly organised with respect to the stimulus' (their p. 313), though there was no doubt that the efferent discharge was reflexly elicited for it ceased on cessation of stimulation. Such behaviour is what would be expected if mono- and polysynaptic pathways were arranged 'in parallel'; Alvord and Fuortes clearly recognised this although they expressed their conclusion slightly differently.

A few years later Granit, Phillips, Skoglund & Steg (1957) published a hypothetical wiring diagram showing such an arrangement. The evidence on which they presented this suggestion was the finding that the reflex response of single units recorded in the ventral root in response to stretching the gastrocnemius muscle might be facilitated for a minute or more following the elicitation of a crossed extensor reflex or a pinna reflex which also caused the unit to discharge. They believed that this prolonged facilitation was due to 'post-tetanic potentiation' of some axon terminal which was common to the stretch reflex and to the other reflexes and so they thought that the facilitation indicated that the Ia fibres elicited the stretch reflex by polysynaptic pathways as well as by the monosynaptic one. However, in the light of further knowledge several other processes in addition to post-tetanic potentiation may be proposed as the basis for their finding of a prolonged facilitation and the need for postulating an interneurone on the Ia pathway then disappears. The chief current interest of their paper is to show that the idea of an exclusive monosynaptic transmission for Ia activity has never been considered inviolable.

Some years later again, Tsukahara & Ohye (1964) repeated Alvord & Fuortes' experiment, apparently in ignorance of its prior performance, and obtained much the same result; from this they drew the explicit conclusion that in the decerebrate cat excitatory Ia autogenetic actions could be transmitted polysynaptically. They confirmed that the response of a motoneurone, judged by single unit recording from the ventral root, could occur with a variable latency when elicited by a half maximal group I volley in the gastrocnemius nerves. Moreover, when a spike was discharged it

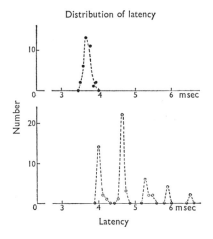

FIG. 7.13. Evidence suggesting that in the decerebrate cat Ia fibres may excite synergists via polysynaptic pathways as well as monosynaptically. The graphs show the distribution of the latencies of the spikes discharged by a single motor fibre, isolated in a ventral root filament, on stimulating a muscle nerve at the strength required to elicit a half-maximal group I volley. Above, on stimulation of the lateral gastrocnemius nerve which elicited a response of constant short latency which was presumably transmitted monosynaptically. Below, on stimulation of the plantaris nerve which elicited responses occurring either with the short latency appropriate to monosynaptic transmission or with longer latencies suggesting transmission via interneurones. The nerves were stimulated at 50/sec but the motor fibre responded at only about a quarter of this rate. The injection of a sub-anaesthetic dose of nembutal (5 mg/kg) blocked the presumed polysynaptic responses. The absence of a demonstrable polysynaptic response from gastrocnemius may perhaps merely have been due to greater strength of its monosynaptic excitatory pathway to the particular motoneurone studied. (Tsukahara & Ohye, 1964, Fig. 2.)

tended to occur at certain fixed intervals after the stimulus; the intervals increased in steps of 0·6 msec which they saw as the time required for transmission via a further interneurone for each increase in latency. This is illustrated in Fig. 7.13. The only puzzling thing about this interpretation is that there should be such a chain of interneurones standing by to provide so many alternative pathways.

Quite recently, Pacheco & Guzmán (1969) recorded intracellularly from motoneurones in cats which had been made spastic by a lesion of the sensori-motor cortex some 2–4 months before-hand; the lesion might have led to trophic changes in the pre-dominance of alternative spinal pathways. In these animals they found EPSPs to be evoked with such a long latency that poly-synaptic transmission seemed inevitable even with stimuli to the nerve which were well below group I maximum. Thus there seems a real possibility that Ia fibres may have poly- as well as monosynaptic pathways available for eliciting autogenetic excita-tion. It would be valuable to have more detailed work explicitly directed towards exploring whether or not this is so.

'Direct' inhibitory actions of Ia fibres. It is now generally accepted that as well as producing autogenetic excitation Ia fibres also inhibit the motoneurones of antagonistic muscles via a disynaptic pathway, with a single interneurone intercalated between the afferent fibre and the motoneurone. Once again, agreement on an apparently simple matter was slow to achieve. The story started in 1940 with Lloyd's description of what he called 'direct inhibition'. He introduced this term on the basis of recording the motor dis-charge in the S1 ventral root on stimulating the L6 and S1 dorsal roots at various time intervals. On its own, the S1 stimulus elicited the usual polyphasic segmental reflex discharge of which the earliest component had at that time just been shown to be attributable to monosynaptic action. When the S1 stimulus was preceded by the L6 stimulus the monosynaptic reflex was inhi-bited to a variable degree depending upon the separation between the two volleys. Lloyd's important contribution was to show that, as the shocks were approximated in time, an inhibitory action could be detected up to and until the moment when the two shocks were delivered simultaneously. This made untenable earlier suggestions that central inhibition arose merely from the refractoriness of some interneurone which lay on the reflex arc in question and which had just been activated in the course of a quite different reflex, elicited by the preceding stimulus that inhibited the reflex in question. Clearly a monosynaptic reflex could not be so depressed, nor at such a short latency could dis-facilitation or other such mechanism be responsible. Thus Lloyd established the existence of a specific inhibitory process operating within the central nervous system. In support of this apparently, he called the short latency inhibition by the name

'direct' in order to forcefully contrast it with any indirect inhibitory effects resulting from non-specific processes. A specific process had long been assumed by many workers but, remarkably in modern eyes, others had been reluctant to accept any process underlying central inhibition which had not already by established as being involved in the conduction of an impulse along an axon; such an approach tended to be linked with the belief that electrical transmission was likely to be the normal mode of synaptic transmission.

At the time of his discovery and for the ensuing few years, Lloyd (1941, 1946a) did not feel able to specify the precise site of his direct inhibition though he felt that the process probably acted directly upon the motoneurone. Nor did he explicitly state whether or not he believed that the inhibition was conveyed monosynaptically. Later accounts by various authors including Lloyd himself, however, tended to treat the phrase 'direct' as if it were synonymous with monosynaptic. Rather oddly, in his original summary Lloyd simply stated that the 'inhibition occurs without measurable latency', which meant no more than that the synchronous delivery of two stimuli led to a detectable inhibition. Later he systematically charted the distribution of the inhibition (Lloyd, 1946b) and showed that in this it was largely the inverse of monosynaptic excitation, going to antagonists rather synergists. The inhibition like monosynaptic excitation was only elicitable from group I fibres and thus only from muscle nerves. Lloyd also charted the time-course of the decay of the inhibition following a single inhibitory afferent volley.

A few years later and in the absence of any new evidence the conclusion from Lloyds' experiments of 1941–1946 had been transmuted with apparently general greement into a belief that group I fibres produce 'monosynaptic reflex inhibition of antagonists' (Laporte & Lloyd, 1952, p. 620), and Lloyd himself continued to propagate this view for at least the next decade. The belief, however, was based on a misinterpretation of the evidence and the fallacy had actually been pointed out by Renshaw (1943) shortly before his premature death at the very beginning of the work using monosynaptic reflexes for testing motoneuronal excitability. Renshaw emphasised that the essential thing to compare with the time of arrival of the inhibitory volley at the cord is the time at which the departing motor volley is initiated, rather than the moment at which the excitatory afferent volley reaches the cord. On this basis he concluded for a related inhibitory effect, which we can now recognise to be basically the same as Lloyd's, that 'a condition for the appearance of demonstrable inhibitory action was that the conditioning volley arrive at least one msec before the firing of the tested motoneurones'. Renshaw left it open whether or not this left time for transmission of the inhibitory action across an intervening interneurone.

The advent of intracellular recording immediately brought the question of the existence of an inhibitory interneurone to the forefront. This was because it was then found that the latency of the IPSP evoked in a motoneurone on stimulating Ia fibres from antagonists was invariably about 0·8 msec longer than of the EPSP evoked in the same motoneurone by the monosynaptic action of the autogenetic Ia fibres. After some initial special pleading aimed at retaining the idea that direct inhibition was mediated mono-synaptically (cf. Eccles, 1953), it was recognised that the explana-tion for the greater latency of the IPSP was simply that direct inhibition was mediated via an interneurone and was not mono-synaptic after all (Eccles, Fatt & Langdren, 1956). As illustrated in Fig. 7.14 the finite rising time of the EPSP ensures that the last

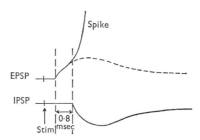

FIG. 7.14. Diagram of the interaction between an EPSP and an IPSP to explain the muddle that occurred over whether or not the Ia direct inhibitory pathway contains an interneurone. Because of the finite rise time of the EPSP the generation of a spike can be inhibited by an IPSP which begins appreciably after the beginning of the EPSP. Thus there is no incompatibility between the experimental observation that an inhibitory stimulus is effective when delivered to one afferent nerve at the same time as an excitatory stimulus is delivered to another, and the belief that the inhibitory pathway contains an interneurone while the excitatory pathway does not.

spikes to be discharged by monosynaptic action are sufficiently late to be inhibited by an IPSP, even though the latter does not begin until some 0·8 msec after the beginning of the EPSP. Thus the inhibitory pathway is allowed to be longer than the excitatory one and to contain an interneurone, even though both afferent volleys enter the cord simultaneously.

In the face of this argument Lloyd objected that the whole problem had been side-stepped by falsely equating inhibitory action with motoneuronal hyperpolarisation. This was answered by comparing the motor discharges in the ventral root in the presence and absence of inhibition, and thereby deciding upon the earliest appearance of the inhibitory action as judged by the suppression of firing (Araki, Eccles & Ito, 1960); this confirmed that the latency of inhibition was indeed the same as that of the IPSP. In addition, Eccles, R. M. & Lundberg (1958b) showed that an Ia-evoked IPSP could not be recorded until the afferent volley eliciting it was of appreciable size. This would not be expected if the IPSP was elicited monosynaptically, but was readily explained by supposing that in their preparations the relevant interneurones required an appreciable facilitatory afferent input before they fired and so inhibited the motoneurones. This view was favoured by finding that post-tetanic potentiation of the afferent fibres could lead a previously inadequate volley to produce an IPSP. Moreover, on a single occasion a particular cell was found to have an IPSP when five subdivisions of the appropriate antagonistic nerve were stimulated together but not when they were stimulated individually, and so unable to facilitate each other's action. The interneurones mediating inhibition are believed to lie in the dorsolateral grey matter of the cord in the so-called intermediate nucleus of Cajal and they have now been studied to some extent by electrophysiological methods (see Eccles, 1969). Of particular interest for the present argument is that stimulation in this region in preparations in which the Ia fibres have been removed by previous de-afferentation evokes an IPSP with a latency of only 0·5 msec, which would appear to be the latency for monosynaptically mediated inhibitory action (Eide, Lundberg & Voorhoeve, 1961). The latency for inhibition on Ia stimulation is over 1 msec thus making it unlikely to be mediated monosynaptically. This view now seems to have gained virtually complete acceptance.

Integrative function of the interneurone. The existence of an interneurone on the Ia inhibitory pathway was initially seen largely as a convenient way of enabling the body to use a single afferent input to produce excitation of one set of motoneurones and inhibition of another set. This could then be done without requiring, either that a single chemical transmitter liberated at different sites by the Ia fibres should have sometimes an excitatory and sometimes an inhibitory action, or that the different branches of a single afferent fibre should have to liberate different transmitters. All this remains true, but the chief current interest in the existence of an interneurone on any nervous pathway is that it allows 'integration' to occur through the interaction of several different kinds of input to the interneurone. The Ia inhibitory interneurone has now been shown to receive a number of inputs additional to the Ia fibres, but the full functional meaning of their various actions remains to be elucidated (Lundberg, 1970). The most intriguing of the other inputs to these interneurones is the recently discovered inhibitory one from the Renshaw cells, for this seems simple enough to offer a chance of functional understanding in the fairly near future as it will be brought into play via the recurrent axon collaterals whenever a motor discharge occurs. Figure 7.15 illustrates the action of this pathway by showing

test Q   cond L6 VR + test Q

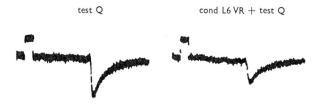

FIG. 7.15. The blockage of Ia direct inhibitory action by an antidromic motor volley, demonstrating that the Renshaw cells can inhibit the interneurone on the Ia inhibitory pathway. Left, the IPSP recorded intracellularly from a hip flexor motoneurone on stimulating the nerve to quadriceps and which demonstrates Ia inhibitory action. Right, the reduced IPSP elicited by the same stimulus when it was preceded by a conditioning stimulus to the central end of the severed L6 ventral root. This depression had a latency of about 2 msec and lasted for some 50 msec. Calibrating pulse on left, 1 mV and 2 msec; the records shown are the mean of 20 responses obtained with an averager. (Hultborn, Jankowska & Lindström, 1968, Fig. 1.)

the inhibition of an Ia-evoked EPSP as a result of ventral root stimulation. The pattern of connections from the motor fibres of a particular muscle to the interneurones on particular Ia pathways is also beginning to yield interesting results with the suggestion that the main feature is the regular and strong effects from efferents to muscles whose Ia afferents excite the interneurone in question (Hultborn, Jankowska & Lindström, 1971*a,b*).

Several other inputs to the same Ia interneurones have also been demonstrated to exist by studying the effects of central stimulation on the effect of Ia volleys in producing an IPSP, and in inhibiting the monosynaptic reflex produced by antagonistic Ia fibres. So far all the effects discovered have proved to be excitatory and to facilitate the transmission of Ia inhibitory effects. This was first shown on stimulating the sensorimotor cortex, when the effects were almost entirely mediated via the pyramidal tract, and has since also been found on exciting rubro-spinal and vestibulo-spinal fibres; all these results were obtained for the cat hindlimb. For the pyramidal and rubro-spinal tracts no differences were observed in the actions on Ia interneurones excited from flexors and from extensors (Lundberg & Voorhoeve, 1962; Hongo, Jankowska & Lundberg, 1969). In contrast, the vestibulo-spinal tract excited the interneurones lying on the inhibitory pathway from extensor Ia fibres to flexor motoneurones without affecting the mirror image ones on the pathway from flexor Ia fibres to extensor motoneurones (Grillner, Hongo & Lund, 1966; Lundberg, 1970). It seems likely that the Ia inhibitory interneurones can also be influenced by several other purely spinal inputs as well as the Ia fibres. Intracellular recording from interneurones has shown that virtually all those in the region of the intermediate nucleus which are excited by Ia fibres, presumably some of which lay on the Ia inhibitory pathway, could have either an EPSP or an IPSP or both on stimulating various afferent nerves (Hongo, Jankowska & Lundberg, 1966). In addition, strong contralateral stimulation may facilitate transmission in the ipselateral pathway from extensor Ia fibres to flexor motoneurones, presumably by exciting the relevant interneurones (Bruggencate, Burke, Lundberg & Udo, 1969). Such an action would appear to be a component of the crossed extensor reflex for the stimulation did not affect the ipsilateral inhibitory pathway from flexors to extensors.

A simple point following from all this is that the absence of an

Ia inhibitory action in any particular circumstance does not guarantee the absence of an Ia inhibitory connection, for it may merely have been inadequately facilitated to display itself. Thus the charting of the distribution of Ia inhibitory effects is necessarily less complete than is that for their monosynaptic excitatory action. However, as far as can be currently seen, they appear largely to inhibit antagonists in the way originally described by Lloyd, and with about as many exceptions as for his Ia excitatory actions (Eccles, Eccles & Lundberg, 1957a; Hongo, Jankowska & Lundberg, 1969). A notable example of the absence of Ia inhibition between apparent antagonists was provided by Sears (1964) who found no such connection between the expiratory and inspiratory intercostal muscles of the same segment even though each had the normal autogenetic Ia monosynaptic excitatory action. It is all becoming unpleasantly complicated and it seems unlikely that the normal mode of operation of even this simple reflex pathway can be sorted out simply by the continued use of the technique of activating it by single synchronous afferent inputs, but no better method is yet to hand.

Contralateral actions. Group I fibres also produce effects on contralateral motoneurones. The stimulation of any particular nerve usually produces a mixture of excitatory and inhibitory actions on any particular group of motoneurones, in both cases with a latency suggesting polysynaptic transmission. Perl (1958, 1959) believed that the Ia fibres of any particular muscle produced an inhibition of the motoneurones of the equivalent contralateral muscle and the Ib fibres produced an excitation. This view was based on the effects of grading the strength of an electrical stimulus to a muscle nerve and also on the effects of grading the strength of a pull applied to a muscle. Holmqvist (1961), however, was subsequently unable to separate the contralateral actions of Ia and Ib fibres on using electrical stimulation and so the matter remains in the air.

Reflex effects of group II muscle afferents as seen with electrical stimulation

Flexor reflex actions. At first sight electrical stimulation appears to offer a safe way of differentiating group II reflex effects from those of other afferents, for the wide range of diameters of group

II fibres (4–12 μm) means that it should be relatively easy to increase the strength of a stimulus so that group II fibres are recruited to the afferent volley without either group I or group III fibres. Unfortunately, once again the progress of understanding has advanced fitfully. Figure 7.16 shows the earliest determination

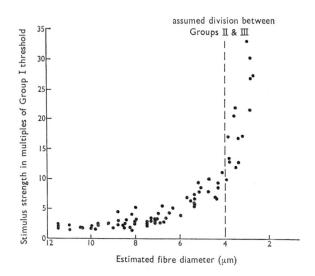

FIG. 7.16. The strengths of stimuli required to excite different sizes of muscle afferents of groups II and III from ankle extensors. The stimuli were condensor discharges with a half-time of decay of 45 μsec and were applied to the nerves to triceps surae. Each point shows the threshold for excitation of a single afferent fibre, whose action potential was recorded from a dorsal root filament. The size of the fibres were estimated on the basis of measurement of their conduction velocity. See Fig. 7.12 for similar data for semitendinosus fibres. (Eccles, R.M. & Lundberg, 1959a, Fig. 1 redrawn.)

of the thresholds for a number of single group II fibres which provided the basis for much subsequent experimentation. It can be seen that in these particular experiments increasing the stimulus from 2 to 6 times group I threshold recruited most of the group II fibres. Hunt's (1954) prior single fibre recordings suggested that for the soleus and gastrocnemius muscles virtually all these group II fibres originated in the spindle, and presumably from secondary endings. Similar results have been obtained more recently by Coppin, Jack & McIntyre (1969) for the semitendinosus. However, MacLennan (1971) has found for the tibialis anterior that up to about a third of the group II fibres do not originate in spindle endings. Sources of sampling error would appear to have been avoided in these various experiments and so it is hard not to accept them at their face value and believe that for some muscles the group II fibres are almost entirely derived from spindle secondary endings. But it should be remembered that the balance of histological evidence suggests that even the soleus and gastrocnemius nerves may contain some non-spindle group II fibres and that for many other nerves such contamination is a virtual certainty (see Chap. 2). Moreover, Paintal (1960) found in a sample of 31 afferents from 'pressure–pain receptors' in the lateral gastrocnemius and soleus muscles that seven had conduction velocities which placed them in the group II or even just in the group I range. Thus though it can be confidently accepted that increasing the strength of an electrical stimulus so as to excite group II fibres does excite the afferent fibres from the spindle secondary endings, their excitation cannot usually be guaranteed to be unaccompanied by that of afferent fibres from other types of receptor. The ascription of any reflex effect to the type of afferent fibre which is in the majority, in this case the spindle group II fibres, has no basis in logic and requires to be supported by experimental evidence for each particular case.

Some slightly puzzling findings in the rat have also been taken to show that an appreciable number of group I and II muscle afferents terminate in free nerve endings rather than the usual stretch receptors (Hník & Payne, 1965, 1966). The observation is that from one week to two months after de-efferenting the triceps surae the number of afferent units with a spontaneous discharge increases and up to half of those which were studied were not excited by stretching the muscle, even though they had large afferent fibres and so might have been expected to originate in spindles or tendon organs. These stretch-unresponsive large afferents were suggested to come from free nerve endings which had begun to fire as a result of metabolic changes induced in the muscle by de-efferentation and so had brought themselves to the attention of the physiologist. These atypical afferents were felt not to come from stretch receptors which were 'sick' and so had ceased to respond to their normal stimulus largely because the numerous stretch receptors which were studied had become more and not less sensitive to mechanical stimulation (Hník, 1970). In the normal rat all spontaneously firing units appear to come from the usual stretch receptors, but as yet no systematic search has been made in

the way pioneered by Hunt to see whether all the large afferents supply
stretch receptors. Until this has been accomplished judgement may
reasonably be reserved on the interpretation of the results found in de-
efferented muscles.

Only too often, however, the difficulties have been brushed
aside and the muscle group II fibres talked about as if they were
invariably a functionally homogeneous group. This was so in the
original experiments based on monosynaptic testing and the
recording of frank discharges by Lloyd and by Eccles which have
already been described. The next stage was the intracellular study
of the reflex effects of muscle group II afferents, and initially this
was largely taken to confirm what was already believed. Thus,
Eccles & Lundberg (1959a) on the basis of recording IPSPs and
EPSPs in a variety of motoneurones on stimulating a variety of
nerves concluded that in spinal animals in good condition group II
muscle afferents 'evoked excitatory action in motoneurones classified as flexors by Sherrington and inhibitory in those classified as
extensors'.

On the basis of further similar work Holmqvist & Lundberg
(1961) later found it convenient to define a system of 'flexor reflex
afferents' or FRA. Electrical stimulation of any part of the FRA
elicited a non-specific flexor reflex accompanied by the excitation
of several spinal pathways ascending to higher centres. (The
definition is actually introduced obliquely by reference to two
earlier papers, but these do not appear to state it in any explicit
manner or to employ the term systematically.) The FRA com-
prised group II and III muscle afferents along with those from
joint and from skin which had an electrical threshold slightly
above that of the most excitable fibres. All these were seen as
producing central actions in 'a pattern of functional unity', though
this was not felt to exclude the possibility that each of these
receptor systems might also have some other more specialised
central action (Holmqvist & Lundberg, 1961, p. 43). Since then,
scant attention has often been paid to any different actions of sub-
groups within the FRA. In particular, in investigating the actions
of the FRA the stimulus does not always appear to have been
finely adjusted so as to separate the effects of group II and group
III muscle afferents; the implicit assumption then seems to have
been made that their functions were indeed the same and so did
not merit individual scrutiny. Thus a fully justified term of con-

venience tended to become a strait-jacket restricting thought and hence the precision of experimentation.

The supraspinal control of the relevant interneurones. However, Eccles & Lundberg (1959*a*) in performing the experiments which helped usher in the concept of the FRA and its applicability to muscle afferents also sowed the seed which led to its destruction, for they found that the reflex effects of muscle nerve stimulation depended crucially upon the condition of the preparation. In contrast to their normal result they found that in some spinal animals, usually ones which happened to have an unduly low blood pressure, volleys in group II and III muscle afferents produced inhibition of flexor motoneurones rather than the usual excitation. To explain this paradoxical finding they suggested that a single group of afferent fibres could influence flexor motoneurones via two separate pathways which lay 'in parallel' but which produced opposite effects, the one producing excitation and the other inhibition. Since they could never detect any sign of inhibition and excitation directly competing against each other on the motoneurone soma they suggested that at any particular time one pathway was switched off while the other one was switched on.

They supported this line of thought by re-investigating with modern methods the differing reflex behaviour of spinal and decerebrate preparations and confirmed that flexor actions are largely suppressed in the decerebrate (Eccles & Lundberg, 1959*b*, see also Kuno & Perl, 1960). This had been emphasised long before by Sherrington & Sowton (1915) who found that a single shock to a peripheral nerve became much more efficient at eliciting a flexor reflex when a decerebrate cat was spinalised, and who concluded that in the decerebrate the flexor reflex centres were under a steady inhibition. More recently, Job (1953) had shown by monosynaptic testing that in the decerebrate cat the excitability of extensor motoneurones was barely affected by nociceptive stimuli, whereas in the same preparation made spinal they were inhibited in the accustomed way. Job thus suggested that the interneurones involved in mediating the extensor inhibition could be tonically controlled from higher centres (the stimuli used were strong electrical stimulation of the gastrocnemius nerve or the combination of cooling and vascular congestion of the gastrocnemius muscle). Figure 7.17 illustrates the converse effect, namely that nerve

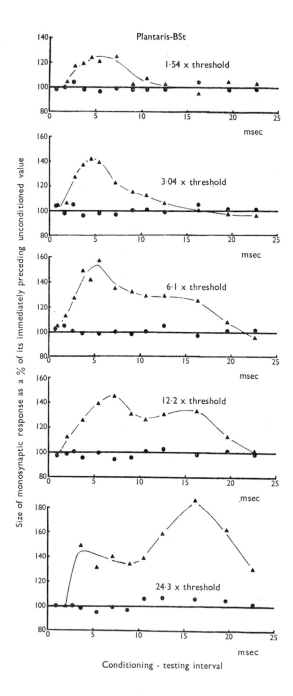

Size of monosynaptic response as a % of its immediately preceding unconditioned value

Plantaris-BSt

1·54 x threshold

3·04 x threshold

6·1 x threshold

12·2 x threshold

24·3 x threshold

Conditioning - testing interval

stimulation of a strength sufficient to excite the FRA may fail to excite flexor motoneurones in the decerebrate cat though it does so in the spinal animal. Furthermore, in decerebrate preparations with an additional mid-pontine lesion Holmqvist & Lundberg (1961) found the muscle group II afferents might actually inhibit flexor motoneurones instead of exciting them. This is illustrated in Fig. 7.18 where the triangles show the flexor inhibition in the animal with the mid-pontine lesion and the crosses the responses to the same stimuli when the animal was made spinal. They made out a convincing case for most such effects being due to a 'switching' between two alternative reflex pathways both of which were activated by the same afferent input.

On some occasions it seems possible, however, that similar results could be obtained by an alteration in the relative strengths of the responses elicited from two different sets of afferent fibres. More specifically, the effects of spindle group II afferents might sometimes be masked by the effects of a small number of group II afferents supplying pressure–pain receptors. At any rate, the demonstration of a particular reflex effect in a particular type of preparation clearly provides no guarantee that the central action of a particular set of afferent fibres is restricted to the one observed, or even to somewhat similar patterns of action. Moreover, the experiments performed to date leave no conviction that the flexor effects observed on group II stimulation are always part of a non-specific flexor reflex attributable to the FRA, rather than a more specific reaction involving excitation of particular flexor moto-neurones as part of a different pattern of control.

FIG. 7.17. The absence in the decerebrate of various reflex actions found in the spinal preparation; the difference is believed to be due to the inhibition in the decerebrate of the relevant interneurones by tonic discharges from higher centres. The graphs show the effect on the monosynaptic reflex elicited on stimulating the nerve to the posterior biceps-semitendinosus muscle of a prior single conditioning shock to the nerve to plantaris. The strength of the conditioning shock, in multiples of the group I threshold, is shown to the right of each graph. The results were obtained from a single decerebrate cat before (●) and after (▲) transecting the spinal cord at L1. The excitation produced by a stimulus of strength 1·5 is attributable to excitation of Ib fibres, group II fibres produced the additional effect on increasing the stimulus to ×6, and group III fibres the still greater effects on further increase of the stimulus. (Eccles, R. M. & Lundberg, 1959b, Fig. 1.)

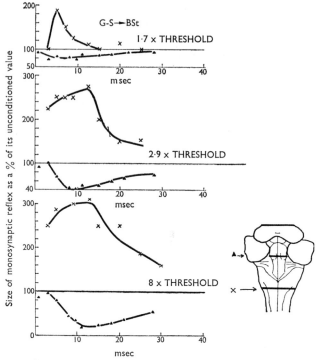

FIG. 7.18. A reversal of reflex action found with alteration of the central state of the preparation. The graphs show the effect on the monosynaptic reflex elicited on stimulation of the nerve to biceps-semitendinosus of a prior conditioning shock to the gastrocnemius nerve of the strength indicated to the right. This was done first when the preparation was decerebrate, when no effect at all was found (not illustrated); again after a mid-pontine lesion (▲); and again after making the preparation spinal (x). Opposite effects were produced in the mid-pontine and the spinal preparation by each of the three strengths of conditioning stimulus; possibly, however, the small inhibition observed in the mid-pontine state with the weakest stimulus was a Renshaw inhibition consequent on some motor discharge elicited by the conditioning stimulus, rather than a direct reflex action. (Holmqvist & Lundberg, 1961, Fig. 5.)

Even in the spinal cat, the reflex action of group II afferents is not restricted to the production of a flexor reflex, for Wilson & Kato (1965) regularly found that stimulation of group II fibres in the nerve to biceps-semitendinosus (a flexor) excited motoneurones of gastrocnemius and soleus (extensors). In addition, Pacheco & Guzmán (1969) have recently recorded polysynaptically evoked EPSPs in extensor motoneurones of chronically spastic cats on stimulating the gastrocnemius nerves at group II strength. Thus the supposition, which originated 25 years ago with Lloyd (1943b), that the sole reflex action of the muscle group II afferents is to produce a generalised flexor response can now be seen to be but a partial and simplified view. Experiments with physiological stimulation (see later) suggest that under some conditions they may also contribute to autogenetic excitation of extensors though the synaptic pathways which might produce such an effect remain unknown.

Reflex effects of group III fibres, including on the cardiovascular and respiratory systems

The somatic reflex effects of group III muscle afferents are still seen very much as Lloyd described them in the 1940's, namely as a generalised flexor response accompanied by inhibition of extensors, mediated via polysynaptic pathways, and occurring whatever the muscle of origin of the group III fibres stimulated. Subsequent intracellular studies have supported this conclusion by showing the appearance of the appropriate EPSPs and IPSPs, occurring with a suitably long latency, on increasing the strength of a stimulus so as to excite group III fibres (for example Eccles & Lundberg, 1959a; Holmqvist & Lundberg, 1961). The labelling of group III fibres as 'flexor reflex afferents' therefore seems appropriate and is useful in bringing together the effects of stimulating muscle, skin and joint nerves with strong shocks.

Even here, however, the attachment of the label FRA has its dangers for it emphasises the lowest common denominator resulting from stimulating small medullated fibres, namely their prepotent nociceptive actions, and tends to distract attention from the possibility that this may be the action of only a fraction of the group III fibres. Others among them may perhaps be subserving a quite different and more interesting function. However, there seems little doubt that many of the group III fibres do supply nociceptors and Paintal (1961) showed that squeezing of the tendo achilles or of the belly of gastrocnemius produces flexor effects which appear to be largely mediated via group III fibres. As with group II actions, changes in the central state of the preparation

Nм

leading to changes in the excitability of different kinds of inter-neurone may block or change the character of the reflex response to group III fibre stimulation, thus suggesting that their functional role can be adjusted to some extent to suit the needs of the body (Eccles & Lundberg, 1959b; Kuno & Perl, 1960). In particular, the switching off of crude nociceptive responses when there is a continuing need for controlled muscular action as in fight or flight seems a prerequisite for survival in a hostile world. The recordings so far made from single afferent fibres argue against any of the group III fibres themselves having a significant role to play in muscular control. Only a few fibres have shown even a weak response to muscle stretch or muscle contraction and these would appear to have been adventitious (see chap. 3).

On the other hand, it remains quite conceivable that group III includes fibres specifically concerned in mediating respiratory or cardiovascular reflex responses via mid-brain centres. The tele-ological value of such responses is simply that an increase in muscle activity needs to be accompanied by an increase in ventila-tion, an increase in cardiac output, and a rise in blood pressure, and these reactions could usefully be initiated in part by reflexes from the working muscles themselves. On somewhat circumstan-tial evidence it is now widely believed that such muscle reflexes do indeed exist and play a significant part in cardiovascular and reflex regulation (for example: Kao, 1963; Asmussen & Nielsen, 1964; Dejours, 1964; Coote, Hilton & Perez-Gonzalez, 1971).

The investigation of such possible controlling processes by electrical stimulation of muscle nerves has so far been relatively fruitless. This is largely because stimulation of afferents from nociceptors has profound reflex effects on the respiratory and cardiovascular systems which, though of considerable interest in themselves, are likely to mask any more refined control mediated by any other small muscle afferents. Thus repetitive stimulation of group III fibres certainly evokes a large increase in ventilation as may also the manual squeezing of a muscle (Bessou, Dejours & Laporte, 1959; Senapati, 1966; Hodgson & Matthews, 1968), but at present it seems impossible to decide whether these effects are the result of stimulating fibres specifically responsible for respira-tory control or simply those from nociceptors. Smaller respiratory effects may be produced by stimulating group I and II fibres but these also seem as likely to be due to contamination of groups I and

II with 'pressure–pain' afferents as due to a specific response and at any rate appear unlikely to be due to primary spindle afferents (Hodgson & Matthews, 1968; Hornbein, Sørensen & Parks, 1969). In the cardiovascular system, as illustrated in Fig. 7.19,

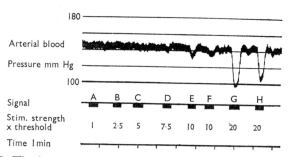

FIG. 7.19. The hypotensive effect of stimulating small muscle afferents. The hamstring nerve was stimulated at 9/sec for the periods indicated at successively greater intensity. The first clear effect was seen when the stimulus was 10 times group I threshold, which should have been just enough to excite some of the group III fibres. The recordings were made in the cat anaesthetised with chloralose and also paralysed with curare; both vagi had been cut. (Johansson, 1962, Fig. 4, reversed in contrast.)

stimulation of group III afferents usually causes a fall of blood pressure. This occurs in the vagotomised animal and is atropine resistant and seems to be due to removal of pre-existing sympathetic tone (Johansson, 1962; Laporte, Bessou & Bouisset, 1960; Skoglund, 1960; Coote & Perez-Gonzalez, 1968). Again, this effect could be a nociceptive response rather than a specific cardiovascular adjustment to muscle activity, in which case a rise in blood pressure would seem the more appropriate, as of course occurs in exercise.

The action of presumed nociceptive fibres in giving a depressor response contrasts with the pressor response normally obtained with electrical stimulation of presumed nociceptive fibres in cutaneous nerves. Johansson argued that this difference reflected the difference between the effect of nociceptive stimuli applied to a deep and to a superficial tissue; the one elicits responses aimed at producing rest to aid recovery from injury, the other at mobilising resources to deal with a crisis. However, a stimulus to a muscle nerve which is strong enough to excite non-medullated fibres does cause the more familiar nociceptive increase in blood pressure

(Johansson, 1962) and increasing the frequency of stimulation of group III fibres may also do so (Laporte, Bessou & Bouisset, 1960). High-frequency group II stimulation may also have a slight pressor effect, but group I stimulation appears to be completely without action (Laporte, Bessou & Bouisset, 1960; Laporte, Leitner & Pagès, 1962).

Much current work is still quite properly concerned in establishing whether or not muscular reflexes are definitely involved in helping to regulate the respiratory and cardiovascular systems. Only as such effects are shown to exist can the attack properly be directed to the two ensuing questions which are of more immediate concern for the present review but which are still largely unanswered. These are first, which kind of receptors are involved and, second, by what change in their environment are they excited. On current evidence free nerve endings and the extracellular accumulation of potassium would appear to be possible answers to these two questions, but much more experimental work is required to establish anything definite. It is heartening to see that such problems are now being attacked on a broad front by several groups of workers (for example: Achar, 1968; Coote, Hilton & Perez-Gonzalez, 1971; Hník & Hudlická, 1969; Kučera, 1969; Wildenthal, Mierzwial, Skinner & Mitchell, 1968).

Reflex effects of non-medullated fibres

The common view of the reflex action of the numerous non-medullated afferent fibres from muscle is that they produce a non-specific flexor reflex; but there appear to be no definitive experiments on muscle nerves establishing this view and in and case it seems unlikely to be applicable to all the non-medullated fibres. Lloyd (1943b) in redefining C fibres as his group IV felt that their 'afferent and reflex function . . . is proven' but did not investigate it by the methods he was then pioneering. Earlier experiments had shown effects on respiration and blood pressure on increasing the strength of a stimulus to a cutaneous or mixed nerve so as to excite C fibres as well as A fibres; these effects were also observable after blocking the nerves so that only C fibres were presumed to be capable of transmitting impulses from the site of stimulation to the spinal cord (Bishop & Heinbecker, 1935; Clark, Hughes & Gasser, 1935).

The matter then rested until the mid 1950's when Laporte &

Boer (1954a,b) showed that in the acute spinal cat increasing the strength of a stimulus to a dorsal root so as to excite C fibres as well as A fibres elicited a discharge in the nerves to flexor muscles additional to that elicited by stimulation of A fibres on their own. Moreover, the C fibre effect far out-lasted that of the A fibres and a frank motor discharge could continue for up to 100 msec after a single stimulus. Subsequently, Laporte & Bessou (1958) were able to produce a similar prolonged flexor reflex on stimulating C fibres in the sural nerve after blocking all the medullated fibres by a brief period of repetitive stimulation with rather strong shocks (30 volts at 50/sec for 0·25 sec) in the way introduced by Bishop & Heinbecker (1935). However, even in the spinal cat Laporte & Bessou found that these C fibre volleys produced an increase in the excitability of gastrocnemius motoneurones as judged by monosynaptic testing. In the decerebrate cat similar C fibre excitation could produce a frank contraction of gastrocnemius as shown by electromyographic recording. Thus the reflex actions of non-medullated fibres may be presumed to be regulated by supraspinal centres just as are those of medullated fibres.

Unfortunately these elegant experiments just quoted can no longer be accepted entirely at their face value for Mendell & Wall (1964) were subsequently unable to repeat the findings using simple polarisation block of the sural nerve, rather than strong stimulation, to eliminate the action of medullated fibres. They firmly stated that for the spinal cat 'we saw no reflex effects of C fibres if they were fired in isolation. We have tried single volleys, multiple bursts, and continuous tetanus' none of which evoked a detectable discharge in ventral root filaments 'although an output was easily recorded if any A fibre impulses were present in the afferent volley' (p. 287). They found, however, that C fibre activity potentiated the response to A fibre activity and suggested that possibly Laporte & Bessou's results were due to such an indirect action of C fibres, for they found that in their hands the blocking by strong repetitive stimulation always led to an asynchronous discharge in some of the blocked medullated fibres; such asynchronous firing would not have been detected with the diphasic recording used by Laporte & Bessou. On the other hand, Franz & Iggo (1968) subsequently detected motor discharges in the ventral root on stimulating cutaneous C fibres supposedly on their own after blocking the A fibres by cold. Moreover, other recent work has shown certain reflex effects on the autonomic system on stimulating both cutaneous and muscular C fibres on their own after blocking the medullated fibres by polarisation (Fussey, Kidd & Whitwam, 1969; Collin, Kaufman & Koizumi, 1969; Schmidt & Weller, 1970). In addition, Mendell & Wall's work has been questioned in another respect. They found that in their hands a C fibre volley produced a dorsal root potential which was 'entirely positive' and stated that 'so far, this is the only central effect of such a volley that we have detected'. Subsequent work, however, has shown that C fibres often produce the more usual negative going dorsal root potential, and the precise factors that determine which type of response will occur have yet to be sorted out (Burke, Rudomin, Vyklický & Zajac III, 1971; Dawson, Merrill & Wall, 1970; Franz & Iggo, 1968; Mendell, 1970; Zimmermann, 1968). Positive going dorsal root potentials have now been seen on stimulating muscle C fibres as well as on stimulating cutaneous C fibres (Mendell, 1970), but as yet the muscle C fibres have not been activated on their own without the A fibres. And there the matter currently rests, with the knowledge of the reflex action of muscle non-medullated afferents based by implication on experiments which involved stimulation of cutaneous non-medullated fibres, and which moreover have themselves been questioned. The rise in blood pressure originally noted to be produced by the combined stimulation of A and C fibres has, however, been confirmed to be produced by stimulation of pure muscle nerves and of muscle C fibres on their own (Johansson, 1962; Coote & Perez-Gonzales, 1968; Collin, Kaufman & Koizumi, 1969).

Reflex effects of joint afferents

It might be expected that joint afferents would take part in the reflex control of movement, but as yet there has been no indubitable demonstration of effects significant in this respect. Gardner (1950) appears to have been the first to observe the flexor effects of electrical stimulation of the posterior nerve to the knee joint, which is the most convenient articular nerve for experimental use. The flexor effects were prominent in the acute spinal cat but were largely absent in the decerebrate preparation. He showed this by visually observing the contraction of various muscles and by recording the discharges in various nerves. Skoglund (1956) re-investigated the matter with monosynaptic testing of motoneuronal excitability in both kinds of preparation but only found 'small and variable effects', which might be excitatory for either flexors or extensors. These different results by different investigators probably simply reflected the strength of the stimuli employed. Gardner would appear to have used rather strong shocks, whereas Skoglund appears to have restricted himself to those which were only slightly above the threshold of the most excitable fibres. Slightly later Eccles, R. M. & Lundberg (1959a) recorded intracellularly in the lightly anaesthetised spinal cat from a variety of motoneurones on stimulating the posterior nerve to the knee with shocks of graded strength. Shocks stronger than about 2·5 times the threshold of the most excitable fibres in the nerve consistently produced large flexor reflex actions. Thus joint afferents with a high threshold to electrical stimulation came to be included under the umbrella label of FRA. Again, the experimental findings themselves can provide no indication whether or not all the smaller afferents should be lumped together as flexor reflex afferents. The wide distribution of the diameters of the afferents connected to different receptors suggests that such lumping together is unlikely to be a proper thing to do.

As with muscle nerves, the effects of stimulation of joint nerves were subsequently shown to be highly dependent on the central state of the animal, and to be largely absent in the decerebrate preparation as originally noticed by Gardner (Eccles, R. M. & Lundberg, 1959b; Holmqvist & Lundberg, 1961). Figure 7.20 shows the contrasting effects obtained on biceps semitendinosus motoneurones of stimulating the nerve to the knee joint under three sets of conditions. These were firstly, with the animal decerebrate when there was no observable action, secondly, with a superadded mid-pontine lesion when these flexor motoneurones were inhibited, and thirdly, with the animal made spinal when the familiar flexor excitation finally made its appearance. Eccles, R. M. & Lundberg (1959a) in their original work never found 'any indication that larger afferents, presumably with Golgi and Ruffini endings, evoke synaptic actions in motoneurones' (p. 209). This, however, was probably simply due to the relevant interneurones being insufficiently excitable in their preparations. Subsequently effects were found on stimulating the joint nerve at below 2·5 times threshold provided the stimulus was preceded by a conditioning train of stimuli to the red nucleus (Hongo, Jankowska & Lundberg,

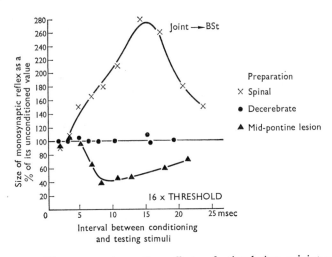

FIG. 7.20. The contrasting reflex effects of stimulating a joint nerve found on changing the central state of the preparation. The graph shows the effect on the monosynaptic reflex elicited by stimulating the nerve to biceps-semitendinosus of a prior conditioning shock to the posterior nerve to the knee joint at a strength 16 × threshold for the most excitable fibres. This was done in the simple decerebrate (●), when there was no effect; again after a mid-pontine lesion (▲), when inhibition was produced; and again after making the preparation spinal by transection the cord at about C1 (×), when excitation was produced. Tests with different strengths of the conditioning stimulus suggested that the effects were due to fibres of 2–7 μm diameter. (Holmqvist & Lundberg, 1961, Fig. 9.)

1969). This seems unlikely to have been due to facilitation of the effects of any few FRA fibres which happened to be of large diameter, for the FRA effects elicited by strong stimulation were not so facilitated. No systematic pattern of reflex connections was, however, then determinable and 'following rubral stimulation volleys in low threshold joint afferents were found to evoke excitation or inhibition in flexor as well as extensor motoneurones' (p. 378). This is hardly surprising since a joint nerve is not even as homogeneous from the functional point of view as is a muscle nerve, for it contains afferents which discharge optimally at quite different positions of the joint and which would be expected to have correspondingly varied reflex actions; for example, a fibre firing at full extension would hardly be expected to have the same actions as one firing at full flexion. Electrical stimulation is thus once again seen to be a peculiarly inappropriate method for elucidating the full range of natural reflex action.

Physiological stimulation of the receptors by movement of the joint presents certain technical problems and has as yet been little employed. Moreover in order to limit the stimulus solely to the joint receptors the surrounding muscles probably require to be denervated, but this may of itself alter the responsiveness of the receptors by changing the tension in the capsule (see Chap. 3). Cohen & Cohen (1956) found infinitesimal effects of doubtful significance in the decerebrate on moving the knee joint and observing the effect on the contraction of the quadriceps muscle. Skoglund (1956) showed that altering the steady position of the knee joint sometimes produced maintained changes in the excitability of various motoneurone pools as shown by monosynaptic testing. These effects were presumably mediated by the excitation of proprioceptors rather than nociceptors. Skoglund stated that he generally observed reciprocal effects on extensors and flexors. But more complex reflex patterns may also be expected to exist for he illustrates an experiment (his Fig. 27) in which on fully extending the knee the quadriceps motoneurones were inhibited while the gastrocnemius ones were excited, yet these are both extensors. The semi-physiological stimuli of pulling on the severed medial collateral ligament of the knee joint or inflating the joint capsule with saline produce a flexor action in both the decerebrate and the spinal preparation (Ekholm, Eklund & Skoglund, 1960). This action, however, seems as likely to be due to an excitation of nociceptors as of proprioceptors. In any case, the latter must be excited in an unnatural physiological combination and so might not be able to produce the full range of their normal action. It would be premature to write off the joint afferents as playing no part in the spinal reflex control of movement, though in view of their relatively small number in comparison to muscle afferents and the general dearth of effects obtained so far they may reasonably be suspected to play only a minor role.

Muscle afferents and presynaptic inhibition

For the first twenty years after the discovery of the mono-synaptic reflex, measurement of its size in response to a standard testing group I volley was thought to provide a reliable way of estimating the excitability of motoneurones, for in spite of some evidence to the contrary it was widely believed that nothing could interfere with the Ia afferent volley on its way to the moto-neurones. Now, however, there is a variety of physiological evidence showing that the synaptic efficacy of a Ia volley may be altered by a process operating on the primary afferent terminals themselves, as well as by those acting directly upon the moto-neurones. An anatomical basis for this has been provided by the observation of synaptic terminals ending upon the presumed Ia terminals, which could be identified by their showing degenerative changes after dorsal root section (Conradi, 1970). The active process is usually thought to be restricted to an inhibition of synaptic transmission, rather than a facilitation, and has thus been given the name presynaptic inhibition. However, presynaptic facilitatory effects can probably be reflexly induced by dis-inhibition, that is by the inhibition of a pre-existing presynaptic inhibition. Presynaptic inhibition is most likely to be brought about by the synapses on the Ia terminals liberating a chemical trans-mitter which depolarises the terminal and thereby leads to a diminution of the quantity of transmitter released by the Ia fibre at its own synaptic terminal. The details of the mechanism and its physiological importance are unfortunately still far from settled. The disagreements between those who have worked on these matters have been aired in several symposia and will not be presently discussed (Eccles, 1964b; Wall, 1964; Kellerth, 1968). It does seem appropriate, however, to retail some of the observations relating to muscle afferents. These can be crudely summarised by saying that apparently every kind of muscle afferent fibre may be presynaptically inhibited by itself and/or some other kind of muscle afferent, and likewise that activity in every kind of muscle afferent may lead to presynaptic inhibition of some muscle afferents somewhere; but proper physiological meaning has yet to be attached to the various patterns of interaction that have been observed.

Methods of study. The occurrence of presynaptic inhibition of a particular afferent pathway is most directly shown by observing a diminution of its synaptic action upon any cell that it influences monosynaptically, without there being any observable change in the post-synaptic cell itself as a result of the inhibition acting on its own. The requirements for demonstrating the complete absence of a post-synaptic effect have tended to become progressively more stringent with the passage of time. In any case there seems no reason why fibres producing a particular presynaptic effect should not often also have post-synaptic action on the very neurones innervated by the presynaptic fibre in question, so the two mechanisms might be experimentally nearly inseparable though completely distinct in themselves. Thus presynaptic inhibition may well occur at sites at which it cannot be readily recognised by the application of the usual tests. The most rigorous test for presynaptic action requires that the monosynaptically evoked synaptic action of an afferent input on a single neurone should be resolvable into a measurable number of quanta each due to a unit of presynaptic influence, whether of synaptic vesicles liberated or afferent terminals activated. Presynaptic inhibition then shows itself as a reduction in the average number of quanta resulting from a constant excitatory afferent input, rather than by a diminution in the average quantal size. Except for a limited success with the Ia fibres acting on motoneurones (Kuno, 1964) such a demanding criterion of presynaptic action has not been successfully met. To apply the same rigorous approach to other types of primary afferent fibre would require stable intracellular recording from interneurones, which is only rarely achievable.

In the face of the experimental difficulties of a truly rigorous approach it is usual and perfectly acceptable to recognise the occurrence of presynaptic inhibition of an afferent fibre by its partial depolarisation occurring as the result of activity of some other afferent fibres and not itself, thereby avoiding confusion with the various after-potentials following a spike. Such depolarisation passes under the name of primary afferent depolarisation or PAD for short. The simplest way of detecting a primary afferent depolarisation is to place electrodes on the central end of a cut dorsal root and record the dorsal root potential which is produced by the electrotonic spread of the depolarisation from its site of generation in the nerve terminals into the inactive more peripheral regions of the fibres. The recording of a dorsal root potential on exciting a particular group of afferent fibres suggests that these fibres are evoking a presynaptic inhibition of some group of afferent fibres, but such an observation on its own is incapable of identifying the kind of afferent fibre being influenced. Under favourable circumstances this may be determined by recording intracellulary from a number of identified single afferent fibres within the cord and seeing which ones are depolarised; the fibres may be readily categorised according to their conduction velocity and muscle of origin by stimulating a variety of peripheral nerves.

A less direct but experimentally less demanding method was introduced by Wall (1958) who stimulated the afferent fibres somewhere near their terminals by a microelectrode inserted into the spinal cord. The resultant afferent volley is recorded from a peripheral nerve as it courses antidromically; the ventral roots are cut to eliminate motor responses. The strength of the stimulus is adjusted so that it excites some but not all of the particular group of fibres investigated. In consequence, if for any reason the threshold of the fibres is lowered then more of them are excited by the standard stimulus. The size of the compound antidromic action potential thus measures the excitability of the terminals and this is taken to reflect their state of polarisation. Hence, at one stage further removed from the truly rigorous test the degree of presynaptic inhibition is equated with the increase in afferent fibre excitability. An impressive correspondence has been obtained between the duration and extent of the presumed presynaptic inhibitory depression of the EPSP elicited by Ia action on the motoneurone, and the duration and extent of the depolarisation and excitability changes of the afferent fibres. Thus measurement of the latter may reasonably be used to chart the extent of pre-synaptic inhibition in kinds of fibre whose synaptic action cannot be studied as directly as that of the Ia fibres. But it should be recognised that not all presynaptic inhibitory mechanisms need manifest themselves in this way by afferent depolarisation coupled with increased excitability. For example, a presynaptic fibre might perfectly well be 'inhibited' by a chemical transmitter which acted so as to increase the membrane conductance of the fibre without altering its membrane potential. This would be especially effective if the spike were normally to fail to propagate itself actively to the very end of the presynaptic fibre. Moreover, a depolarisation of afferent fibres with resultant changes in their excitability might be partly due to non-synaptic influences such as the liberation of potassium from other afferent fibres.

For technical simplicity the group I fibres have been the most intensively investigated of the muscle afferents with regard to being acted upon by presynaptic inhibition, and relatively little is known about the presynaptic inhibition of the smaller muscle afferents. Ia fibres can have their excitability tested independently of that of the Ib fibres by placing the stimulating microelectrode near the motoneurones; this produces a selective excitation because the Ia fibres are the only afferents that penetrate so far into the cord. Alternatively, the electrode may be placed so as to excite all group I fibres, and the Ia and the Ib contributions to the antidromic potential differentiated by a collision technique. The colliding orthodromic volley of approximately known composition is set up by stimulating peripheral nerves in the usual way with graded shocks. These then are the methods which have been employed hitherto and they have yielded a valuable harvest. But equally clearly present knowledge rests on slightly insecure foundations and can make no claim to be final or comprehensive.

Patterns of action shown by electrical stimulation. These various methods were first systematically applied to muscle afferent fibres by Eccles and his colleagues. They investigated presynaptic inhibition in anaesthetised spinal cats and evoked different kinds of afferent volley in the usual way by stimulating a variety of peripheral nerves with graded shocks. The presynaptic actions of the muscle afferents usually only manifested themselves after several successive afferent volleys at high frequency and then showed a rise and fall of action which was an order of magnitude slower than that previously known for the more direct synaptic actions of the large muscle afferents. The slowness of the decay of presynaptic inhibitory action is illustrated in Fig. 7.21. All this bespeaks an appreciable dependence of presynaptic inhibition upon the prolonged activity of interneurones. But there is still disagreement as to how far the prolonged decay of the presynaptic action following a brief afferent input reflects the gradual decay of interneuronal activity, and as to how far it reflects the tardy disappearance of a transmitter chemical liberated soon after the arrival of the afferent volleys at the spinal cord. Yet another possibility is that the slow decay of some part of the presynaptic effects reflects a slow reabsorption of K^+ ions which have 'leaked' into the extracellular space during the initial neural discharges and then tend to depolarise all surrounding elements.

Figure 7.22 summarises Eccles' conclusions about the pattern of presynaptic effects produced by and on muscular afferents. Ib

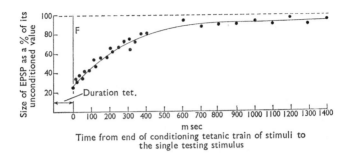

FIG. 7.21. Prolonged depression of reflex action of Ia fibres attributable to presynaptic inhibition elicited by a brief tetanus. The graph shows the size of the EPSP monosynaptically elicited in a gastrocnemius moto-neurone by stimulation of the gastrocnemius nerve. The presynaptic inhibition of the gastrocnemius Ia fibres was produced by stimulating the biceps semitendinosus nerve at 210/sec for the period indicated and at a strength just adequate to elicit maximal Ia volleys in it. Anaesthetised cat with transection of the spinal cord at about L2. (Eccles, Eccles & Magni, 1961, Fig. 6.)

fibres can be seen to be particularly effective at producing inhibi-tion, and especially those from flexor muscles which strongly influence both Ia and Ib fibres whereas those from extensors chiefly inhibit Ib fibres. A particular kind of afferent fibre appeared to be inhibited by a particular input without regard to whether the inhibited fibres supplied flexor or extensor muscles; doubtless, however, the finer details of such patterns of action remain to be worked out. The effect of Ib fibres back on to themselves can of course be re-described as a 'negative feedback' pathway; but it should not be confused with the type of restricted feedback used by engineers, for the Ib fibres of any particular muscle appear to influence the Ib fibres of a wide and functionally diverse range of other muscles. Interestingly, however, in spite of their strong ipsilateral actions Ib fibres appear to have no contralateral action at all though muscle group II and III afferents do so (Eccles R. M., Holmqvist & Voorhoeve, 1964). Ia fibres were found to have a weak ipsilateral action which was restricted to Ia fibres. The effects from extensor Ia fibres were thought to be very small, as judged by the size of the depolarisation recorded with intrafibre recording. The Ia/Ib subdivision of the responsible exciting afferents was however based on the usual criterion of stimulus

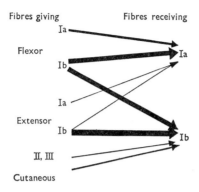

FIG. 7.22. Diagram showing the distribution of ipsilateral presynaptic inhibitory effects arising from and terminating in muscle afferents. The width of the arrows show the approximate strengths of the effects; no differentiation was found on the receiving side for fibres from flexors and from extensors. The diagram is based on the amount of primary afferent depolarisation (PAD) observed in a number of single fibres with intracellular recording on stimulating a variety of nerves. (Eccles, Schmidt & Willis, 1963, Fig. 15.)

strength, and so may well not have been entirely reliable. This is particularly so because the observed response depends upon the activity of interneurones which require appreciable facilitation in order to be made to discharge. Thus a half-maximal Ia volley might fail to produce an action when a maximal one did so. Such an action might, however, perhaps be mistaken for a Ib action for Ib fibres would be recruited as the Ia volley was increased from submaximal to maximal. Subsequently Decandia, Provini & Táboříková (1967) found quite definite effects on extensor Ia fibres on stimulating extensor group I fibres (from medial head of gastrocnemius to lateral head of gastrocnemius plus soleus), showing that group I effects are not the prerogative of flexors.

Lundberg (1964, 1966) and his colleagues have largely confirmed Eccles' findings using broadly similar methods. In addition they have shown, as might be expected, that the chain of interneurones mediating presynaptic inhibitory action does not behave as an invariant and secure transmission line but may also be influenced by various other inputs. For example, the pathway from Ia afferents may be greatly depressed by a single preceding shock to the sural nerve of sufficient intensity to activate flexor reflex afferents (Lund, Lundberg & Vycklický, 1965). The inter-neuronal pathways would also seem to be under higher control so that a particular afferent input may produce different effects under different conditions. In line with this is the finding that stimulation of the cerebral cortex may produce presynaptic inhibition.

More direct evidence for such higher control of spinal pre-synaptic inhibitory pathways has been obtained by studying the action of DOPA (dihydroxyphenylalanine). This is believed to act either by mimicking, or by producing an increase in, the activity of nerve terminals which liberate monoamines as chemical trans-mitter. In the spinal cord all such terminals are believed to arise from fibres descending from supraspinal centres (Lundberg, 1966). At any rate, along with a variety of other actions the intra-venous injection of DOPA may transform the presynaptic inhibitory actions of flexor reflex afferents. In the acute spinal cat these normally depolarise other flexor afferents and Ib fibres, but have no detectable action on Ia fibres. After DOPA they no longer produce either of these effects but instead depolarise Ia fibres, though with a longer latency than their normal actions. In line with previous thought on the more direct reflex pathways it was suggested that the same group of flexor reflex afferents fed into two separate and disparate pathways mediating presynaptic inhibition, and that sensible functioning at any time was ensured by the existence of suitable inhibitory cross-connections arranged so that only one pathway could function at a time.

It may also be noted that presynaptic inhibition appears to be sufficiently localised along the length of a fibre for it to be possible for one set of terminals of a particular fibre to be influenced in one way, and another set of terminals from the same fibre to be in-fluenced in another way. Jankowska, Jukes & Lund (1965) sug-gested that such differences were found between the Ia terminals ending on the motoneurones and those ending on the neurones of the dorsal spino-cerebellar tract. Another complication has recently been raised by Mendell (1970) who has found that group III and non-medullated muscle afferents can produce a positive dorsal root potential rather than the usual negative going one produced by the large fibres; the fine afferents may thus be pre-sumed to produce a presynaptic facilitation rather than an inhibition. This was demonstrated on increasing the strength of the stimulus so as to excite the small fibres along with the large ones, but without the use of selective blocking techniques to eliminate the central action of the large fibres. It may be noted that the bulk of the early experiments on presynaptic inhibition were performed on cats anaesthetised with barbiturate which tends to favour the appearance of negative going dorsal root potentials at the expense of positive going ones (Mendell & Wall, 1964). Mendell (1970) also emphasised that the negative dorsal root potentials produced by the large muscle afferents were, volley for volley, much smaller than those produced by the large cutaneous of nerves of comparable size. In the face of all the above complexities it is clearly premature to attempt a final assessment of the relative strengths and importance of the various patterns of presynaptic effect which have currently been described.

Response to physiological stimulation of receptors. Since the effects described so far were elicited by the unnatural afferent input set up on electrical stimulation of afferent nerves it is interesting and valuable that depolarisation of primary afferent fibres has also been observed with more natural physiological stimuli. Thus, R. M. Eccles and her colleagues found that a brief stretch of various flexor muscles, probably exciting both Ia and Ib fibres, could depolarise the Ia and the Ib fibres of both flexor and extensor muscles (Devandan, Eccles & Yokota, 1965a, b; the stretch lasted about 20 msec and was sufficiently large to increase the tension in the muscle by around 100 g and so was probably several millimetres in extent). Likewise, the contraction of either a flexor or an extensor muscle, elicited by stimulation of the peripheral end of a cut ventral root, evoked a depolarisation of the Ia and the Ib fibres of both flexor and extensor muscles. The contractions would undoubtedly have powerfully excited Ib fibres, but as the authors pointed out may well also have excited some Ia fibres (Devandan, Eccles, R. M. & Stenhouse, 1966). None of these papers provided a detailed description of the pattern of effects produced on the afferent fibres of each of a series of muscles on physiologically activating each of another set of muscles. The production of such data on the distribution of a particular action is particularly laborious when physiological methods of stimulation are used rather than electrical stimulation. However, contraction of the medial head of gastrocnemius was noted as having a pronounced effect on Ia fibres of lateral gastrocnemius plus soleus, whereas in the earlier work with electrical stimulation (cf. Fig. 7.22) such interactions between synergistic extensor muscles had been rather small. This is of particular interest for it is important to find out whether presynaptic inhibitory effects are always widespread in their distribution, or whether they can also provide a localised control of the afferent feedback from a particular region.

Quite recently, Barnes & Pompeiano (1970a,b) have used selective activation of Ia fibres by high-frequency vibration to investigate presynaptic inhibition. First, as illustrated in Fig. 7.23, they confirmed that Ia fibres from the hip flexor semitendinosus produce depolarisation of Ia fibres of gastrocnemius. This was worthwhile because this method of stimulation is probably better at exciting nearly maximal Ia volleys than is electrical stimulation. Second, they found that the Ia fibres from the medial head of gastrocnemius had a pronounced action on Ia fibres from the lateral head of gastrocnemius and so would presumably also have had one back on to themselves. This cannot be demonstrated directly because repetitive activity in a fibre produces prolonged changes in its state of polarisation and synaptic efficacy thereby precluding the testing for presynaptic inhibitory action by the usual methods. Thus, both Ia and Ib fibres would appear to produce a certain amount of presynaptic inhibition back on to themselves, but whether this is part of a specific mechanism or merely part of a widespread action is at the moment quite undecided.

Whatever its precise mechanism presynaptic inhibition is certainly established as one of the basic mechanisms available to play a part in the reflex control of muscle; but as yet it is uncertain whether it produces effects of appreciable magnitude in relation to the longer known synaptic interactions occurring on the somata of motoneurones and interneurones. Barnes & Pompeiano (1970b) found that during repetitive firing of medial gastrocnemius Ia fibres the excitability of lateral gastrocnemius motoneurones was increased, as judged by monosynaptic testing. They considered that this showed that the monosynaptic excitatory effects on lateral gastrocnemius motoneurones from medial gastrocnemius Ia fibres had overwhelmed the presynaptic inhibitory action evoked by the same input on the testing Ia volley in lateral gastrocnemius Ia fibres. On the other hand, some ten msec or so after stopping the

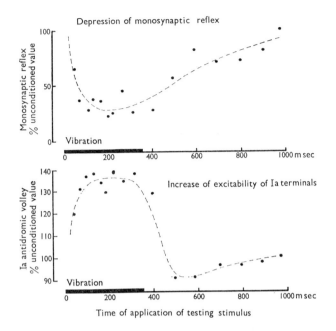

FIG. 7.23. The effect of a pure Ia input in eliciting presynaptic inhibition of other Ia fibres. The Ia input was produced by vibrating the semitendinosus muscle at 200/sec with the appropriate amplitude to selectively excite Ia fibres for the period indicated by the bars. This produced presynaptic inhibition of gastrocnemius Ia fibres as shown firstly, by recording the size of the monosynaptic reflex elicited in L7 ventral root on stimulating the gastrocnemius nerve (above), and secondly, by testing the excitability of the Ia terminals by a stimulating microelectrode inserted into the spinal cord (below). The reason why the time course of the two curves differ is uncertain, but they were obtained at different times. Decerebrate cat with spinal transaction at T10. (Barnes & Pompeiano, 1970a, Fig. 2.)

repetitive Ia bombardment the residual presynaptic inhibition overcame the residual increase in motoneuronal excitability so that the testing monosynaptic reflex became smaller than normal. Another factor to be remembered in assessing the role of presynaptic inhibition in muscular control is that the reactions so far seen to be mediated in this way would appear to be too sluggish, both in their onset and abatement, to play a moment-to-moment part in controlling phasic reactions. At present it is tempting to ignore presynaptic inhibitory mechanisms in formulating ideas as to how the spinal cord reflexly controls movement, but this should be no more than a temporary shelving of the issue until a more quantitative assessment can be made of its role. Moreover, presynaptic inhibition will also affect the transmission of information from muscle afferents to higher centres so it may be a mistake to look for its primary meaning in the way it affects spinal reflex action. For the moment it is cast in the role of a gain control of the afferent input to the spinal cord which is reasonably specific for fibre type, but which does not appear to be particularly spatially organised so as to control differentially fibres of the same type arising from different muscles of the same limb.

Résumé of reflex actions, largely as seen on the electrical stimulation of peripheral nerves

The spinal reflex actions of the muscle receptors have a particular interest from the point of view of motor control for they would appear to provide for the rapid correction of the motor outflow in the light of the moment-to-moment mechanical situation and without the need for troubling the higher centres. Moreover, the higher centres may perhaps produce some of their motor effects by altering the state of balance between antagonistic spinal reflexes as well as by directly exciting the motoneurones themselves. Most of the present chapter is devoted to a description of the reflex actions which may be elicited by the electrical stimulation of muscle nerves. Such work has had a reasonable measure of success in answering the question 'What is the reflex action of each of the known types of muscle receptor?'

The tendon jerk. The brevity and simplicity of the tendon jerk made it an ideal object for the earliest stages of the physiological study of muscle reflexes and helped usher in the systematic use of electrical stimulation as a tool for their study. For the first thirty years or so after the initial description of the jerk in 1875 it was usually believed to be a direct response of muscle to a mechanical stimulus, rather than a reflex response mediated via the spinal cord. This misconception arose from a misplaced confidence in the earliest measurements of its latency which appeared to be so short that reflex action was excluded. The objection was dispelled in 1911 by the electromyographic recording of the latency of the jerk coupled with estimates of the various delays around the reflex arc. At the same time the central latency of the jerk was found to be so short that the reflex was suggested to be transmitted monosynaptically. This supposition was only firmly established some 30 years later after electrical studies had proved that the earliest reflex response elicited in the ventral root on stimulating a dorsal root was transmitted monosynaptically through the cord. The central latency of the jerk response was then shown to be identical.

The next question was which of the various receptors was responsible for the jerk. By the early 1930's the silent period in the electromyogram, which occurred on superimposing a twitch contraction on a steady contraction of a muscle, was widely accepted as showing that the spindle endings were the ones which were responsible. By then the spindle endings were known to fall silent during a twitch and a withdrawal of their tonic excitation of the motoneurone was seen as the cause of the electromyographic silence. In 1941, measurements were made of the conduction velocity of the afferent volley responsible for initiating the jerk response. The value came out at slightly over 100m/sec thus making the primary ending rather than the secondary ending of the spindle the responsible receptor. This has been the accepted view more or less ever since and has been progressively supported by a variety of more rigorous experiments. In particular, some 20 years later still it was shown that only the primary endings are excited by the very small stimuli that are sufficient to elicit a jerk; the other two main types of mechanoreceptor in muscle, namely the tendon organ and the spindle secondary ending, then failed to respond.

The use of electrical stimulation to give a reasonably selective activation of different types of afferent fibre. The threshold of a nerve fibre to electrical stimuli varies inversely with its diameter and so progressive increase in the strength of a stimulus applied to a nerve recruits progressively thinner fibres. Thus the reflex effects elicited by the weakest stimuli may be attributed to the largest fibres, and any new effects appearing with increase of the stimulus strength may be attributed to somewhat smaller fibres, provided that the effect studied does not depend upon a high degree of central facilitation. With this in mind the muscle afferents were classified in the early 1940's into groups I, II, III and IV (see p. 79), and the reflex effects of each of these groups determined by grading of the stimulus strength. The earliest experiments of this kind showed that the monosynaptic reflex was the prerogative of the group I fibres and that an afferent volley in the nerve from a particular muscle monosynaptically excited only the motoneurones of that muscle itself and its close synergists. At the same time the group I volley produced an inhibition of the motoneurones of antagonistic muscles. These two reflex actions of group I fibres were seen as welding together the muscles acting at any particular joint so as to form a functional whole. This was called the 'myotatic unit'. Of course, simple anatomy also ensures that all the members of a unit are influenced together by any gross movement at a joint. The early studies on group II, III and IV fibres suggested that they all had the same function, namely to produce a generalised flexor reflex response consisting of excitation of flexor motoneurones and inhibition of extensor motoneurones, occurring via polysynaptic pathways. This was thought to occur whatever the muscle of origin of the excited afferent fibres.

In the early 1950's, the effects of group I stimulation were found to be divisible into two kinds attributable to different afferent fibres. This work followed on naturally from the recognition that group I fibres supplied two quite distinct types of receptor, namely the spindle primary endings and the tendon organs. The weakest electrical stimuli elicited the well-established autogenetic monosynaptic excitatory effects accompanied by inhibition of antagonists; these were attributed to the Ia fibres from the spindle primary endings. Stronger stimuli would produce additional effects occurring in an almost opposite pattern of action, namely autogenetic inhibition accompanied by excitation of antagonists. This pattern of action was given the name of the 'inverse myotatic reflex' and was attributed to the excitation of the Ib fibres from the tendon organs. Stimulation of nerves to muscles of the thigh (quadriceps, hamstrings) was found to allow a particularly clear separation of these two contrasting effects of group I stimulation and largely confirmed the above description which was initially based largely on work on muscles of the lower leg.

Using triphasic recording from the intact dorsal root it was found on stimulating a nerve to a thigh muscle that the resulting compound action potential was often markedly bifid. The fastest component, which was also quite properly of lowest threshold, was found to be almost entirely due to the activation of Ia spindle afferents. The slower group I wave was mainly due to the activation of Ib fibres from tendon organs, but also included a significant contribution from spindle afferents; the latter were presumably mostly from primary endings but may perhaps also have included some from secondary endings. Investigation of a range of other nerves has shown that in these also it is often possible to excite a nearly pure Ia volley by suitably weak stimulation, but that an increase in the stimulus recruits Ia and Ib fibres together (and possibly also some spindle group II fibres). Thus electrical stimulation can reasily be used to study the action of Ia fibres on their own, but it is impossible to recruit Ib fibres on their own and thereby study their actions in isolation from that of other afferents. None the less, most workers have usually felt confident that they could distinguish the Ib effects from the Ia effects, because they are different, and from group II effects, because these continue to increase on increasing the stimulus above the value required to give a maximum group I volley. Perhaps, however, not all the results in the literature are as secure as they might at first sight appear. A further complication in using electrical stimulation is that a few afferent fibres supplying nociceptors may perhaps be found in all four fibre groups. In certain circumstances these might be able to overwhelm the reflex actions of the other fibres of the same diameter, even though the latter were in the majority.

Further details of Ia action. Intracellular recording has allowed the description of Ia reflex action in more detail than was originally possible with the ventral root recording of massed discharges and the monosynaptic testing of motoneuronal excitability. Both the excitatory and the inhibitory actions were found to be somewhat more widespread than was originally suggested and may sometimes be produced on motoneurones which do not belong to the strictly defined 'myotatic unit'. Thus it has been suggested that the original form of the concept is somewhat over-simplified in relation to reality, particularly for muscles acting at ball and socket joints. This has all been done by charting the size of the EPSP set up in a variety of motoneurones on maximal group I stimulation of a variety of nerves. Such work has also suggested that the smaller motoneurones, which are the ones which supply the more tonically contracting muscle fibres, are more powerfully excited by Ia action than are the larger ones.

The Ia fibres were originally thought to exert their inhibitory action on antagonistic motoneurones via a monosynaptic arc. This view arose from a misinterpretation of certain latency measurements and the fallacy involved was only finally cleared up with the advent of intracellular recording, though it had actually been pointed out rather earlier. There is now a variety of evidence showing that this Ia inhibition of antagonists is mediated via a single interneurone. From one point of view this arrangement may be seen as a convenient way of allowing the inhibition of a motoneurone to be mediated by a separate chemical transmitter from its excitation. But it is now seen to be equally important that the interneurone allows for a certain amount of 'integration' to take place in this apparently straight through reflex arc. These Ia inhibitory interneurones are now thought to be activated also by the cortico-spinal tract, the rubro-spinal tract, the vestibulo-spinal tract, and as part of the crossed extensor reflex, and to be inhibited by the Renshaw cells and thus by the recurrent collaterals of the motoneurones.

There is also a certain amount of indirect evidence that the Ia excitatory actions on motoneurones may perhaps be mediated polysynaptically as well as being mediated monosynaptically.

Ib actions. These have always been accepted as being mediated via one or two spinal interneurones. In the earliest intracellular studies of their pattern of distribution the simple arrangement into an 'inverse myotatic reflex' could not be entirely confirmed, and there was, in fact, a paucity of effects of any kind. Quite recently, Ib effects have been investigated after facilitating the relevant interneurones by stimulation of the rubro-spinal tract. A wide range of Ib actions was then found, but these did not fall into a universal simple pattern and a good deal remains for further study.

Group II and III actions, and the demonstration of the importance of variations of the excitability of interneurones with variations in the central state of the preparation. Intracellular recording in conjunction with the appropriate stimulation of peripheral nerves has confirmed that both group II and group III afferents usually

evoke responses in the pattern of the general flexor reflex via polysynaptic pathways mediated via two or more interneurones. The
technique of electrical stimulation cannot show, however, whether
this is the action of all of the fibres of each of these ranges of
diameter, or whether of only a fraction of them. It seems likely that
the spindle group II fibres have some more rational action than
simply producing a generalised flexor reflex. In the group III
range there seem likely to exist some fibres which subserve
specialised cardiovascular and respiratory regulatory responses.
So far, however, the detection of any such specialised actions has
been almost impossible in the face of the flexor effects of stimulating other fibres of the same diameter. In spite of these complications of interpretation the group II and III muscle afferents have
often each been considered to be a functional unity, and have been
lumped in with afferents from skin and joint nerves which have a
relatively high electrical threshold and which also produce flexor
reflex effects. Together, all these have been given the name of the
Flexor Reflex Afferents, commonly abbreviated to FRA. Such an
umbrella classification is certainly valuable on occasion, but its
systematic use risks confusing the issue because the possibility is
then easily forgotten that fibres of the same size may come from
different kinds of receptor and have different reflex actions.

A further complication in reflex studies is provided by the now
well-documented observation that the reflex response to a particular afferent input depends crucially upon the central state of the
preparation. The simplest demonstration that this is so is provided
by comparing the responses of decerebrate and of spinal preparations. In the decerebrate cat a single volley of impulses in the
flexor reflex afferents is almost without action. When the same
preparation is made spinal the well-known flexor actions make
their appearance in response to the same volley. In the decerebrate
preparation the relevant interneurones appear to be being tonically
inhibited by impulses descending from hyperactive higher centres.
Still more striking observations may be made when a single
preparation is repeatedly studied after making a succession of
different central lesions. The effect of a fixed afferent input on a
fixed group of motoneurones may sometimes then be found to
be transmuted from excitation to inhibition or vice versa. It has
been suggested that this takes place because some kinds of afferent
fibre have alternative reflex pathways available to them which lie

'in parallel' to converge on the same target motoneurones and there produce opposite effects. The higher centres are held to be able to switch on either pathway at will by suitable action on their interneurones; suitable reciprocal inhibitory cross-connections between the two pathways are suggested to ensure that both can never be switched on simultaneously.

Joint afferents. The usual flexor reflex effects can be produced when a moderately strong electrical stimulus is applied to a joint nerve. There may well also be physiologically more interesting reflexes initiated from joints but they have yet to be described.

Presynaptic inhibition. Many or all of the terminals of primary afferent fibres appear to be able to have their synaptic potency decreased by other nerve terminals synapsing upon them and giving rise to what is called presynaptic inhibition. This is believed to take place by a depolarisation of the inhibited terminal leading to a diminution in the number of quanta of transmitter that it liberates. The occurrence and distribution of presynaptic inhibition has been studied in the main by the indirect methods of recording the depolarisation of the primary afferent fibres or by measuring the resulting change in their excitability. Other processes might perhaps also give rise to these second order indicators of presynaptic inhibition and so the methods are not absolutely reliable.

For technical reasons the group I fibres are the only muscle fibres which have been extensively studied in this respect. On the basis of experiments using electrical stimulation in the usual way it has been found that Ib fibres are particularly effective at eliciting presynaptic inhibition. Ib fibres from flexor muscles were the most effective in this respect and inhibited both Ia and Ib fibres. Ib fibres from extensor muscles mainly acted upon other Ib fibres. In both cases, however, the receiving fibres have so far appeared to be more or less equally distributed between flexor and extensor muscles. Ia fibres were found to produce relatively weak presynaptic effects which were mainly restricted to other Ia fibres.

Presynaptic inhibitory effects have also been elicited by the physiological stimuli of muscle stretch and muscle contraction. Moreover, the pure Ia input which may be produced by high-frequency vibration will produce presynaptic inhibition of other

Ia fibres. However, it is still premature to assess the physiological role and importance of presynaptic inhibition with regard to muscle control. It may be noted that as so far studied presynaptic inhibition would appear to be too widespread in its action and too slow in its onset and offset to play a part in the moment-to-moment reflex regulation of muscle. It could perhaps therefore be cast in the role of a gain control.

References

Achar, M. V. S. (1968). Effects of injection of Locke solution with higher concentration of potassium into femoral artery on blood pressure in cats. *J. Physiol.* **198**, 115–116P. [378]

Alvord, E. C. & Fuortes, M. G. F. (1953). Reflex activity of extensor motor units following muscular afferent excitation. *J. Physiol.* **122**, 302–321. [358]

Araki, T., Eccles, J. C. & Ito, M. (1960). Correlation of the inhibitory post-synaptic potential of motoneurones with the latency and time course of inhibition of monosynaptic reflexes. *J. Physiol.* **154**, 354–377. [364]

Asmussen, E. & Nielsen, M. (1964). Experiments on nervous factors controlling respiration and circulation during exercise employing blocking of the blood flow. *Acta. physiol. scand.* **60**, 103–111. [376]

Barnes, C. D. & Pompeiano, O. (1970a). Inhibition of monosynaptic extensor reflex attributable to presynaptic depolarisation of the group Ia afferent fibres produced by vibration of a flexor muscle. *Archs. ital. Biol.* **108**, 233–258. [392, 393]

— (1970b). Presynaptic and postsynaptic effects in the monosynaptic reflex pathway to extensor motoneurons following vibration of synergic muscles. *Archs. ital. Biol.* **108**, 259–294. [392]

Bessou, P., Dejours, P. & Laporte, Y. (1959). Effets ventilatoires réflexes de la stimulation de fibres afférentes de grand diamètre, d'origine musculaire, chez le chat. *C.r. Séanc. Soc. Biol.* **153**, 477–481. [376]

Bishop, G. H. & Heinbecker, P. (1935). The afferent functions of non-myelinated or C fibers. *Am. J. Physiol.* **114**, 179–193. [378, 379]

Boyd, I. A. & Davey, M. R. (1968). *Composition of Peripheral Nerves.* 57 pp. Edinburgh: Livingstone. [339]

Bradley, K., Easton, D. M. & Eccles, J. C. (1953). An investigation of primary or direct inhibition. *J. Physiol.* **122**, 474–488. [342, 343]

Bradley, K. & Eccles, J. C. (1953). Analysis of fast afferent impulses from thigh muscles. *J. Physiol.* **122**, 462–473. [340, 341]

Brock, L. G., Eccles, J. C. & Rall, W. (1951). Experimental investigations on the afferent fibres in muscle nerves. *Proc. R. Soc.* B, **138**, 453–475. [339]

Bruggencate, G. ten, Burke, R., Lundberg, A. & Udo, M. (1969). Interaction between the vestibulospinal tract, contralateral flexor reflex afferents and Ia afferents. *Brain Res.* **14**, 529–532.   [366]

Burke, R. E. (1968). Group Ia synaptic input to fast and slow twitch motor units of cat triceps surae. *J. Physiol.* **196**, 605–630.   [355]

Burke, R. E., Rudomin, P., Vyklický, L. & Zajac III, F. E. (1971). Primary afferent depolarisation and flexion reflexes produced by radiant heat stimulation of the skin. *J. Physiol.* **213**, 185–214.   [380]

Clark, D., Hughes, J. & Gasser, H. S. (1935). Afferent function in the group of nerve fibers of slowest conduction velocity. *Am. J. Physiol.* **114**, 69–76.   [378]

Clough, J. F. M., Kernell, D. & Phillips, C. G. (1968). The distribution of monosynaptic excitation from the pyramidal tract and from primary spindle afferents to motoneurones of the baboon's hand and forearm. *J. Physiol.* **198**, 145–166.   [354, 356]

Cohen, L. A. & Cohen, M. L. (1956). Arthrokinetic reflex of the knee. *Am. J. Physiol.* **184**, 433–437.   [383]

Collin, R., Kaufman, A. & Koizumi, K. (1969). Some sympathetic reflexes produced by varying afferent nerve stimulation. *J. Physiol.* **201**, 49–50P.   [380]

Conradi, S. (1970). Ultrastructure of dorsal root boutons on lumbosacral motoneurons of the adult cat, as revealed by dorsal root section. *Acta physiol. scand.* **78**, suppl. 332, 85–105.   [357, 384]

Coote, J. H., Hilton, S. M. & Perez-Gonzalez, J. F. (1971). The reflex nature of the pressor response to muscular exercise. *J. Physiol.* **215**, 789–804.   [376, 378]

Coote, J. H. & Perez-Gonzalez, J. F. (1968). The response of some sympathetic neurones to volleys in various afferent nerves. *J. Physiol.* **197**, 25–26P.   [377, 380]

Coppin, C. M. L., Jack, J. J. B. & McIntyre, A. K. (1969). Properties of group I afferent fibres from semitendinosus muscle in the cat. *J. Physiol.* **203**, 45–46P.   [349, 369]

Coppin, C. M. L., Jack, J. J. B. & MacLennan, C. R. (1970). A method for the selective activation of tendon organ afferent fibres from the cat soleus muscle. *J. Physiol.* **219**, 18–20P.   [350]

Dawson, G. D., Merrill, E. G. & Wall, P. D. (1970). Dorsal root potentials produced by stimulation of fine afferents. *Science, N.Y.* **167**, 1385–1387.   [380]

Decandia, M., Provini, L. & Táboříková, M. (1967). Presynaptic inhibition of the monosynaptic reflex following the stimulation of nerves to extensor muscles of the ankle. *Expl. Brain Res.* **4**, 34–42.   [389]

Dejours, P. (1964). Control of respiration in muscular exercise. In *Handbook of Physiology, section 3: Respiration*, Vol. 1. ed. Fenn, W. O. & Rahn, H. pp. 631–648. Washington: American Physiological Society.   [376]

Denny-Brown, D. (1928). On inhibition as a reflex accompaniment of the tendon jerk and of other forms of active muscular response. *Proc. R. Soc. B*, **103**, 321–326.   [330]

Denny-Brown, D. E. & Liddell, E. G. T. (1927). Observations on the motor twitch and on reflex inhibition of the tendon jerk of M. supraspinatus. *J. Physiol.* **63**, 70–79. [330]

Devandan, M. S., Eccles, R. M. & Stenhouse, D. (1966). Presynaptic inhibition evoked by muscle contraction. *J. Physiol.* **185**, 471–485. [391]

Devandan, M. S., Eccles, R. M. & Yokota, T. (1965*a*). Depolarisation of afferent terminals evoked by muscle stretch. *J. Physiol.* **179**, 417–429. [391]

— (1965*b*). Muscle stretch and the presynaptic inhibition of the group Ia pathway to motoneurones. *J. Physiol.* **179**, 430–441 [391]

Eccles, J. C. (1953). *The Neurophysiological Basis of Mind: The Principles of Neurophysiology.* 314 pp. Oxford: Clarendon Press. [363]

— (1957). *The Physiology of Nerve Cells.* Baltimore: John Hopkins Press. [326, 342, 358]

— (1964*a*). *The Physiology of Synapses.* 316 pp. Berlin: Springer.

— (1964*b*). Presynaptic inhibition in the spinal cord. In: *Physiology of Spinal Neurones,* Vol. 12, *Progress in Brain Research,* pp. 65–89. ed. Eccles, J. C. & Schadé, J. P. Amsterdam: Elsevier. [384]

— (1969). *The Inhibitory Pathways of the Central Nervous System.* 135 pp. Liverpool: Liverpool University Press. [364]

Eccles, J. C., Eccles, R. M. & Lundberg, A. (1957*a*). Synaptic actions on motoneurones in relation to the two components of the group I muscle afferent volley. *J. Physiol.* **136**, 527–546. [342, 343, 367]

— (1957*b*). The convergence of monosynaptic excitatory afferents on to many different species of alpha motoneurones. *J. Physiol.* **137**, 22–50. [353, 354]

— (1957*c*). Synaptic actions on motoneurones caused by impulses in Golgi tendon organ afferents. *J. Physiol.* **138**, 227–252. [343–345]

Eccles, J. C., Eccles, R. M. & Magni, F. (1961). Central inhibitory action attributable to presynaptic depolarisation produced by muscle afferent volleys. *J. Physiol.* **159**, 147–166. [388]

Eccles, J. C., Fatt, P. & Langdren, S. (1956). The central pathway for the direct inhibitory action of impulses in the largest afferent nerve fibres to muscle. *J. Neurophysiol.* **19**, 75–98. [363]

Eccles, J. C. & Pritchard, J. J. (1937). The action potential of motoneurones. *J. Physiol.* **89**, 43–45P. [325]

Eccles, J. C., Schmidt, R. F. & Willis, W. D. (1963). Depolarization of central terminals of group Ib afferent fibers of muscle. *J. Neurophysiol.* **26**, 1–27. [389]

Eccles, R. M., Holmqvist, B. Voorhoeve, P. E. (1964). Presynaptic depolarisation of cutaneous afferents by volleys in contralateral muscle afferents. *Acta physiol. scand.* **62**, 474–484. [388]

Eccles, R. M. & Lundberg, A. (1958*a*). Integrative pattern of Ia synaptic actions on motoneurones of hip and knee muscles. *J. Physiol.* **144**, 271–298. [353, 354]

— (1958*b*). The synaptic linkage of 'direct' inhibition. *Acta physiol. scand.* **43**, 204–215. [364]

Eccles, R. M. & Lundberg, A. (1959a). Synaptic actions in motoneurones by afferents which may evoke the flexion reflex. *Archs. ital. Biol.* **97**, 199–221.   [368–371, 375, 381]

— (1959b). Supraspinal control of interneurones mediating spinal reflexes. *J. Physiol.* **147**, 565–584.   [371, 373, 376, 381]

Eide, E., Lundberg, A. & Voorhoeve, P. (1961). Monosynaptically evoked inhibitory postsynaptic potentials in motoneurones. *Acta physiol. scand.* **53**, 185–195.   [364]

Ekholm, J., Eklund, G. & Skoglund, S. (1960). On the reflex effects from the knee joint of the cat. *Acta physiol. scand.* **50**, 167–174.   [383]

Franz, D. N. & Iggo, A. (1968). Dorsal root potentials and ventral root reflexes evoked by nonmyelinated fibers. *Science, N.Y.* **162**, 1140–1142.   [379, 380]

Fulton, J. F. & Pi-Suñer, J. (1928). A note concerning the possible function of various afferent end-organs in skeletal muscle. *Am. J. Physiol.* **83**, 554–562.   [329]

Fussey, I., Kidd, C. & Whitwam, J. G. (1969). Evoked activity in efferent sympathetic nerves in response to peripheral nerve stimulation in the dog. *J. Physiol.* **200**, 77–78P.   [380]

Gardner, E. (1950). Reflex muscular responses to stimulation of articular nerves in the cat. *Am. J. Physiol.* **161**, 133–141.   [380]

Gotch, F. (1896). Note on the so-called tendon reflex. *J. Physiol.* **20**, 322–333.   [323]

Granit, R. (1955). *Receptors and Sensory Perception.* 369 pp. New Haven: Yale University Press.   [332]

Granit, R., Phillips, C. G., Skoglund, S. & Steg, G. (1957). Differentiation of tonic from phasic alpha ventral horn cells by stretch pinna and crossed extensor reflexes. *J. Neurophysiol.* **20**, 470–481.   [359]

Grillner, S., Hongo, T. & Lund, S. (1966). Interaction between the inhibitory pathways from the Deiters' nucleus and Ia afferents to flexor motoneurones. *Acta. physiol. scand.* **68**, suppl. 277, 61.   [366]

Hník, P. (1970). The increased response of chronically de-efferented rat muscle spindles to stretch. *Brain Res.* **21**, 448–451.   [369]

Hník, P. & Hudlická, O. (1969). The response of myelinated muscle afferents to non-proprioceptive stimuli. *J. Physiol.* **201**, 92–93P. [378]

Hník, P. & Payne, R. (1965). Spontaneous activity in non-proprioceptive sensory fibres from de-efferented muscles. *J. Physiol.* **180**, 25–26P.
                                                                        [369]

— (1966). The origin of increased sensory outflow from chronically de-efferented muscles. *Physiologia bohemoslov.* **15**, 498–507.   [369]

Hodgson, H. J. F. & Matthews, P. B. C. (1968). The ineffectiveness of excitation of the primary endings of the muscle spindle by vibration as a respiratory stimulant in the decerebrate cat. *J. Physiol.* **194**, 555–563.   [376, 377]

Hoffmann, P. (1920). Demonstration eines Hemmungsreflexes im menschlichen Rückenmark. *Z. Biol.* **70**, 515–524.   [329]

— (1922). *Untersuchungen uber die Eigenreflexe (Sehnenreflexe) Menschlischer Muskeln.* Berlin: Springer.   [325]

Holmqvist, B. (1961). Crossed spinal reflex actions evoked by volleys in somatic afferents. *Acta. physiol. scand.* **52**, Suppl. 181, 66pp. [367]

Holmqvist, B. & Lundberg, A. (1961). Differential supraspinal control of synaptic actions evoked by volleys in the flexion reflex afferents in alpha motoneurones. *Acta. physiol. scand.* **54**, suppl. 186, 51pp. [370–375, 381, 382]

Hongo, T., Jankowska, E. & Lundberg, A. (1966). Convergence of excitatory and inhibitory action on interneurones in the lumbosacral cord. *Expl. Brain Res.* **1**, 338–358. [366]

— (1969). The rubrospinal tract II. Facilitation of interneuronal transmission in reflex paths to motoneurones. *Expl. Brain Res.* **7**, 365–391. [346, 366, 367, 382]

Hornbein, T. F., Sørensen, S. C. & Parks, C. R. (1969). Role of muscle spindles in lower extremities in breathing during bicycle exercise. *J. appl. Physiol.* **27**, 476–479. [377]

Hultborn, H., Jankowska, E. & Lindström, S. (1968). Inhibition in Ia inhibitory pathway by impulses in recurrent motor axon collaterals. *Life Sci.* **7**, 337–339. [365]

— (1971a). Recurrent inhibition from motor axon collaterals of transmission in the Ia inhibitory pathway to motoneurones. *J. Physiol.* **215**, 591–612. [366]

— (1971b). Relative contribution from different nerves to recurrent depression of Ia IPSPs in motoneurones. *J. Physiol.* **215**, 637–664. [366]

Hunt, C. C. (1954). Relation of function to diameter in afferent fibres of muscle nerves. *J. gen. Physiol.* **38**, 117–131. [342, 349, 368]

Hunt, C. C. & Kuffler, S. W. (1951). Stretch receptor discharges during muscle contraction. *J. Physiol.* **113**, 298–315. [342, 349]

Jack, J. J. B. & MacLennan, C. R. (1971). The lack of an electrical threshold discrimination between group Ia and group Ib fibres in the nerve to the cat peroneus longus muscle. *J. Physiol.* **212**, 35–36P. [349]

Jack, J. J. B., Miller, S., Porter, R. & Redman, S. J. (1970). The distribution of group Ia synapses on lumbosacral spinal motoneurones in the cat. In *Excitatory Synaptic Mechanism.* ed. Andersen, P. & Jansen, J. K. S. pp. 199–205. Oslo: Universitetsforlaget. [355, 356]

Jankowska, E., Jukes, M. G. M. & Lund, S. (1965). The pattern of presynaptic inhibition of transmission to the dorsal spinocerebellar tract of the cat. *J. Physiol.* **178**, 17–18P. [390]

Job, C. (1953). Über autogene Inhibition und Reflexumkehr bei spinalisierten und decerebrierten Katzen. *Pflügers Arch. ges. Physiol.* **256**, 406–418. [371]

Johansson, B. (1962). Circulatory responses to stimulation of somatic afferents. *Acta. physiol. scand.* **57**, Suppl. 198, 91 pp. [377–380]

Jolly, W. A. (1911). On the time relations of the knee-jerk and simple reflexes. *Q. Jl. exp. Physiol.* **4**, 67–87. [323–325]

Kao, F. F. (1963). An experimental study of the pathways involved in exercise hyperpnoea employing cross-circulation techniques. In *The Regulation of Human Respiration*. ed. Cunningham, D. J. C. & Lloyd, B. B. pp. 461–502. Oxford: Blackwell.   [376]

Kellerth, J. O. (1968). Aspects on the relative significance of pre- and post-synaptic inhibition in the spinal cord. In *Structure and Function of Inhibitory Synapses*. ed. Euler, C. von, Skoglund, S. & Söderberg, U. pp. 197–212. Oxford: Pergamon.   [384]

Kučera, J. (1969). Vasomotor reflexes from muscles in the spinal cat. *Experientia* **12,** 1267–1268.   [378]

Kuno, M. (1964). Mechanism of facilitation and depression of the excitatory synaptic potential in spinal motoneurones. *J. Physiol.* **175,** 100–112.   [385]

Kuno, M. & Miyahara, J. T. (1969). Analysis of synaptic efficacy in spinal motoneurones from 'quantum' aspects. *J. Physiol.* **201,** 479–493.
          [356]

Kuno, M. & Perl, E. R. (1960). Alteration of spinal reflexes by interaction with suprasegmental and dorsal root activity. *J. Physiol.* **151,** 103–122.   [347, 371, 376]

Laporte, Y. & Bessou, P. (1957). Étude des sub-groups lent et rapide du Groupe I (fibres afférentes d'origine musculaire de grand diamètre) chez le chat. *J. Physiol., Paris* **49,** 1025–1037.   [346]

— (1958). Reflexes ipse-latéraux d'origine exclusivement amyélinique chez le chat. *C.r. Séanc Soc. Biol.* **152,** 161–164.   [379]

Laporte, Y., Bessou, P. & Bouisset, S. (1960). Action réflexe des differents types de fibres afférentes d'origine musculaire sur la pression sanguine. *Archs. ital. Biol.* **98,** 206–221.   [377, 378]

Laporte, Y. & Boer, A. (1954a). Décharge réflexe segmentaire homolatérale provoquée par les fibres amyéliniques chez le chat spinal aigu. *C.r. Séanc. Soc. Biol.* **148,** 793–796.   [379]

— (1954b). Réflexe de flexion ipsilatéral provoqué par les fibres amyélinique chez le chat spinal. *C. r. Séanc. Soc. Biol.* **149,** 808–810. [379]

Laporte, Y., Leitner, L. M. & Pagès, B. (1962). Absence d'effets réflexes circulatoire des fibres afférentes d'origine musculaire. *C. r. Séanc. Soc. Biol.* **156,** 2130–2133.   [378]

Laporte, Y. & Lloyd, D. P. C. (1952). Nature and significance of the reflex connections established by large afferent fibres of muscular origin. *Am .J. Physiol.* **169,** 609–621.   [336–338, 362]

Liddell, E. G. T. (1960). *The Discovery of Reflexes*. 174 pp. Oxford: Clarendon Press.   [322]

Liddell, E. G. T. & Sherrington, C. (1924). Reflexes in response to stretch (myotatic reflexes). *Proc. R. Soc. B.* **96,** 212–242.   [330]

Lloyd, D. P. C. (1941). A direct central inhibitory action of dromically conducted impulses. *J. Neurophysiol.* **4,** 184–190.   [362]

— (1943a). Reflex action in relation to pattern and peripheral source of afferent stimulation. *J. Neurophysiol.* **6,** 111–120.   [334, 336]

— (1943b). Neuron patterns controlling transmission of ipsilateral hind limb reflexes in cat. *J. Neurophysiol.* **6,** 293–315.
          [334, 335, 353, 375, 378]

Lloyd, D. P. C. (1943c). Conduction and synaptic transmission of reflex response to stretch in spinal cats. *J. Neurophysiol.* **6**, 317–326. [327, 334]

— (1946a). Facilitation and inhibition of spinal motoneurons. *J. Neurophysiol.* **9**, 421–438. [334, 335, 342, 362]

— (1946b). Integrative pattern of excitation and inhibition in two-neuron reflex arcs. *J. Neurophysiol.* **9**, 439–444. [334, 335, 353, 362]

Lund, S., Lundberg, A. & Vyklický, L. (1965). Inhibitory action from the flexor reflex afferents on transmission to Ia afferents. *Acta physiol. scand.* **64**, 345–355. [390]

Lundberg, A. (1964). Supraspinal control of transmission in reflex paths to motoneurones and primary afferents. In *Physiology of Spinal Neurones*, Vol. 12 in *Progress in Brain Research*, ed. Eccles, J. C. & Schadé, J. P. pp. 197–219. Amsterdam: Elsevier. [389]

— (1966). Integration in the reflex pathway. In *Muscular Afferents and Motor Control*, ed. Granit, R. pp. 275–305. Stockholm: Almqvist & Wiksell. [389, 390]

— (1970). The excitatory control of the Ia inhibitory pathway. In *Excitatory Synaptic Mechanisms*, ed. Andersen, P. & Jansen, J. K. S. pp. 333–340. Oslo: Universitetsforlaget. [365, 366]

Lundberg, A. & Voorhoeve, P. E. (1962). Effects from the pyramidal tract on spinal reflex arcs: *Acta physiol. scand.* **56**, 201–219. [366]

Lundberg, A. & Winsbury, G. (1960). Selective adequate activation of large afferents from muscle spindles and Golgi tendon organs. *Acta physiol. scand.* **49**, 155–164. [331]

McIntyre, A. K. (1951). Afferent limb of the myotatic reflex arc. *Nature (Lond.)* **168**, 168–169. [331]

MacLennan, C. R. (1971) *Studies on the selective activation of muscle receptor afferents*. Doctoral thesis: Oxford University. [369]

Mendell, L. M. (1970). Positive dorsal root potentials produced by stimulation of small diameter muscle afferents. *Brain Res.* **18**, 375–379. [380, 390, 391]

Mendell, L. M. & Henneman, E. (1968). Terminals of single Ia fibers: Distribution within a pool of 300 homonymous motor neurons. *Science* **160**, 96–98. [355]

Mendell, L. M. & Henneman, E. (1971). Terminals of single Ia fibers: Location, density, and distribution within a pool of 300 homonymous motoneurones. *J. Neurophysiol.* **34**, 171–187. [355, 356]

Mendell, L. M. & Wall, P. D. (1964). Presynaptic hyperpolarisation: a role for fine afferent fibres. *J. Physiol.* **172**, 274–294. [379, 391]

Pacheco, P. & Guzmán, C. (1969). Intracellular recording in extensor motoneurons of spastic cats. *Expl. Neurol.* **25**, 472–481. [360, 375]

Paintal, A. S. (1960). Functional analysis of group III afferent fibres of mammalian muscles. *J. Physiol.* **152**, 250–270. [369]

— (1961). Participation by pressure-pain receptors of mammalian muscles in the flexion reflex. *J. Physiol.* **156**, 498–514. [375]

Perl, E. A. (1958). Crossed reflex effects evoked by activity in myelinated afferent fibres of muscle. *J. Neurophysiol.* **21**, 101–112. [367]

Perl, E. A. (1959). Effects of muscle stretch on excitability of contralateral motoneurones. *J. Physiol.* **145**, 193–203.   [367]

Renshaw, B. (1940). Activity in the simplest spinal reflex pathways. *J. Neurophysiol.* **3**, 373–387.   [325, 326]

— (1943) Reflex discharges in branches of the crural nerve. *J. Neurophysiol.* **5**, 487–498.   [362]

Schmidt, R. F. & Willis, W. D. (1963). Intracellular recording from motoneurons of the cervical spinal cord of the cat. *J. Neurophysiol.* **26**, 28–43.   [353]

Schmidt, R. F. & Weller, E. (1970). Reflex activity in the cervical and lumbar sympathetic trunk induced by unmyelinated somatic afferents. *Brain Res.* **24**, 207–218.   [380]

Sears, T. A. (1964). Some properties and reflex connexions of respiratory motoneurones of the cat's thoracic spinal cord. *J. Physiol.* **175**, 386–403.   [367]

Senapati, J. M. (1966). Effect of stimulation of muscle afferents on ventilation in dogs. *J. appl. Physiol.* **21**, 242–246.   [376]

Sherrington, C. S. (1900). The knee-jerk and allied phenomenon. In: *Textbook of Physiology*, Vol. II, ed. Schäfer, E. A. pp. 870–873. Edinburgh: Pentland.   [322]

— (1906). *The Integrative Action of the Nervous System.* 433 pp. London: Constable.   [322, 333]

— (1909). On plastic tonus and proprioceptive reflexes. *Q. J. exp. Physiol.* **2**, 109–156.   [334]

— (1910). Flexion-reflex of the limb, crossed extension-reflex, and reflex stepping and standing. *J. Physiol.* **40**, 28–121.   [352]

Sherrington, C. S. & Sowton, S. C. M. (1915). Observations on reflex responses to single break-shocks. *J. Physiol.* **49**, 331–348.   [371]

Skoglund, C. R. (1960). Vasomotor reflexes from muscle. *Acta physiol. scand.* **50**, 311–327.   [377]

Skoglund, S. (1956). Anatomical and physiological studies of knee joint innervation in the cat. *Acta physiol. scand.* **36**, Suppl. 124: 101 pp.   [380, 383]

Snyder, C. D. (1910). The latency of the knee-jerk response in man as measured by the thread galvanometer. *Am. J. Physiol.* **76**, 474–482.   [325, 329]

Szentágothai, J. (1958). The anatomical basis of synaptic transmission of excitation and inhibition in motoneurones. *Acta morph. Acad. Sci. hung.* **8**, 287–309.   [357]

Sumner, A. J. (1961). Properties of Ia and Ib afferent fibres serving stretch receptors of the cat's medial gastrocnemius muscle. *Proc. Univ. Otago Med. Sch.* **39**, 3–5. Also cited by McIntyre, A. K. (1965) p. 202 in *Studies in Physiology* ed. Curtis D. R. & McIntyre, A. K. Berlin: Springer.   [347, 348]

Tschirjew, S. I. (1878). Ursprung und Bedeutung des Kniephänomens und verwandter Erscheinungen. *Arch. Psychiat. u. Nervenkrank.* **8**, 689–712.   [322]

Tsukahara, N. & Ohye, C. (1964). Polysynaptic activation of extensor motoneurones from group Ia fibres in cat spinal cord. *Experientia* **20**, 628–629. [359, 360]

Wall, P. D. (1958). Excitability changes in afferent fibre terminations and their relation to slow potentials. *J. Physiol.* **142**, 1–21. [386]

— (1964). Presynaptic control of impulses at the first central synapse in the cutaneous pathway. In: Physiology of Spinal Neurones, Vol. 12, *Progress in Brain Research*, ed. Eccles, J. C. & Schadé, J. P. pp. 92–115. Amsterdam: Elsevier. [384]

Waller, A. D. (1881). On muscular spasms known as 'tendon-reflex'. *Brain*, **3**, 179–191. [323]

— (1890). On the physiological mechanism of phenomenon termed 'tendon-reflex'. *J. Physiol.* **11**, 384–395. [323]

Wildenthal, K., Mierzwial, D. S., Skinner, N. S. & Mitchell, J. H. (1968). Potassium-induced cardiovascular and ventilatory reflexes from the dog hindlimb. *Am. J. Physiol.* **215**, 542–548. [378]

Wilson, V. J. & Kato, M. (1965). Excitation of extensor motoneurons by group II afferent fibers in ipsilateral muscle nerves. *J. Neurophysiol.* **28**, 545–554. [374]

Zimmermann, M. (1968). Dorsal root potentials after C-fiber stimulation. *Science, N.Y.* **160**, 896–898. [380]

8

MUSCLE TONE AS EXEMPLIFIED BY THE TONIC COMPONENT OF THE STRETCH REFLEX

The introduction of the decerebrate preparation

THE tone of skeletal muscle has long been an object of physiological interest. For example, in 1892 Foster with the assistance of Sherrington and Langley devoted four pages of his textbook to a discussion of its properties and origin. His definition of tone remains as clear as any that can be made today, for he stated: 'When we handle the limb of a healthy man, we find that it offers a certain amount of resistance to passive movements. This resistance . . . is an expression of muscular tone.' From a variety of evidence he believed that the 'maintenance of skeletal tone is one of the functions of the cord'. Then, as now, the practical importance to medicine of a study of tone needed little emphasis, since alteration in the tone of skeletal muscle is a common result of disease of the nervous system. Unfortunately the study of the processes underlying muscle tone is difficult in the normal animal. Not only is the degree of tone often slight, but in addition, to anaesthetise an animal is to reduce or abolish the very tone that it is wished to study.

A great advance was made, therefore, when Sherrington (1898) rediscovered and publicised the fact that an abnormally high degree of tone promptly develops in the extensor muscles of an animal on transecting the brainstem in the region of the corpora quadrigemina, and thereby disconnecting the lower centres from the cerebral hemispheres and basal ganglia. According to Granit (1966) the phenomenon had already been observed though not named by several of Sherrington's equally illustrious predecessors including Magendie, Flourens, Claude Bernard and Vulpian, but had then been lost sight of. This decerebrate preparation provides an automaton in which tone may be studied with relative ease, but it would be naive to suppose that its tone is similar in all respects, save in degree, to that of the normal preparation. Nor need it be supposed that pathological increases in tone occurring in human disease all depend upon the same functional aberration as that occurring in the cat decerebrated in the manner described by Sherrington. None the less, analysis of the abnormal tone of the decerebrate cat should help elucidate some if not all of the basic mechanisms underlying normal tone. With luck it should also help throw light upon the reflex control exerted over muscle in the performance of voluntary muscular acts.

FIG. 8.1. The exaggerated postural standing of the decerebrate cat. The picture shows a cat decerebrated by the anaemic method. This produces a preparation which is usually rather more rigid than those decerebrated by transecting the mid-brain between the colliculi, as done by Sherrington. (Pollock & Davis, 1930, Fig. 4.)

Sherrington (1898) immediately used the decerebrate preparation to make an observation of unrivalled importance, namely that section of the appropriate dorsal spinal roots caused a local reduction of rigidity. A single limb might then become flaccid while the rest remained rigid. This occurred the moment the dorsal roots were cut, but local flaccidity was also found when the dorsal roots were cut some days before the decerebration. Sherrington therefore ascribed the reduction of the rigidity to the interruption of a 'tonic' stream of afferent impulses from the limb, rather than to the excitation, by the trauma of sectioning, of fibres with an inhibitory action on the tone. He thus concluded that 'the development of decerebrate rigidity in a limb is largely determined by centripetal impulses coming from the limb in question'. Some ten years later, Sherrington (1909) studied the tone of the vastocrureus portion of the quadriceps in the decerebrate cat after all the other muscles and the skin of the leg had been denervated. The chief afferent activity remaining to be eliminated by dorsal root section was then that from the muscle itself. The increased tone of decerebrate rigidity was found to develop as usual in the isolated muscle and still to be eliminated by dorsal root section. From this Sherrington rightly concluded both that muscle contains receptors which can reflexly produce an autogenetic excitation, and also that the tonic activity of these receptors is important in maintaining decerebrate rigidity. The local reflexes responsible for tone were thus shown to be, at least in part, of a highly specific kind.

Later work has shown, however, that muscle rigidity may survive de-afferentation in decerebrate cats with a superadded lesion of the cerebellum. In addition, the tone of forelimb muscles survives after de-afferentation when the spinal cord has been cut below the brachial enlargement. Terzuolo & Terzian (1953) have also shown that rigidity may persist in a de-afferented limb of a Sherringtonian decerebrate cat for a minute or two following stimulation of the cerebellum. In all these cases there appears to be so much excitation converging upon the extensor α motoneurones from non-local sources that they discharge even in the absence of any reflex excitation, and thus produce a maintained contraction of extensor muscles which manifests itself as an extensor rigidity. Such behaviour, however, in no way contradicts Sherrington's demonstration of the importance of local reflexes, though Pollock & Davis (1930, 1931) seem to have felt so when they found that in cats decerebrated by their anaemic method the rigidity could persist in spite of widespread de-afferentation; they apparently felt that Sherrington's preparations were in a poor state as a result of the traumatic severing of the brainstem and consequent blood loss. Anaemic decerebration is performed by tying both carotid arteries and the basilar artery so as to destroy the brain by depriving it of blood (Pollock & Davis, 1923). In this case the anterior part of the cerebellum is usually killed in addition to the structures removed by the Sherringtonian midcollicular decerebration, thus producing an essentially different preparation (Granit, Holmgren & Merton, 1955). But even in cats which can maintain an 'α rigidity' independent of local reflexes it seems likely that when the dorsal roots are intact muscle afferent activity will increase the rigidity yet further. Autogenetic excitation cannot be dismissed as unimportant for any type of preparation until suitable quantitative studies have been performed to determine the effect of de-afferentation on the degree of rigidity.

The classical description of the stretch reflex with the delimitation of its tonic and phasic components

Sherrington's earlier experiments, which have just been described, depended upon operative skill followed by careful observation of the posture of the resulting preparation and upon the resistance felt on manipulating its limbs. This was soon supplemented by the recording of muscle length with a simple isotonic myograph writing on a smoked drum. With the introduction of the optical isometric myograph Liddell & Sherrington (1924, 1925) were able to study more quantitatively than before the 'development of resistance . . . against . . . passive movement' evoked by extension of the quadriceps muscle of a cat with decerebrate rigidity. In its time this optical myograph provided a considerable advance in the sensitivity and fidelity with which high-speed events could be recorded. It consisted of a torsion wire which was fixed at one or both ends and to which was attached a short lever for the muscle to pull upon. Its movement was recorded by a mirror which deflected a light beam of about a metre in length which impinged on a photographic glass plate. The plate could be made to travel at constant velocity, and so provide the time scale, by being fixed to a mass which fell under gravity at a velocity determined by an oil-filled dash-pot (i.e. the falling plate camera). This now seemingly cumbrous recording system was used to record the contraction by being attached to the distal tendon of the muscle. Not surprisingly it then proved easier to stretch the muscle by moving its other end, i.e. its origin, along with the rest of the cat. This was done by rigidly fixing the preparation to the so-called 'falling table', the top of which was allowed to fall a fixed distance under gravity at a velocity controlled by a dash-pot. The table was lifted back to its original position by a Lab. boy, and the particular one then employed has, so it happens, only just retired (1971) after over 50 years in the service of physiology. The man concerned, Mr. E. T. Giles, will also be remembered by some thousand or so Oxford medical graduates as the man who was in charge of the 'frog room'. Nowadays, small myographs utilising semiconductor strain gauges or other transducers are readily moved at high frequency and the conduct of such experiments has been greatly facilitated.

In this way Liddell & Sherrington (1924, 1925) were able to

confirm that extension of the quadriceps in the decerebrate cat caused it to contract, even though it remained 'the only hind-limb structure still retaining its afferent connections with the spinal cord'. The occurrence of a reflex contraction was demonstrated by showing that stretching the muscle produced appreciably more tension when it was innervated than when its nerve was cut. It is droll to note, however, that if they had happened to have performed the same experiment on preparations decerebrated by the anaemic method then the same finding would have been inconclusive. This is because some discharge of quadriceps motoneurones would probably then have occurred with the muscle at its initial length, thereby leading to an increase of contractile tension when the muscle was stretched as a result of purely muscular properties (see later). Fortunately, in cats decerebrated by Sherrington's method such tonic contraction only rarely occurs when the muscle is allowed to assume a reasonably short initial length. Thus their conclusions were impeccable and have been entirely substantiated by later work.

Liddell & Sherrington (1924) introduced the name stretch reflex for the responses they studied and also gave them the alternative name of the myotatic reflex from the combination of the greek words for muscle and extended (μυο- and τακτικός), because it was convenient in adjectival form. The combination had originally been introduced 40 years earlier by Gowers in describing tendon jerks as a 'myotatic contractions'. Liddell & Sherrington proceeded to study the time-course of the reflex contraction occurring during a prolonged extension of the muscle. They distinguished, as subdivisions of the stretch reflex, 'two modes of reaction—(1) "phasic" or short-lasting but relatively intense reaction; (2) "postural" or tonic, often less powerful but much longer lasting'. Both components were found irrespective of whether the muscle was extended slowly or rapidly, though the phasic component could be very small on the completion of a slow stretch. They concluded that the tonic component, at least, was a response to the maintained extension (static stretch), rather than to the movement required to reach the new length (kinetic stretch). The relative development of the two components varied in different preparations (see Fig. 8.2) and seemed to depend upon 'central neural conditions of the preparation, difficult sometimes to trace and control'. The tonic component was regularly accentuated

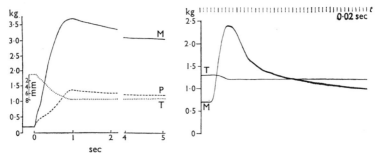

FIG. 8.2. Classical myographic records of the stretch reflex of the quadri-ceps muscle in the decerebrate cat showing the different degree of the development of the tonic and phasic components of the reflex in different preparations. M, muscle tension; T, muscle extension ('less than 1 mm in B'). P, passive tension produced by same extension after muscle denervated. (Liddell & Sherrington, 1924, Figs. 2 and 7.)

in decerebrate rigidity and practically abolished by spinal section, though a weak phasic reaction sometimes still persisted on spinalisation. The two components were none the less seen as two facets of the same reflex, rather than as two separate reflexes, and they blended into each other without any discontinuity. The tendon jerk, however, was seen by Liddell & Sherrington as only a 'fractional manifestation' of the more comprehensive stretch reflex which had been 'reduced and simplified by the extreme brevity and slightness of the mechanical stretch'; they had the same feeling about the clonus which was sometimes observed when the myograph spring was not particularly stiff.

In the summary of their first paper, Liddell & Sherrington (1924) stated that 'When the application of the stretch is confined to a portion only of the muscle, the reflex contraction is also con-fined to that portion.' This generalisation has rightly received much prominence in general accounts of the stretch reflex. It was, however, based solely on observing that a stretch confined to the vastrocrureus portion of the quadriceps evoked a stretch reflex from this portion of the quadriceps alone without evoking a con-traction in the rectus femoris portion of the quadriceps, and vice versa. These muscles are however fairly distinct, and the degree of localisation occurring in the stretch reflex has still not been intensively investigated. The matter remains of some interest since the monosynaptic connections of the Ia fibres are now well-known to have a relatively wide distribution and so at first sight the same might be expected for the stretch reflex. Cohen (1953, 1954) stretched a strip of the quadriceps which had been somewhat isolated from the rest of the muscle by inserting a thread around a fasciculus of muscle fibres. He found that though the resulting reflex contraction was sometimes limited to this strip, on other occasions it was not. Roberts (1952) found that slow stretch of one head of a muscle could excite another head of the muscle to contract, provided that the latter was under suitable initial tension (cf. gastrocnemius to soleus, vastus medialis or lateralis to crureus). It would be particularly interesting to know if the localisation of the tonic stretch reflex, which probably depends on complex central interactions, differs from that of the tendon jerk which depends upon monosynaptic connections by Ia fibres. Cohen's results at first sight appear to suggest that the tendon jerk spreads the further, but it is probably impossible to reach any firm conclusion on this basis. His stretched portion of muscle was still mechanically connected to the rest of the muscle and it seems inevitable that the effect he observed depended as much upon mechanical spread of the stimulus as upon any neural spread of the response.

Denny-Brown (1929) extended the work of Liddell & Sherrington by recording the stretch reflex in more than one muscle and found that red muscles tended to have more pronounced stretch reflexes than pale muscles acting at the same joint. For example, the soleus developed a tonic stretch reflex 'over ranges in length at which it is loose and folded if the motor nerve be sectioned'. When its stretch reflex was well developed extension of soleus might cause it to develop reflexly 'over 90 per cent of its maximal tension' as determined by electrical stimulation of its nerve at 100/sec; thus just about every motor unit of the soleus may be recruited in the stretch reflex. In contrast, gastrocnemius responded with a stretch reflex 'only when section of its nerve reveals that some passive tension is being exerted on the inactive fibres at that length'. The largest stretch reflex then found developed only 1500 g of active tension while the maximal tension which gastrocnemius could develop was 'well over 10 Kg'. All this accords with the present author's experience, though somewhat larger reflexes have sometimes been observed in gastrocnemius. These differential responses of different muscles fit in with the more recent demonstration that motoneurones with a high input resistance and smaller axons tend to have a lower reflex threshold and to supply more slowly contracting muscle fibres than do large fibres (see Chap. 7). This correlation has been shown to hold on exciting motoneurones by stretching the triceps surae in the decerebrate as well as on using other methods of reflex activation (Henneman, Somjen & Carpenter, 1965). Denny-Brown (1929) also showed that the tonic stretch reflex was not the prerogative of extensor muscles but could also occur in flexors; indeed some decerebrate cats may show flexor rather than extensor spasms, at any rate of the forelimbs.

The relation between muscle extension and reflex tension

In their original description, Liddell & Sherrington (1924) stated that 'so long as the stretch increases, the reflex continues to increase'. This was based on observing the response throughout the course of a single progressive slowly applied stretch. Subsequent more detailed investigation of the relation between the magnitude of the stimulus (muscle extension) and the resulting reflex response (muscle contraction) showed that the relation is often approximately linear as illustrated in Fig. 8.3 (Granit, 1958; Matthews, 1959). This is found both when the muscle is stretched to a series of different lengths and the tension measured at each, or when the tension is measured throughout the course of a single slowly applied stretch. When this latter is applied sufficiently slowly (2 mm/sec) it elicits largely the tonic component of the stretch reflex, for there is then an absence of any initial rapid phasic decay of tension on completion of the dynamic phase of stretching. Measurements made during a more rapid stretch usually give a steeper tension–length relation and there is then an appreciable phasic decay of tension on completion of the extension (Takano & Henatsch, 1971). In Fig. 8.3 the slope of the relation between active tension and extension was 75 g/mm, which is a fairly typical value for a soleus muscle with a moderately well developed stretch reflex; however, values up to 200 g/mm have been observed for the soleus. In one series the mean value was 90 g/mm which is 5% of the maximal tetanic tension per mm of extension (Matthews, 1959).

The linear relation should not however be taken to be completely exact, and deviations in both directions have been observed. At

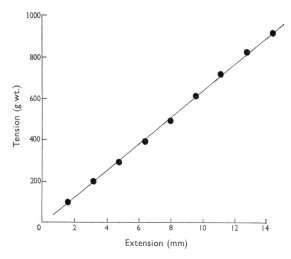

FIG. 8.3. An example of the frequent remarkable linearity of the stretch reflex elicited by large extensions of increasing extent. The graph shows the 'active' tension produced in the soleus muscle of a decerebrate cat plotted against the extension applied to the muscle. The results were obtained during the course of a single stretch of 14 mm applied at 1·6 mm/sec; this largely measures the extent of the tonic component of the stretch reflex. (Matthews, 1959, Fig. 3, redrawn.)

small reflex tensions the curve almost always slopes progressively upwards. At large tensions, when the passive tension begins to become prominent, the curve of active tension against length may slope downwards as if increase in the passive tension were having an inhibitory action (as could occur by an increasing excitation of tendon organs). In view of the various elements contributing to the stretch reflex it seems unwise to take up a definite stand, but the relation certainly often looks simple enough to lend itself to analysis. This caution is particularly necessary because the stretch reflex is by no means an invariant response though it sometimes appears to be so from the usual textbook précis of its properties. If the same stretch is repeatedly applied to an extensor muscle then in some preparations it may elicit virtually the same response for an hour or more, but in others the size of the reflex and the relative preponderance of its tonic and phasic components may vary from trial to trial without apparent rhyme or reason. Micturition or defecation are regularly accompanied by augmentation of the stretch reflex, and any sensory stimulation usually changes its size, so some apparently spontaneous alterations are presumably due to undetected peripheral stimuli (such as flea-bites); but most of the variability is probably due to sporadic changes in purely central function, particularly in the partially mutilated structures lying just below the level of section. One feels that if conditions were constant the reflex would be constant, and that the variability of the reflex is of little theoretical significance though a considerable experimental nuisance.

The apparently static equilibrium found in the tonic stretch reflex none the less results from the continual interplay of dynamic processes. For one thing, the tension trace observed on high gain is never completely still. The irregularities of tension development give the impression of being greater than would be expected from the mere beating against each other of the discharges of different motor units firing below their fusion frequency; moreover, in so far as this occurs it must inevitably influence the spindle afferent discharge and thus influence the reflex discharge (i.e. incipient clonus or tremor, see later). More importantly, release of the stretched muscle gives an immediate decrease in reflex discharge and the moment the stretch is removed the reflex ceases without after discharge, as is best shown electromyographically (Liddell & Sherrington, 1924; Denny-Brown, 1929).

The quasi-linear relation of Fig. 8.3 obtains its simplicity largely because of a restriction of the form of the stimulus, namely to large stretches of progressively increasing extent, and because no attention is paid to what happens on releasing the muscle or with the very smallest stretches. Like the spindle primary ending (see Chap. 4), the stretch reflex has been found to behave slightly differently when presented with alternate small stretches and releases. This is shown in Fig. 8.4 where stretches of 0·2 mm extent were superimposed on three different mean extensions. The small stretches can be seen to produce a relatively much larger effect than the large stretches. The peak tension produced by the small stretch applied at a mean extension of 4 mm was nearly the same as the trough tension at the longest length, and the trough tension at 4 mm was nearly the same as the peak tension at the shortest length. In this particular experiment increasing the size of the small stretches up to about 0·4 mm produced a proportional increase in the response, but the response increased relatively less

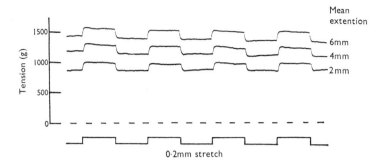

FIG. 8.4. The relatively large stretch reflex response to alternate small stretches and releases. Myographic records of the reflex responses to alternately stretching and releasing the soleus muscle by 0·2 mm when it was at three different mean lengths. Separate records were obtained for each extension and subsequently superimposed. Passive tensions produced by the same stretches were inappreciable. (Matthews, 1969, Fig. 8.)

for larger stretches. The sensitivity to small alternating stretches was about four times that to large stretches. The superimposition of small stretches on a muscle contracting in response to stimulating its nerve does not produce this effect, so it is shown to be a property of some other part of the reflex arc and may reasonably be attributed to a similar behaviour of the primary endings. In fact, the non-linearity is often more marked for the primary endings than it is for the reflex. This is probably a result of the stretch reflex depending upon the secondary endings as well as the primary endings (see later). At any rate, the stretch reflex is seen to have the valuable property of being at its best in resisting disturbance from a set point, but without being driven into the saturation which would occur if the same high sensitivity were maintained for stretches of all sizes.

The roles of the various receptors in the stretch reflex

An immediate question about the stretch reflex is 'which of the various receptors in muscle is responsible for it?' Liddell & Sherrington wisely refrained from comment on this, but with the passage of time it came to be equated with the question as to which receptor was responsible for the tendon jerk, even though the latter was only a 'fractional manifestation' of the more comprehensive stretch reflex. Lloyd, in particular, apparently helped to promulgate this view with the establishment of the monosynaptic transmission of the tendon jerk and his bald characterisation of it as the 'reflex response to stretch'. Thus in the 1950's and 1960's it was widely believed that the Ia fibres were the sole origin of the tonic as well as the phasic component of the stretch reflex, and that there was no more to it than that. This, however, neglected factors which may contribute to the tonic component of the stretch reflex even though they have little or no opportunity to do so overtly to the tendon jerk, as for example any slow changes in Ia synaptic potency as a result of presynaptic inhibitory processes. Of course, it has always been recognised that stretch of a muscle is liable to set up inhibitory as well as excitatory autogenetic effects, but though Granit (1955) emphasised their existence they were usually relegated to a minor role. The essential thing to be kept in mind in thinking about the tonic component of the stretch reflex is that it represents a steady motor output in response to a steady barrage of afferent input. This allows for integrative neural mechanisms of a far higher order of complexity than one can hope to find displayed in the tendon jerk resulting from a single synchronous volley.

Steady stretch of a muscle will usually excite a steady afferent discharge in each of the three main types of proprioceptive afferent, namely the Ia, the Ib and the spindle group II fibres. Each of these is signalling a different facet of the mechanical state of the muscle and all three would be of use to an engineer faced with the problem of controlling muscle contraction. *A priori*, therefore, and from what has already been described of their reflex actions we might expect each of these inputs to be playing some part in modulating the stretch reflex. The current problem is to determine the precise role of each. This is to ask of each one, firstly, whether it is excitatory or inhibitory; secondly, by what interneuronal pathways the effect is mediated; and thirdly, how strong the effect is and how widely it is distributed. These last quantitative questions become of particular interest the moment it is desired to elaborate a model to mimic and thus 'explain' the response of the stretch reflex to a variety of inputs. The tendency to concentrate attention on the Ia fibres alone is tantamount to accepting the special case in which the reflex effects of the other inputs are zero. This seems unreasonable and is certainly not proven. The tacit acceptance of such a restricted view of the

stretch reflex came about partly from a general ignorance of anything better to put in its place, partly because the threshold of the
Golgi tendon organs was for long felt to be too high for them to
play a role in the moment-to-moment control of muscle responses,
and partly because the reflex response of the decerebrate cat to
single volleys in group II afferent fibres is almost absent, due to a
blockade of the relevant interneurones by inhibitory impulses
originating in mid-brain centres.

The Ia fibres and their excitatory contribution to the stretch reflex.
The Ia fibres can be confidently ascribed an excitatory role in the
stretch reflex because of their autogenetic monosynaptic connection; as already discussed it is possible that this short latency
route is backed up by polysynaptic spinal pathways. Whether the
Ia fibres also have further effects via yet other pathways, such as
the mid-brain or cerebellum, remains an open question. However,
the Ia fibres would certainly appear to produce a certain amount
of self-inhibition via presynaptic inhibition (see p. 392). There is
thus no logical necessity for a maintained Ia input to lead to a
maintained motor output. However, that it actually does so can
be demonstrated rather readily by using high-frequency vibration
as a stimulus instead of simple stretch (Matthews, 1966a,b;
Gillies, Burke & Lance, 1971). This is shown in Fig. 8.5 where
prolonged vibration is seen to cause a prolonged reflex contraction.
Afferent recording has shown that an input of 10 μm amplitude
vibration is an entirely selective stimulus for Ia fibres and so the
small maintained response of Fig. 8.5a is guaranteed to be the
response to a Ia input. Increasing the amplitude of vibration to
100 μm makes it a more powerful stimulus for the Ia fibres, and
may also have excited some other kinds of receptor; even so the
type of response does not seem to have changed and it has merely
increased in size. Thus part at least of the steady contraction seen
in the tonic stretch reflex must be due to a steady Ia input. In this
respect it is interesting that the response to vibration never shows
a rapid phasic decline with time even when the stretch reflex of
the same preparation does so. This suggests that the decline of the
stretch reflex cannot be due to a central adaptation to a steady Ia
input. Furthermore, no phasic decline is seen when vibration is
applied throughout the rising phase of the stretch and continuing
on its completion so that the Ia firing should then show no

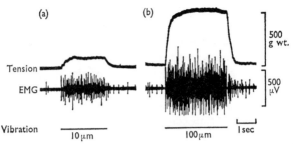

FIG. 8.5. The reflex response to high-frequency vibration applied in the decerebrate cat. During the signal a longitudinal vibration at 200 Hz was applied to the tendon of soleus which was connected to a myograph mounted on a vibrator. The peak-to-peak amplitude of vibrations was 10 μm in *a* and 100 μm in *b*. (Matthews, 1966*a*, Fig. 1.)

adaptation at the final length. This suggests that when a phasic decline is present in response to simple stretch it merely reflects a phasic diminution of Ia firing.

Vibration also provides a ready way of determining the power of the Ia fibres in producing a reflex contraction of the muscle. Such a determination is of particular interest in relation to the servo hypothesis of muscle control via the stretch reflex. It is performed by plotting the size of the vibration-induced reflex against the frequency of vibration when its amplitude is fairly large. On increasing the amplitude of vibration at any particular frequency the resulting reflex response first increases in size but then reaches a plateau value, so that as illustrated in Fig. 8.6 the response is approximately constant for amplitudes of from about 100–200 μm. The occurrence of such a plateau may be taken to show that the vibration is then sufficiently powerful to drive every primary ending in soleus to discharge an impulse on every cycle of the vibration, so that the overall Ia firing becomes constant in spite of changes in the size of the vibration. Smaller amplitudes of vibration probably fail to produce secure driving of every ending. Larger amplitudes lead to a diminution of the reflexly developed tension, but this is probably because of a direct action on the contractile strength of the muscle rather than a reflex action (Matthews, 1966*b*; Rack & Westbury, 1969).

Figure 8.6 also shows that the plateau size of the reflex increases with the frequency of vibration. Figure 8.7 shows further that the relation is approximately linear. In this particular case the slope

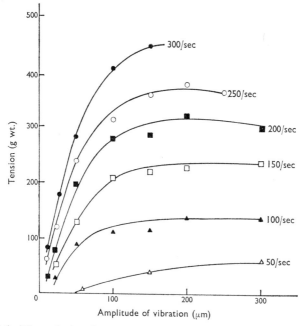

FIG. 8.6. The relation between the size of a vibration-induced reflex contraction and the amplitude of vibration for a series of different frequencies of vibration. Measurements made 1·5 sec from beginning of vibration. (Matthews, 1966b, Fig. 9.)

was 1·6 g tension per Hz increase in vibration frequency. Accepting that the vibration was driving all the Ia fibres this may be transmuted into 1·6 g reflex per impulse/sec Ia firing in all of the 50 or so soleus Ia fibres. This is equivalent to 30 mg for each individual Ia impulse, though of course the contraction is unlikely actually to be so finely gradable in practice because of the finite size of the motor unit and the variability in their frequency of discharge. As discussed later this figure for Ia action is rather low both in relation to strength of the reflex response to simple stretch and to that employed in many human engineered control systems, which employ negative feedback to achieve fidelity of response. It should also be emphasised that these figures are for measurements of the tonic or maintained response to vibration, and that the phasic response of the reflex arc is likely to be more appreciable but has not yet lent itself to analysis in such terms.

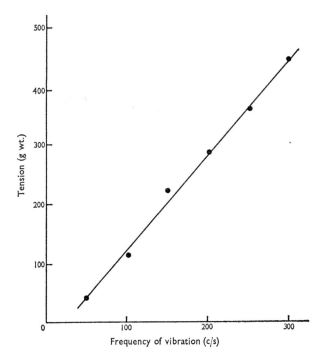

FIG. 8.7. The relation between the reflex response to vibration and the frequency of vibration. The measurements were of the response elicited by vibration of 150 μm amplitude; this was sufficient to elicit a 'plateau' response which did not alter with small alterations in the amplitude. (Matthews, 1966b, Fig. 10.)

The Ib fibres and their inhibitory contribution to the stretch reflex. The next point is that the muscle contraction occurring as a result of Ia excitation by stretch or vibration must inevitably excite the Ib fibres via the Golgi tendon organs with a resulting reflex autogenetic inhibition. This must lead to a diminution of the reflex contraction from what it otherwise would have been, for the Ib inhibition will counteract the Ia excitation. Houk, Singer & Goldman recently (1970) estimated that the contraction would be about half as large again if Ib feedback did not exist. Figure 8.8 illustrates the principle of their method for determining this figure which was to study the effect on a pre-existing reflex contraction of introducing some additional Ib excitation. The extra

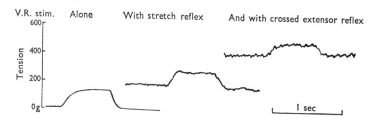

FIG. 8.8. Demonstration of the presence of 'tension feedback' reflexly modulating the strength of muscle contraction in the decerebrate cat. The records show the increase of contractile tension in the soleus muscle on stimulating a ventral root filament containing about 10% of its α motor fibres. The dorsal roots and the rest of the ventral root outflow were intact. The stimulation, which was at 20/sec, was repeated under three sets of conditions all with the muscle at the same length; on the left, when all pre-existing stretch reflex activity had been abolished by stimulating an inhibitory nerve; in the middle, when a small stretch reflex was present; on the right, when the stretch reflex had been combined with a crossed extensor reflex produced by stimulating the contralateral peroneal nerve. The ventral root stimulation produced a smaller increase in tension when it was superimposed on a pre-existing reflex contraction than it did on its own, even though its direct action on the muscle fibres it supplied must have been the same in all cases. The reduction must thus be attributed to the additional contraction reflexly reducing any pre-existing physiologically induced contraction. (Houk, Singer & Goldman, 1970, Fig. 2.)

Ib excitation was produced by the reasonably physiological method of eliciting a muscle contraction by stimulating the peripheral end of a small filament of severed ventral root. This was done in the decerebrate cat with its reflex connection otherwise intact. First, the true strength of the additional contraction was determined by performing the stimulation when the stretch reflex had been abolished by stimulating an inhibitory nerve. The contraction was then elicited during a stretch reflex, and again when the stretch reflex had been augmented by being combined with a crossed extensor reflex. The resulting increase in contractile tension was found to be smaller when the contraction was superimposed on the stretch reflex than when occurring in its absence, even though the stimulation of the filament must have excited the self-same muscle fibres in the two cases. The diminution of the tension increment is of course due to the extra contraction 'inhibiting' some of the pre-existing stretch reflex contraction.

The contraction was presumed to have this 'inhibitory' effect partly by the direct action of exciting Ib fibres and so producing a true inhibition, and partly by the indirect action of slightly relieving the pre-existing strain on the muscle spindles thereby decreasing their firing and producing a disfacilitation of the pre-existing motor discharge. These two factors were separated by calculations based on estimates of the stiffness of the stretch reflex, the length-tension curve of the contracting muscle fibres, and the value of the series compliance of the tendon. These calculations suggested that the observed 'inhibition' of the superadded counteraction was slightly more due to a true Ib inhibition than to a disfacilitation from reduced Ia firing. The 'gain' round the Ib loop was estimated to be of the order of 0·5 (the only two complete estimates achieved were 0·135 and 0·61). The meaning of this dimensionless figure of gain is that under open loop conditions (i.e. with ventral roots severed) the Ib firing elicited by a contraction of 100 g would inhibit 50 g's worth of any pre-existing motor firing. Approximately the same value was found for a range of muscle lengths and sizes of initial stretch reflex studied. Such treatment of the reflex centres as a relatively linear feedback loop is inevitably based on various assumptions and raises a good many problems which cannot be considered here. But such an approach seems likely to yield an understanding of the reflex in a different realm from that achieved by the unravelling of the number of synaptic relays involved, and would seem as important for the understanding of muscle control. This is not, however, to decry the more classical approach and the two methods essentially complement each other.

The spindle Group II fibres and their probable excitatory contribution to the stretch reflex. As already discussed, the experiments using electrical stimulation of nerve trunks led to the belief that the group II muscle afferents, including those from the secondary endings of the spindle, merely produced a non-specific flexor reflex. This view was fortified by Laporte and Bessou in 1959 when they found the appropriate effects on supposedly exciting the group II fibres by the more physiological method of stretching a muscle after blocking its group I fibres. Group I activity was eliminated by Bishop & Heinbecker's method of applying a short period of repetitive stimulation with rather strong shocks; in this case stimulation at 20–40/sec for about 0·5 sec with 100 μsec shocks of 20–30 V was deemed to provide a temporary paralysis of group I fibres while the group II fibres still conducted. Considerable attention had to be paid to every experimental detail to achieve selectivity and even so the method was not apparently invariably successful. The block was monitored solely by recording triphasically from the muscle nerve on stimulating the dorsal root and its efficacy was not tested by any recordings of single units. Laporte and Bessou found that when the group I fibres were blocked moderate stretching of soleus by a weight of 200 g produced autogenetic inhibition of its motoneurones, as judged by monosynaptic testing (for this the common nerve to lateral gastrocnemius and soleus was stimulated above block). Repetition of the experiment upon the tibialis anterior muscle produced an autogenetic excitation.

These actions are certainly those found in the flexor reflex, but there seems to be no guarantee that they were actually part of such a general pattern rather than of some more localised and specific response; no further muscles were studied, nor was the effect tested of stretching one muscle on the motoneurones of the other. Moreover, the experiments were restricted to the acute spinal cat. As has now become abundantly clear the finding of a reflex effect in any one type of preparation provides no surety that it will occur also in all others. None the less, perforce from the evidence it was widely accepted from about 1945 to 1970 that the spindle group II afferents merely produced a flexion reflex. This view, however, became progressively less satisfying as successive single unit recordings showed that the message transmitted from the spindle secondary endings was quite unnecessarily refined for such a non-specific purpose, as it provided such an accurate indication of muscle length, albeit under fusimotor control. Indeed, for many people the accuracy of response of the secondary ending made it appear inevitable that, like the primary ending, it must be designed to play a part in normal muscle control rather than to be reserved for emergencies. The limited evidence on its flexor reflex function was accordingly treated with reserve.

In 1969 the matter was put on a new footing by the suggestion that in the decerebrate cat the spindle group II fibres of extensor muscles produce autogenetic excitation rather than inhibition, and thereby help to produce the characteristic rigidity of the decerebrate preparation (Matthews, 1969). The evidence was indirect

and was based on a novel line of argument so that the new hypothesis has not yet found acceptance in all quarters (see for example,
Grillner, 1970; Grillner & Udo, 1971a) and at the present time it
still awaits confirmation by more conventional techniques. The
starting point for the suggestion was the new finding that in the
decerebrate cat the reflex response to simple stretch was often
rather stronger than the reflex response of the same muscle to
high-frequency vibration. Stretch excites both Ia and II fibres
whereas vibration powerfully excites the Ia fibres without significantly affecting the group II fibres. Thus, if the group II fibres
should indeed be excitatory, stretch would be a more potent stimulus than vibration. Figure 8.9 illustrates the type of record on

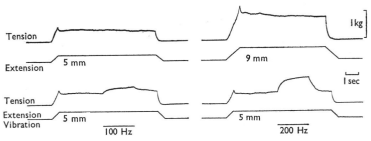

FIG. 8.9. The reflex response of a single preparation to simple stretch
(above) and to stretch plus vibration (below). Soleus muscle of decerebrate cat vibrated by 150 μm at the two frequencies shown. (Matthews,
1969, Fig. 1.)

which the reflex responses to stretch and vibration were determined and shows among other things that the responses to stretch
and to vibration were both well maintained with time. The
amplitude of vibration was 150 μm which was sufficient to produce
a maximal reflex response. Thus all the soleus Ia fibres may be
assumed to have been driven at the frequency of the vibration.
Figure 8.10 compares graphically the relative strengths of the two
kinds of reflex and thereby furthers the argument. As noted earlier
the stretch reflex tension is approximately linearly related to the
extension. In this particular case the slope is 90 g/mm which is a
very typical value. The vibration reflex response is also linearly
related to the frequency of vibration; in this case the slope is 3·9
g/Hz. As before, this value may be transmuted to 3·9 g reflex
contraction per impulse/sec increase in firing for all the soleus Ia

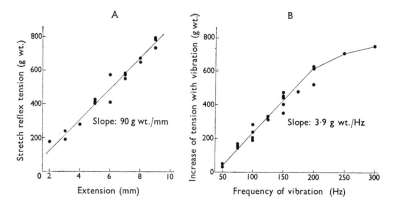

FIG. 8.10. Comparison of the relative strengths of the maintained reflex response to stretch and to vibration, derived from records like those of Fig. 8.9. A, extension increased in the absence of vibration. B, frequency of vibration increased with a constant extension of 5 mm (amplitude of vibration 150 μm, Matthews, 1969, Fig. 2).

fibres. On this basis one can estimate the increase of Ia firing required to produce the stretch reflex of Fig. 8.10A, which works out at 23 impulses sec^{-1} mm^{-1}. At first sight this seems a very reasonable figure, but in fact the experimentally observed values in comparable experiments are often very much lower for stretches of large amplitude. For example, Granit (1958) found an average of only 3·5 impulses sec^{-1} mm^{-1}. Taken on its own, however, this discrepancy might not appear especially serious, since the Ia firing was not recorded in the particular preparations in which the reflexes were studied, and since any increase in muscle strength with muscle length contributes to the strength of the stretch reflex but not to that of the vibration response (see later).

More compelling evidence was obtained by studying the inter-action between the reflex responses to stretch and to vibration. If they both depended solely upon the Ia pathway any increase in the stretch reflex with increasing stretch should occlude the response to vibration by an equivalent amount. This is because any increase in Ia firing with stretch will leave so much less addi-tional excitatory effect available for the action of vibration on the Ia fibres. However, as shown in Fig. 8.11 no gross occlusion occurs on combining stretch and vibration. On the left, the muscle was

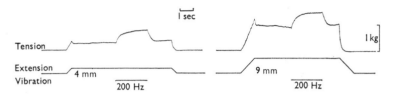

FIG. 8.11. The effect of the same vibration at two different extensions showing an absence of mutual occlusion between the reflex responses to stretch and to vibration. (Same experiment as Figs. 9 and 10, Matthews, 1969, Fig. 3.)

vibrated at 200 Hz after extending it by 4 mm. During the combined stimuli of stretch plus vibration the muscle developed 750 g of active tension; accepting that the vibration was driving all the Ia fibres this is shown to be the response to a Ia input at 200/sec. On the right, is the response to an extension of 9 mm, which on its own elicited a stretch reflex of 740 g (the records show the total tension elicited by the stretching, including the passive tendon). Assuming that the Ia fibres are the only excitatory input and neglecting any slight increase of muscle strength with muscle length one would thus conclude that the stretch on its own was then exciting the Ia fibres to fire on average at 200/sec. Granting this, vibration at 200 Hz would produce no appreciable further increase in the afferent input but would merely synchronise the discharges in the different fibres. Little or no increase in reflex contraction would then be expected with the vibration. In fact, the superadded vibration response was slightly larger than before. Putting it another way, the total reflex response to vibration of 200 Hz plus stretch of 4 mm was 750 g while the response to vibration plus 9 mm stretch was 1280 g, yet the Ia input should have been the same in both cases and consisted of synchronised volleys at 200/sec. There seems no ready explanation for all this if the Ia fibres provide the only excitatory component of the stretch reflex, but any problem is removed if the spindle group II fibres also produce autogenetic excitation in this preparation.

The attribution of the missing excitatory action to the spindle group II fibres rests on argument by exclusion, for no other kinds of afferent fibres are suitably stretch sensitive. Various control experiments made it unlikely that any increase of muscle strength with muscle length could have had a significant part to play in the genesis of the observed results (Matthews, 1969, 1970). More recently, Westbury (1971) has greatly strengthened the whole argument by eliminating muscle as the indicator of stretch reflex action and recording intracellularly from motoneurones in the anaesthetised cat. On applying stretch and vibration either separately or in combination to the triceps surae he found that the resulting depolarising response approximately summed when they were superimposed and that 'little or no occlusion was found between them'.

Further support for an autogenetic excitatory action of the spindle group II fibres has been obtained by studying the effect of the application of procaine to the nerve to the soleus on the reflex response of the muscle to the combined stimuli of stretch and vibration (McGrath & Matthews, 1970). As long known, progressive procaine paralysis diminishes the reflex response to simple stretch at a time when the α motor fibres appear to be still conducting quite normally (Matthews & Rushworth, 1957). This is illustrated in Fig. 8.12. The recording of the compound action potentials in separate experiments has shown that the γ efferents are paralysed long before the α motor fibres and the group I afferents, and that these two groups of large fibres are about equally sensitive to the procaine. Thus the initial early decline in the stretch reflex appears at least partly due to an equivalently early paralysis of the γ efferents. This would abolish the pre-existing γ bias of the spindle and would thus lead to a decrease in the spindle afferent firing elicited by a standard stretch. As far as one can tell from observing the stretch reflex on its own the early decline could perfectly well be entirely attributed to a reduction of Ia firing, and this indeed is what was originally believed. But such a suggestion has now become untenable because procaine causes a similar early diminution in the reflex response to the combined stimuli of stretch plus vibration; this is also shown in Fig. 8.12. In this case, however, there should be no change in Ia firing on γ efferent paralysis. The amplitude of vibration may be presumed to have been sufficiently large to ensure that all the Ia fibres of soleus were being 'driven' to discharge at the vibration frequency, irrespective of whether or not the γ fibres were conducting. But vibration has no significant action on secondary endings so that during the combined stimuli of stretch plus vibration, γ efferent paralysis will, as usual, reduce the response

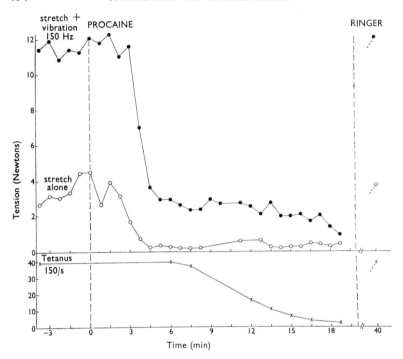

FIG. 8.12. Effects of the progressive narcotisation of the soleus nerve with procaine which suggest that the stretch reflex depends upon spindle group II as well as Ia activity. The bottom graph (x) shows the time course of paralysis of the motor fibres; this was determined by recording the contraction of the muscle on stimulating its nerve at 150/sec above the anaesthetised region. The middle curve (o) shows the reflex contraction elicited by an extension of 6 mm. The top curve (●) shows the reflex response to the combined stimuli of a strength of 6 mm and a vibration of 150 Hz, 150 μm, which should have been sufficient to drive all the Ia fibres at 150/sec. The early phase of reflex diminution is attributed to a paralysis of γ efferents (and possibly also to some paralysis of group II fibres themselves). This leads to a decrease of both Ia and II firing in response to simple stretch; during vibration the Ia discharge should be unaffected by the γ block while the group II discharge would still be diminished. (McGrath & Matthews, unpublished.)

of the group II fibres to the stretch component of the combined stimuli. Thus the finding of an early phase of action of procaine on the response to the combined stimuli supports the belief that the spindle group II fibres may make an appreciable contribution to the stretch reflex. Of course, once this is accepted it seems possible that some degree of paralysis of the group II fibres themselves may be contributing to the early phase of reflex paralysis; but the matter has yet to be investigated in detail and is in any case immaterial to the conclusion that the stretch reflex cannot be attributed solely to Ia action. It should finally be emphasised that the group II fibres need not necessarily produce their postulated excitatory action by a straight-through chain of synaptic connections. Instead, they might perhaps act primarily by operating upon a reflex pathway from some other group of afferents. In this respect it may be noted that, as happens in Fig. 8.12, procaine paralysis may sometimes reduce the increment of tension produced by vibration over and above the prevailing level produced by simple stretch. This suggests that the group II discharges might perhaps partly have their excitatory action by facilitating group Ia action.

The various arguments favouring the newly suggested role of the spindle group II fibres have been slightly simplified in the present account and may be found more fully developed elsewhere (Matthews, 1969, 1970; McGrath & Matthews, 1970). They are probably not completely watertight, but even so the new hypothesis has the merit that it enables a variety of experimental results to be brought into line without further ado. No other single suggestion seems able to do so. The original early experiments with electrical stimulation are sufficiently uncertain in their interpretation to prevent them having the power of veto over the present suggestion; they could, however, usefully be repeated with the new suggestion in mind. For the time being the newly suggested autogenetic excitatory role for the spindle group II fibres provides a reasonable working hypothesis which can be expected to stimulate further investigation. Whatever then transpires, it would be surprising if further experiment did not help kill the old idea of the exclusive flexor reflex action of the spindle group II fibres and replace it by some more rational concept. The whole matter awaits further detailed investigation.

The role of the contractile properties of muscle in automatically resisting stretch

The stretch reflex has a finite latency so that for the first few milliseconds the resistance of a muscle to any newly applied force can depend only upon its mechanical properties, hence the muscle is, so to speak, 'on its own' and cannot be helped by the CNS. As recently emphasised the behaviour of contracting muscle is then more complicated than might be supposed, but fortunately in a way which helps to oppose any alteration of its length (Rack, 1970; Joyce, Rack & Westbury, 1969; Joyce & Rack, 1969). This is illustrated in Fig. 8.13 which shows the tension developed in a

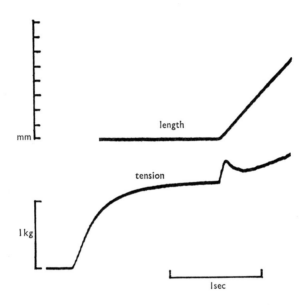

FIG. 8.13. The effect of forced lengthening of a contracting muscle in producing an initial overshoot in tension. The contraction of the soleus muscle was elicited by asynchronous stimulation of several different ventral root filaments at 10/sec (see Fig. 8.14). The overshoot would have been much less prominent if the muscle had been activated at a higher frequency. (Rack, 1970, Fig. 2.)

contracting muscle on its forcible extension, when it develops a greater tension at the beginning of the deformation than it does later on. Conversely, if a constant force is applied to a contracting muscle it initially yields more slowly than it does as it progressively gives way. Such behaviour is readily interpreted in terms of the sliding filament hypothesis of muscle action in conjunction with the supposition that the rate of breakdown of bonds between the actin and myosin filaments is relatively slower when the muscle is at a constant length than when it is being extended. Thus at the beginning of a forced movement there are a greater number of bonds in existence than there are later on, when some of them have been ruptured by the movement and failed to reform. At any rate, whatever its precise molecular origin, the initial rigidity of the muscle serves to increase its stiffness (force required for unit extension) in the short period before the stretch reflex comes into action. It will have a particularly important part to play in resisting deformation on the occasions when the applied disturbance is small. The muscle by itself may then be able to prevent significant deformation occurring before the stretch reflex comes into action.

The mechanical properties of muscle must also play a part in determining the force developed by large stretches maintained over an appreciable time. As long recognised, a contracting skeletal muscle develops a force which varies with its length. Figure 8.14 illustrates such behaviour. Because the rising limb of the length–tension relation falls within the physiological range, a constant a motor discharge can lead to the development of a 'pseudo stretch reflex' consisting of an increase in muscle tension with muscle extension in a preparation in which the dorsal roots are cut, and thus any true reflex response excluded. The filled circles of Fig. 8.15 illustrate such behaviour for the triceps of the de-afferented forelimb of the decerebrate cat.

This leads to the question as to how far the increase in tension seen in the ordinary stretch reflex, which is recorded when the dorsal roots are intact, is due to purely muscular properties and how far it is a genuine reflex effect. Unfortunately there seems to be no simple answer to this question. The difficulty in answering it is chiefly because the increase of muscle strength with muscle length depends both on the range of lengths studied and on the frequency of activation of the individual motor units (see Fig. 8.14). For the soleus muscle in the last few millimetres of its physiological range the curves run nearly flat for all frequencies of activation likely to be physiologically important. Since this is often the only range over which its stretch reflex is well-developed purely muscular properties would often seem to be relatively unimportant in the development of the stretch reflex of this muscle. On the other hand, in very rigid cats a stretch reflex may be found when soleus is considerably shorter, and different

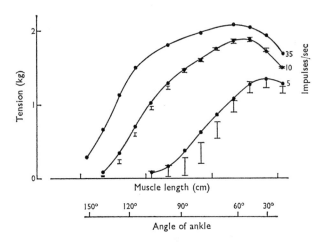

FIG. 8.14. The effect of muscle length on the tension developed by the soleus muscle during its contraction. The motor fibres to soleus were activated by stimulating 5 different ventral root filaments via 5 pairs of electrodes. The solid circles joined by lines show the result when the stimuli to the different filaments were delivered out of phase with each other so as to give a smooth overall contraction approximating to the normal (distributed stimulation). The vertical bars join the peak and trough tensions of the contractions elicited when the various filaments were stimulated in phase (synchronous stimulation). In both cases each of the individual filaments was stimulated at the frequency shown on the right. The maximum length of the muscle which is possible in the body corresponds to an angle of about 30° at the ankle. (Rack & Westbury, 1969, Fig. 8.)

muscles might well have the maximum of their tension–length curves differently situated with regard to their working ranges. What happens then will depend very much upon the frequency of firing of individual motor units in relation to their fusion frequency, for the contractile tension falls off much more rapidly with shortening when the frequency of motor discharge is low. But as yet the relevant data are fragmentary.

Since Denny-Brown's (1929) early measurements it has been generally accepted that the frequency of firing of units discharging tonically in response to muscle stretch is generally rather low, and moreover that once the threshold of a unit is reached its discharge is relatively unaffected by the precise degree of stretch. Thus increasing reflex activity is usually attributed more to the recruitment of new units than to an increase in the firing of those already active. Denny-Brown (1929, p. 271) found frequencies of 5–20/sec for different units and similar values have been sporadically reported by a number of other workers (for example: Granit, 1958; Roberts, 1958; Henneman, Somjen & Carpenter, 1965; Matthews & Stein, 1969). Since a large stretch reflex can lead to a nearly maximal contraction of the soleus muscle it appears that in this muscle the reflexly induced frequency of firing is adequate to cause a fused tetanus and that the lowness of some of the observed values of the frequency of motor discharge merely reflects the slowness of the muscle fibres of soleus. In other muscles the slower motor fibres are the ones most involved in the tonic stretch reflex, as they are the more easily recruited. These supply the most slowly contracting muscle fibres, and so a discharge frequency of around 5/sec may be sufficient to elicit a fused contraction. None the less, even though many motor units may be contracting in a nearly fused tetanus it seems likely that purely muscle properties must on occasion contribute some part of the increase in tension occurring on extending a muscle with a stretch reflex, as recently re-emphasised by Grillner & Udo (1971a,b).

Contribution of autogenetic inhibition. But a peripherally-originating increase in tension cannot be thought of in isolation from the genuine stretch reflex. Any excess of muscular tension resulting from muscle properties will excite an additional Ib discharge from the tendon organs and so inhibit a certain amount of the reflex discharge which would have occurred if the muscle had not increased in strength. Thus some part of the variation of muscle strength with muscle length must be counteracted by the system studied possessing tension feedback as well as length feedback. This seems the most plausible interpretation of the otherwise surprising finding that the 'true' stretch reflex, seen with the dorsal roots intact, may on occasion lead to an increase in tension which is the same as that found in the 'pseudo' stretch reflex seen with the dorsal roots severed. This is illustrated in Fig. 8.15. At first sight such a finding might be taken to suggest that reflex action had no part to play in the development of the apparently 'true' stretch reflex. However, in the experiment of Fig. 8.15 afferent activity was indeed shown to be important for the true reflex. This was because cutting the dorsal roots greatly diminished the

PM

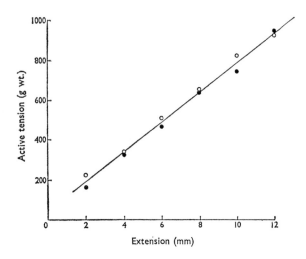

FIG. 8.15. Pompeiano's paradox of the equality of the true and the pseudo stretch reflexes. The graph shows the relation between the extension applied to the triceps muscle of the forelimb of the decerebrate cat and the resulting 'active' tension. This was determined, first, when the stretch reflex may be presumed to have been in operation (o) and second, after any true reflex had been abolished by cutting the appropriate dorsal roots (●) and the previous level of 'tone' restored by the combined procedures of cerebellectomy and section of the contralateral dorsal roots. (Pompeiano, 1960, Fig. 9, as redrawn in Matthews, 1967, Fig. 3.)

motor discharge, and it was subsequently only restored to its original high level by the two facilitatory procedures of removing the cerebellum and sectioning the contralateral dorsal roots. Moreover, there seems no reason to believe that the spindle afferents were failing to increase their firing in the usual way when the muscle was extended. Rather, it seems likely that the stretching excited fibres with opposed excitatory and inhibitory actions. If these approximately balanced each other out there would be little change in the overall motor discharge on extension of the muscle. The Ib fibres appear to provide a possible source for such inhibition but for their action to have been so effective would appear to require that their central gain should be rather greater than that found by Houk, Singer & Goldman (1970); who, of course, studied another muscle under rather different conditions.

The existence of Ib inhibitory feedback may also help to

explain the commonly observed approximately linear relation between tension and extension found in the stretch reflex. At first sight this seems unremarkable because the spindle afferent firing also increases approximately linearly with extension, and so might be expected to reflexly elicit a linearly increasing motor discharge. But if muscle strength increases with muscle length, a linearly increasing motor output would be expected to cause the tension to increase more rapidly than linearly with extension. This is because with each increase in the length of the muscle there would be some increase in the motor discharge and so, due to the length–tension properties of muscle, the next increment of length would automatically elicit a peripheral increment of tension which was greater than that occurring at shorter lengths. Precise prediction of what would happen is complicated by the difficulty in defining a clear measure of motor discharge in a system where the different motor units have different strengths and where each may vary its frequency of discharge; such problems have been tackled in more detail by Houk, Singer & Goldman (1970). Anyhow, in so far as they behave linearly, the negative tension feedback from the Golgi tendon organs must tend to linearise the stretch reflex in face of variations of muscle strength with muscle length; this is one of the basic actions of negative feedback. The value of the Ib gain so far observed would, however, have only a moderate action in this respect.

Sinusoidal studies. Another familiar property of muscle whose importance has recently been emphasised in relation to the stretch reflex is that, on activation of a muscle, its contractile tension only builds up relatively slowly (Poppele & Terzuolo, 1968; Rosenthal, McKean, Roberts & Terzuolo, 1970). One way of demonstrating this is to stimulate a motor nerve with a repetitive pulse train whose frequency at any moment is modulated sinusoidally. This leads to an approximately sinusoidal modulation in contractile tension, as recorded under isometric conditions. As the frequency of stimulus modulation is increased the rhythmic change in muscle tension becomes progressively smaller. In addition, the peak in tension lags progressively further and further behind the peak in stimulus frequency, provided the delay is expressed as a fraction of a cycle rather than an absolute time (phase lag). The lower curve of Fig. 8.16 shows the effect of the frequency of stimulus modulation on the amplitude of the response.

In contrast, neither the size nor the phase of the stretch reflex elicited by small amplitude sinusoidal stretching changes appreciably on increasing the frequency of stretching from 1 to 10 Hz, even though the stretching may be presumed to be causing a sinusoidal modulation in the motor discharge from the reflex centres. This constancy of the reflexly elicited tension seems to occur largely because the spindle primary endings show a response to sinusoidal stretching which is the inverse of that shown by the muscle. They thereby compensate for the phase lags introduced by the slowness of the muscle and thus lead to a flat frequency–response curve for the overall response of the stretch reflex system. This is all illustrated in Fig. 8.16 and provides an interesting new way of looking at the physiological significance of the dynamic sensitivity of the primary ending. It would be interesting to have the measurements of muscle properties extended to a range of motor units with different contraction times. If, as might be expected, these were found to show different frequency–response curves it would be pertinent to ask to which of them the spindles were adjusted.

However, a certain caution is necessary in thinking about such findings as it is still not clear how far a sinusoidal modulation of the frequency of firing of a large number of motor units properly mimics what happens in the stretch reflex. Individual units may then fire at a relatively constant frequency and variations in reflex strength be achieved by recruitment of new units. All this goes to show that one should not underrate the complexity of the mechanisms underlying 'tone' as exemplified by the apparently simple response observed when a muscle is stretched and its tension recorded. Even this simple stretch reflex can now be seen as an example of reflex integration which has still not been fully unravelled and requires further quantitative analysis of the contribution provided by each of its components.

Reflexly mediated 'plastic' responses of muscle to lengthening and shortening

Another indication of the complexities underlying the stretch reflex is provided by the so-called plastic tonus which was described by Sherrington in 1909 and does not seem to have been explicitly investigated again since that time. The experiments

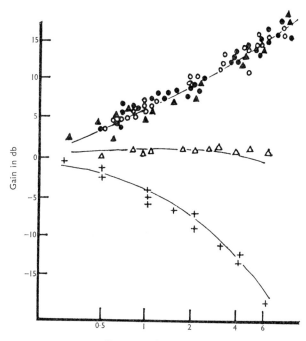

FIG. 8.16. Compensation by the primary ending for the loss of sensitivity and phase lags introduced into the stretch reflex loop by the slowness of muscle contraction. The middle curve (△) shows the tension developed by the stretch reflex on stretching the triceps surae of the decerebrate cat at frequencies from 0·5 to 6 Hz (amplitude several mm). The ordinate has been normalised to give the response at each frequency relative to that at the lowest frequency used, and is on a logarithmic scale (i.e. a Bode plot with 'gain' expressed in decibels). The bottom curve (+) shows, in a similarly normalised manner, the tension excursion produced by the muscle on sinusoidally modulating the frequency of stimulation of its nerve (mean frequency of stimulation 20–35/sec modulated up to 15%, recording isometric). The top curve shows the response of a primary ending in the anaesthetised cat to sinusoidal stretching (●, amplitude below 100 μm) and also the reflex effects of this in producing a modulation of the membrane potentials of individual motoneurones (o) and the summed electromyographic activity of the muscle (▲). The similarity of the three sets of points suggests that the central components of the reflex loop did not contribute to the transformation of the signal in these particular experiments. The middle curve is equal to the sum of the top and bottom curves. Similar results were obtained for measurements of phase (i.e. the phase lag introduced by the muscle contraction was counteracted by the phase advance introduced by the spindle afferent endings. Poppele & Terzuolo, 1968, Fig. 2).

demonstrating plastic tone were performed on the vastocrureus muscle of the decerebrate cat with the rest of the hindlimb denervated and with the muscle still attached to the body at both ends. The recording was isotonic rather than the now usual isometric arrangement. When the knee joint was initially in the fully extended position, and the muscle consequently at its shortest physiologically possible length, the limb was able to maintain its position against a moderate external force, thereby showing that its extensor muscles possessed a fair degree of tone. However, when the experimenter forcibly flexed the knee, and overcame the tonic resistance, the muscle reflexly adjusted itself to the new length so that when the limb was released it showed little or no tendency to return to its original short length. This adjustment was favoured by forcibly maintaining the muscle at the new length for a short time before releasing it. The tension developed at the new greater length was then approximately the same as that originally demonstrated at the original shorter length. Sherrington called this response the lengthening reaction. The converse response was seen on approximating the ends of a previously extended muscle. Again it was soon able to adjust itself so as to develop its original degree of tone and once more maintain the shorter length against moderate external forces. This was called the shortening reaction.

By their combined action the lengthening and shortening reactions endowed the tone of the muscle with a 'plastic' quality which was quite different from that which would be shown by a simple spring. Any such plastic behaviour was conspicuously absent after the dorsal roots had been cut and the muscle induced to contract tonically by eliciting a crossed extensor reflex in it. The reflex origin of the lengthening reaction was further suggested by the occurrence of contraction of knee and ankle extensor muscles of the opposite limb when the ipsilateral muscle was forcibly stretched. This was seen as a typical example of crossed excitation accompanying ipsilateral inhibition. The crossed response had been described just beforehand by Philippson and so Sherrington called it Philippson's reflex, by which name it is still usually known. It was first described in the chronic spinal animal, but it is also 'usually obtainable with ease' in the decerebrate preparation after a full bilateral hindlimb denervation sparing only the two vastocrurei.

However, plasticity was not a *sine qua non* of an intact reflex arc for in some of the preparations in which the rigidity was very appreciable the lengthening reaction was then absent. In Sherrington's words 'a plastic tonus' had 'been replaced by an elastic tonus'. In these cases the muscle apparently simply reverted to its previous length when it was released after forcible extension. Thus the occurrence of plasticity depends upon an appropriate condition of the controlling neural apparatus.

In the chronic spinal dog, without isolation of single muscles, Sherrington found that on forced flexion of the knee the initial reflex resistance soon gave way abruptly so that flexion could then be continued without meeting further resistance. This is now commonly known as the 'clasp-knife' effect by analogy with the way a pocket-knife behaves when it is being opened or closed. It is also well developed in spastic human patients (see, for example, Burke, Gillies & Lance, 1970). Sherrington considered the clasp-knife reaction to be an integral part of the lengthening reaction. Unfortunately, however, he neither described its occurrence for the quadriceps muscle which had been fully isolated by denervation of other muscles in the decerebrate, nor did he explicitly deny its absence in this preparation. While the sudden melting of resistance to stretching and the ability of a muscle to retain a new length would appear to be closely related, they are not necessarily identical. It is perhaps unfortunate, therefore, that these possibly distinct phenomena are often given only a single name, for this may lead to confusion in discussing their origin, as also noted by Rademaker (1947).

These various reactions have as yet remained almost unstudied by modern methods. Only Roberts (1963) appears to have used isotonic recording to study tone in the decerebrate animal, but without apparently furthering the problem of the origin of plastic tone. However, such an approach is not closed for Roberts' work is currently a little difficult to assess; among other things he failed to obtain regular responses to sinusoidal stretching applied via an isometric system, whereas other workers have subsequently succeeded in this and thereby submitted the stretch reflex to detailed analysis (Jansen & Rack, 1966; Poppele & Terzuolo, 1968; Rosenthal, McKean, Roberts & Terzuolo, 1970.)

Records taken under isometric conditions might be expected to show phenomena related to plasticity, though no author appears to have drawn attention to this. Looked at *a priori* it seems likely that the lengthening reaction may be largely an expression, under different experimental conditions, of the phasic component of the stretch reflex seen under isometric conditions. When this is prominent steady extension leads to a reflex response which decays more or less rapidly with time to leave a residual contraction which is often little larger than that present at a shorter length. As noted earlier, this phasicity of response may well be due to a decline in the response of the spindle rather than of the reflex centres themselves, though whether because of a high level of dynamic fusimotor bias or because of a stretch-evoked fusimotor inhibition remains unknown. In addition, the stretch reflex recorded isometrically would appear often to lead to a 'hysteresis' type of response from the muscle so that on releasing a stretched muscle through a short distance it develops rather less tension than if it had just been stretched up to the same length (i.e. it tends to retain its pre-existing length; Matthews, 1959, and Roberts, 1963, suggest this on the basis of dynamic rather than static studies and the point could usefully be looked at more carefully). In the process of demonstrating the lengthening reaction a slight muscular shortening must almost inevitably occur on letting go the stretched muscle, and so allow any 'hysteresis' to manifest itself with an abrupt fall of muscle tension and little consequent tendency for it to shorten much further. 'Elastic tone' with an absence of a lengthening reaction is probably the prerogative of decerebrate preparations with well-marked tonic stretch reflexes without a significant phasic component; such stretch reflexes may show little hysteresis and develop much the same tension at a given length when the muscle is being allowed to shorten as when it is being stretched.

The shortening reaction probably shows itself under isometric conditions as the slow redevelopment of tension which occurs after the release of a stretched muscle. This is favoured if, after its release, the muscle is again very slightly stretched so as to take in slack; this would probably have been brought about by gravity in Sherrington's preparations.

The clasp-knife effect, however, does not yet appear to have found expression with isometric recording. At some stage on slowly stretching a muscle a clasp-knife action would be expected to lead to an abrupt decrease in the tension recorded isometrically, but this certainly does not occur for the soleus muscle as studied by the present author (Matthews, 1959). The absence of the clasp-knife effect may perhaps be because it requires a wider receptive field for its elicitation than the receptors of a single muscle. It would also appear to be a reaction of rather greater complexity than the lengthening and shortening reactions. It is often asserted that the clasp-knife effect is simply due to the progressive stretch mobilising sufficient autogenetic inhibition via the Ib fibres to overcome the Ia excitation resulting from the same stretch. On this view the sudden appearance of inhibition at a certain tension tended to be equated with the threshold of the tendon organs, which was, mistakenly, long believed to be rather high. It certainly seems likely that the Ib fibres do have a part to play in the mediation of the clasp-knife reaction but the simple pitting of Ia and Ib effects against each other on the motoneuronal soma would not appear sufficient to explain the switch-like behaviour of the clasp-knife effect. The subjective experience on the part of the experimenter is that the muscle almost stops contracting altogether as the limb gives way in the experimenter's hand. As already discussed an algebraical summation of inhibition and excitation should lead merely to a reduction of the reflex contraction below what it would have been without any inhibition.

The abruptness of the disappearance of contraction in the clasp-knife reaction suggests that the threshold level has just been exceeded of some 'all-or-nothing' central mechanism which turns off the excitatory side of the stretch reflex. Whether or not it does this by direct action on the motoneurone is another matter. In this respect, considerable interest attaches to Eldred, Granit & Merton's (1953) observation on the behaviour of a spindle afferent during the elicitation of a clasp-knife response; this is illustrated in Fig. 8.17. About half-way through the stretch the spindle firing became intermittent. It then ceased altogether at about the time that the muscle stopped contracting as the clasp-knife reaction developed. This cessation of spindle firing shows that the fusimotor fibres must have been inhibited, and suggests that the cessation of muscular contraction may have been as much due to a withdrawal of spindle excitation as to a frank inhibition of the α motoneurones. At any rate it is clearly unduly simple to equate the clasp-knife effect with disynaptically mediated Ib autogenetic inhibition. Further recording of reflexes under isotonic conditions

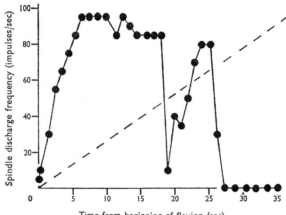

FIG. 8.17. An experiment suggesting that the clasp-knife reaction is at least partly due to fusimotor inhibition. The graph shows the spindle firing occurring during a slow forcible manual stretch of the ankle extensors in a decerebrate cat; the dotted line indicates the time-course of the stretching. The decrease in spindle firing which occurred as the stretch progressed can only have been due to fusimotor inhibition. The reflex arc was intact except for the small filament used for recording the afferent discharge and the muscle did show the clasp-knife effect; judging by the firing of a tendon organ the contraction of the muscle suddenly lessened at about the same time as the spindle firing decreased. Decerebrate cat without denervation of the hindlimb and with the ankle extensors still attached to the calcaneum. (Eldred, Granit & Merton, 1953, Fig. 8.)

would clearly be interesting, for the suspicion remains that the small movements that occur in tremor etc. might have physiologically interesting effects, for the resulting rhythmic bursts of afferent input to the cord might produce a different response from those obtained with steady discharges. Further investigation of the clasp-knife effect might also be rewarding for the interaction between the pushing of the experimenter's limb and the yielding of the animal's provides a complexity which has not yet been reproduced instrumentally.

Fusimotor neurones and the question of their autogenetic reflex responses

This leads on to the vexed question as to the existence and nature of any autogenetic reflexes to fusimotor neurones. About the only clear statement that can be made is that no sign of autogenetic Ia excitatory action has ever been observed in spite of its being appropriately sought. Thus it has not been seen on recording intracellularly from γ motoneurones in the anaesthetised cat on stimulating various nerves (Eccles, Eccles, Iggo & Lundberg, 1960; Grillner, Hongo & Lund, 1968), nor does such stimulation alter the rhythm of a fusimotor fibre isolated in a muscle nerve (Hunt & Paintal, 1958; Voorhoeve & van Kanten, 1962). Moreover, section of the appropriate segmental dorsal roots in the decerebrate produces little change in fusimotor firing though it abolishes the Ia input to the cord and leads to a great reduction or abolition of α motor firing (Eldred, Granit & Merton, 1953). Hunt & Paintal (1958), by virtue of the shortest latency with which excitatory effects were observed on γ efferent fibres isolated from the muscle nerve, concluded that no primary afferent of any kind had a monosynaptic action on γ motoneurones. Their findings also make it unlikely that Ia fibres can have an appreciable polysynaptically mediated autogenetic excitatory action.

Group I volleys have been thought to produce inhibition of fusimotor neurones, but this effect has yet to be allocated to a particular type of fibre, notably Ia or Ib, and have its pattern of distribution delimited. Possible group I inhibitory effects were reported originally with recording from fibres isolated in the peripheral nerve in the course of the various work mentioned above. Group I inhibitory effects have definitely been seen on recording intracellularly from a total of 5 γ motoneurones by Grillner, Hongo & Lund (1968). In addition, the relatively pure Ia input elicited by high-frequency vibration of the triceps surae has been shown to produce inhibition of a certain number of fusimotor fibres in the decerebrate cat, though unfortunately their muscle of destination was unknown as they were isolated in ventral root filaments (Brown, Lawrence & Matthews, 1968a). Moreover, it was then impossible to decide whether this was a direct reflex action of the Ia input, or an indirect one occurring as a result of the excitation of α motoneurones leading to a Renshaw inhibition of the fusimotor neurones via the recurrent collaterals of the α fibres. Renshaw inhibition of γ motoneurones definitely appears to exist but seems to be much less strong than that of α motoneurones. It passed unobserved in the several independent sets of experiments in which it was first sought, and thus for some years it was thought to be totally absent (Eccles, Eccles, Iggo & Lundberg,

1960; Granit, Pascoe & Steg, 1957; Hunt & Paintal, 1958; Voorhoeve & van Kanten, 1962). However, subsequent search in the decerebrate showed that it can certainly occur on occasion from α motoneurones to γ motoneurones, though whether it may also occur from γ motoneurones back on to themselves remains uncertain. (Brown, Lawrence & Matthews, 1968a,b; Ellaway, 1971.) Thus what at one time seemed to be an absolute difference between α and γ motoneurones now appears to be merely one of degree, though more detailed study is necessary to allow this to be categorically asserted and in particular it seems possible that static and dynamic fusimotor neurones might have different properties in this respect.

The action of the spindle group II fibres on fusimotor neurones, if any, also remains obscure. The actions of group III muscle afferents, genuine flexor reflex afferents and non-medullated afferents also all remain open for study. However, judging by what has been done so far, a detailed attack on these matters by conventional techniques would be arduous and possibly relatively unrewarding. It could well yield no more than a mixed bag of excitatory and inhibitory effects, depending upon the muscle studied and the central state of the preparation. However, stimulation of nociceptive afferents might be expected to give a predominant excitation of flexor fusimotor neurones with inhibition of those to extensors, just as it usually does for α motoneurones. Indeed, one of the few generalisations that has emerged about the reflex actions of other than autogenetic stimuli is that the fusimotor neurones very often behave in the same way as the α motoneurones of the same muscle, as emphasised in the pioneer studies (Hunt, 1951; Eldred & Hagbarth, 1954). Very often, however, the fusimotor neurones are the more easily influenced, which is perhaps no more than an expression of the fact that they are frequently discharging spontaneously. This provides a background against which small effects, whether excitatory or inhibitory, are the more easily recognisable.

The reflex effect of stretch itself on fusimotor discharge also still remains somewhat uncertain. Hunt (1951) originally claimed that stretch of a muscle had an autogenetic inhibitory action on its own fusimotor neurones in both the spinal and in the decerebrate cat. However, in a subsequent fuller study with Paintal (1958) he was unable to confirm this for the spinal cat. By implication it was still suggested to occur in the decerebrate preparation but as this was not then re-investigated the matter merits repeated study. Brown, Lawrence & Matthews (1968a) certainly observed inhibitory fusimotor effects on stretching gastrocnemius in the decerebrate cat but it was not shown whether or not these were autogenetic. The effects seen by Eldred, Granit & Merton (1953) and shown in Fig. 8.17 also may not have been entirely autogenetic for in their experiments the limb was not denervated in any way. Fusimotor neurones are readily reflexly influenced by cutaneous stimuli or by squeezing tendons. Thus a thorough denervation is required to ensure that the effects observed with stretch are truly autogenetic. Fusimotor fibres supplying intercostal muscles have been found to have their discharge rate reflexly altered by pulling on adjacent ribs and so altering the width of intercostal spaces. These effects were suspected to be proprioceptive reflexes mediated by the receptors in muscle, tendon or joint (Eklund, Euler & Rutkowski, 1964). A contribution from spindle afferents was supported by the finding that the intravenous injection of suxamethonium also reflexly altered the fusimotor discharges, including in the acute spinal preparation; however, this drug is no longer believed to be completely specific in producing spindle excitation (see Chap. 5).

In conclusion, it may be pointed out that the reasonably straightforward reflex actions of stretch on α motoneurones would have a completely different significance if they were also to occur for γ motoneurones. The reflexes would then be controlling the chief transducer upon which the reliability of the feedback system depends, rather than compensating for externally imposed disturbances or a weakness of the muscle. It may therefore be emphasised that so far the chief finding of interest in relation to autogenetic fusimotor reflexes is that they do appear to be different from those to α motoneurones, and that monosynaptic Ia excitation is absent. In contrast, as also makes sense from the above point of view, reflexes elicited by cutaneous or nociceptive stimulation and stimulation within the central nervous system often influence α and γ motoneurones similarly.

Possible functional derangements responsible for the appearance of decerebrate rigidity and the tonic stretch reflex

There are two quite different kinds of answer to the question

'What is the cause of decerebrate rigidity?'. The first and historic-
ally more usual one consists simply of a description of which
central structures must be destroyed and which must be left in
intact in order for the rigidity to appear. In spite of the demonstrated importance of the vestibulo-spinal tract this basically
anatomical problem is still not fully resolved and, though of the
utmost importance, seems outside the scope of the present work.
Progressive investigation along these lines may well help to
throw light on the interactions normally taking place between
various higher motor centres, and so help to elucidate their
functions. It may be noted in this respect that the presence or
absence of rigidty is not an all-or-none phenomenon and that
different central lesions may produce different patterns of rigidity.
In the normal decerebrate cat extensor rigidity usually prevails;
but, for as yet undetermined reasons, some preparations may
temporarily show a rigidity predominantly of the flexors as first
noted by Bazett & Penfield in 1922.

The second and currently more interesting way of replying
when asked the cause of rigidity is to attempt to describe the
nature of the functional derangement of the spinal motor centres
which leads them to discharge in the abnormal and uncontrolled
way that manifests itself as rigidity. Sherrington's (1898) classical
demonstration that the rigidity could usually be abolished by
local de-afferentation immediately casts doubt on the obvious idea
that the excessive discharge of α motoneurones merely reflects their
direct excitation by an untrammelled flow of impulses descending from higher centres. Undoubtedly there is such a flow of
impulses from centres which have been 'released' from an inhibition normally mediated by structures that are destroyed in the
decerebrate; but the descending action is unlikely to be restricted
to a direct one on the α motoneurone. Thus the second more
functional type of answer requires present discussion, even
though no very definite conclusions can as yet be reached. Moreover there may be no universal answer applicable to all types of
preparation; the occurrence of an abnormally high degree of
muscle tone may well be a somewhat non-specific sign of derangement of function, rather than a specific defect with a single cause.

Sufficiency of purely spinal mechanisms when suitably facilitated.
The first point is that all the essential mechanisms required for

the development of excessive muscle tone appear to exist within the spinal cord itself. This is believed to be so in spite of the fact that the acute spinal preparation is almost toneless. To begin with, the spinal animal possesses a tendon jerk and, even on the most pessimistic view, this depends in good measure on the same mechanisms as the tonic stretch reflex and tone. Next, the chronic spinal animal becomes hypertonic with the passage of time as spinal 'shock' wears off. This is usually attributed to the return of function to pre-existing spinal mechanisms rather than to the development of new ones; for example, this was the view of Denny-Brown & Liddell (1927) when they used the standard myographic techniques to demonstrate the existence of a tonic stretch reflex in the chronic spinal cat. The idea that the tonic stretch reflex is basically a spinal process is supported by the occasional finding that it may persist for a short time after making a decerebrate preparation spinal (for example, by implication, Fulton, Liddell & Rioch, 1930, p. 322; Matthews, 1966b, for the tonic response to vibration). This presumably occurs because of a temporary injury discharge of some of the severed descending fibres maintaining the excitability of the spinal reflex centres and so momentarily staving off the appearance of spinal shock. In addition, Pompeiano (1960, Fig. 11) has illustrated the appearance of a 'tonic' stretch reflex on stretching the long head of the triceps of the forelimb at 1 mm/sec in the acute spinal preparation in which the local spinal excitability has been increased by post-brachial section of the spinal cord. The ability of the spinal cord to maintain a tonic stretch reflex on its own, provided it is appropriately facilitated, has recently been further demonstrated by Grillner (1969a,b) who found that the injection of DOPA (dihydroxyphenylalanine) into the acute spinal cat leads to the temporary appearance of a tonic stretch reflex in both flexor and extensor muscles of the hindlimb, provided they are suitably isolated for myographic recording; the whole animal, however, does not become grossly rigid. DOPA is believed to have this effect by mimicking the action of a monoaminergic descending pathway consisting of small fibres, and whose activity in the decerebrate preparation might be a factor in the development of its rigidity.

Thus there is no need to suggest that the development of rigidity depends upon reflex activity traversing higher centres, rather than simply passing round suitably facilitated segmental reflex arcs. But, of course, it remains possible that when the higher centres remain connected to the cord then some high-level reverberatory activity may also take place and contribute to the rigidity. Indeed, it would be surprising if the multifarious proprioceptive excitation of various ascending tracts, which has been established experimentally, has no effect on those higher centres whose unbridled downwards discharge leads to the development of rigidity. It might be thought an easy matter to settle whether or not this occurs by electromyographically recording the latency of the onset or the offset of the stretch reflex at the beginning and end of a stretch; but the response of the muscle is then so dominated by local spinal reflexes that it has not yet been possible to decide whether or not supraspinal circuits are also in operation. Indeed, even when more prolonged changes in excitability have been found following proprioceptive stimuli (stretching, vibration, nerve stimulation), it is not easy to exclude the possibility of some long-lasting change restricted to the spinal cord, such as for example post-tetanic potentiation.

In addition to the activity of higher centres, the appearance of rigidity in a limb may also depend upon what is happening in parts of the spinal cord not directly concerned with the control of the limb itself. Most notably, the rigidity of the forelimbs of the decerebrate cat is increased by severing the spinal cord below the brachial enlargement. Ruch & Watts (1934) named this effect the Schiff–Sherrington phenomenon to commemorate its earlier description in the frog and the mammal by these two great men respectively. It appears to depend upon the abolition of a tonic inhibition of the forelimb centres by the lower spinal centres. The relevant activity of the lower centres would appear to be initiated by descending activity rather than reflexly, for the tonic inhibition of the forelimb by the lower part of the cord continues after bilateral section of the lumbo-sacral dorsal roots (Ruch, 1936). In contrast, in decerebrate cats with a lesion of the fastigial nucleus the rigidity of one forelimb appears to be being reflexly inhibited by the activity of receptors in the other forelimb. This was shown by Moruzzi & Pompeiano (1957) who found that cutting the dorsal roots contralaterally increased the rigidity ipsilaterally. It appears to remain to be established that these relatively distant spinal actions depend upon direct intraspinal connections, as would be expected, rather than by feedback to higher centres. At any rate it seems clear that the appearance of rigidity or otherwise in a limb depends upon a balance struck between excitatory and inhibitory influences arising from a number of sources.

Thus the development of rigidity in any particular case seems likely to depend partly upon an excess of excitatory factors, and partly upon a deficit of inhibitory factors, in relation to the normal. However, these factors need not all have the same kind of action, such as a direct synaptic action on the α motoneurone, and some may help increase or decrease hypertonia in some quite different sort of way, such as by acting on the interneurones via which some other pathway operates. This turns the search for the cause of rigidity into a general hunt for all the various contributory factors; each then needs to be assessed to decide upon its relative importance. In particular, the recognition that the problem is potentially complex and that there may be several causes argues for caution in accepting the conventional tendency of attributing a unique importance to any particular factor whose removal suffices to abolish rigidity; other factors which are less amenable to current investigation may be just as important, and this could be so even if they were unable to act on their own.

Particular factors

Individual factors possibly contributing to rigidity are discussed serially below, but from what has just been said they need not be thought of as mutually exclusive.

1. *α hyperactivation.* A sufficient amount of direct excitation reaching the α motoneurones from supraspinal or distant spinal sources should obviously be able to make them fire, even when they are not also being excited by local proprioceptive feedback. This has been found to occur in decerebrate cats which have had the anterior lobe of the cerebellum damaged, whether by frank surgery or by the anaemic method of decerebration which deprives part of the cerebellum of blood along with the rest of the forebrain. These preparations show what is frequently termed 'α rigidity' for, in contrast to the normal decerebrate, the rigidity usually persists in a limb after all its dorsal roots have been cut; this was demonstrated, for example, by Pollock & Davis (1931) shortly after they introduced the anaemic decerebrate. The Schiff–

Sherrington phenomenon probably also depends partly upon a release of an α rigidity for it can apparently continue to make a contribution to the motor discharge of a de-afferented segment of the spinal cord (Pompeiano, 1960). Moreover, intracellular recording has shown that post-brachial section leads to a de-polarisation of forelimb motoneurones of some 10–15 mV (Gidlöf, 1966). Thus in some cases decerebrate type rigidity can occur independently of any derangement of autogenetic muscle reflexes or over-activity of the γ loop. As discussed earlier, the purely peripheral length–tension properties of muscle may then produce a 'pseudo stretch reflex' which develops an increasing force as the tonically active muscle is forcibly elongated and which may be myographically indistinguishable from a true stretch reflex; the true and the pseudo reflexes should, however, usually be dis-tinguishable electromyographically. The pseudo reflex is likely to show itself best when the tonically contracting muscles have suc-ceeded in shortening to the minimum length allowed in the body, for their tension–length curve is then likely to be at its steepest. All this is not to say, however, that preparations with enough direct 'α excitation' to produce an 'α rigidity' lack a true stretch reflex. Rather this seems likely also to be present and to serve to intensify the rigidity yet further.

2. *γ hyperactivation.* For no very good reason, γ hyperactivity has often been taken to be the cause of rigidity which may be abolished by de-afferentation or fusimotor paralysis, on the implicit assump-tion that these tests are adequate to establish that the rigidity primarily depends upon an over-activity of γ motoneurones. Such γ hyperactivity is, of course, seen as secondary to their synaptic excitation by an abnormally great descending activity rather than to truly spontaneous fusimotor discharge. The ordinary decere-brate cat prepared by inter-collicular section of the mid-brain is often seen as the prototype of γ mediated rigidities for its excess of tone is abolished by dorsal root section. In addition, afferent fibre recording shows that it does possess a very appreciable spon-taneous fusimotor discharge, and more than that found in cats decerebrated by anaemia or acute spinal animals (Eldred, Granit & Merton, 1953; Granit, Holmgren & Merton, 1955; Alnaes, Jansen & Rudjord, 1965). This view of the origin of decerebrate rigidity was backed up by Henatsch & Ingvar's (1956) demonstra-

tion that the drug chlorpromazine both reduces the rigidity of the ordinary decerebrate and abolishes its fusimotor activity. In contrast, chlorpromazine fails to abolish the rigidity of the anaemic decerebrate and so seems unlikely to have any major action on α motoneurones or spinal interneurones. More recently, Maxwell & Rhodes (1970) confirmed that a related compound, dimetho-thiazine, abolishes both static and dynamic activity in the decere-brate. It may be noted in passing that the paired terms 'α rigidity' and 'γ rigidity' stem from Granit's (1955) work, though they were not then given formal definition.

Further support for the importance of fusimotor activity in maintaining the enhanced stretch reflex of the inter-collicular decerebrate was provided by the experiments of Matthews & Rushworth (1957) in which procaine was applied to the nerve to the soleus muscle. As already illustrated (Fig. 8.12) this procedure was found to abolish or greatly reduce the tonic stretch reflex at a time when the α motor fibres and the group I afferent fibres were still functioning normally. Cats decerebrated by anaemia showed the effect much less if at all (Matthews, 1958). In the light of the then current knowledge, the early paralysis of the stretch reflex in the ordinary decerebrate was originally attributed to a reduc-tion of Ia firing following an early selective paralysis of the γ efferents; and this remains acceptable as a part of the explanation. In addition, however, it now seems likely that the reduction of spindle group II firing on γ efferent paralysis may also play a part in reducing the stretch reflex, and a yet further contribution may perhaps be made by a relatively early paralysis of the group II fibres themselves.

On all the evidence it seems reasonable to continue to believe that the steady γ discharge found in the ordinary inter-collicular decerebrate cat plays an important part in maintaining its rigidity. This, however, is quite different from suggesting that its rigidity is solely or even primarily due to an abnormally great fusimotor activity which, by producing a 'spindle cramp', reflexly drives the main muscle into the same state. As Granit (1955, p. 274) empha-sised from the very beginning, an appreciable fusimotor activity is often found in the absence of rigidity. Moreover, in so far as fusi-motor activity is important in maintaining rigidity, it probably does so as much by increasing group II activity as by increasing Ia dis-charges. But in accepting this, one is also tacitly accepting the importance for the development of rigidity of the supraspinal control of the excitability of spinal pathways. In addition, there is further evidence to show that the increased Ia firing found in the decerebrate cannot be allocated the sole responsibility for the development of its rigidity. This is that the high-frequency vibration of muscles in the spinal animal does not elicit a tonic stretch reflex type of contraction, as it does in the decerebrate, even though the Ia discharge on vibrating in the spinal animal is greater than it is on simple stretching in the decerebrate. Thus fusimotor activity cannot be taken as a universally sufficient cause for the appearance of rigidity, even though it sometimes provides an essential factor without which the rigidity will not appear.

This is all on the supposition that the group II fibres produce autogenetic excitation in the decerebrate. If the classical view is retained that the group II fibres of extensor muscles produce autogenetic inhibition then a complication arises, namely that their excitation by the static fusimotor discharge of the decerebrate cat should tend to annul the production of rigidity by the γ route. This difficulty often tends to be ignored on the assumption that the central action of group II fibres is too weak to matter, because in the decerebrate the interneurones through which spindle group II fibres produce flexor effects are tonically inhibited by supraspinal action. However, in accepting that such a supraspinal switching of interneurones is important for the development of rigidity then, *ipso facto*, the rigidity is no longer being attributed to the single cause of γ hyperactivity. At the moment it seems most likely that in the ordinary decerebrate cat a moderately enhanced fusimotor firing assists in the development of a rigidity which is equally due to other aberrations in nervous function. A purely γ mediated rigidity has yet to be shown to exist under any set of conditions, and to establish its occurrence in a suspected case will require more crucial experiments than have yet been performed. Those done so far have been suitable for analysing a unifactorial rather than a multifactorial situation. Among other things, there are at present no systematic figures available showing the amount of fusimotor firing occurring in preparations with and without rigidity, but these are obviously needed to decide just how far the fusimotor fibres are hyperactive in each case.

3. *Switching of reflex pathways by descending action on inter-neurones.* Another possible kind of cause for the appearance of decerebrate rigidity is the switching of a reflex pathway so that the action of a particular afferent input is changed so as to favour the development of autogenetic excitation on stretching a muscle. This could be done either by facilitating an excitatory pathway or by blocking an inhibitory one. As already discussed it is now commonplace that descending pathways can have this sort of action. *A priori*, this kind of thing can be expected to play some part in the development of rigidity, for autogenetic reflexes often provide an essential contribution to the production of rigidity, and the patterns of reflex activity in the decerebrate are quite different from those of, for example, the acute spinal preparation. Moreover, by extracellular recording in the spinal cat, Kolmodin (1957) showed some time ago that a wide variety of interneurones are tonically excited by maintained muscle stretch and so provide candidates for mediating relatively complex reflex responses to stretch. Simple consideration of the known reflex pathways suggests the various possibilities given below, though the present list can hardly be expected to prove comprehensive. Unfortunately, there is so little definite to say about the precise role of any of these factors in the development of rigidity that it has seemed unnecessary to provide detailed reference to the present state of knowledge on their supraspinal control. Also, because of the different patterns of reflex behaviour of flexor and extensor muscles some of the possibilities are not equally applicable to both kinds of muscle. Various possibilities for the production of rigidity by the switching of reflex pathways are as follows:

(*a*) The opening of polysynaptic pathways mediating Ia autogenetic excitation, supposing that these exist. This would clearly allow the 'normal' amount of Ia input to have a more powerful effect on the motoneurone than when its action is restricted to the monosynaptic pathway, and so would assist in the development of a stretch reflex.

(*b*) The opening of pathways mediating autogenetic excitation from spindle group II fibres, again supposing that these exist. The author is personally committed to the view that such an occurrence is of some importance, but further evidence is required for it to be regarded as fully established.

(*c*) The closing of pathways mediating autogenetic inhibition from spindle group II fibres. Most would agree that this provides an acceptable mechanism for facilitating the stretch reflex. But it seems unlikely to be sufficient on its own to lead to the appearance of a stretch reflex *de novo*.

(*d*) The closing of pathways mediating Ib autogenetic inhibition. This would make the Golgi tendon organs less effective at antagonising spindle excitation when a muscle is stretched and so would again favour the stretch reflex. As Eccles & Lundberg (1959) first showed there is no doubt that such an inhibition of the Ib inhibitory pathway does occur in the decerebrate. Thus the only question is as to how large a contribution the inhibition of the Ib pathway makes to the production of the stretch reflex. This awaits detailed study; as already described, the residual Ib inhibition of the decerebrate still serves to approximately halve the stretch reflex.

(*e*) The diminution of the action of the Renshaw negative feedback pathway to the motoneurones. A given afferent excitation of any particular motoneurone pool would then be less effectively opposed by recurrent inhibition, and so would elicit a greater motor discharge.

(*f*) The blocking of the reflex pathways from nociceptive afferents which normally mediate an ipsilateral flexor reflex accompanied by the reciprocal inhibition of extensor muscles. Such a supraspinal action would again favour the development of rigidity of extensor muscles by removing the possibility of an unwanted antagonistic reflex being set up by adventitious stimuli. This might be quite important in animals prepared for experimentation by extensive peripheral dissection, but seems unlikely to be a prime factor in more intact preparations with the operative interference restricted to the head. In widely dissected preparations there is a possibility of the excitation of nociceptive afferents from damaged skin, muscle and tendons or from the pins used for fixation. If an extensive denervation is performed to eliminate such 'physiological' excitation of nociceptors affecting the CNS, then there is the risk of injury discharges being initiated at the cut ends of nerve fibres, including of genuine 'flexor reflex afferents'. Fortunately, the flexor actions of nociceptive afferents are definitely blocked in the decerebrate, and this seems likely to have the favourable effect of removing a potential artefactual complication from the study of stretch reflexes. But it seems unlikely to provide a prime cause for the appearance of rigidity in the whole animal.

(g) Changes in the pattern or degree of presynaptic inhibition might also play a part in favouring the development of rigidity. For example, autogenetic inhibitory pathways (like the Ib one) might be blocked, or autogenetic pathways (like the Ia one) might be relieved of a presynaptic inhibition found in other preparations. In particular, it would help the development of the stretch reflex if supraspinal action were to block the negative feedback pathway by which Ia fibres produce a presynaptic inhibition of themselves. There is no doubt that presynaptic inhibition can be produced more or less directly by descending action. In addition, supraspinal centres can modify the action of the spinal reflex pathways which set up presynaptic inhibition on receipt of the appropriate afferent input. But the experiments performed so far have given no encouragement to the idea that such happenings might play a significant part in the development of rigidity. In particular, there seems to be no appreciable change in the presynaptic actions of group I afferents on making a decerebrate animal spinal, even though brainstem pathways which might control such actions are known to exist (Carpenter, Engberg, Funkenstein & Lundberg, 1963; Lundberg & Vyklický, 1966). In man, however, Delwaide (1970) has recently obtained suggestive evidence that certain presynaptic inhibitory processes are blocked in the spastic patient, for in this state high frequency vibration fails to inhibit the Hoffmann reflex in the way that it does in the normal.

(h) The foregoing mechanisms could all remain potentially effective when only a single muscle in a limb is left innervated. In many experiments this is brought about by widespread denervation so as to increase the precision of analysis. However, it is regrettably familiar to the experimentalist that after such a widespread denervation the tonic stretch reflex may be reluctant to make its appearance, even though there is a reasonable degree of rigidity in other limbs which have been left fully innervated. The more ready appearance of rigidity in a fully innervated limb might perhaps be because it is favoured by the mutual facilitatory effects between synergistic muscles; nor need the facilitation be restricted to muscles which all act at the same joint. The extent of spread of such facilitation might well be under supraspinal control by the action of descending fibres upon any interneurones mediating

widespread facilitatory actions. It is well known for the somaesthe-
tic system that the receptive field of neurones responding to
cutaneous stimuli may alter with the central state of the preparation. In addition, the appearance of rigidity in a whole limb would
be favoured if the motoneurones of certain muscles were relieved
of any direct Ia inhibition from their antagonists. On the other
hand, in the intact limb, relatively distant reflex interactions might
sometimes serve to diminish rigidity in comparison with that of a
single muscle isolated for myography. This is possibly the case
after giving DOPA to the spinal animal in which both flexors and
extensors may be found to have a stretch reflex when isolated for
myography, even though the hindlimbs of the animal are not
always grossly rigid and electromyographic recording confirms
that there is little resting muscle activity (Grillner, 1969b).

In spite of such a bewildering variety of potential mechanisms
it remains an open question whether the switching of spinal reflex
pathways by descending activity really plays a significant part in
the development of decerebrate rigidity. And quite naturally a
certain amount of evidence can be adduced against several of the
above possibilities having anything to do with the matter. However, Grillner & Udo (1970) recently noted that the stiffness of the
stretch reflex could be reduced by lesions of the spinal cord which
spared the vestibulo-spinal tract. On indirect evidence they suggested that the severed tracts had assisted the development of
rigidity by interfering with autogenetic inhibition rather than by
directly exciting either α or γ motoneurones. It will clearly take
some time before our understanding of what is happening in
rigidity has caught up with the advances of the last decade showing
so many ways in which so many higher motor centres can control
the reflex behaviour of the spinal cord. At any rate, it no longer
seems good enough to think of rigidity merely in terms of the
direct excitation of α motoneurones by descending pathways,
supplemented by a variable amount of Ia monosynaptic excitation
triggered by fusimotor overactivity.

With so many factors capable of contributing to the development of rigidity it would be surprising if any one of them should
ever prove to be solely responsible in any particular case. Rather,
varying mixtures might be expected to be found in different kinds
of preparation. But the range of combinations of different factors
is likely to prove limited in practice. This is so partly for the

obvious reason that only a limited range of central lesions will be readily producible, and partly for the more interesting reason that apparently different kinds of supraspinal action may prove to be regularly linked together because they form a functional entity. It is currently convenient for us to think separately about the actions of a particular higher centre on each of a number of different kinds of interneurone, but in normal function several of these actions might be found to be regularly combined just as they are on using electrical stimulation within the CNS. This might occur for the simple anatomical reason that the branches of an individual descending fibre end on several different kinds of neurone, and so have several different kinds of action; such an occurrence is commonplace for the numerous terminals arising from a single Ia afferent fibre. Alternatively, the individual descending fibres from a particular 'higher centre' might fall into groups each with a different and relatively circumscribed action, but the higher centre involved might only rarely activate them independently. This might be because it was often too difficult for the centre concerned to arrange its internal interactions on a sufficiently fine scale, or more probably because it did not usually wish to do so because the different groups of fibre were required to act together.

With our present limited understanding of the internal working of the spinal cord we can do little better than recognise as functional units groups of neurones having precisely the same function, such as all the interneurones lying on a particular reflex pathway; for example, such a unit is provided by all the interneurones lying on the Ia pathway mediating the 'direct' inhibition of one muscle by another. But the higher centres may be operating with broader terms of reference and able to see the spinal cord as made out of more complicated functional units, each of which comprises a number of synaptic elements that at the moment still appear to us to have diverse functions. We may perhaps still be unable to see the wood for the trees and not yet have succeeded in recognising the higher-level functional units existing within the spinal cord, even though we are making steady progress in studying their elements. By analogy, in examining an electronic circuit we are being quite successful in recognising capacitors and resistors etc. and so building up a detailed wiring diagram, even though we have not yet learnt to recognise blocks of circuitry performing a single kind of elementary function such as a flip-flop or an operational amplifier, let alone realising that these functional elements can perform quite different jobs on different occasions. (For example, an operational amplifier can be used for integrating or for differentiating, and flip-flops may be used as counters or as logic elements.) It is to be hoped that progressive analysis of the combinations of functional derangements that occur in different rigidities may lead on to a further understanding of the kinds of functional units which the spinal cord is employing for its various operations.

Additional mechanisms possibly helping to produce chronic increases in muscle tone

A further reason for interest in the origin of decerebrate rigidity is to help in the search for the causes of pathological increases of tone in man. Here yet other mechanisms may be at work, for the rigidities of human disease often develop slowly and persist indefinitely rather than appearing abruptly and being studied only in the acute state, as is usual for decerebrate rigidity. The passage of time allows for the degeneration of the spinal terminals of damaged neurones thus leaving the surface of motoneurones and interneurones somewhat bare of synaptic contacts. On the one hand, this has been suggested to lead to a denervation super-sensitivity, as occurs on complete denervation in the peripheral nervous system. This might possibly enable the remaining synaptic contacts to exert an abnormally great action (Teasdall & Stavraky, 1953). Why this should have a net excitatory rather than an inhibitory effect remains to be specified. On the other hand, the bare synaptic areas have been suggested to be filled up by new synaptic knobs arising from sprouts growing *de novo* from nearby fibres, and thus again to lead to a greater synaptic activation of the motoneurones than just before (McCouch, Austin, Liu & Liu, 1958). Once more it remains to be explained just why this should have an overall excitatory effect in any particular case.

The part such 'trophic' processes play in the development of spasticity following supraspinal lesions is quite problematical and there is as yet no significant evidence in their favour. However, temporary local asphyxiation of the spinal cord leads to the development of an intense and indefinitely prolonged extensor rigidity which in its later stages may quite possibly be associated with a hyper-excitability of the motoneurones as a result of their losing the majority of their normal synaptic contacts. The asphyxiation may be produced either by occluding the thoracic aorta or by raising the pressure in the dural sac surrounding the spinal cord. When either procedure is performed for the appropriate period the majority of spinal interneurones are destroyed while most of the α and γ motoneurones manage to survive. The resulting rigidity has been intensively studied by Van Harreveld (1965) and by Gelfan & Tarlov (1959) among others. It is described as having various stages, and different causal factors may be predominating in each of them. When well developed in its later stages the rigidity will survive local de-afferentation and so is an 'α rigidity'. But unlike that of the anaemic decerebrate it may perhaps be one depending upon a truly spontaneous discharge of α motoneurones, for the rigidity persists after separating the spinal cord from all higher centres; however, it is not entirely clear if this remains true after de-afferentation, as well as before. A truly spontaneous discharge would be expected to occur in all kinds of motoneurones whatever muscle they supply. In line with this the rigidity has been thought to occur simultaneously in both flexors and extensors, and the extensor posture to result from the greater strength of the latter; this again could perhaps be more fully studied. Polysynaptic reflexes such as the flexor reflex are virtually absent in these preparations, as would be expected from the destruction of the interneurones upon which they depend. Monosynaptic Ia reflexes tend to be enhanced, suggesting that when the dorsal roots are intact the rigidity should be heightened by the presence of a true stretch reflex. This view is supported by the finding that the rigidity may be reduced without loss of direct motor function by applying local anaesthetic to the nerve of a spastic muscle, though it remains to sort out the relative contributions to this effect of γ efferent blockade and the Wedensky inhibition of afferent fibres (Trubtach & Van Harreveld, 1970). At any rate, this experimental rigidity of purely spinal origin, and apparently occurring in the virtual absence of interneuronal activity, provides a further argument that hypertonia is a relatively non-specific response which may arise from a variety of causes.

Difficulties of application of physiological knowledge to human disease

The application of all these ideas to the elucidation of the derangements underlying human hypertonias so far seems to have led to little more than a wide range of more or less controversial assertions. Thus it has been variously stated for both the spasticity of an upper motor neurone lesion and the rigidity of Parkinson's disease that, on the one hand, they are due to a fusimotor over-activity and, on the other hand, that they occur in association with no special change in fusimotor activity or even with a decrease. No attempt will now be made to review the discordant literature of this important but difficult field. Part of the confusion arises because the clinical literature grows too easily by feeding upon new physiological knowledge rather than by any new analysis of the diseased state itself. This is because improved understanding of the underlying normal physiological mechanisms readily lends itself to fresh speculation on the origin of well-known clinical syndromes, even when no new clinical observation has been made and the physiological work has not been fully digested.

The real trouble arises quite simply from the paucity of methods currently available for studying human beings who naturally wish to suffer no permanent ill effects as the result of investigation; this equally limits the scope of the few methods which do exist. Most of the methods which are applicable to animals can no longer be employed with precision even if they can be used at all. The best hope is that suitable 'model syndromes' can be developed in animals each of which closely resembles some human malfunction. After a full analysis of a 'model' it might then be possible to decide on the basis of a few relatively simple confirmatory proce-dures whether the conclusions for the model could be transferred more or less *in toto* to the human syndrome. Thus, arising from Granit's separation of animal rigidities into α and γ types similar attempts were made for man, only to be overtaken by the realisa-tion that even in the experimental animal things are not quite so simple. At present, there are probably unfortunately too few methods available to allow at all a thorough correspondence to be established between a model syndrome in an animal and the real syndrome in man.

Study of the mechanism of reinforcement of the tendon jerk. The difficulties and false turnings associated with human studies may be illustrated by a cautionary tale about the mechanism of the reinforcement of tendon jerks which occurs on clenching the fists. For a time this was believed to be a purely fusimotor mediated reaction, and to be brought about by an increased γ efferent firing raising the sensitivity of the spindle and so augmenting the Ia afferent discharge elicited by a fixed mechanical stimulus. This view was based partly on the fact that reinforcement occurs without any observable increase in muscle contraction, though this is largely irrelevant, and partly on a comparison of the effects of reinforcement on the tendon jerk and on the H reflex, when there was originally thought to be no action on the latter. The H reflex is named by abbreviation after Paul Hoffmann, its discoverer. It is simply the monosynaptic reflex seen in man with electromyographic recording of the response of the ankle extensors on stimulating their Ia fibres via an electrode placed at the back of the knee. Because the nerve is intact, the motor fibres to the ankle extensors inevitably tend to be stimulated along with their Ia fibres. This limits the range of stimulus strengths that can be used so that it is not necessarily possible to initiate a maximal Ia volley. Too strong a stimulus completely occludes the reflex response by directly exciting all the α motor fibres. Even with weak stimuli a few motor fibres are excited along with the Ia fibres giving an M wave (direct muscle response) slightly preceding and so interfering with the H wave (reflex muscle response). Probably because of such difficulties only one stimulus strength appears to have been used in the earlier experiments on the effects of reinforcement.

When Landau & Clare (1964) used a range of strengths of stimuli to elicit the H reflex they found it to be reinforced in the same way as the tendon jerk, provided that the H reflex was initially sufficiently small to leave a subliminal fringe of motoneurones available to show up the effect of a central facilitation. This is illustrated in Fig. 8.18 and disposes of any possibility of reinforcement depending uniquely upon fusimotor action. It was further shown that reinforcement of the tendon jerk could persist long after all the γ efferent fibres could be presumed to have been paralysed by procaine injected into the motor point of the muscle (Clare & Landau, 1964). However, in view of the usual central coactivation of α and γ motoneurones some contribution to the reinforcement of the jerk would be expected to be provided by fusimotor action, and has certainly not been excluded by these

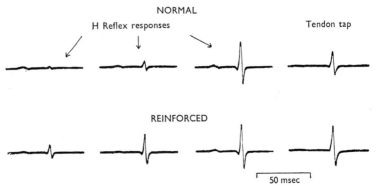

FIG. 8.18. The occurrence of reinforcement of the H reflex at the same time as that of the tendon jerk. This shows that the effect on the jerk cannot be attributed solely to a fusimotor excitation. The records show the electromyographic responses recorded with surface electrodes from the calf muscles of a normal human subject. The subject reinforced his responses by clenching his fists and jaw. The tendon jerk was the largest which could be elicited under the prevailing conditions. Starting from the left the three H responses in each row were elicited by stimuli of increasing strength. The stimulus artefact is too small to be seen. The initial low deflection is the M response due to the direct stimulation of a few α motor fibres along with Ia fibres. It can be seen that the largest H reflex was not influenced by reinforcement thus explaining the earlier statements in the literature that reinforcement acts solely through the fusimotor fibres. (Landau & Clare, 1964, Fig. 1, retouched.)

experiments. In addition, suitably trained subjects might perhaps be able to produce reinforcement of the jerk by purely fusimotor pathways. With this example in mind, it may be suggested that, pending the development of better experimental methods, the understanding of the underlying basis of the rigidities of human disease is likely to be more rapidly advanced by continued animal work rather than by the apparently more direct study of patients.

Résumé of the properties and origin of the tonic stretch reflex

The decerebrate preparation has long provided an ideal object for the study of muscle tone. Immediately on its introduction it was used to demonstrate the importance of local reflexes for the maintenance of tone. This was done by showing that cats decerebrated in the classical manner by transecting the brainstem become locally flaccid on cutting the appropriate dorsal roots. Some at least of the responsible receptors were soon shown to lie in the hypertonic muscles themselves, for decerebrate rigidity is still found in a muscle when all nearby muscles have been denervated, and it is still abolished in the usual way by de-afferentation. However, in cats decerebrated by the anaemic method, which destroys the anterior lobe of the cerebellum as well as the structures rostral to the colliculi, some rigidity usually survives de-afferentation. Thus local reflexes cannot always be held to be solely responsible for rigidity for in this and other types of preparation α motoneurones can be excited to discharge tonically by purely central mechanisms acting without local proprioceptive support.

The introduction of the optical isometric myograph allowed fuller analysis than before of the reflex response of a muscle to stretching. This led to the formal description of the stretch, or myotatic, reflex. Its existence was demonstrated by showing that an extensor muscle in the decerebrate produced a greater tension when it was stretched with the reflex arc intact than it did when its nerve was cut. The stretch reflex may be subdivided into tonic and phasic components which blend into each other, but whose relative preponderance varies with the central state of the preparation. Stretch reflexes are particularly well shown by red muscles. In the decerebrate they are largely the prerogative of extensor muscles, though weaker ones may also be seen in flexors. The stretch reflex is a rather highly localised reflex, for on stretching one head of a muscle it is rarely overtly present in another head of the same muscle. It is rather closely related to the magnitude of the stimulus. On applying a series of stretches of increasing amplitude of several millimetres extent the reflexly elicited tension is often found to be more or less linearly related to the extension. However, the reflex response evoked by small alternating stretches and releases is often rather larger than might have been expected on the basis of the response to large stretch reflexes. In this respect the behaviour of the stretch reflex mirrors that of the spindle primary endings. Thus the stretch reflex seems to have the valuable property of being at its best in resisting disturbance from a set point, but without being driven into the saturation which would be shown if the same high sensitivity were maintained for stretches of all sizes.

Contribution provided by the various types of afferent fibre. Steady stretch of a muscle normally excites a steady afferent discharge in each of the three main types of proprioceptive afferent fibre, namely the Ia, the Ib and the spindle group II fibres; each of these may be expected to play some part in modulating the stretch reflex. The current problem is to determine the precise role of each one; this means assessing its action as quantitatively as possible, as well as discovering the particular synaptic connections through which it acts. The Ia fibres provide a steady excitatory contribution to the stretch reflex and one which appears to show little central fatigue with time. This can be demonstrated most directly by exciting the Ia fibres by high-frequency vibration rather than by simple stretch; as described earlier, vibration provides a relatively specific stimulus for the spindle primary endings. The Ib fibres provide, it is believed, a steady inhibitory feedback so that the stretch reflex develops consistently less tension than it would in the absence of Ib action. A recent attempt to estimate the magnitude of this effect suggests that the stretch reflex would be about half as large again if the Ib inhibition were to be suddenly removed.

The spindle group II fibres have long been believed to contribute inhibition to the stretch reflex of extensor muscles by being part of a widespread system of flexor reflex afferents. This view was based largely on the reflex effects of graded electrical stimulation of muscle nerves. As already discussed, the interpretation of any such findings is equivocal. Certain recent experiments have favoured precisely the opposite idea, namely that in the decerebrate preparation the spindle group II fibres produce autogenetic excitation rather than inhibition. This seems a more rational function for an afferent fibre which carries a signal so accurately related to the length of the muscle. The evidence for the new view is, however, still somewhat indirect and it has not yet won universal acceptance. The starting point for the suggestion is the finding that in the decerebrate cat the reflex response to simple stretch is often rather greater than the reflex response of the same muscle to high-frequency vibration, though the latter excites the Ia fibres the more powerfully. Stretch, however, excites the spindle group II fibres as well as the Ia fibres thus raising the possibility that they are contributing positively rather than negatively to the stretch reflex. The Golgi tendon organs are excluded from providing the missing excitatory contribution since there is a variety of evidence to show that they produce autogenetic inhibition. No other types of receptor is currently believed to be significantly excited by stretch thus leaving it by exclusion to the spindle group II fibres.

More cogent evidence for an excitatory role for the group II fibres is provided by studying the interaction between the reflex responses to stretch and to vibration. If they both depended solely upon the Ia pathway an increase in the stretch reflex with increasing stretch should occlude the response to vibration by an equivalent amount. In practice, however, such occlusion does not occur. This is so whether the interaction between the two reflexes is studied in the decerebrate cat with the recording of muscle contraction or in the anesthetised cat with intracellular recording from motoneurones. Analysis of the action of procaine applied to the nerve to the soleus muscle also supports the idea that the stretch reflex cannot be attributed solely to Ia action. However, the provisional acceptance of an excitatory role for the group II fibres carries with it no particular implication about the particular synaptic pathways via which they have this action and the matter remains for study.

The importance of the contractile properties of muscle for the stretch reflex. The resistance to stretching of a muscle with a preexisting tonic contraction is partly due to its mechanical properties as well as to any reflex response. Thus if a constant force is applied to a contracting muscle it initially yields rather slowly, but as it begins to yield it does so ever the faster. This behaviour must help the muscle to resist deformation in the short time before assistance arrives from the CNS via the stretch reflex. It can be plausibly explained in terms of the sliding filament hypothesis of muscle contraction.

The tension produced by a contracting muscle also varies with the absolute value of the length of the muscle—the classically known length–tension relationship. This means that when a constant motor discharge occurs after dorsal root section, as it may do in the anaemic decerebrate, then an increasing tension can still be observed on extending a muscle even though any true reflex action is excluded. This 'pseudo-stretch reflex' may be indistinguishable from a true one on simple myographic recording, but the true reflex can usually be recognised as such by electromyographic recording. However, it is still uncertain just how large a contribution the peripheral length–tension properties of muscle play in the development of tension in the 'true' stretch reflex seen when the dorsal roots are intact. For the soleus muscle near its physiological maximum length the peripheral contribution would appear to be rather slight, since its tension–length curve is then rather flat. Near its physiological minimum length, however, the tension–length curve may be quite steep, particularly for low frequencies of muscle activation as occur in the stretch reflex; thus an appreciable peripheral contribution to the stretch reflex tension might then be expected, though it should be noted that the stretch reflex is only rarely well developed at such short lengths. The tension feedback from the Ib fibres will, moreover, tend to reflexly counteract the effects on the stretch reflex of the peripheral properties of muscle, for any excess of muscle strength with extension will lead to a reflex inhibition of some part of the motor discharge which would otherwise have occurred.

Reflexly mediated plastic behaviour of muscle. When the tone of the decerebrate is studied under approximately isotonic conditions it shows the so-called plastic behaviour of the lengthening and shortening reactions. To elicit a lengthening reaction a tonically contracting muscle is forcibly extended and held for a short time at a new longer length. When released it then fails to shorten down to its original length and develops no more reflex tension at the new longer length than it had previously done at the old shorter length. To elicit the shortening reaction the now stretched muscle is manually helped to assume once more its original shorter length; after a short interval it will then once again develop the same tension as before. These reactions are not shown by a de-afferented muscle which is induced to contract tonically by eliciting a crossed extensor reflex; the plastic reactions are thereby shown to be reflexly mediated.

A frequent concomitant of the lengthening reaction is the clasp-knife response. It consists of the muscle suddenly ceasing to resist forcible extension so that the limb abruptly gives way. The clasp-knife response is often attributed merely to a Ib disynaptic autogenetic inhibition which is thought to manifest itself at the moment when the increasing stretch reflex tension reaches the threshold of the Golgi tendon organs. This view, however, completely overlooks the switch-like character of the

ME473

clasp-knife effect which leads to a turning off of the pre-existing reflex response and not just an inhibition of that fraction of the stretch reflex which exceeds the threshold of the inhibitory mechanism. This betokens a more complicated spinal mechanism than the simple summation of excitatory and inhibitory actions on the motoneurone soma.

There is some evidence that a 'switch-like' inhibition of fusimotor discharge may play a part in the clasp-knife effect. The present state of knowledge about autogenetic fusimotor reflexes is, however, unfortunately confused. The only definite point is that the Ia autogenetic pathway succeeds in by-passing the fusimotor neurones even though they are anatomically intermingled with the α motoneurones. Group I inhibition of some fusimotor neurones has, however, been suggested to occur. In addition, there appears to be a weak and variable recurrent motor collateral inhibition of fusimotor neurones which escaped detection in the earliest experiments. Cutaneous reflexes appear to influence the fusimotor neurones of a muscle in very much the same way as its α motoneurones, though the fusimotor neurones often have the lower threshold.

Possible functional derangements underlying decerebrate rigidity. All the essential mechanisms required for the development of hypertonia would appear to exist within the spinal cord itself, but hypertonia only occurs when they are suitably facilitated. It remains an open question whether some part of the stretch reflex neural activity traverses the higher centres as well as the spinal centres. Three rather different kinds of central action would appear to be able to lead to the appearance of rigidity. First, an excessive excitation of α motoneurones by purely central pathways can lead them to fire spontaneously in the absence of any reflex support; in addition, such central excitation might so lower their, threshold that they fired excessively in response to the normal amount of proprioceptive feedback. Second, an excessive excitation of fusimotor neurones can probably reflexly elicit an excessive α motor discharge via its effect on the spindle afferent fibres (Ia certainly, II possibly). Third, descending central activity may act on spinal interneurones so as to switch the overall action of the normal afferent input and so favour autogenetic excitation over autogenetic inhibition; numerous ways in which this might happen are readily suggested. These various kinds of factor probably act in combination rather than independently. However, the hypertonias of different types of preparation seem unlikely all to be based on the same balance of the various possible functional derangements. In the chronic state, denervation-supersensitivity and the sprouting of afferent terminals have also been suggested to contribute to the development of hypertonia.

There is naturally a particularly strong desire to elucidate the functional derangements underlying the various hypertonic states of human disease. For the time being, however, progress is likely to be more rapid by the continuation of animal work rather than the direct study of man. This is because of the paucity of the methods available in clinical practice in relation to the complexity of the problems.

References

Alnaes, E., Jansen, J. K. S. & Rudjord, T. (1965). Fusimotor activity in the spinal cat. *Acta physiol. scand.* **63**, 197–212.   [456]

Bazett, H. C. & Penfield, W. G. (1922). A study of the Sherrington decerebrate animal in the chronic as well as the acute condition. *Brain* **45**, 185–265.   [452]

Brown, M. C., Lawrence, D. G. & Matthews, P. B. C. (1968*a*). Reflex inhibition by Ia afferent input of spontaneously discharging motoneurones in the decerebrate cat. *J. Physiol.* **198**. 5–7P.   [449–451]

— (1968*b*). Antidromic inhibition of presumed fusimotor neurones by repetitive stimulation of the ventral root in the decerebrate cat. *Experientia* **24**, 1210–1211.   [450]

Burke, D., Gillies, J. D. & Lance, J. W. (1970). The quadriceps stretch reflex in human spasticity. *J. Neurol. Neurosurg. Psychiat.* **33**, 216–223.   [445]

Carpenter, D., Engberg, I., Funkenstien, H. & Lundberg, A. (1963). Decerebrate control of reflexes to primary afferents. *Acta physiol. scand.* **59**, 424–437.   [461]

Clare, M. H. & Landau, W. M. (1964). Fusimotor function. V. Reflex reinforcement under fusimotor block in normal subjects. *Archs. Neurol. Chicago* **10**, 123–127.   [467]

Cohen, L. A. (1953). Localization of stretch reflex. *J. Neurophysiol.* **16**, 272–285.   [417]

— (1954). Organization of stretch reflex into two types of direct spinal arcs. *J. Neurophysiol.* **17**, 443–453.   [417]

Delwaide, P. J. (1970). *Étude expérimentale de l'hyperréflexie tendineux en clinique neurologique.* Brussels: Arscia, S.A. Paris: Maloine, S.A. [461]

Denny-Brown, D. (1929). Nature of postural reflexes. *Proc. R. Soc.* B **104**, 252–301. [417–420, 438, 439]

Denny-Brown, D. E. & Liddell, E. G. T. (1927). The stretch reflex as a spinal process. *J. Physiol.* **63**, 144–150. [453]

Eccles, J. C., Eccles, R. M., Iggo, A. & Lundberg, A. (1960). Electrophysiological studies on gamma motoneurones. *Acta physiol. scand.* **40**, 32–40. [449, 450]

Eccles, R. M. & Lundberg, A. (1959). Supraspinal control of interneurones mediating spinal reflexes. *J. Physiol.* **147**, 565–584. [460]

Eklund, G., Euler, C. von & Rutkowski, S. (1964). Spontaneous and reflex activity of intercostal gamma motoneurones. *J. Physiol.* **171**, 139–163. [451]

Eldred, E., Granit, R. & Merton, P. A. (1953). Supraspinal control of the muscle spindles and its significance. *J. Physiol.* **122**, 498–523. [447–451, 456]

Eldred, E. & Hagbarth, K. E. (1954). Facilitation and inhibition of gamma efferents by stimulation of certain skin areas. *J. Neurophysiol.* **17**, 59–65. [450]

Ellaway, P. H. (1971). Recurrent inhibition of fusimotor neurones exhibiting background discharges in the decerebrate and the spinal cat. *J. Physiol.* **216**, 419–439. [450]

Foster, M. (1892). *A Text Book of Physiology*, part III. *The Central Nervous System*, 6th ed. London: Macmillan. [411]

Fulton, J. F., Liddell, E. G. T. & Rioch, D.McK. (1930). The influence of experimental lesions of the spinal cord upon the kneejerk. I. Acute lesions. *Brain* **53**, 311–326. [453]

Gelfan, S. & Tarlov, I. M. (1959). Interneurones and rigidity of spinal origin. *J. Physiol.* **146**, 594–617. [465]

Gidlöf, A. (1966). Intracellular aspects of 'release' phenomena in α-extensor motoneurones of the cat. *Acta physiol. scand.* **68**, suppl. 277, 58. [456]

Gillies, J. D., Burke, D. J. & Lance, J. W. (1971). Tonic vibration reflex in the cat. *J. Neurophysiol.* **34**, 252–262. [423]

Granit, R. (1955). *Receptors and Sensory Perception.* New Haven: Yale University Press. [422, 457]

— (1958). Neuromuscular interaction in postural tone of the cat's isometric soleus muscle. *J. Physiol.* **143**, 387–402. [418, 431, 439]

— (1966). *Charles Scott Sherrington, an Appraisal.* London: Nelson. [411]

Granit, R., Homgren, B. & Merton, P. A. (1955). Two routes for excitation of muscle and their subservience to the cerebellum. *J. Physiol.* **130**, 213–224. [413, 456]

Granit, R., Pascoe, J. E. & Steg, G. (1957). The behaviour of tonic alpha and gamma motoneurones during stimulation of recurrent collaterals. *J. Physiol.* **138**, 381–400. [450]

Grillner, S. (1969a). The influence of DOPA on the static and dynamic activity to the triceps surae of the spinal cat. *Acta physiol. scand.* **77**, 490–500. [453]

— (1969b). Supraspinal and segmental control of static and dynamic γ-motoneurones in the cat. *Acta physiol. scand.* **76**, Suppl. 327, 34 pp. [453, 462]

— (1970). Is the tonic stretch reflex dependent upon group II excitation? *Acta physiol. scand.* **78**, 431–432. [430]

Grillner, S., Hongo, T. & Lund, S. (1968). Descending monosynaptic and reflex control of γ-motoneurones. *Acta physiol. scand.* **75**, 592–613. [449]

Grillner, S. & Udo, M. (1970). Is the tonic stretch reflex dependent on suppression of autogenetic inhibitory reflexes? *Acta physiol. scand.* **79**, 13–14A. [462]

Grillner, S. & Udo, M. (1971a). Motor unit activity and stiffness of the contracting muscle fibres in the tonic stretch reflex. *Acta physiol. scand.* **81**, 422–424. [430, 439]

— (1971b). Recruitment in the tonic stretch reflex. *Acta physiol. scand.* **81**, 571–573. [439]

Henatsch, H. D. & Ingvar, D. H. (1956). Chlorpromazin und Spastizität. *Arch. Psychiat. Zt. Neurol.* **195**, 77–93. [456]

Henneman, E., Somjen, G. & Carpenter, D. O. (1965). Functional significance of cell size in spinal motoneurones. *J. Neurophysiol.* **28**, 560–580. [418, 439]

Houk, J. C., Singer, J. J. & Goldman, M. R. (1970). An evaluation of length and force feedback to soleus muscles of decerebrate cats. *J. Neurophysiol.* **33**, 784–811. [426, 427, 440, 441]

Hunt, C. C. (1951). The reflex activity of mammalian small-nerve fibres. *J. Physiol.* **115**, 456–469. [450]

Hunt, C. C. & Paintal, A. S. (1958). Spinal reflex regulation of fusimotor neurones. *J. Physiol.* **143**, 195–212. [449, 450]

Jansen, J. K. S. & Rack, P. M. H. (1966). The reflex response to sinusoidal stretching of soleus in the decerebrate cat. *J. Physiol.* **183**, 15–36. [445]

Joyce, G. C. & Rack, P. M. H. (1969). Isotonic lengthening and shortening movements of cat soleus muscle. *J. Physiol.* **204**, 475–491. [436]

Joyce, G. C., Rack, P. M. H. & Westbury, D. R. (1969). The mechanical properties of cat soleus muscle during controlled lengthening and shortening movements. *J. Physiol.* **204**, 461–474. [436]

Kolmodin, G. M. (1957). Integrative processes in single spinal interneurones with proprioceptive connections. *Acta physiol. scand.* **40**, Suppl. 139, 89 pp. [459]

Landau, W. M. & Clare, M. H. (1964). Fusimotor function. IV. Reinforcement of the H reflex in normal subjects. *Archs Neurol. Psychiat.*, Chicago **10**, 117–122. [467, 468]

Laporte, Y. & Bessou, P. (1959). Modification d'excitabilité de moto-neurones homonymes provoquées par l'activation physiologique de fibres afférentes d'origine musculaire du groupe II. *J. Physiol.*, Paris **51**, 897–908. [428]

Liddell, E. G. T. & Sherrington, C. (1924). Reflexes in response to stretch (myotatic reflexes). *Proc. R. Soc.* B, **96**, 212–242. [414–420]

— (1925). Further observations on myotatic reflexes. *Proc. R. Soc.* B, **97**, 276–283. [414]

Lundberg, A. & Vyklický, L. (1966). Inhibition of transmission to primary afferents by electrical stimulation to the brainstem. *Archs. ital. Biol.* **104**, 86–97. [461]

McCouch, G. P., Austin, G. M., Liu, C. M. & Liu, C. Y. (1958). Sprouting as a cause of spasticity. *J. Neurophysiol.* **21**, 205–216. [464]

McGrath, G. J. & Matthews, P. B. C. (1970). Support for an autogenetic excitatory reflex action of the spindle secondaries from the effect of gamma blockade by procaine. *J. Physiol.* **210**, 176–177P. [433–435]

Matthews, P. B. C. (1958). The effect of the local application of procaine on the stretch reflex of the soleus muscle of the cat decerebrated by anaemia. *J. Physiol.* **140**, 408–420. [457]

— (1959). The dependence of tension upon extension in the stretch reflex of the soleus muscle of the decerebrate cat. *J. Physiol.* **147**, 521–546. [418, 419, 446, 447]

— (1966a). Reflex activation of the soleus muscle of the decerebrate cat by vibration. *Nature, Lond.* **209**, 204–205. [423, 424]

— (1966b). The reflex excitation of the soleus muscle of the decerebrate cat caused by vibration applied to its tendon. *J. Physiol.* **184**, 450–472. [423–426, 453]

— (1967). Vibration and the stretch reflex. In *Myotatic, Kinesthetic and Vestibular Mechanisms*. Ed. de Reuck, A. V. S. & Knight, J. pp. 40–50, London: Churchill. [440]

— (1969). Evidence that the secondary as well as the primary endings of the muscle spindles may be responsible for the tonic stretch reflex of the decerebrate cat. *J. Physiol.* **204**, 365–393. [421, 429–435]

— (1970). A reply to criticism of the hypothesis that the group II afferents contribute excitation to the stretch reflex. *Acta physiol. scand.* **79**, 431–433. [433, 435]

Matthews, P. B. C. & Rushworth, G. (1957). The selective effect of procaine on the stretch reflex and tendon jerk of soleus muscle when applied to its nerve. *J. Physiol.* **135**, 245–262. [433, 457]

Matthews, P. B. C. & Stein, R. B. (1969). The regularity of primary and secondary muscle spindle afferent discharges. *J. Physiol.* **202**, 59–82. [439]

Maxwell, D. R. & Rhodes, K. F. (1970). The effects of dimethothiazine on muscle spindle activity in the decerebrate cat. *Br. J. Pharmac. Chemother.* **39**, 520–532. [457]

Moruzzi, G. & Pompeiano, O. (1957). Inhibitory mechanisms underlying the collapse of decerebrate rigidity after unilateral fastigial lesions. *J. comp. Neurol.* **107**, 1–25. [454]

Pollock, L. J. & Davis, L. (1923). Studies in decerebration I. A method of decerebration. *Archs. Neurol. Psychiat., Chicago* **10**, 391–398. [413]

Pollock, L. J. & Davis, L. (1930). The reflex activities of a decerebrate animal. *J. comp. Neurol.* **50**, 377–411.   [412, 413]

— (1931). Studies in decerebration. VI. The effect of deafferentation upon decerebrate rigidity. *Am. J. Physiol.* **98**, 47–49.   [413, 455]

Pompeiano, O. (1960). Alpha types of 'release' studied in tension–extension diagrams from cat's forelimb triceps muscle. *Archs ital. Biol.* **98**, 92–117.   [440, 453, 456]

Poppele, R. E. & Terzuolo, C. A. (1968). Myotatic reflex: its input–output relation. *Science, N.Y.* **159**, 743–745.   [441–445]

Rack, P. M. H. (1970). The significance of mechanical properties of muscle in the reflex control of posture. In *Excitatory Synaptic Mechanisms*, ed. Andersen, P. & Jansen, J. K. S. pp. 317–321. Oslo: Universitetsforlaget.   [436]

Rack, P. M. H. & Westbury, D. R. (1969). The effects of length and stimulus rate on tension in the isometric cat soleus muscle. *J. Physiol.* **204**, 443–460.   [424, 438]

Rademaker, G. G. J. (1947). On the lengthening and shortening reactions and their occurrence in man. *Brain* **70**, 109–126.   [445]

Roberts, T. D. M. (1952). Reflex interaction of synergic extensor muscles of the cat hind limb. *J. Physiol.* **117**, 5–6P.   [417]

— (1958). The assessment of changes in the sensitivity of a stretch reflex. *J. Physiol.* **144**, 2–5P.   [439]

— (1963). Rhythmic excitation of a stretch reflex, revealing (a) hysteresis and (b) a difference between the responses to pulling and to stretching *Q. Jl exp. Physiol.* **47**, 328–345.   [445, 446]

Rosenthal, N. P., McKean, T. A., Roberts, W. J. & Terzuolo, C. A. (1970). Frequency analysis of stretch reflex and its main subsystems in triceps surae muscles of the cat. *J. Neurophysiol.* **33**, 713–749.   [441, 445]

Ruch, T. C. (1936). Evidence of the non-segmental character of spinal reflexes from an analysis of the cephalad effects of spinal transection (Schiff–Sherrington phenomenon). *J. Physiol.* **114**, 457–467.   [454]

Ruch, T. C. & Watts, J. W. (1934). Reciprocal changes to reflex activity of the fore limbs induced by post-brachial 'cold-block' of the spinal cord. *J. Physiol.* **110**, 362–375.   [454]

Sherrington, C. S. (1898). Decerebrate rigidity and the reflex co-ordination of movements. *J. Physiol.* **22**, 319–322.   [411, 412, 452]

— (1909). On plastic tonus and proprioceptive reflexes. *Q. Jl. exp. Physiol.* **2**, 109–156.   [412, 442]

Takano, K. & Henatsch, H. D. (1971). The effect of rate of stretch upon the development of active reflex tension in hind limb muscles of the decerebrate cat. *Expl. Brain Res.* **12**, 422–434.   [418]

Teasdall, R. D. & Stavraky, G. W. (1953). Responses of de-afferented spinal neurones to corticospinal impulses. *J. Neurophysiol.* **16**, 367–375.   [464]

Terzuolo, C. & Terzian, H. (1953). Cerebellar increase of postural tonus after de-afferentation and labyrinthectomy. *J. Neurophysiol.* **16,** 551–561. [413]

Trubtach, J. R. & Van Harreveld, A. (1970). Effect of procaine on asphyxial rigidity. *Exptl. Neurol.* **27,** 76–89. [465]

Van Harreveld, A. (1965). Effects of spinal cord asphyxiation. In *Progress in Brain Research,* Vol. 12, Physiology of Spinal Neurones, ed. Eccles, J. C. & Schadé, J. P. pp. 280–307. Amsterdam: Elsevier. [465]

Voorhoeve, P. E. & Van Kanten, R. W. (1962). Reflex behaviour of fusimotor neurones of the cat upon electrical stimulation of various afferent fibres. *Acta physiol. pharmacol. néerl.* **10,** 391–407. [449, 450]

Westbury, D. R. (1971). A comparison of stretch and vibration responses at the motoneurone. *J. Physiol.* **213,** 25–26P. [432]

9

THE RELATIONSHIPS OF THE MUSCLE AFFERENTS WITH THE HIGHER PARTS OF THE CENTRAL NERVOUS SYSTEM

THE spinal reflex actions of the muscle afferents clearly represent only a part of their central function. In addition, they also project to higher centres, notably the cerebellum and cerebral cortex, and practically everything remains to be discovered about their actions at these levels. At the moment the neurophysiological study of central structures is quite properly concerned with details of anatomical localisation and synaptic connections; but even when these have been established relatively completely it will remain to show the use to which the higher centres put the information provided by the muscle receptors about the state of the muscle. Equally, the conditions under which, and the reasons why, the higher centres activate the fusimotor neurones also remain largely obscure. The present chapter will attempt to do no more than detail the current state of knowledge.

The cortical projection of muscle afferents

Multiplicity of receiving areas shown by the recording of evoked potentials. In the 1940's, with the refinement of recording techniques, the detection of a potential wave on the cortical surface in response to a peripheral stimulus became the standard way of showing that an afferent input sent its signal to the cerebral cortex by a reasonably direct pathway. When the muscle afferents were first examined in this way no responses were found on stretching and prodding muscles, but stimulation of muscle nerves at group III strength elicited evoked potentials in both tactile areas I and II of the contralateral cortex (Mountcastle, Covian & Harrison, 1952; Gardner & Haddad, 1953). Group I afferent stimulation was not then found to produce a detectable response. Small responses to group II stimulation were seen at about the same time by McIntyre (1953, 1962) but he felt that they were unlikely to have been due to the excitation of the spindle group II afferents and attributed them to other fibres of the same diameter. The thalamic relay for the group III effects has subsequently been described by Mallart (1968). On the basis of electrical stimulation experiments he felt that the 'central organisation' concerned with group III inputs was similar to that of 'the other somesthetic inputs', i.e. the cutaneous ones. This fits in with the idea that many group III fibres supply endings mediating the sensation of 'pressure–pain'.

However, cortical responses on group I stimulation are now well known to exist and were presumably missed in the pioneer work because they are rather small and rather highly localised. The original work was largely performed on the hindlimb. Shortly afterwards, Amassian & Berlin (1958) looked at the effect of stimulating forelimb nerves and then found surface positive cortical waves in the contralateral cortex with a latency of some 6–8 msec after stimulating group I fibres in several different muscle nerves. The response was suggested to be due to the excitation of afferents from stretch receptors (i.e. Ia or Ib) because the evoked response was reduced by pulling on the appropriate muscle when its nerve was intact. Oscarsson & Rosén (1963) soon confirmed the existence of a group I cortical projection and provided a much fuller description and the first illustrations of the responses. Figure 9.1 shows the type of response and their restriction to a

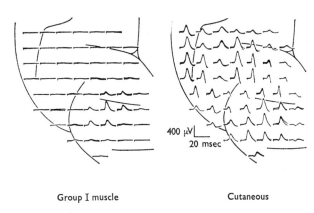

Group I muscle   Cutaneous

FIG. 9.1. Comparison of the cortical potentials evoked by stimulation of group I muscle afferents and of comparatively low threshold cutaneous afferents, both from the forelimb. Left, group I stimulation by single shock to the deep radial nerve at 1·8 × threshold. Right, cutaneous stimulation by single shock to superficial radial nerve at 5 × threshold. The potentials recorded from different parts of the sensori-motor cortex of the cat are superimposed on a plan view of the anterolateral part of the cortex. The muscular potentials are clustered just rostral to the post-cruciate dimple. (Oscarsson & Rosén, 1963, Fig. 3.)

small region which is just rostral to the post-cruciate dimple and which lies in the classical somatic sensory area one (S1).

Oscarsson & Rosén further showed that Ia fibres were likely to be responsible, at least in part, for they found that the responses evoked by nerve stimulation were occluded by exciting spindle afferents by the intra-arterial injection of suxamethonium. In addition they found that a cortical wave was elicited by a rapid pull of only 60 μm extent which may be presumed to have produced a nearly pure Ia input. The electrical stimulation experiments had already shown that a very small group I volley would suffice to give a cortical response, thus betokening a considerable security of synaptic transmission and a slight need for spatial summation; this parallels the behaviour of some ascending sensory systems but contrasts with the excitatory action of the Ia fibres on moto-neurones. The sensitivity of the ascending pathway activated by group I stimulation further highlights the necessity for careful controls to demonstrate that the cortical effects so elicited are indeed due to stretch receptor afferents and not to any few fibres supplying other types of receptor, and notably the Pacinian corpuscle. McIntyre, Holman & Veale (1967), using a localised mechanical stimulus, found that a single impulse in a single corpuscle afferent was sufficient to evoke a detectable cortical potential. However, under normal conditions such one-to-one transmission seems unlikely to occur for the discharge of stretch receptors since any additional impulse will usually be super-imposed on a maintained barrage of afferent firing, rather than on the completely quiescent background of the anaesthetised cat with severed peripheral nerves.

Like others before them, Oscarsson & Rosén failed to find a hindlimb group I projection, and so for a time it appeared that a cortical group I action was a facultative phenomenon associated with a more refined cortical control of movement than that exerted over the hindlimb. However, further persistent study by Landgren & Silfvenius (1969) duly demonstrated a hindlimb projection on stimulating several of the standard nerves (quadriceps, biceps-semitendinosus, gastrocnemius-soleus, peroneals) and using an averager to help the small evoked potentials to stand out from the background disturbances; in addition to recording from the cortical surface they used a microelectrode to record from the depths of the sulci. By the usual grading of stimulus intensity they were able to show that both Ia and Ib fibres projected to the cortex, apparently by rather separate pathways for they did not occlude each others' actions.

Such successful demonstration of a role for Ib as well as for Ia fibres has not yet proved possible for the forelimb group I cortical projection; in forelimb nerves evidence is still lacking to show whether or not the two kinds of fibre differ in their thresholds to electrical stimulation. Hindlimb group II fibres were found to project to around the borders of the group I locus, but were not thought to project to the precise regions where the group I responses were maximal because increasing the strength of the stimulus so as to recruit group II fibres produced no increase in the size of the potentials evoked in the centre of the group I region; this, however, may merely have been due to an occlusion of the group II action by the prior group I activity. The hindlimb group I afferents were found to project to two separate areas on the contralateral cortex with no overlap between them. One lay on the dorsal surface of the hemisphere just medial and rostral to the post-cruciate dimple, and largely overlapped the originally described forelimb group I area. The other hindlimb area lay on the medial surface of the hemisphere adjacent to the cruciate sulcus and did not receive a forelimb group I projection, though it did receive hindlimb cutaneous fibres. The hindlimb group I responses elicited in the two areas were indistinguishable in character.

The pathway via which the hindlimb group I responses reach the cortex has yet to be fully described. It certainly does not include the dorsal columns, for the cortical response is unaffected by their transection in the cervical region. The response is abolished, however, by a superficial section of the dorsolateral fascicle at C1. Since this is where the dorsal spino-cerebellar tract runs it seems possible that the cortex may be fed by branches of this tract after suitable but unknown synaptic relay (Landgren & Silfvenius, 1969). The forelimb group I pathway to the cortex has been studied in some detail and is via the dorsal columns, the deep part of the cuneate nucleus, the medial lemniscus and a small part of the nucleus ventralis posterolateralis of the thalamus (Oscarsson & Rosén, 1963; Andersson, Landgren & Wolsk, 1966; Mallart, 1968; Rosén, 1969a, b).

Andersson, Landgren & Wolsk (1966) found that some of the single units in the thalamus which could be excited by forelimb group I fibres could be antidromically excited on stimulating two separate regions of the cortex; this may be taken to show that individual ascending thalamic fibres branched to supply the two different receiving areas. One region was the then familiar group I projection area near the post-cruciate dimple; the other was in the neighbourhood of the suprasylvian sulcus. Recording from the depths of the sulcus with a penetrating microelectrode subsequently showed that group I fibres from the forelimb produced potential changes here also, but ones which could not readily be picked up by the previously employed surface recording (Landgren, Silfvenius & Wolsk, 1967). Thus to date three separate cortical regions have been described for the receipt of the information transmitted by group I fibres. The largest lies just rostral to the post-cruciate dimple and is common to both fore- and hindlimbs, though their respective areas are not precisely coterminous. One lies in the suprasylvian sulcus and is fed by the forelimb. One lies on the medial surface of the hemisphere adjacent to the cruciate sulcus and is supplied by the hindlimb. The approximate location of these various regions is shown in Fig. 9.2. This enumeration is not final, for in addition, in a single experiment, Landgren, Silfvenius & Wolsk (1967) observed potentials elicited by hindlimb group I stimulation in the suprasylvian sulcus close to the

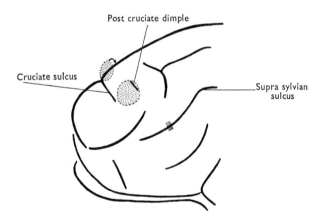

CAT CEREBRAL CORTEX
Lateral view of anterior half

FIG. 9.2. The chief places on the cerebral cortex to which group I muscle afferents have been found to project. The stippling shows where evoked potentials have been recorded on stimulating various peripheral nerves at group I strength. The post-cruciate dimple region is common to both fore- and hindlimbs. The suprasylvian region is for the forelimb, and the cruciate region for the hindlimb. Two further small forelimb areas have been described and yet others are thought to exist.

forelimb group I region; large potentials were also produced here on stimulating cutaneous nerves of both fore- and hind-limbs. Moreover, Silfvenius (1968) has briefly described two further small forelimb areas.

The situation in the monkey (Macaque) has been studied by Albe-Fessard and her colleagues who found that, in preparations anaesthetised with chloralose, group I stimulation may excite localised potentials in the classical motor area (Albe-Fessard, Liebeskind & Lamarre, 1965; Albe-Fessard & Liebeskind, 1966; Albe-Fessard, Lamarre & Pimpaneau, 1966). Their main work, however, was an extensive single unit analysis of cells activated by physiological stimuli such as altering the angle of a joint, pulling on an isolated tendon or lightly pressing on the surface of a muscle. All of these proprioceptive stimuli sufficed to excite dis-charges from a number of cells lying in the motor area. Some at least of these responses were argued to have been due to spindle afferents, for some cells could be excited by a presumed selective activation of spindle afferents; this was done by stimulating fusi-motor fibres in the ventral root along with alpha fibres whose action had been blocked by curarisation of just sufficient degree to eliminate overt muscle contraction. The pathways for such effects of coure remain unknown and might involve several inter-neurones; but even so the findings seem as interesting as the demonstration of a direct short-latency response on electrical stimulation. In the baboon anaesthetised with nembutal, a short-latency group I projection from forelimb group I afferents has been described in area 3a which lies in the depths of the central fissure (Phillips, Powell & Wiesendanger, 1971); again some of these responses were argued to depend upon Ia afferents for they could also be elicited by small rapid stretches or by high-frequency vibration.

Single unit analyses, including those in the relay nuclei. Single unit analysis, mostly with extracellular recording, has confirmed and extended many of the findings obtained with grosser recording methods, though there has as yet been no serious study of the responses to controlled physiological stimuli. On stimulating various forelimb nerves, Oscarsson, Rosén & Sulg (1966) found some cortical cells to be excited and some to be inhibited by group I action. On the basis of latency measurements they suggested that the excited cells were the ones which were directly acted upon by the ascending thalamo-cortical fibres and that some if not all of these 'fourth order' neurones then inhibited the 'fifth order' neurones upon which they impinged. Neither order neurone, however, appeared to be particularly concerned with what was happening in any one single muscle, for most of the cells were usually affected by a number of different muscle nerves, including those from antagonists; they were also influenced by cutaneous inputs. Widespread though slightly less marked convergence is found for the thalamic relay cells lying on the group I pathway (Andersson, Landgren & Wolsk, 1966; Rosén, 1969b). However, the equivalent relay cells in the cuneate nucleus show appreciably less convergence from different inputs.

In spite of marked convergence on many of the cells in the thalamus and the cuneate, about half of those studied by Rosén (1969a,b) in either relay site could be excited to discharge impulses by only one out of the six forelimb nerves then stimulated. Each of these nerves supplied a group of synergistic muscles rather than just a single muscle. When nerves to individual muscles were studied an appreciably higher degree of convergence was observed, particularly in the thalamus. Thus with ascent of the central sensory pathway there appears to be a progressive convergence of group I inputs from different sources. Transmission at these nuclei is unlikely, however, to be restricted to a progressive invariant funnelling of information from group I fibres. Many of the relay cells in both sites were also influenced by cortical stimulation. Those in the thalamus were almost invariably synaptically excited. In contrast, cortical stimulation often inhibited the response of those in the cuneate to a peripheral stimulus; this inhibition was possibly largely due to a presynaptic inhibition of the primary afferent terminals which were bearing the excitatory input. In addition, both nuclei contained a number of group I activatable cells which could not be antidromically excited by stimulation upstream, and so were presumably interneurones mediating 'integrative' reactions, quite possibly by inhibition. These interneurones were often also influenced by cortical and by cutaneous stimulation. The thalamic relay cells were usually excited by cutaneous stimulation whereas the cuneate ones were less often so; in addition cutaneous stimulation seemed to produce a pre-synaptic inhibition of the group I terminals in the cuneate.

Of especial interest from the point of view of muscular control is Rosén's (1969a,b) finding that, particularly in the cuneate, group II fibres often excite the same relay cells that are activated by group I fibres of the same nerve; such relay cells thus fire a greater number of impulses in response to a strong than to a weak stimulus. As group III stimulation had no further excitatory action on these cells, the group II effects seem almost certain to have depended upon spindle group II fibres rather than upon any group II fibres from free nerve endings etc. Such similarity of group I and group II action is a further sign that group II fibres should not be written off as simply a part of a system of flexor reflex afferents (FRA). It seems likely that, for once, an action which is genuinely due to spindle group II fibres has proved demonstrable by electrical stimulation without being overpowered by the concomitant activation of true flexor reflex afferents of group II diameter.

The greater paucity of such superadded group II actions in the thalamus may perhaps reflect yet another limitation of electrical stimulation as a tool for investigating such complicated systems. Namely that in these experiments the group II action was recognised by any increase in the number of impulses fired by the cell studied when the strength of the peripheral stimulus was increased. The difficulty with this is that a combination of refractoriness and the action of the well-known recurrent inhibitory pathway in the thalamus will tend to block the initiation of impulses by any more tardily arriving excitatory action, such as that provided by the group II fibres. Thus a group II action on group I activated cells may perhaps sometimes fail to be detected because it does not lead to the discharge of any further impulses. On the other hand, if the cells fail to fire in response to the group I volley they would be facilitated in their response to the subsequent arrival of the group II excitation. A related indication of the complexities of the whole situation is illustrated in Fig. 9.3 which shows the cortical potentials evoked by stimulating a muscle nerve at various strengths. In the intact animal group II stimulation produced no increase in the size of the evoked potential, whereas after transecting the dorsal funiculi group I stimulation became ineffective and group II stimulation then evoked a response! This appears to betoken an interference with group II action by prior group I activity. In life, of course, group I and group II afferents will

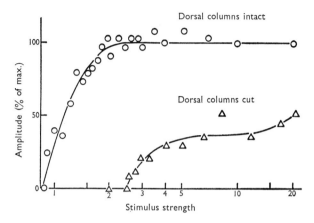

FIG. 9.3. The normal masking of a cortical response to group II nerve stimulation, presumably by the prior arrival of a group I volley. The graphs show the size of the surface positive cortical potential elicited by stimulating the deep radial nerve at a variety of strengths. This was done; first with the dorsal columns intact, when there was a large response on group I stimulation but no increase on increasing the stimulus so as to excite group II fibres; and second after cutting the dorsal columns when the group I response was abolished but a group II response made its appearance. It seems likely that in the intact animals the group II fibres influence the cortex also, but in this particular experimental situation had their action occluded by the group I activity. (Oscarsson & Rosén, 1963, Fig. 2.)

often both be discharging tonically so that neither can really be said to precede the other in its time of arrival at, and thus influence on, any particular central station; thus their mutual interactions can proceed more fairly than when the group I volley is allowed the first word. The proprioceptive ascending systems appear ripe for study with controlled physiological inputs which should allow central integrative processes to take place more normally than they can ever do when presented with a single pseudo-synchronised afferent volley, with the inputs arriving at the cord in order of fibre size.

Relation to cortical motor output. Returning to the cortex, a brief comment may be made on the relation of the afferent input to motor function. Oscarsson, Rosén & Sulg (1966), using cats anaesthetised with pentobarbitone, found no sign that the group I activated cells sent their axons down the pyramidal tract for they could not be antidromically excited by stimulating the pyramidal tract in the upper cervical region (C2, C3). Very shortly afterwards, however, Swett & Bourassa (1967a) found pyramidal excitation with a latency of 7–11 msec on group I forelimb stimulation in cats anaesthetised with chloralose. They did this by recording extracellularly from single cells in the cortex which had been identified as pyramidal tract neurones by their antidromic response on stimulating the bulbar pyramids. In addition, on using an averaging computer, they were able to record a small multi-unit motor discharge with an electrode in the bulbar pyramid itself on stimulating group I afferents in the deep radial nerve. The reason for the absence of any group I excitation of pyramidal tract cells in Oscarsson, Rosén & Sulg's careful study is not clear: possibly they had an unrecognised sampling bias against such units; possibly they stimulated the pyramidal tract below the point of termination of the relevant fibres; possibly their preparations were too deeply anaesthetised with barbiturate, for Swett & Bourassa on using this anaesthetic appear then not to have obtained any prominent effects, though this is not made quite explicit. On the other hand, it is conceivable though unlikely that Swett & Bourassa's stimulus may have spread so as to activate other than group I fibres, for group III stimulation has been shown to elicit a pyramidal discharge in the cat under chloralose (Megirian & Troth, 1964). The role of any such short-latency pyramidal discharge remains obscure and it should be remembered that not all cortical responses seen under chloralose anaesthesia need represent a normal function, as shown by the gibe that 'chloralose is a convulsant, not an anaesthetic'. In the baboon under barbiturate, Andersen & Phillips (1971) failed to find any effect on the electrical excitability of the cortical cells which project monosynaptically to spinal motoneurones either when they stimulated the relevant group I afferent fibres or when they stimulated their cortical projection area (3a). At any rate, on the present multifarious evidence the group I projection would appear to lack the spatial specificity required to provide a simple negative feedback loop for regulating the cortical motor discharge in the way the monosynaptic stretch reflex elicited by the Ia fibres operates. However, even this idea cannot be excluded until better understanding has been obtained about the nature of the command signals issued by the motor cortex, and in particular how far they are specifically destined for individual motoneurone pools. Anyhow, as in both cat and monkey proprioceptive messages appear to reach the 'motor' areas, they may be presumed to have a part to play in motor control, particularly as they have no simple part to play in consciousness (see later).

An interesting sidelight on the role of muscle afferents in motor control has been thrown by some recent experiments of Abrahams (1970). In the whole animal, stimulation of the nerve to one of the small muscles of the neck (biventer cervicis) produces a facilitation of lumbar motoneurones, both to flexor and extensor muscles, as shown by monosynaptic testing. This action is abolished by ablating a small area of cortex just above the suprasylvian sulcus which corresponds approximately to the second area for forelimb muscle afferents in Fig. 9.2. The cervico-lumbar interaction was thus suggested to have taken place via a pathway involving this area of cortex. The region ablated, moreover, was one from which potentials had previously been recorded on stimulating the nerve to another muscle of the neck, but they had only been found on stimulation at group III strength (Landgren & Silfvenius, 1968). Group I neck afferents project weakly to the postcruciate dimple region, but ablation of this area had no lasting effect on the cervico-spinal interactions. Thus the interpretation of these effects leaves a good deal for further study, and in particular it would be interesting to know which precise groups of neck afferents are responsible for the lumbar actions (the strength of the stimuli used hitherto does not seem to have been calibrated in terms of the groups of fibre excited). It appears unlikely, however, that any great progress can be made in understanding the use to which the cortical motor mechanisms put the afferent feedback from muscles while exclusive reliance has perforce to be placed on results obtained by the stimulation of peripheral nerves with single shocks.

Cortical projection of joint afferents

Gardner was the first to show in 1952–3 that stimulation of the posterior nerve to the knee joint evoked potentials in the sensory cortex of the cat. He would appear to have used strong stimuli and to have paid no particular attention to which groups of fibres were being excited (Gardner & Noer, 1952; Gardner & Haddad, 1953).

Shortly afterwards, Skoglund (1956) graded the strength of a stimulus to the medial nerve to the knee joint and was able to evoke a cortical response with a single shock which was only just above threshold for the most excitable fibres in the nerve and so could be presumed to have its effect by exciting the afferents from the proprioceptive Golgi and Ruffini endings, rather than the smaller ones from nociceptors. A response from the afferents from the paciniform corpuscles would however also seem likely and so the precise fibres of origin of the cortical responses would not appear to be settled. Skoglund found potentials with a latency of some 10–15 msec in both cutaneous sensory areas I and II of the contralateral cortex (approximately in post-cruciate and anterior ectosylvian regions respectively), and sometimes somewhat smaller responses in area I of the ipsilateral cortex when the cat was anaesthetised with chloralose as well as with nembutal. Essentially similar responses were obtained in the contralateral hemisphere in a subsequent study in which a purely articular nerve in the forelimb was used, namely the branch from the musculo-cutaneous nerve to the elbow joint (Andersen, Korner, Landgren & Silfvenius, 1967).

As yet there appears to have been no single-unit study of the cortical response to nerve stimulation, but Mountcastle and his colleagues have extensively studied the response of single units in the cat and monkey sensory cortices and the monkey thalamus occurring on passive movements of the limbs and which were presumed to be initiated by joint receptors (Mountcastle, 1957; Mountcastle & Powell, 1959; Mountcastle, Poggio & Werner, 1963). As illustrated in Fig. 9.4 such units gave slowly adapting responses when the limb was moved, and their frequency of firing was found to alter systematically with the angle of the joint. The units were not excited by manipulation of muscles through the skin. Thus the joint mechanoreceptors are the obvious candidates for the origin of the afferent excitation; in a few cases this was confirmed by evoking the responses by poking the surface of the joint and by showing that they persisted after widespread tenotomy.

The repeated experimental testing of traditional beliefs appears to be an unfortunate necessity of life; such probing has recently thrown doubt on the classical assumption that the joint receptors project to higher levels predominantly via the dorsal columns. This

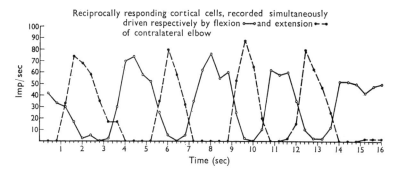

FIG. 9.4. The responses of two single cortical units in the cat which signalled the position of the elbow, presumably because they were activated by joint receptors. The two units lay close enough together for their spikes to be recorded simultaneously by the same electrode. The elbow was moved backwards and forwards by hand, except at the end of the time shown when it was held in full flexion. (Mountcastle, 1957, Fig. 5.)

was done by Burgess & Clark (1969) who found that only about 10% of knee joint afferents project upwards in this manner. Moreover, virtually all of these were afferents from paciniform corpuscles rather than those from the receptors signalling the angle of the joint. This was shown by stimulating the dorsal columns and recording from single fibres in the nerve with a microelectrode, thus permitting both the detection of any response to the stimulation and the determination of the nature of the receptor of origin of each fibre studied. Thus once again a good deal of uncertainty remains to be cleared up.

The apparent lack of access to consciousness of the group I cortical projection

The preferred view at the turn of the century, as exemplified in Sherringtons's textbook description (1900), was that the various sense endings in both muscles and joints combined in their action to subserve muscle position sense or kinesthesia. The subserving of kinesthesia is still believed to be a major function of the joint afferents, but there is now certain evidence against the muscle afferents playing any clear-cut role in this respect. Instead, they are usually seen as reserved for the control of movement and posture without producing any conscious sensation at all, in spite of demonstrably projecting to the cerebral cortex; indeed, their action there provides an interesting example of cortical activity occurring without a simple counterpart in consciousness.

The first reason for believing that muscle afferents play no in kinesthesis is a purely theoretical one and on its own is far from convincing. It is that at first sight the signals carried by the muscle afferents appear quite unsuited to provide the accurate estimation of limb position which is demonstrably present in the normal human subject (Mountcastle & Powell, 1959). However, this argument can be largely overridden by postulating that the muscle afferent signals are read by a decoding device which has access to a variety of other information in addition to that from the afferents themselves. But the postulated system then becomes so complex that it may be felt to be implausible to suggest it.

To begin with the simplest case it is now well established that the signals from the tendon organs give a measure of muscle tension and not of muscle length. Thus they at any rate cannot provide direct information about the position of a limb. Muscle length might, however, possibly be deducible from additional knowledge about the amount of motor firing, the tension–length and force–velocity properties of various muscles, and the velocity of any movement. The spindle endings do give signals related in part to the instantaneous value of the length of the muscle in which they lie so that they provide a more hopeful source of information on muscle sense. However, the signal from the primary endings appears almost unusable for this purpose because it also depends upon so many other factors. It is non-linear with regard to the amplitude of movement, it is dependent on the velocity and direction of movement and it is influenced by two separate kinds of fusimotor control system. The secondary ending, however, gives a much simpler signal and one which is fairly directly related to the length of the muscle, and which is relatively unaffected by movement; moreover, it is influenced by only a single kind of fusimotor fibre. Thus it would be fairly easy to work out the lengths of various muscles on the basis of the firing of their spindle group II afferents and a knowledge of the amount of static fusimotor discharge directed to each one of them. But there is not the slightest indication that any central structure is equipped to carry out such a computation.

Experimental evidence is naturally far to be preferred to speculative discussion and was first provided by Browne, Lee &

Ring (1954) who anaesthetised the metatarsophalangeal joint of the big toe in man by infiltrating it with procaine. They found that the subject then became completely unaware of whether or not his toe was being moved, often even until it had been displaced to one or other extreme of its normal range when other sensory clues became available; normally, the threshold for detection of movement under their particular conditions was about 5°. The procaine would, of course, have paralysed the joint and local cutaneous afferents without influencing the afferents from the appropriate muscles since these lie far away. Their results thus suggested that joint afferents could provide position sense while muscle afferents could not. However, they failed to make the latter deduction, for on quite indirect evidence they believed that during contraction the muscles acting at a joint could take over the task of supplying the sensorium with positional information. They did not, unfortunately, test this idea by seeing whether tensing the appropriate muscles could restore the position sense which had been abolished by anaesthetising the joint.

It remained for Provins (1958) to perform similar experiments on the metacarpophalangeal joint of the index finger and show that a gross impairment of position sense was produced by anaesthetising the joint, irrespective of whether or not the muscles acting at the joint were voluntarily tensed; the interference with the kinesthesis of the finger does not, however, appear to have been quite as great as that previously described for the toe. Likewise, Butt, Davies & Merton (Merton, 1964) subsequently tested position sense after producing an asphyxial block of all the nerve fibres in the hand by inflating a pressure cuff around the wrist to above the arterial pressure and waiting the appropriate time. This procedure abolished all position sense in the thumb without obviously impairing its voluntary control.

These various experiments argue first, that muscle afferents on their own are unable to mediate position sense, and second that joint afferents provide an essential contribution to kinesthesia and indeed are likely to be solely responsible. Cutaneous afferents would not yet seem to have been firmly eliminated by direct experiment, even though this should be easy to do. Again on theoretical grounds they appear to be an unsuitable source of information for kinesthesia. Moreover, the accuracy of position sense at the shoulder joint has been shown to be relatively little affected by applying sticking plaster to the overlying skin, though this might be expected to significantly change the cutaneous afferent discharges occurring at any given shoulder position (Cohen, 1958).

The belief that muscle afferents have no access to consciousness was subsequently consolidated by Gelfan & Carter (1967) who pulled upon various tendons exposed via a skin incision in the awake human subject (Flexor Digitorum Sublimis and Palmaris Longus usually tested). If they pulled upon a finger flexor tendon in the direction of contraction of the muscle, the fingers flexed as normal and their position was correctly recognised by the subject, as might be expected whatever the responsible receptor. But if the tendons were pulled in the other direction so as to stretch the muscle, while leaving the position of the fingers unaltered, the subject then had no perception of the muscle changing its length or of the fingers taking up a new position. This was so even when the tendon was rapidly pulled by an amount corresponding approximately to the whole of its normal range of movement and which should have excited all three types of stretch receptor (Ia, Ib, II). There were, however, sometimes various somewhat indefinite or somewhat painful sensations localised to the skin over the muscles or around the skin incision required to expose the tendons. Direct squeezing of the belly of the muscles through the skin produced the normal localised subjective sensations. Thus a muscle could be stretched over the whole of its physiological range without producing any clear kinesthetic sensation and so Gelfan & Carter concluded that 'there is no muscle sense in man', meaning by this that there is no conscious awareness of limb position as a result of muscle afferent discharges.

Brindley & Merton (1960) had earlier performed a similar experiment on the extrinsic eye muscles, which in man possess a rich complement of spindles. After anaesthetising the conjunctiva and occluding vision with an opaque contact lens, to eliminate the normal sensory clues, they were able to seize the sclera with toothed forceps and move the eyeball around without producing any subjective awareness of the movement. In addition, if the subject tried to move his eyes while they were both held he was quite unaware that he had failed to do so, again demonstrating that he had received no direct sensory clues from his eye muscles to show him in which direction his eyes were pointing. Thus, whatever else they may do, muscle spindles and Golgi tendon organs would appear to have no part to play in the development of our immediate conscious awareness of the position of different parts of our body. This is not to deny, however, that they may not play some part in the development of yet more elaborate perceptions. For example, we can gauge the stiffness of a spring by deforming it or the weight of an object by handling it. This is presumably done by assessing the effectiveness of the motor commands on which our manipulation of the objects depends, and thus must be based on some sort of feedback mechanism. It is still perhaps premature to deny muscle afferents a role in all such tasks, for an out-of-balance motor-sensory signal might be what was transmitted to the 'sensorium' rather than a simple afferent response.

Experiments performed since the above went to press have fortified the view that under appropriate conditions spindle afferent discharges can influence perception. Vibration of the tendon of the biceps or of the triceps muscle in the normal human subject has been found to produce a systematic mis-judgement of the angle at the elbow, which under certain circumstances when the muscle is contracting may be as great as 40° (Goodwin, McCloskey & Matthews, 1972). Under all the conditions so far studied the arm was felt to be in the position it would have been if the vibrated muscle had been more stretched than it actually was. This is what would be experienced if the vibration-induced Ia discharges were to be interpreted by the sensorium as due to a stretch of the muscle. In addition, it is interesting that Paillard & Brouchon (1968) found that position sense is more accurate when a limb moves actively than when it is passively positioned. But it remains unknown how far this latter effect depends upon peripheral feedback from the muscle receptors, and how far upon the sensory centres being informed via recurrent pathways of the despatch of command signals from the higher motor centres.

Lack of arousal by group I volleys in animals. In animals also it has proved possible to show that group I afferents do not contribute to 'consciousness'. This has been done by stimulating a muscle nerve in the awake animal with a previously implanted electrode and demonstrating that a stimulus which excites only the group I fibres produces no change in the behaviour of the animal or alteration in its electroencephalogram (Pompeiano &

Swett, 1962; Giaquinto, Pompeiano & Swett, 1963); this is illustrated in Fig. 9.5. Both low- and high-frequency repetitive stimuli

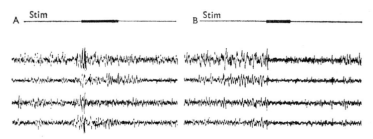

FIG. 9.5. The ineffectiveness of group I stimulation in desynchronising the electroencephalogram. A, stimulation of the right deep radial nerve at 200/sec with shocks exciting the majority of group I afferent fibres (1·91 × threshold for period indicated above) failed to produce desynchronisation; B, a stronger stimulus does so. The cat was unanaesthetised but lightly asleep. The EEG records are from above downwards, parieto-temporal and temporo-occipital for the left and right sides in turn. (The stimulus in B was only 1·93 × threshold and it probably produced its action by exciting non-spindle group II fibres. The largest EEG waves are about 200 µV total extent; time scale given by second period of stimulation which lasted 2 sec, Giaquinto, Pompeiano & Swett, 1963, Fig. 3.)

were applied to the central end of the severed nerve (4 to 100/sec to hamstring or deep radial nerves) and the afferent volley was monitored shortly afterwards by anaesthetising the animal and exposing the brachial plexus or lumbar dorsal roots. Group III stimulation readily produced 'arousal' of the animal. This was recognised by observing its behaviour and by the EEG showing desynchronisation, that is the replacement of large slowish waves by very small higher-frequency ones. 'Arousal' was more readily produced when the animal was initially awake, and the frequency of stimulation was high, but even under the most favourable conditions there was no sign of it being produced by maximal group I volleys.

Subsequently, Swett & Bourassa (1967b) found it impossible to condition a cat to respond by pressing a bar to group I stimulation at 100/sec by electrodes implanted on the hamstring or the deep radial nerves, even though the stimulation could be shown to produce an evoked potential in the cortex. The conditioned response, moreover, could be easily produced on stimulating cutaneous afferents, or muscle afferents with a higher electrical threshold than the group I fibres. They suggested that spindle group II fibres were also inadequate as a conditioning stimulus since group II stimulation of the hamstring nerve was ineffective in this respect. As group III hamstring stimulation could elicit the conditioned response, they attributed the responses they obtained on group II strength stimulation of the deep radial nerve to some other type of group II fibre, possibly joint afferents. This also was the view of Giaquinto, Pompeiano & Swett (1963) on finding that group II stimulation of the deep radial nerve often produced arousal, whereas that of the hamstring nerve only did so as it approached group III strength.

More recently, the effect of group I stimulation was tested in the acute thalamic preparation which has a propensity to go into sham rage on weak peripheral stimulation and so was felt to provide a sensitive indicator of any arousal produced by group I action (Malliani, Carli, Mancia & Zanchetti, 1968). Repetitive stimulation of the hamstring nerve was then regularly found to produce effects on blood pressure and respiration provided that the majority of the group I fibres were activated; such effects were never found with stimuli which were below 1·35 times the group I threshold. Unfortunately, however, the experiments performed so far have been restricted to electrical stimulation and so cannot guarantee that these arousal actions of group I volleys were genuinely due to afferents from stretch receptors, rather than to any few afferents from pressure–pain receptors which happened to be of group I diameter and which were able to manifest themselves because of the heightened excitability of the preparation. This latter possibility would appear to be the most probable interpretation of the findings.

The cerebellar projections of signals from the muscle afferents

The directness of their projection and the large size of many of their fibres made the dorsal and ventral spino-cerebellar tracts well known to the classical anatomists. It has thus long been accepted that the cerebellum has a need for proprioceptive information in regulating muscle contraction. The effects of its damage show the great importance of the cerebellum in motor regulation, but precisely what it does and how it does it remains almost entirely mysterious. Thus it is hardly surprising that knowledge is almost totally lacking about the use to which the cerebellum puts the information that it receives from the muscle afferents. At present, experimental analysis is largely restricted to the study of the type of message which is being transmitted along the various spino-cerebellar pathways, and even these are proving fairly hard to understand in their entirety. It is droll to note that if investigation were to have been restricted to the recording of evoked potentials the recognition of the importance of the spino-cerebellar tracts would probably have been delayed, for a single group I volley in a peripheral nerve elicits a rather small change of potential on the cerebellar surface in comparison with that evoked by stimulation of cutaneous nerves.

The large size of many of the spino-cerebellar fibres makes recording of their discharges relatively easy, whether by a micro-electrode inserted into a fibre itself as it runs in the appropriate tract, or with more difficulty into a cell body in the grey matter. In both cases stimulation of the cerebellar surface can be used to prove that the unit studied is indeed a spino-cerebellar one for it can then be activated antidromically. Thus starting in 1956 with the paper by Laporte, Lundberg & Oscarsson there has been a continuing flood of largely Scandinavian work describing how single units in the spino-cerebellar tracts respond to a variety of peripheral stimuli, including both electrical stimulation of nerves and more physiological stimuli applied to muscle or skin. It seems redundant to give all this important work the attention it deserves for little has changed since it was reviewed in detail by Oscarsson (1965, 1967) who has been personally involved in it from the very beginning. A brief synopsis of some of the major findings may however currently prove helpful, but no attempt will be made to give detailed reference to the original on matters to be found in Oscarsson's discussion.

After entering the spinal cord the muscle afferent fibres from the hindlimb ascend a short distance in the dorsal columns and then feed activity into the separate dorsal and the ventral spino-cerebellar tracts (abbreviated DSCT and VSCT respectively). These differ from each other in a number of ways, both physiologically and anatomically. Both tracts have their cell bodies on the side of the spinal cord on which they lie, but they differ in that the DSCT terminates almost entirely on the ipsilateral side of the cerebellum, whereas the VSCT terminates largely contra-laterally; its fibres cross the spinal cord almost immediately after their origin. Each tract has its distinctive region of termination and their individual fibres differ also in the size of the area over which their terminations are spread. Fibres from the DSCT terminate in a highly circumscribed region (? around a millimetre), whereas those from the VSCT cover a much larger area ('several square mm', in the extreme about 25 mm²); this is based on deter-mining the area from which individual fibres may be excited on stimulating the cerebellar surface and so takes no account of what happens in the depth of the folia. Collaterals from the fibres of either tract may well also terminate in the deep cerebellar nuclei or even outside the cerebellum altogether. The VSCT appears to consist entirely of large fibres (conduction velocity 70–120 m/sec, equivalent to 11–20 μm diameter), whereas the DSCT contains small fibres as well as very large ones (conduction velocity range at least 30–110 m/sec, equivalent to 5–18 μm). The DSCT is the simpler to understand physiologically, as the discharges of individual fibres depend upon a more restricted afferent input, both with regard to the region influenced and the type of fibre activated.

The discrete monosynaptic activation of various subdivisions of the dorsal spino-cerebellar tract. Different cells of the DSCT respond to different kinds of peripheral stimuli. The first subdivision which may be made is into units which respond to proprioceptive stimulation and those which respond to cutaneous stimulation. There appears to be little or no overlap between these two groups. The cutaneous DSCT units need not detain us here. Of the proprioceptive units, many are activated monosynaptically on stimulating muscle nerves at a strength which would excite only group I fibres. On the usual basis of the grading of stimulus strength these group I activated DSCT cells may be further sub-divided into those activated by Ia fibres and those activated by Ib fibres respectively. On applying physiological stimuli (muscle stretch, muscle contraction) and observing the discharge of impulses in DSCT fibres these two categories of unit appear to be quite distinct, and a group I activated DSCT unit behaves as if it were connected either to Ia fibres or to Ib fibres but not to both. This is also the usual finding on recording intracellularly and looking for the appearance of an EPSP on nerve stimulation (Eccles, Oscarsson & Willis, 1961). Intracellular recording provides the more sensitive method for detecting weak synaptic connections for they do not have to be potent enough to be able to make the cell fire an impulse. A few units then appear to be connected to both Ia and Ib fibres, but it may be questioned whether the nerve stimulation actually provides a sufficiently selective activation of the two kinds of afferent fibre for such a conclusion to be considered secure. This is particularly so because cells excited by Ia fibres are commonly found also to be excited by group II fibres of the same nerve, and some group II fibres are probably recruited when the stimulus strength is increased so as to recruit the Ib fibres.

When group II convergence occurs it may be sufficiently powerful for group I plus II stimulation to cause a DSCT fibre to fire a larger number of spikes than it does in response to group I stimulation alone. The latency for the superadded group II excitation is sufficiently short to suggest that their action is also mediated monosynaptically and this is confirmed by the intracellular recording of EPSPs. This convergence of group Ia and II excitation onto the same DSCT cells provides a clear-cut example of the two kinds of fibre having a similar central action. In this case the similarity perhaps has the opportunity of manifesting itself in response to electrical stimulation of muscle nerves because, unlike the arrangement in the stretch reflex, the genuine flexor reflex afferents of group II diameter are probably not wired up so as to overwhelm the action of the spindle group II afferents on the DSCT cells. There would also appear to be a certain number of DSCT cells which receive group II excitation without receiving significant group I excitation, for Jansen & Rudjord (1965b) found that on stretching a muscle some units mirrored the dynamic responsiveness of the secondary rather than of the primary spindle endings; they did not, however, record intracellularly to detect any weak group I effects. When the action of a range of muscle nerves is tested, any particular DSCT unit is usually found to receive monosynaptic excitation solely from a single muscle. Thus, in so far as excitation is concerned, the discharge of a single DSCT fibre serves to show what is happening in a particular muscle, and moreover as seen either by spindle endings or by tendon endings.

It may next be mentioned that, unlike motoneurones, DSCT

cells commonly fire more than one spike when presented with a more or less synchronous presynaptic input volley. Again unlike motoneurones, DSCT cells are able to respond securely to every one of a repetitive input for frequencies up to several hundred per second. This presumably helps them to signal rapid events the more fully and effectively. VSCT neurones share these properties and the motoneurone would appear to be the atypical nerve cell and to have had its range of firing frequencies unusually restricted in order to fit in with the requirements of skeletal muscle.

Variability of discharge introduced by synaptic transmission. One interesting difference between the DSCT discharges and those of the primary afferents eliciting them lies in the degree of regularity of the spike trains fired by individual units. In the de-efferented preparation the Ia discharge is rather regular. In contrast, as first noted by Jansen, Nicolaysen & Rudjord (1966*a*,*b*), the discharge of the DSCT neurones excited by the self-same afferents is highly irregular, as illustrated in Fig. 9.6. The coefficient of variation of the interspike intervals of the two types of discharge averages

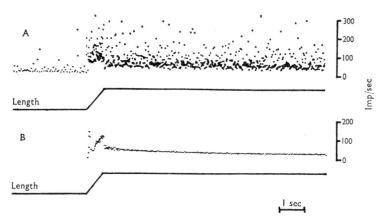

FIG. 9.6. The increase in the variability of nervous discharge introduced by synaptic transmission from Ia fibres to a DSCT neurone. Above, the 'instantaneous' frequency of a Ia activated DSCT fibre on stretching the triceps surae 15 mm. Below, the typical response of a Ia fibre to similar stretching. Both records taken in the cat with fusimotor action eliminated by section of the ventral roots. (Jansen, Nicolaysen & Rudjord, 1966*b*, Fig. 1.)

RM

about 0·06 and 0·4 respectively, showing that synaptic transmission increased the variability nearly sevenfold.

Detailed analysis shows that the greater variability of the DSCT discharges can be accounted for by the 'beating' of a comparatively small number of regular Ia trains impinging upon a single DSCT neurone so that the neurone usually fires only when several Ia impulses arrive at nearly the same time (Walløe, Jansen & Nygaard, 1969). A particular feature which pinpointed this explanation was the finding that the value of successive DSCT intervals showed a high degree of negative correlation (i.e. long intervals followed by short intervals and vice versa); the value of the first serial correlation coefficient was often around − 0·6. This could not be reproduced by allowing the synaptic input to consist of a single non-rhythmic spike-train which had the same interval histogram as the aggregate of the Ia discharges, but which took no account of the correlations produced by their regular 'beatings'. Computer simulation showed that the observed patterns of variability would arise if about 15 Ia fibres supplied each neurone, and if the synchronous arrival of impulses in about 3 of them were enough to fire the neurone. Subsequent intracellular recording showed that these values were indeed approximately correct (Eide, Fedina, Jansen, Lundberg & Vyklický, 1969).

The increased variability in the DSCT neurone as opposed to the Ia fibre would seem to imply a considerable decrease in the accuracy with which it can signal what is happening in the muscle. Precise determination of such 'information loss' on synaptic transmission is, however, far from easy but Walløe (1970a,b) has provided estimates for certain rigidly defined conditions. So far these estimates have been based on the behaviour of the de-efferented spindle. Under normal conditions the spindle will always discharge appreciably less regularly, and then the contrast with the DSCT discharge would probably be less extreme; because of its origin the variability of the DSCT discharges might be expected to be relatively little greater when initiated by irregular Ia discharges, but the matter has yet to be tested. It would appear that a price has to be paid for the advantages of having a synaptic relay on an ascending afferent pathway. The abstraction of certain qualitative features of the stimulus and the opportunity for supraspinal control have to be paid for by a loss in the fidelity with which certain quantitative aspects of the stimulus are signalled to higher centres.

Comparison of the ventral spino-cerebellar tract with the dorsal tract, particularly with regard to the complexity of their organisation. The cells in the ventral spino-cerebellar tract are also mono-synaptically activated by group I afferents, but in this case the excitation is almost exclusively from Ib afferents; Ia fibres, certainly, and spindle group II fibres, probably, appear to make so rare a contribution as to be physiologically insignificant ('functional aberration'). However, unlike DSCT cells, individual VSCT cells are regularly excited by the group I afferents from a number of widely separated muscles (for example, knee, ankle and toe extensors), though such convergence appears to be absent for antagonist muscles acting at the same joint. Thus there would appear to be little possibility of the discharge of any particular single VSCT unit preserving information about what is happening in an individual muscle. Moreover, whereas stretch of a single muscle may be adequate to evoke a discharge in a DSCT fibre, the simultaneous contraction of several muscles is usually required to persuade a VSCT cell to fire, suggesting that any given unit is signalling the stage of a movement (Oscarsson, 1965) rather than the contraction of a particular muscle. These statements, however, all appertain to the VSCT largely as it has been studied by Oscarsson. More recently, certain 'spinal border cells' have been shown to project to the cerebellum along with the VSCT and so must be considered to belong to it. Yet intracellular recording from these cells has shown that many of them may be mono-synaptically excited by Ia fibres rather than by the usual Ib fibres. On demonstrating such a connection Burke, Lundberg & Weight (1968, 1971) concluded that the 'VSCT has many different subdivisions'.

All that has been said so far relates to monosynaptic excitation, but both the DSCT and the VSCT relays may also be influenced by a number of other inputs. Individual DSCT neurones may be inhibited by proprioceptive stimuli applied to various muscles other than the one whose afferents monosynaptically excite it; sometimes the inhibition is mediated by Ia fibres and sometimes by Ib fibres, and is often weak. In addition, Ib fibres and 'flexor reflex afferents' may produce a presynaptic inhibition of both Ia and Ib fibres at their termination on the DSCT neurones. It may be noted that the pattern of this action is different from that found on the same kinds of fibre when they are terminating elsewhere (Jankowska, Jukes & Lund, 1965). Presumably the space constant of the afferent fibres is short enough to allow their different terminals to be depolarised to varying degrees, and in addition any localised change in conductance of the presynaptic fibre will have a predominantly local effect in reducing the size of the presynaptic spike.

Group I activated DSCT cells may also be inhibited, as shown by the appearance of an IPSP, on repetitive stimulation of the contralateral motor cortex. Such stimulation may also produce a presynaptic inhibition of the group I terminals ending on the DSCT neurones (Hongo & Okada, 1967; Hongo, Okada & Sato, 1967). Both types of effect have been shown to be mediated by the pyramidal tract. Their appreciable latency and considerable duration of action indicate that interneurones are involved. A few DSCT units may be excited on pyramidal stimulation, but with a shorter latency than that with which they are inhibited by the same stimulation.

All this makes things very hard to understand. In discussing the behaviour of DSCT units on stretching a pair of muscles, one excitatory and the other inhibitory, Jansen, Nicolaysen & Walløe (1967) said 'This means that the signals mediated by the DSCT Ia units are not simply functions of length and rate of change of length of the appropriate muscle, but are instead rather more complicated functions of length, velocity and tension in a number of interrelated muscles. Most appropriately the DSCT signals should probably be described in relation to limb position, movement, and degree of contraction in the various muscles. A very extensive piece of work remains before the full complexity of the situation has been revealed'. In other words, we have not yet really understood the language in which the DSCT is speaking to the cerebellum. The discharge in individual DSCT units has been recoded by the synaptic transfer so that it means something rather different from the very similar discharges occurring in the primary afferent fibres, and we have not yet grasped the essential difference between them. None the less, it remains a most striking and important finding that when the input is restricted to that from a single muscle the discharge of a DSCT fibre is remarkably like that of whichever of the Ia, Ib or II fibres is predominantly feeding it.

The interactions taking place on the VSCT neurones appear to be altogether more complex than are those occurring on the DSCT neurones. To begin with, as already mentioned, the group Ib excitatory input always comes from a number of well separated muscles. Next, the VSCT neurones may be inhibited by group I afferents of yet other muscles, sometimes by Ia fibres and sometimes by Ib fibres. Moreover, individual cells of the 'spinal border' contribution to the VSCT have recently been shown to be disynaptically inhibited by the self-same group I fibres that excite them monosynaptically (Lundberg & Weight, 1971). More striking still are the powerful effects of cutaneous stimulation which may either excite or inhibit any particular VSCT neurone depending upon the region of skin stimulated. Moreover, the precise extent of the receptive field for eliciting these different effects varies with the central state of the preparation. The inhibitory effects are particularly widespread and may often be produced from the contralateral hindlimb. All this has been found using physiological stimulation, as well as with electrical stimuli to nerves which were of sufficient strength to excite the flexor reflex afferents. Thus in the VSCT, unlike the DSCT, proprioceptive and cutaneous information would appear to have become mixed up. In addition, on stimulating various other afferent fibres there is sometimes a weak presynaptic inhibition of the Ib fibres directly impinging on the VSCT neurones. Next, the VSCT neurones are greatly influenced by descending fibres, and at least three different systems seem to be involved, all acting via interneurones. One pathway produces excitation of VSCT neurones, one produces inhibition, and another one or more pathways inhibit the interneurones lying on both the excitatory and the inhibitory pathways from flexor reflex afferents to the VSCT cells; these latter control mechanisms possibly serve to regulate the relative preponderence of the cutaneous and the proprioceptive inputs to the VSCT cells. As with their peripheral inputs, individual 'spinal border' VSCT cells would appear commonly to receive both excitatory and inhibitory influences from each one of their descending inputs (Lundberg & Weight, 1971).

It seems quite impossible to hope to be able to decide from all this just what the VSCT is trying to tell the cerebellum.

Oscarsson (1965) was forced into suggesting that the discharges are somehow appropriately organised so as to be 'used in postural adjustments including the whole body and the limbs bilaterally', which is clearly to leave the matter largely open for subsequent more detailed speculation. However, these present difficulties in trying to form a general view of function should not be allowed to obscure the great extent to which our understanding has advanced as a result of the last 15 years of patient and thorough electrophysiological work. The uncovering of so much complexity is probably the inevitable result of electrophysiological methods being progressively applied to problems which are truly physiological rather than largely anatomical.

Other ascending spinal tracts influencing the cerebellum. The muscle afferents of the forelimb do not make use of the DSCT and VSCT to transmit their signals upwards to the cerebellum. Instead they feed into two other tracts which appear to be functionally similar to the DSCT and the VSCT, even though they take a rather different course to the cerebellum. The homologue of the DSCT is the cuneo-cerebellar tract and that of the VSCT is the-rostral spino-cerebellar tract. In so far as it has been investigated the cuneo-cerebellar tract seems closely similar to the DSCT, but the rostral spino-cerebellar tract shows certain differences from the VSCT. To begin with, unlike the VSCT, the rostral tract ascends on the same side of the spinal cord as that on which its cell bodies lie, and its termination in the cerebellum is predominantly ipsilateral, though like the VSCT it has an appreciable projection to the less preferred side of the cerebellum. In addition, the rostral tract lacks the widespread inhibitory effects from cutaneous afferents which are found for the VSCT, and receives somewhat more marked excitatory effects. The similarity between the rostral tract and the VSCT lies largely in that both receive monosynaptic excitation from the group I fibres of an appreciable number of muscles and in both cases the Ib fibres appear to be those that are chiefly responsible. It will be interesting to have the rostral tract investigated in yet more detail. Further comparison with the VSCT may help to demonstrate which of the properties of the two tracts are fundamental to their main job and which of them are to some extent incidental.

All the four tracts which have just been discussed terminate in the cerebellar cortex as mossy fibres. The cortex also receives the climbing fibres from the inferior olive. These are particularly potent in exciting the Purkinje cells, so considerable interest attaches to their activation by peripheral afferent inputs. To date, five routes have been described whereby climbing fibres may be brought to discharge following stimulation of a peripheral nerve. Each of them would appear to transmit a different sort of message for they are all activated by different ranges of stimuli (Larson, Miller & Oscarsson, 1969). Many of these pathways, however, have so far only been demonstrated to be active when the peripheral stimulus is sufficiently strong to activate the majority of the group III fibres in the nerve tested; physiological stimuli applied to skin or muscle have been largely ineffective. It is thus a little hard to assess how far these various pathways have a part to play in transmitting signals related to the activity of stretch receptors in muscle; the failure to see responses with weak stimulation might merely be a result of an inadequate central facilitation. However, the classical spino-olivary tract which runs on the ventral surface of the spinal cord does seem to be regularly excited by group II volleys from a variety of hindlimb nerves, and also sometimes by group I volleys—particularly from the quadriceps nerve (Armstrong, Eccles, Harvey & Matthews, 1968; Oscarsson, 1968). Brief trains of stimuli were required to elicit these responses and it is uncertain just which kind of afferent fibre was responsible, though spindle afferents seem a definite possibility. Stimulating the nerve to the knee joint, however, produces powerful olivary excitation, so some of the effects from muscle nerves may have depended upon their 'contamination' by joint afferents. In this respect, it is interesting that the afferents from the main joint receptors do not seem to project into the DSCT and may therefore perhaps be especially dependent upon the olivary route to the cerebellum. Recording from single olivary neurones showed that they could usually be influenced via the ventral tract by each one of the muscle or cutaneous nerves tested, including those from more than one limb, thus indicating a widespread convergence of action.

It appears that, as with the VSCT, the individual spino-olivary fibre is transmitting a message which is far too complicated for us yet to be able to grasp its full significance. Conditioned by knowledge of the somato-sensory system one tends to assume that any ascending tract which can be activated by a peripheral stimulus is primarily concerned with forwarding a message from the periphery, albeit in a suitably concise form. However, the higher motor centres probably also require to be informed about how the lower motor centres are getting on, and for this would require specialised information about the degree of excitation in various pools of interneurones. The activity of those spinal interneurones that are concerned with motor control seems likely to be influenced by a variety of descending and afferent inputs, and except under artificial conditions no one of these inputs alone would decide their behaviour; an ascending signal related to interneuronal activity would thus be inevitably complex. Put another way, some ascending messages may well show the state of, and the error signals occurring within, various servo-loops which lie partly in the spinal cord and partly at the periphery; this might, for example, help the higher centres to issue suitable command messages or appropriately to alter the value of various parameters of the loops (most simply their gain).

There seems little hope of understanding the messages being sent up and down various motor and 'proprioceptive' pathways until the signals can be listened in to under more or less normal conditions, such as in the conscious animal doing something, when they could perhaps be related to what is going on. Even then the messages might only be recognisable for what they were by an observer who had already guessed the right kind of thing to look for. Things are not as likely to proceed as smoothly as they have with the somato-sensory system, where no particular activity is often required of the animal and where attention has been profitably directed towards things which are known to have physiological meaning because of introspection and prior psychophysical studies.

The central control of fusimotor neurones

Methods of study. The central nervous system, including its higher centres, has of course a dual relation with the muscle afferents. In addition to being informed by them about the state of the muscles it also regulates what it receives from them by using the fusimotor fibres to modulate the responsiveness of the muscle spindles. Thus in thinking about the functional role of muscle afferents it is necessary to enquire into the central mechanisms involved in fusimotor regulation, and this is bound up with the whole problem of central motor control. The little that has so far been found out has, as usual, been determined by the available techniques. The restricted value of ablation and stimulation as tools for the study of central motor action does not merit present discussion. It does seem appropriate to discuss the problems which are specifically involved in recognising that central stimulation or ablation has had a fusimotor action.

The activity of fusimotor neurones has been studied in two main ways, each with its own particular advantages. The most direct method was introduced by Hunt (1951) and is simply the recording of the discharge of functionally single fusimotor fibres from ventral root or muscle nerve filaments. The identification of a single unit as a γ motor fibre rather than an α motor fibre can usually only be done with certainty by measuring its conduction velocity, though if the unit which is functionally single consists of an anatomically single fibre then equal certainty can be achieved by measuring its diameter. A less reliable method is to compare the sizes of the various spikes recorded in a multi-fibre preparation and allocate the large ones to α fibres and the small ones to γ fibres. This is perfectly acceptable when the filament recorded from is a naturally occurring one, but becomes hazardous when the filament studied has been split off a larger one by dissection in order to decrease the number of responding units. An injured large fibre may then give a smaller spike than an uninjured small fibre. A complementary procedure is to apply a local anaesthetic to the nerve trunk some way away from the recording site and assume that it blocks small fibres before large ones; it then no longer matters if the fibre has been slightly injured at the recording site.

Because of the smallness of their spikes, such recordings of γ efferent activity have usually been made monophasically from the cut end of a filament, for this improves the signal-to-noise ratio. But if a sufficiently fine nerve is used, such as that to the inter-transverse muscles of the rats tail studied by Steg (1964), then satisfactory diphasic records may be obtainable from the nerve while it remains intact. This has the advantage of permitting the simultaneous recording of afferent and efferent spikes, which are distinguishable by the direction of their initial deflection, and does not entail interrupting the reflex arc. Recording with a microelectrode from the nerve trunk offers similar advantages, but has as yet not been done for the γ efferents, though it has been achieved for spindle afferent fibres in man (Vallbo, 1970).

In the earlier work, because of the greater ease of their isolation, γ efferents were often isolated from ventral root filaments rather than from muscle nerves. But with root recording it is usually difficult to determine the conduction velocity of the fibres studied and thereby reliably classify them into a and γ fibres. In addition, their muscle of destination is usually unknown so that it often becomes rather difficult to draw any very specific conclusions from the point of view of central control. Ventral root recordings have therefore now largely been supplanted by those taken from muscle nerve filaments where these objections do not apply. Samples of γ efferent fibres, wherever isolated, often tend to be biassed in favour of those which are discharging spontaneously. This can be circumvented by initially seeking the fibres for isolation on the basis of their slowness of conduction, as may be done by looking for delayed spikes in nerve filaments on stimulating ventral roots, which of course have to be left intact. The isolation of single units in this way may be simplified by severing a large part of the ventral root outflow and stimulating the remainder, thereby restricting study to only a proportion of fibres in the nerve. Recordings may also be made from the soma of γ motoneurones with microelectrodes inserted into the cord. This mostly yields extracellular recordings as the γ neurones are too small to readily withstand penetration by the electrode; even extracellular records may be hard to come by. The great advantage of recording directly from γ fibres or γ motoneurones is that it permits the exact determination of latencies of response and absolute frequencies of firing; and, moreover, it is immaterial whether or not some a motor fibres of the same muscle are simultaneously excited.

The second method of studying the activity of γ motoneurones is indirect and consists of recording the discharge of a muscle spindle afferent from a dorsal root filament, while leaving the ventral roots and muscle nerve intact. At the same time a sensitive myograph is used to record the tension in the muscle in which the spindle studied has been shown to lie. Any change in spindle responsiveness that occurs in the absence of a contraction of the main muscle may be confidently ascribed to a change in the discharge of specific fusimotor neurones. The classical criterion for recognising fusimotor activation on central stimulation is simply to observe an increase in the discharge of the ending above its pre-existing value which occurs in the absence of contraction and while the length of the muscle remains constant. The existence of a tonic fusimotor discharge may be recognised and measured by the decrease of afferent discharge which occurs on interrupting the efferent pathway to the spindle by cutting the ventral roots or by curarising the preparation. Such abolition of pre-existing fusi-motor activity also produces a regularisation of the afferent dis-charge. Indeed, any gross irregularity in the discharge of spindle afferents when the ventral roots are intact and the muscle is not contracting provides a sure sign of fusimotor activity without the need for severing the roots; though de-efferentation is still required to assess its degree.

It should be remembered, however, that because of certain prolonged mechanical changes in the intrafusal fibres following their activation (p. 284) the frequency of discharge of a primary ending may remain raised for some time after a period of intense fusimotor activity. Hence measurement of the afferent firing occur-ring after a period of central stimulation need not accurately reflect the time-course of any fusimotor after-discharge. Afferent record-ing is moreover an unreliable way of attempting the precise timing of central latencies; this is because there is an inevitable uncer-tainty about the value of the delay in the muscle spindle itself, since there is a variable delay between the beginning of an intra-fusal contraction and the resulting afferent excitation.

Afferent recording is also unusable, at any rate in its theoreti-cally purest form, in order to obtain information about the dis-charge of mixed skeleto-fusimotor fibres. Changes in afferent discharge are then inevitably accompanied by a concomitant extra-fusal contraction making it difficult to guarantee that the afferent response is genuinely due to fusimotor action, rather than to a mechanical action on the spindle of the contracting extrafusal fibres. If desired, however, it is usually possible to eliminate the extrafusal contraction selectively by curarising the preparation just sufficiently to block the extrafusal end-plates; this usually leaves the intrafusal end-plates transmitting tolerably. The same problem of a concomitant extrafusal contraction also arises when the central action investigated leads to a simultaneous discharge of both α and γ motoneurones, as happens in the extreme on stimulating a tract which monosynaptically excites both kinds of neurone; this has been suggested to be the action of the vestibulospinal tract.

In such cases it is a mistake to restrict one's attention to proving the occurrence of a genuine fusimotor action by the use of selectively curarised preparations. It is of equal interest to determine just how effectively the fusimotor action can overcome the unloading produced by the concomitant extrafusal contraction. Indeed, if the spindle afferent discharge still increases when muscle shortening is allowed, as well as under strictly isometric conditions, the fusimotor action is shown to be of such power that it may be judged to be playing a physiologically significant part in reflexly assisting the contraction via the monosynaptic reflex. The finding of spindle slowing during muscle contraction is also of interest in this respect, but has no value for attempting to decide whether or not a fusimotor inhibition occurs concurrently with an α excitation; the extreme sensitivity of spindle afferents to unloading, particularly of the primaries, makes it virtually impossible to exclude simple mechanical interaction as the cause of any such slowing.

Distinguishing between static and dynamic fusimotor activation

Originally, the recording of afferent rather than efferent discharges was sometimes chosen for studying fusimotor activity because it is easier to isolate large spindle afferents in the dorsal roots rather than small γ efferents in the muscle nerve. After the foregoing recital of the shortcomings of afferent recording as a way of studying fusimotor activity the method might be thought to be obsolete and to continue to find favour merely with those who wished to avoid the full rigours of experimentation. This is not so, for it can provide information that is still unobtainable by the apparently more direct recording of efferent discharges. In the first place, the afferent recording shows the combined action of several γ efferents on a sensory ending. This is of more physiological interest in relation to the 'servo theory' of motor control than is a simple description of the discharges in individual fusimotor fibres. In addition, afferent recording is of crucial importance for determining whether a given fusimotor effect depends primarily upon static or upon dynamic fusimotor action. This

cannot be settled by measuring the conduction velocity of individual γ efferents for the two kinds of fusimotor fibre show no
absolute difference in this respect. With the progress of understanding, however, it is to be hoped that the two kinds of γ efferent
will become recognisable by their particular patterns of behaviour;
this is already so in the special case of the spinal preparation in
which any fusimotor fibre which is found to be discharging spontaneously may be presumed to be a dynamic fibre (see later). On
the basis of afferent recording, however, several criteria are available for distinguishing between static and dynamic actions, even
though they both produce the classical sign of fusimotor activity,
namely an increase in spindle primary firing accompanied by an
irregularity of discharge. The methods are as follows:

1. Any centrally elicitable fusimotor action which can be shown
to influence the secondary endings of the spindle as well as the
primary endings is guaranteed to have been mediated at least
partly by the static fusimotor neurones, since these are the only
ones which can influence the secondary endings. Thus any fusimotor induced increase in secondary firing demonstrates static
excitation, and conversely any decrease demonstrates static inhibition; moreover, an irregularity of secondary discharge betokens a
tonic static firing. The recording from secondary endings thus
possesses a unique value for determining whether static fusimotor
activity changes, for this can be decided upon irrespective of whether
or not there is a concomitant change in dynamic fusimotor activity.

2. Static fusimotor activity may be assessed with rather less
certainty by observing the behaviour of the primary ending on
releasing a stretch of large amplitude. In the absence of all fusimotor activity the ending stops firing abruptly at the beginning of
the release. Static fusimotor activity readily overcomes such
depression so that the ending then fires throughout the release,
albeit at a lower frequency than during stretching. Dynamic fusimotor action is very much less powerful in this respect, and even
when effective cannot prevent an abrupt fall in discharge at the
beginning of the release. Thus a smooth decrease in primary
firing on release can be taken to indicate an appreciable firing of
static fusimotor fibres.

3. Static fusimotor activity can further be shown by observing
a reduction in the dynamic sensitivity of a primary ending occurring at the same time as an increase in its static firing. A tonic static

discharge is demonstrated by finding more static discharge but less dynamic sensitivity for an ending than it shows when rendered 'passive' by sectioning the ventral roots or by curarisation of sufficient degree to block intrafusal transmission.

4. Dynamic fusimotor activity is shown by an increase of the dynamic sensitivity of the primary above its pre-existing level that occurs at the same time as an increase in static firing. Tonic dynamic activity is recognisable by the same criteria on comparing the behaviour of the ending at any time with its 'passive' behaviour observed after cutting the ventral roots.

The dynamic sensitivity of the primary ending may be assessed in several different ways which are all more or less equivalent. The longest-established method is to record the response of the primary ending to a stretch of the muscle of large amplitude and applied at a constant velocity. The 'dynamic index' may then be measured as was originally done to define the two kinds of fusimotor fibre (dynamic index = decrease in the discharge occurring in the first 0·5 sec of completion of stretching). Subsequently, sinusoidal stretching of the muscle at around 1 Hz has been found a convenient way of expeditiously testing the endings, as may be seen in Fig. 9.7. Since the stretching and releasing alternate so rapidly this provides a more nearly continuous assessment of fusimotor activity than the testing of the behaviour of the ending with isolated ramp stretches. The simplest method of testing dynamic sensitivity avoids the need for any controlled device for stretching the muscle. It simply consists of making the muscle contract by stimulating its nerve and observing the behaviour of the primary ending on the falling phase of the twitch. The contraction first unloads the spindle thus silencing it, and then rapidly re-extends it again to produce a burst of impulses on the falling phase of the twitch. An increase in dynamic responsiveness is shown by an enhancement of this burst, as shown in Fig. 9.8. Conversely a diminution of the burst betokens a decrease in dynamic sensitivity. This test is thus somewhat akin to applying half a cycle of a sinusoidal stretch, starting with release. None of these measures has as yet been employed in more than a semi-quantitative manner for the recognition of gross changes.

5. A further method which has been suggested but not yet systematically employed is the determination of the frequency-gram (see p. 226) of a primary ending on reflexly eliciting a

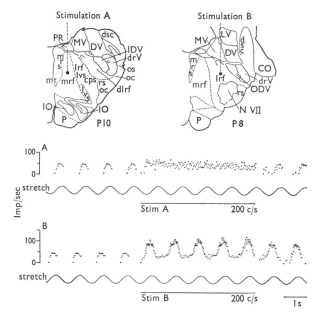

FIG. 9.7. The use of sinusoidal stretching to show whether spindle excitation on central stimulation is mediated primarily by static or by dynamic fusimotor fibres. A, static effect on a primary ending on stimulating in the medial part of the bulbar reticular formation. B, dynamic effect on stimulating in the lateral part of the reticular formation. Cat soleus stretched with 2 mm amplitude at about 1 Hz. (Vedel & Mouillac-Baudevin, 1969b, Fig. 5.)

fusimotor discharge by applying a shock to a peripheral nerve. The time-course of the frequencygram is then compared with those obtained on stimulating single fusimotor fibres (static, quick; dynamic, slow; Lewis, 1969). Yet another potential method is the assessment of the degree of irregularity of the discharges of a primary ending. A gross irregularity in primary firing seems more likely to be due to static than to dynamic action.

All the various methods of separating static and dynamic action are reasonably satisfactory when the central action studied expresses itself predominantly via only one or other of the two fusimotor systems, as may be seen in Figs. 9.7, 9.8, 9.11 and 9.12. Figure 9.9 summarises the way these sort of findings may be used to decide whether static or dynamic fusimotor fibres are the ones which are chiefly influenced in any particular situation. The

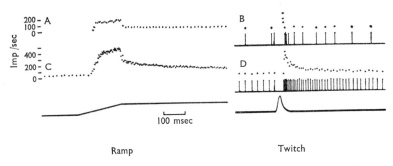

Ramp   Twitch

FIG. 9.8. The use of a twitch contraction to provide a simple way of testing the dynamic responsiveness of a primary ending. A, B, responses to a
ramp stretch and to a twitch in the 'resting' preparation. The dots show
the 'instantaneous' frequency of firing; the actual spikes are also shown
for the records accompanying the twitch. C, D, responses to similar stimuli
applied during activation of dynamic fusimotor fibres by central stimulation. Results obtained from the flexor digitorum longus of the hindlimb
of the anaesthetised cat with intact ventral roots on stimulating in the
mesencephalon. The stretch was 3 mm. (Appelberg & Molander, 1967,
Fig. 1.)

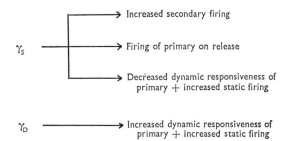

FIG. 9.9. Summary of tests for deciding whether a given fusimotor excitation is primarily due to static or to dynamic fusimotor activation. The
dynamic responsiveness of the primary ending may be assessed by observing its behaviour during a ramp stretch, or during a sinusoidal stretch,
or during the falling phase of a twitch contraction. These are variously
illustrated in Figs. 9.7, 9.8, 9.10, 9.11 and 9.12.

difficulties arise when the activity of the two systems changes
simultaneously, whether the changes are in sympathy or in opposi-
tion. For example, dynamic responsiveness as assessed by the
dynamic index may be reduced either by an increased static discharge or by a decreased dynamic discharge. Thus once an increase

of static fusimotor firing has been shown to occur by recording from the secondary ending then any reduction of the dynamic index fails to show whether or not there has been a simultaneous reduction in dynamic fusimotor firing. Fortunately in this particular case a further test is provided by measuring the peak frequency of discharge during a ramp stretch, for this is decreased by a reduction of dynamic activity but not by an increase of static action. In combination with the other appropriate tests this has been used to show that the injection of DOPA in the spinal cat switches any 'spontaneous' fusimotor discharges to the tenuissimus muscle from dynamic to static fibres (Bergmans & Grillner, 1968a, 1969; Grillner, Hongo & Lundberg, 1967). It would obviously be useful to have some quantitative way of assessing the precise degree of activity occurring simultaneously in each of the fusimotor systems. Sinusoidal stretching would appear to be the most hopeful basis for such a measure, but as yet the response of the spindle to such stretching has been insufficiently studied to decide whether it could be made the basis of an effective method of measuring simultaneously what is happening in both of the fusimotor systems. Further, it appears possible that a powerful action by one system may sometimes completely swamp that occurring in the other.

Effects of central stimulation. As first shown by Granit & Kaada (1952), by recording both from γ fibres and from the spindle afferents, stimulation within the central nervous system may either excite or inhibit the γ motoneurones. The strength of such effects was emphasised by Eldred, Granit & Merton (1953) who found that, with the muscle at a constant length, the discharge of a spindle primary ending in a decerebrate cat could be increased by 100 impulses/sec on stimulation of a certain region of the midbrain, and decreased by 40–50 impulses/sec by stimulating another region nearby which inhibited the pre-existing fusimotor activity. In the decerebrate cat such central effects on the γ motoneurones may persist virtually unchanged after section of the dorsal roots of the segments of spinal cord in which the studied fusimotor neurones lie. They thus appear to depend very little, if at all, upon support from the muscle proprioceptors. This is in keeping with the apparent absence of significant autogenetic reflexes from muscles to their fusimotor neurones, but contrasts with the behaviour of α motoneurones whose responses are greatly affected by local de-afferentation and by autogenetic reflexes. Regions of the central nervous system where stimulation has been found to have effects on fusimotor neurones include the reticular formation, the motor cortex, the pyramidal tract, the basal ganglia, the thalamus, the red nucleus, the cerebellum, the amygdala and the hypothalamus. Many other sites, when investigated, will no doubt prove also to have an influence.

As so often happens on applying electrical stimulation to so complex a structure as the CNS the effect produced from a particular site is often far from constant. Sometimes it may even change from static to dynamic or from γ excitation to γ inhibition on altering the strength or frequency of stimulation, the depth of anaesthesia, or even on simple repetition of the stimulus. Not surprisingly, therefore, no meaningful pattern has yet emerged of which regions control the fusimotor neurones, and in what manner and for what purposes. Achieving such understanding can only be expected as part and parcel of an understanding of motor control mechanisms as a whole. But it is to be hoped that detailed information about the patterns of fusimotor excitation and inhibition that are produced by different parts of the CNS will help in developing the story. For the time being one may be content that it is now reasonably well established that the CNS can control the fusimotor neurones independently of the α motoneurones, and that it can also exert a separate control over the static and the dynamic fusimotor neurones. The established anatomical independence of the three different pathways in each peripheral nerve (skeleto-motor and static and dynamic fusimotor fibres) carries with it the implication that each should be independently controllable by the others, for otherwise there would be no point in their separate existence; but only direct experiment can show how far the CNS actually achieves such a separate control in practice.

The existence of an independent central control of the α and the γ motoneurones of the same muscle. As on reflex activation, the fusimotor neurones can often be excited by central stimulation which does not cause any frank discharge from α motoneurones of the same muscle. In addition, when both are excited the discharge of the fusimotor neurones may precede that of the α motoneurones.

In many instances the effects produced on the fusimotor neurones in the absence of α firing are so powerful that it would appear that the central stimulation has excited descending pathways which are specific for fusimotor neurones and without action on α motoneurones. But whether this is really so is not at all easy to prove. This is because many fusimotor neurones have a low threshold for central activation and discharge spontaneously in the common laboratory preparations. Thus any new synaptic influence upon them produces an effect which is immediately detectable as a change in their discharge. In contrast, alpha motoneurones only rarely discharge spontaneously so that on recording their spikes in peripheral nerves excitation can be detected only when it exceeds their firing threshold and inhibition cannot show itself at all. Of course this limitation is introduced by recording peripherally and is readily overcome by recording intracellularly from the α motoneurones themselves or by testing their excitability by means of the monosynaptic reflex. But as yet such additional procedures have hardly been performed in experiments in which fusimotor activity has been studied.

Fortunately, however, there seems little doubt that α and γ motoneurones can be controlled independently, for in one situation at least they are influenced in opposite ways by manipulation of the central nervous system. This was described by Granit, Holmgren & Merton (1955) who found that, on cooling or ablating the anterior lobe of the cerebellum in the decerebrate cat, the discharge of α motoneurones increased while that of γ motoneurones decreased; the latter conclusion was based on observing a decrease in spindle discharge which was too marked to have been caused mechanically by the extrafusal muscle contraction. In addition, they found that relative to the activity of the α motoneurones there was rather little activity of γ motoneurones in cats decerebrated by the anaemic method of Pollock & Davis (which destroys the anterior lobe of the cerebellum), compared to the activity found in cats decerebrated by the classical method of mid-brain section (which spares the anterior lobe of the cerebellum). This was so, both when the muscle was 'at rest', and when it was contracting reflexly in response to various stimuli and thus may betoken a switching of spinal interneurones differentially influencing α and γ motoneurones as well as showing that α's and γ's can be controlled independently from higher centres. Rather similarly,

Corda, von Euler & Lennerstrand (1966) investigated the effect on spindles in respiratory muscles of cooling, ablating or stimulating the anterior lobe of the cerebellum. They were thereby able to alter the pattern of spindle firing which occurred during normal respiratory movements, and felt that the results indicated that the cerebellum could exert 'an influence on the balance between the two systems', that is α and γ, though their findings were nothing like as dramatic as those previously described for the hindlimb. In the baboon, stimulation of the motor cortex may produce relatively different effects on muscle contraction and on spindle firing when the parameters of stimulation or the depth of anaesthesia are varied, further suggesting a degree of independence of the pathways to α and γ motoneurones (Koeze, 1968; Koeze, Phillips & Sheridan, 1968). Such studies could usefully be fortified by studying fusimotor as well as afferent discharges, for this would eliminate the complications produced by the mechanical action of the extrafusal contractions on the spindle. Moreover, a clear-cut demonstration has yet to be provided that both kinds of fusimotor fibre can be controlled independently of α fibres; *a priori* both might be expected to be so controllable, especially since each may be powerfully excited in the absence of the other, and of muscle contraction.

The central co-activation of α and γ motoneurones. On the other hand, it is notable and α and γ fibres often fire 'in parallel'. Moreover, this still occurs after the dorsal roots have been cut so as to eliminate the possibility that the α firing is merely initiated via the 'γ loop', with increased Ia firing leading to the monosynaptic excitation of the α motoneurones. Granit (1955) coined the phrase 'α–γ linkage' in respect of all such co-activation of the two types of neurone. Unfortunately he appears to have used the term 'linkage' somewhat indiscriminately both for the experimentally observed patterns of common firing of α and γ neurones, and for the neural mechanisms lying behind this shared behaviour. In the latter case there was the implication that the similar behaviour of the α and γ motoneurones was ensured by some unspecified physical neural linkage between them, such as a fixed arrangement of shared input fibres or even some interconnection between the α and γ motoneurones themselves; all this was additional to the functional linkage from the γ to the α motoneurones produced by the Ia monosynaptic pathway. This original failure to give the term 'α–γ linkage' a precise definition has robbed it of much of its value and led to some confusion in its use by others, so that it now requires to be used with caution if at all. It is usually better replaced by the more direct term 'co-activation' of α and γ fibres. That such co-activation usually occurs would appear to be an important feature in the organisation of the motor system. A noteworthy example of it is provided by the rhythmic discharges to the intercostal muscles which occur during normal respiration (Eklund, Euler & Rutkowski, 1964; Sears, 1964).

But co-activation of α and γ motoneurones is not invariable and so it remains important to ask of any particular reflex or descending action on fusimotor neurones whether it depends upon pathways acting also upon α motoneurones, or whether upon those that are specifically devoted to fusimotor control. Conversely, it should be asked of any α action whether or not it occurs concomitantly with a fusimotor action. As the body appears often to require α and γ motoneurones to behave similarly an economy would be achieved by their having some of their inputs in common, for example by their receiving different branches of the same fibre. Thus it may be suspected that some descending pathways are devoted equally to the control of both types of neurone. Independence of α and γ action could remain assured by other pathways which acted selectively upon the two types of neurone. In addition, other descending pathways might act on α and γ motoneurones via separate spinal relay interneurones which could be selectively switched 'on' and 'off' by yet other descending pathways.

Three examples have now been found of a descending tract which produces a monosynaptic and hence an invariant activation of both the α and γ motoneurones to the same muscle; that their individual fibres can have such a dual action remains to be proved. The vestibulo-spinal tract was the first to be suggested to have a parallel action on α and γ neurones. This was done by Carli, Diete-Spiff & Pompeiano (1967) who were often unable to separate its actions in producing contraction of the gastrocnemius and excitation of its spindles. Subsequent microelectrode recording from α and from γ motoneurones proved that fast vestibulo-spinal fibres could indeed excite them both monosynaptically (Grillner, Hongo, & Lund, 1969; Grillner, 1969). A further point of interest was that in the spinal preparation stimulation of the region of cord in which the tract runs could only excite those motoneurones which were not firing spontaneously; those that were already discharging were unaffected by the stimulation. As only the dynamic fibres discharge spontaneously in the spinal preparation this suggested that the vestibulo-spinal tract terminated on static fusimotor neurones as well as on alpha motoneurones, but that it did not terminate upon dynamic fusimotor neurones.

Another example of a parallel monosynaptic excitation of static fusimotor neurones and of α motoneurones is provided by the action on tenuissimus neurones of the large fibres in a tract which descends from the lower brainstem (region of medial longitudinal fasciclus) and runs in the ventrolateral funicle of the cord (Bergmans & Grillner, 1968b). Again, dynamic fusimotor neurones were thought to be uninfluenced. This conclusion was slightly more firmly based than that for the vestibulo-spinal tract as the fusimotor neurones of tenuissimus could be categorised by the action of DOPA as well as by their spontaneous discharge (see later). In the baboon, stimulation of the motor cortex may monosynaptically excite both α and γ motoneurones of finger flexor muscles, though in this case the type of γ neurone remains to be established and only a fraction of the γ motoneurones appear to be so excited (Grigg & Preston, 1971; Clough, Phillips & Sheridan, 1971). In the cat, the pyramidal tract would appear to contain separate sets of fibres devoted to the control of both static and dynamic fusimotor neurones, though presumably not by monosynaptic action, and it would be surprising if primates were to be less well equipped (Vedel & Mouillac-Baudevin, 1970; Yokota & Voorhoeve, 1969).

On the present limited evidence the control of static fusimotor discharge would appear to be the more strongly linked with ordinary motor discharge, and this has interesting implications (see later). It would be valuable to have other descending pathways investigated in similar detail, but the experimental difficulties are so formidable that progress is likely to be slow. Afferent fibre recording is not really enough on its own for establishing a coactivation of α and γ motoneurones, and is at its best in identifying pathways exclusively devoted to fusimotor control; the hazards of interpreting a change in spindle firing in the presence of a concomitant muscle contraction are then absent. Microelectrode recordings, particularly intracellular ones, are difficult to obtain, and the type of fusimotor neurone studied is not then easily established.

Existence of an independent central control of static and dynamic fusimotor neurones. Jansen & Matthews (1962) based the original suggestion that the two kinds of intrafusal muscle fibre permit an independent control of the static and dynamic behaviour of the primary ending on observations that its dynamic responsiveness could be changed by central stimulation. Figure 9.10 shows their

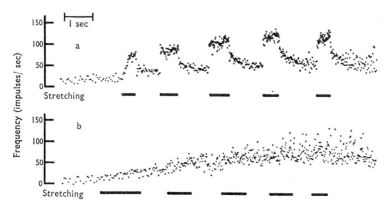

FIG. 9.10. The earliest example of the central control of the dynamic responsiveness of the primary ending of the spindle, and now indicating that static and dynamic fusimotor fibres can be controlled independently by the CNS. (*a*) Response of a primary ending in the decerebrate cat to successive small stretches; the horizontal bars mark the periods of dynamic stretching during each of which the muscle was stretched 1–2 mm at 3 mm/sec. (*b*). Response of same ending to similar stretching applied during repetitive stimulation of the anterior lobe of the cerebellum. (Jansen & Matthews, 1962, Fig. 9.)

most striking example of such an effect, and provides the earliest evidence that the static and dynamic fusimotor fibres can be controlled independently by the central nervous system; at the time the two kinds of fusimotor fibre still awaited description. Subsequent work has consolidated this view and provided several well-documented examples of relatively pure static or dynamic activation.

Immediately afterwards, Appelberg (1962) described an increase in the dynamic sensitivity of primary endings on stimulating in the region of the red nucleus in the cat anaesthetised with pentobarbitone; this original effect appears most likely to have been due to an inhibition of pre-existing static fusimotor discharge as it was accompanied by a reduction of spindle static firing and an inhibition of certain unidentified γ fibres which had been isolated in ventral root filaments. Later work showed that, in cats lightly anaesthetised with halothane, stimulation in nearby regions in the mesencephalon could excite dynamic fusimotor fibres largely without static fibres, as judged by the response of primary endings to stretching or to twitch contractions of the muscle studied (Appelberg & Emonet-Dénand, 1965; Appelberg & Molander, 1967). Similar dynamic activation could then also be produced by stimulating the caudal part of the inferior olive, which incidentally is the part of the olive which receives ascending spinal fibres. Lesions in the olive diminished the effect of the near-rubral stimulation, so that the olive was suggested to lie on the downward pathway from the mesencephalon.

Attempts to trace the pathway in more detail showed that it lay in the dorsal part of the lateral funicle of the cord, but that it was neither the pyramidal nor the rubro-spinal tract; thus the original ascription of dynamic effects to the red nucleus may have been unfounded. The fibres in the tract would appear to be rather small for on its activation no definite wave could be detected when recordings were made from the surface of the cord over the region where the tract lay; potentials were readily so-recorded from other tracts which consisted of large fibres but which were not responsible for the dynamic effect (Appelberg & Jeneskog, 1969); alternatively, the tract for the dynamic effect may just contain rather few fibres. In contrast, the two pathways mentioned earlier (p. 524) which monosynaptically excited static neurones were both fast conducting. As neither of these latter tracts appeared to influence dynamic neurones they provide a further instance of a differential control of the two kinds of fusimotor neurone.

Vedel and his colleagues have provided various further examples of a rather selective central activation of either static or dynamic neurones; this was again done by using afferent recording from primary endings in cats under halothane. Initially, a rather pure dynamic action was described on repetitively stimulating the motor cortex and a rather pure static action on stimulating the caudate nucleus (Vedel & Paillard, 1965). In later work a variety of powerful effects, some static and some dynamic, were obtained on stimulating the reticular formation at various sites in the medulla, pons and mesencephalon, and their locations described; two such examples have already been illustrated in Fig. 9.7 (Vedel & Mouillac-Baudevin, 1969a,b). The responses tended to be rather labile and at some sites the effect might change from predominantly static to predominantly dynamic merely on repeated application of the stimulus. Following this, a more thorough investigation of the effects of cortical stimulation showed that on varying the depth of anaesthesia static effects could sometimes be obtained instead of the more usual dynamic effect previously described (Vedel & Mouillac-Baudevin, 1970). Figures 9.11 and 9.12 illustrate these different actions, both of which were only elicited on

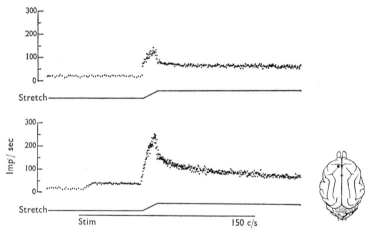

FIG. 9.11. The usual dynamic action on a primary ending on stimulating the sensori-motor cortex. Cat soleus stretched 3 mm. Point of stimulation shown to the right. (Vedel & Mouillac-Baudevin, 1970, Fig. 2.)

stimulating the classical motor areas. Both were abolished on destroying the pyramidal tract and both could also be produced on its stimulation. Thus the pyramidal tract would seem to be established as the pathway responsible for the fusimotor effects of cortical stimulation. The lability of the response with the depth of anaesthesia is apparently at least partly due to alterations in the excitability of the spinal cord rather than the motor cortex. Yokota & Voorhoeve (1969) also obtained evidence of excitation of both static and dynamic fusimotor fibres on cortical stimulation, but they do not seem to have observed any appreciable selectivity in their activation; static effects were shown by an increased discharge of the secondary ending, and dynamic activation by an increased discharge of the primary ending on the falling phase of the twitch. In the light of all this work there can no longer be any

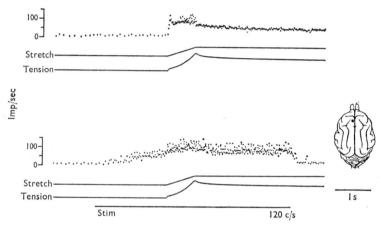

FIG. 9.12. A static action on another soleus primary on stimulating the cortex at nearly the same point as in Fig. 9.10, but under different conditions. Such static effects were only rarely observed. Cat soleus stretched 4 mm. (Vedel & Mouillac-Baudevin, 1970, Fig. 3.)

doubt that, if and when it so requires, the central nervous system can activate static and dynamic fusimotor neurones largely independently of each other. It remains to chart the various pathways involved in more detail and to investigate more thoroughly how selectively each acts upon just one or other kind of fusimotor neurone.

Study of the patterns of 'spontaneous' fusimotor firing occurring in different kinds of preparation has further served to confirm the independence of the central control of static and dynamic action. In addition, it suggests that some descending pathways may be arranged so as to have a reciprocal action on the two kinds of neurone. Alnaes, Jansen & Rudjord (1965) showed that the small amount of spontaneous firing which occurred in the spinal preparation is likely to be restricted to dynamic fibres, both for flexor and extensor muscles; this was done by recording from afferent fibres. Subsequently, it was found that the injection of DOPA (dihydroxyphenylalanine) reversed the pattern of behaviour of tenuissimus neurones so that the dynamic ones became silent and the static ones began to fire; this was amply established by a full battery of tests on recording from γ motoneurones and from both primary and secondary afferents (Bergmans & Grillner, 1968a, 1969; Grillner, Hongo & Lundberg, 1967). DOPA is thought to mimic the action of a descending pathway of small fibres which acts via the liberation of mono-amines. Thus the findings suggest that this pathway has an inverse action on the two kinds of fusimotor neurone of flexor muscles, though whether by a relatively direct synaptic action upon them or by influencing interneurones remains unknown. In line with this Jansen & Rudjord (1965a), in studying a flexor muscle (tibialis anterior) by afferent fibre recording in the decerebrate cat, found signs of a slight spontaneous static activity but no signs of dynamic activity, and in reflex activation only the static fibres were influenced. This suggested that, in comparison with the spinal preparation, the flexor static neurones in the decerebrate had become more excitable while the dynamic ones had been inhibited, which again requires an inverse control of the two kinds of fusimotor neurone. It may be noted that, as might be expected, any spontaneous fusimotor firing is not truly spontaneous but reflects the activity reaching the fusimotor neurones both from spinal reflex pathways and from a variety of higher centres; the latter can have an effective action even when the cord is widely de-afferented (Hunt, 1951; Hunt & Paintal, 1958; Eldred, Granit & Merton, 1953; Appelberg & Jeneskog, 1968; Voorhoeve, 1960).

Discrete and diffuse fusimotor activation. The functional significance of fusimotor activation depends a good deal upon whether the fusimotor neurones of different muscles can be excited independently, or whether they are forcibly activated together by the action of a single descending pathway. Independent activation would be required if they were to form part of a 'follow-up servo' for producing movement, while simultaneous diffuse activation would probably be adequate to produce a widespread increase in receptor sensitivity such as might be appropriate when an animal becomes alert. The present limited evidence is already enough to show that some reasonably discrete pathways to different muscles must exist, for on occasion the fusimotor fibres to flexors and extensors have been found to be influenced independently; but this does not disprove the existence of other more diffusely organised pathways which are probably also present.

For obvious reasons experimentation has only too often been restricted to a single muscle, so that evidence for or against the discreteness of any action observed is then totally lacking. Shimazu, Hongo & Kubota (1962a,b), however, on stimulating the brain-stem recorded simultaneously the discharge of a flexor and of an extensor spindle afferent (gastrocnemius and tibialis anterior respectively). Sometimes both endings increased their discharge more or less 'in-parallel', and this was then attributed to the activation of a 'diffuse' non-specific descending system. However, on varying the strength of stimulation or depth of anaesthesia opposite effects were sometimes obtainable on the spindles in the two muscles, with those from one being excited and from the other inhibited, in either combination. This was attributed to the excitation of descending systems which were reciprocally organised with regard to flexor and extensor fusimotor neurones. Since these effects were all elicitable from secondary as well as from primary endings they must have been mediated at least in part by static fusimotor neurones. On stimulation in the ventral part of the red nucleus, Appelberg & Kozary (1963) again found flexor fusimotor neurones to be excited at the same time as those to extensors were inhibited. However, Vedel & Mouillac-Baudevin (1970) found that, although cortical stimulation regularly produced excitation of flexor fusimotor neurones, this could be accompanied either by an inhibition or by an excitation of extensor fusimotor neurones depending upon the depth of anaesthesia. This is illustrated in Fig. 9.13. Again in the 'pyramidal preparation' (cortex connected to lower centres only via basis pedunculi), Fidone & Preston (1969) found that cortical stimulation inhibited the majority of extensor fusimotor fibres, isolated in filaments of the gastrocnemius nerve, while it excited the majority of peroneal fusimotor fibres; however, about a third of the fibres of each kind were influenced in the opposite manner. All this argues that different fibres in the pyramidal tract differ in their action on the fusimotor neurones of different muscles.

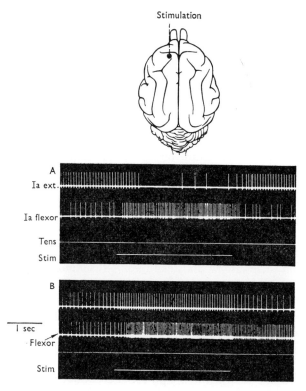

FIG. 9.13. Evidence suggesting independent cortical control of fusimotor fibres to flexor and extensor muscles. The records show the discharges from an extensor primary ending (soleus) and a flexor primary ending (tibialis anterior) on stimulating the cortex at 110/sec. This was done first (A) with the animal very lightly anaesthetised and again (B) with the animal more deeply anaesthetised. Increasing the depth of anaesthesia reversed the action on the extensor spindle from inhibition to excitation, whereas the flexor spindle was excited on both occasions. (Vedel & Mouillac-Baudevin, 1970, Fig. 6.)

Another example of differentiation is provided by the two descending pathways described by Bergmans & Grillner (1968*b*) which monosynaptically activated static fusimotor neurones. The vestibulo-spinal tract excites extensor fusimotor neurones but not flexor ones, while the mid-brain tract has the opposite action. The action of DOPA in the spinal cat provides yet another example of the differential control of flexors and extensors for it leads to an excitation of the static neurones of both kinds of muscle, while inhibiting the dynamic neurones of flexor but not extensor muscles. In the decerebrate cat, both kinds of fusimotor neurones of extensor muscles may be found to be discharging spontaneously, whereas there is little fusimotor discharge of either kind to flexor muscles (Jansen & Rudjord, 1965a); this again suggests that flexor and extensor fusimotor actions can be differentially controlled. It may be finally noted that the γ motoneurones which supply the external and the internal intercostal muscles also show reciprocal behaviour. Both during normal breathing and on the electrical stimulation of the appropriate medullary centres the fusimotor discharge to one muscle increases while that to the other decreases (Sears, 1964; Eklund, Euler & Rutkowski, 1964; Andersen & Sears, 1970). The simplest explanation of such behaviour would be the existence of separate 'inspiratory' and 'expiratory' reticulo-spinal fibres each of which had a reciprocal action on 'inspiratory' and 'expiratory' fusimotor neurones, and probably also on the respective α motoneurones.

On the other hand, it seems likely that some descending pathways have a non-specific effect and activate the fusimotor neurones of a wide range of muscles, though whether both the static and the dynamic ones is unknown. This was suggested by Shimazu, Hongo & Kubota (1962a,b) who, by making various central lesions, could abolish the reciprocal effects of central stimulation (flexor excitation with extensor inhibition, or vice versa), while leaving the diffuse effects of central stimulation (excitation or inhibition of both). This made it unlikely that their diffuse effects were due to the excitation of a number of discrete pathways each to a different muscle. The diffuse effects, moreover, tended to have a greater latency and to persist for much longer after the cessation of stimulation. Rather similarly, Granit & Holmgren (1955) had earlier distinguished two types of pathway from the mesencephalon to γ efferents. One conducted at a high velocity, could 'drive' the γ motoneurones, and could be interrupted by a single deep incision into the lateral column of the spinal cord. The other had a long latency, had an action which was only manifest on repetitive stimulation, and tended to give a slowly increasing excitation of γ motoneurones which persisted long after the stimulation had stopped. This pathway appeared to be diffusely organised for it could not be interrupted by several incisions which together covered the whole cross-section of the spinal cord; it may be suspected to have produced effects on flexors as well as extensors though this was not then tested.

Another pointer to the existence of non-specific systems is that the changes in spindle firing which may occur in association with spontaneous changes in the pattern of the EEG, or on handling the pinna, are not restricted to one type of muscle and so probably represent diffuse effects (for example, Hongo, Kubota & Shimazu, 1963; Granit, Job & Kaada, 1952; Schomburg, 1970). At the spinal level, Jansen (1966) commented on 'the small degree of reciprocity in effects on flexor and extensor spindles during electrical stimulation of spinal nerves' in both the decerebrate and spinal preparation as also earlier noted by Hunt & Paintal (1958). However, at the very outset of such studies Hunt (1951) found that the physiologically natural stimuli that reflexly elicit the flexor and crossed responses from α motoneurones evoke similarly organised reciprocal responses from fusimotor neurones, as illustrated in Fig. 9.14. Slightly afterwards, Eldred & Hagbath (1954)

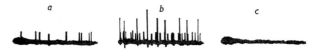

FIG. 9.14. Similarity of reflex responses of α and γ fibres to physiological stimuli in the spinal cat, and conforming to the expected physiologically meaningful pattern. Records from the central end of the cut nerve to tenuissimus. The small spikes are attributable to γ fibres and the large spikes to α fibres. a, spontaneous background firing in γ fibres alone. b, co-activation of α and γ fibres on squeezing the ipsilateral foot to elicit a flexor response. c, parallel inhibition of both kinds of fibre on squeezing the opposite foot to elicit a crossed extensor response with inhibition of flexor motoneurones. (Hunt, 1951, Fig. 2, reversed in contrast.)

extended this demonstration of reciprocal action by showing that natural nociceptive stimulation of the skin overlying an extensor muscle (gastrocnemius) could produce excitation of extensor fusimotor neurones with inhibition of those to flexors (tibialis anterior), just as it did for α motoneurones.

Thus there would appear to be a vast amount of detailed anatomy to be discovered, namely just how specifically various pathways and interneurones are connected to the two types of fusimotor neurone of the same and of different muscles. At present

such things can only be inferred from extremely laborious physiological experimentation so there appears little prospect of rapid
progress. For the time being it seems safe to believe that under
some or other circumstance the nervous system is able to regulate
the α fibres and both kinds of fusimotor fibre of each muscle
relatively independently of each other and of those in all other
muscles. This is the gist of the present limited evidence, and if
such independent central control could never occur there would
be no reason for the separate existence of the three different kinds
of peripheral motor fibre. But the compulsory motor interactions
that are probably constrained to occur in many circumstances
remain almost entirely unfathomed. With the example of the
tardy recognition of the widespread distribution of Ia monosynaptic excitatory actions on α motoneurones it would be foolish
to jump to conclusions about the precise distribution of the fibres
and pathways that excite fusimotor neurones.

*Résumé of the inter-relationships between the muscle afferents and
the higher levels of the CNS*

    Cortical projections. Group III stimulation has long been recog-
nised to give rise to an evoked response in the sensory areas of the
contralateral cortex. Initially, such responses were thought to be
absent on group I stimulation but with the refinement of technique they have now been found on stimulating both fore- and
hindlimb muscle nerves. In the cat, the main receiving area for
both the fore- and the hindlimbs lies just rostral to the post-
cruciate dimple. Several other smaller areas have also been described. In the monkey under chloralose anaesthesia proprioceptive
stimuli have been found to excite large numbers of units lying in
the classical motor area but their response to nerve stimulation
has not been systematically studied. In the baboon under barbiturate anaesthesia only one receiving area has so far been detected
on stimulating peripheral nerves electrically; it lies in area 3a deep
in the central sulcus. Single-unit analyses of the group I evoked
responses in the cat cortex show an extensive convergence of the
action of different muscle nerves upon the same single unit.
Similar analyses in the thalamic and cuneate relay nuclei, which
lie on the route for the forelimb projection, have shown that the
convergence becomes progressively greater with ascent of the
central sensory pathway. There is currently some uncertainty

about whether or not the excitability of cortico-spinal neurones is influenced by the cortical activity set up on group I stimulation. Joint afferents also project to the cerebral cortex. It has recently been questioned how far they do so via the dorsal columns as has long been believed.

Lack of access to consciousness. In spite of their cortical projection the muscle stretch receptors would appear to have no simple part to play in the conscious perception of limb position (kinesthesia). The subjective appreciation of joint angle is abolished by locally paralysing the nerves to a joint, together with the sensory fibres to the nearby skin, even though the muscles concerned, along with their proprioceptors, remain completely untouched. In addition, there is no sensation of a change in finger position in the conscious human subject when one of the finger flexor muscles is stretched throughout its physiological range without altering the angle of the finger joints; this can be done by pulling upon a tendon which has been exposed through a skin incision. In animals, group I stimulation fails to evoke 'arousal', nor can it be used to produce a conditioned reflex; group III stimulation, however, is effective in both respects. This again fits in with the idea that the information provided by the muscle stretch receptors is used for motor control rather than for elaborating conscious sensations. However, certain recent experiments suggest that spindle discharges can influence the perception of joint angle, and so the whole matter is reopened.

The spino-cerebellar tracts. The dorsal and ventral spino-cerebellar tracts have now been reasonably extensively studied by recording the responses of single units within them with a micro-electrode. The dorsal tract has proved to be the simpler in its organisation. Many of its cells are monosynaptically activated by group I muscle afferents, usually from only a single muscle. Such excitation appears to be derived either from Ia fibres or from Ib fibres but not from both. Some of the group I activated cells seem to be further excited by group II fibres. In addition, some DSCT units appear to be monosynaptically excited by spindle group II fibres without being monosynaptically excited by group I fibres. When a DSCT unit is excited trans-synaptically by maintained muscle stretch its discharge is found to be appreciably less regular

Sм

than the spindle afferent discharges which feed onto the cell. This increase in variability has been satisfactorily simulated by the beatings of about 15 presynaptic inputs which converge upon the same cell and where each produces an EPSP of appreciable size. The DSCT cells do not, however, provide a purely private line to the cerebellum from each kind of receptor of each individual muscle. They may be inhibited by afferents from other muscles and also by stimulating the contralateral motor cortex.

The cells of the ventral spino-cerebellar tract are also monosynaptically excited by group I afferents but in this case the excitation is almost exclusively from Ib fibres. Unlike DSCT units individual VSCT units are usually excited by the group I afferents from a number of widely separated muscles and most of these require to be active simultaneously in order to induce the VSCT neurone to fire an impulse. The other synaptic influences impinging on the VSCT neurones are also appreciably more complicated than those impinging on the DSCT. The VSCT cells are powerfully influenced by cutaneous inputs, which may have either an excitatory or an inhibitory action depending upon the area of skin stimulated. They are also influenced by at least three different descending pathways. In addition, there is a newly recognised contribution to the VSCT from certain 'spinal border cells'; these receive a quite different input from the rest of the VSCT. At present we really have very little idea what the VSCT is trying to tell the cerebellum.

The DSCT and the VSCT are hindlimb tracts and are not supplied by afferents from the forelimb. These instead feed into two other tracts, namely the cuneo-cerebellar tract and the rostral spino-cerebellar tract, which appear to be the homologues of the DSCT and VSCT respectively. The cerebellum is also informed about the state of the periphery and of the spinal interneurones by various spino-olivary pathways; five separate such pathways have been described to date.

The central control of fusimotor neurones. The most direct method of studying the central excitation of fusimotor neurones is to record the discharges of single γ motor fibres. Unfortunately it is then usually impossible to characterise the single unit studied as a static or a dynamic fibre for these both have a similar range of conduction velocities. This difficulty can be circumvented by studying the activity of fusimotor neurones by the indirect method of recording the discharges of single afferent fibres while the ventral roots remain intact. The occurrence of fusimotor excitation on central stimulation is then shown by an increase in afferent firing which occurs in the absence of any overt muscle contraction that could influence the spindles from outside. The effect may be categorised as static or dynamic by also studying the responsiveness of the primary ending to dynamic stimuli. Ramp stretches, sinusoidal stretches, and muscle twitches have all been found suitable for this purpose. In addition, since the static fibres are the only ones which excite the secondary endings, any increase in secondary firing reliably demonstrates the presence of static fusimotor excitation.

Stimulation of many different regions within the CNS has now been demonstrated to influence the discharge of γ motoneurones and a range of excitatory and inhibitory effects have been described. Very often the excitatory effects on fusimotor neurones occur in the absence of contraction of the main muscles. This can occur partly because the threshold of the γ motoneurones appears to be lower than that of α motoneurones so they are often firing 'spontaneously'; thus a weak synaptic action on γ motoneurones is more readily detected than it is for α motoneurones. But, in addition, there is evidence for the existence of central pathways which can control the activity of the γ motoneurones independently of that of the α motoneurones. The best example of this is that cerebellar ablation leads to an increase in the discharge of α motoneurones at the same time as it leads to a decrease in the discharge of γ motoneurones. On the other hand, some descending pathways would appear to excite both α and γ motoneurones together, so that they are 'co-activated'. Three examples have now been found of a monosynaptic co-activation of α and γ motoneurones by a descending pathway, possibly by the self-same fibres. These are the action of vestibulo-spinal fibres on cat lumbar extensor motoneurones, the action of a tract from the lower brain stem on cat lumbar flexor motoneurones, and the action of the pyramidal tract on forelimb motoneurones in the baboon. However, in each case only a proportion of the fusimotor neurones were found to be excited. It is of particular interest that in the cat the activated fusimotor neurones all appeared to be static ones and the dynamic ones appeared to be uninfluenced; in the baboon, the matter has yet to be tested.

There is now ample evidence that the static and the dynamic fusimotor neurones can be independently controlled by the CNS. This has been shown by stimulating at various sites in the CNS and finding that some produce dynamic activation and some produce static activation. For example, stimulation in the region of the red nucleus produces a fairly pure dynamic activation, whereas stimulation at certain other sites in the mid-brain may produce a marked static activation. The responses tend to be rather labile and are particularly dependent upon the type and depth of anaesthesia. Repetitive stimulation of the cat motor cortex normally produces a dynamic effect, but can sometimes produce a static effect; both actions are mediated via the pyramidal tract.

Thus there is no doubt of the existence of descending pathways which have quite different actions upon the two types of fusimotor neurone; some descending pathways may possibly be organised reciprocally so as to excite one kind of fusimotor neurone while inhibiting the other. This would fit in with the action of the drug DOPA and with the different patterns of spontaneous fusimotor firing which is found in different types of preparation. Other pathways, however, may perhaps be organised diffusely so as to simultaneously activate both kinds of fusimotor neurone, and possibly also so as to simultaneously excite the fusimotor neurones of antagonistic muscles. But the gist of the present evidence is that if and when the central nervous system so desires it is able to regulate the α fibres and both kinds of γ fibres to each muscle relatively independently of each other and of those in other muscles. Indeed, if it could not the body would appear to gain little by possessing the three different kinds of motor fibre.

References

Abrahams, V. C. (1970). Cervico-lumbar reflex interactions involving a proprioceptive receiving area of the cerebral cortex. *J. Physiol.* **209**, 45–56.   [491]

Albe-Fessard, D., Lammarre, Y. & Pimpaneau, A. (1966). Sur l'origine fusoriale de certaines afférences somatiques atteignant le cortex moteur du singe. *J. Physiol., Paris* **58**, 443–444.   [486]

Albe-Fessard, D. & Liebeskind, J. (1966). Origine des messages somato-sensitifs activant les cellules du cortex moteur chez le singe. *Expl. Brain Res.* **1**, 127–146. [486]

Albe-Fessard, D., Liebeskind, J. & Lamarre, Y. (1965). Projection au niveau du cortex somato-moteur du singe d'afférences provenant des récepteurs musculaires. *C.r. hebd. Séanc. Acad. Sci., Paris* **261**, 3891–3894. [486]

Alnaes, E., Jansen, J. K. S. & Rudjord, T. (1965). Fusimotor activity in the spinal cat. *Acta physiol. scand.* **63**, 197–212. [528]

Amasssian, V. E., & Berlin, L. (1958). Early cortical projection of group I afferents in the forelimb muscle nerves of cat. *J. Physiol.* **143**, 61P. [482]

Andersen, H., Körner, L., Landgren, S. & Silfvenius, H. (1967). Fibre components and cortical projections of the elbow joint nerve in the cat. *Acta physiol. scand.* **69**, 373–382. [492]

Andersen, P. & Phillips, C. G. P. (1971). Unpublished observations cited in Phillips, Powell & Wiesendanger, 1971. [490]

Andersen, P. & Sears, T. A. (1970). Medullary activation of intercostal fusimotor and alpha motoneurones. *J. Physiol.* **209**, 739–755. [532]

Andersson, S. A., Landgren, S. & Wolsk, D. (1966). The thalamic relay and cortical projection of group I muscle afferents from the forelimb of the cat. *J. Physiol.* **183**, 576–591. [484, 487]

Appelberg, B. (1962). The effect of electrical stimulation in Nucleus Ruber on the response to stretch in primary and secondary muscle spindle afferents. *Acta physiol. scand.* **56**, 140–151. [526]

Appelberg, B. & Emonet-Dénand, F. (1965). Central control of static and dynamic sensitivities of muscle spindle primary endings. *Acta physiol. scand.* **63**, 487–494. [526]

Appelberg, B. & Jeneskog, T. (1968). Variations in the dynamic sensitivity of hindlimb muscle spindles in the anaesthetized cat with deafferented lumbo-sacral cord. *Acta physiol. scand.* **73**, 39A. [529]

— (1969). A dorso-lateral spinal pathway mediating information from the mesencephalon to dynamic fusimotor neurones. *Acta physiol. scand.* **77**, 159–171. [526]

Appelberg, B. & Kozary, Z. (1963). Excitation of flexor fusimotor neurones by electrical stimulation in the red nucleus. *Acta physiol. scand.* **59**, 445–453. [530]

Appelberg, B. & Molander, A. (1967). A rubro-olivary pathway. I. Identification of a descending system for control of dynamic sensitivity of muscle spindles. *Expl Brain Res.* **3**, 372–381. [518, 526]

Armstrong, D. M., Eccles, J. C., Harvey, R. J. & Matthews, P. B. C. (1968). Responses in the dorsal accessory olive of the cat to stimulation of hindlimb afferents. *J. Physiol.* **194**, 125–145. [509]

Bergmans, J. & Grillner, S. (1968a). Changes in dynamic sensitivity of primary endings of muscle spindle afferents induced by DOPA. *Acta physiol. scand.* **74**, 629–636. [519, 529]

— (1968b). Monosynaptic control of static γ-motoneurones from the lower brain stem. *Experientia* **24**, 146–147. [524, 531]

Bergmans, J. & Grillner, S. (1969). Reciprocal control of spontaneous activity and reflex effects in static and dynamic γ-motoneurones revealed by an injection of DOPA. *Acta physiol. scand.* **77**, 106–124.
[519, 529]

Brindley, G. S. & Merton, P. A. (1960). The absence of position sense in the human eye. *J. Physiol.* **153**, 127–130.   [496]

Browne, K., Lee, J. & Ring, P. A. (1954). The sensation of passive movement at the metatarsophalangeal joint of the great toe in man. *J. Physiol.* **126**, 448–458.   [495]

Burgess, P. R. & Clark, F. J. (1969). Dorsal column projection of fibres from the cat knee joint. *J. Physiol.* **203**, 301–315.   [493]

Burke, R., Lundberg, A. & Weight, F. (1968). Gower's tract and 'spinal border cells'. *Acta physiol. scand.* **74**, 16A.   [505]

— (1971). Spinal border cell origin of the ventral spinocerebellar tract. *Expl Brain Res.* **12**, 283–294.   [505]

Carli, G., Diete–Spiff, K. & Pompeiano, O. (1967). Responses of the muscle spindles and the extrafusal fibres in an extensor muscle to stimulation of the lateral vestibular nucleus in the cat. *Archs ital. Biol.* **105**, 209–242.   [523]

Clough, J. F. M., Phillips, C. G. & Sheridan, J. D. (1971). The short-latency projection from the baboon's motor cortex to fusimotor neurones of the forearm and hand. *J. Physiol.* **216**, 257–279.   [524]

Cohen, L. A. (1958). Contributions of tactile, musculo-tendinous and joint mechanisms to position sense in human shoulder. *J. Neurophysiol.* **21**, 563–568.   [496]

Corda, M., von Euler, C. & Lennerstrand, G. (1966). Reflex and cerebellar influences on α and on 'rhythmic' and 'tonic' γ activity in the intercostal muscle. *J. Physiol.* **184**, 898–923.   [522]

Eccles, J. C., Oscarsson, O. & Willis, W. D. (1961). Synaptic action of group I and II afferent fibres of muscle on the cells of the dorsal spinocerebellar tract. *J. Physiol.* **158**, 517–543.   [502]

Eide, E., Fedina, L., Jansen, J., Lundberg, A. & Vyklický, L. (1969). Unitary components in the activation of Clarke's column neurones. *Acta physiol. scand.* **77**, 145–158.   [504]

Eklund, G., Euler, C. von, & Rutkowski, S. (1964). Spontaneous and reflex activities of intercostal gamma motoneurones. *J. Physiol.* **171**, 139–163.   [523, 532]

Eldred, E., Granit, R. & Merton, P. A. (1953). Supraspinal control of the muscle spindles and its significance. *J. Physiol.* **122**, 498–523.
[519, 529]

Eldred, E. & Hagbarth, K. E. (1954). Facilitation and inhibition of gamma efferents by stimulation of certain skin areas. *J. Neurophysiol.* **17**, 59–65.   [533]

Fidone, S. J. & Preston, J. B. (1969). Patterns of motor cortex control of flexor and extensor cat fusimotor neurons. *J. Neurophysiol.* **32**, 103–115.   [530]

Gardner, E. & Haddad, B. (1953). Pathways to the cerebral cortex for afferent fibres from the hindleg of the cat. *Am. J. Physiol.* **172**, 475–482. [481, 491]

Gardner, E. & Noer, R. (1952). Projection of afferent fibres from muscles and joints to the cerebral cortex of the cat. *Am. J. Physiol.* **168**, 437–441. [491]

Gelfan, S. & Carter, S. (1967). Muscle sense in man. *Exptl Neurol.* **18**, 469–473. [496]

Giaquinto, S., Pompeiano, O. & Swett, J. E. (1963). EEG and behavioural effects of fore and hindlimb muscular afferent volleys in unrestrained cats. *Archs ital. Biol.* **101**, 133–148. [498, 499]

Goodwin, G. M., McCloskey, D. I. & Matthews, P. B. C. (1972). A systematic distortion of position sense produced by muscle vibration. *J. Physiol.* Proceedings, in the press. [497]

Granit, R. (1955). *Receptors and Sensory Perception.* 369 pp. New Haven: Yale University Press. [522]

Granit, R. & Holmgren, B. (1955). Two pathways from brain stem to gamma ventral horn cells. *Acta physiol. scand.* **35**, 93–108. [532]

Granit, R. Holmgren, B. & Merton, P. A. (1955). Two routes for excitation of muscle and their subservience to the cerebellum. *J. Physiol.* **130**, 213–224. [521]

Granit, R., Job, C. & Kaada, B. R. (1952). Activation of muscle spindles in pinna reflex. *Acta physiol. scand.* **27**, 161–168. [533]

Granit, R. & Kaada, B. R. (1952). Influence of stimulation of central nervous structures on muscle spindles in cat. *Acta physiol. scand.* **27**, 130–160. [519]

Grigg, P. & Preston, J. B. (1971). Baboon flexor and extensor fusimotor neurons and their modulation by motor cortex. *J. Neurophysiol.* **34**, 428–436. [524]

Grillner, S. (1969). The influence of DOPA on the static and the dynamic fusimotor activity to the triceps surae of the spinal cat. *Acta. physiol. scand.* **77**, 490–509. [523]

Grillner, S., Hongo, T. & Lund, S. (1969). Descending monosynaptic and reflex control of γ-motoneurones. *Acta physiol. scand.* **75**, 592–613. [523]

Grillner, S., Hongo, T. & Lundberg, A. (1967). The effect of DOPA on the spinal cord. 7. Reflex activation of static γ-motoneurones from the flexor reflex afferents. *Acta physiol. scand.* **70**, 403–411. [519, 529]

Hongo, T., Kubota, K. & Shimazu, H. (1963). EEG spindle and depression of gamma motor activity. *J. Neurophysiol.* **26**, 568–580. [533]

Hongo, T. & Okada, M. (1967). Cortically evoked pre- and postsynaptic inhibition of impulse transmission to the dorsal spinocerebellar tract. *Expl. Brain Res.* **3**, 163–177. [506]

Hongo, T., Okada, Y. & Sato, M. (1967). Corticofugal influences on transmission to the dorsal spino-cerebellar tract from hindlimb primary afferents. *Expl. Brain Res.* **3**, 135–149. [506]

Hunt, C. C. (1951). The reflex activity of mammalian small-nerve fibres. *J. Physiol.* **115**, 456–469.   [511, 529, 533]

Hunt, C. C. & Paintal, A. S. (1958). Spinal reflex regulation of fusimotor neurones. *J. Physiol.* **143**, 195–212.   [529, 533]

Jankowska, E., Jukes, M. G. M. & Lund, S. (1965). The pattern of presynaptic inhibition of transmission to the dorsal spinocerebellar tract of the cat. *J. Physiol.* **178**, 17–18P.   [506]

Jansen, J. K. S. (1966). On fusimotor reflex activity. In *Muscular Afferents and Motor Control*, ed. Granit, R. pp. 91–105. Stockholm: Almqvist and Wiksell.   [533]

Jansen, J. K. S. & Matthews, P. B. C. (1962). The central control of the dynamic response of muscle spindle receptors. *J. Physiol.* **161**, 357–378.   [525]

Jansen, J. K. S., Nicolaysen, K. & Rudjord, T. (1966a). Discharge patterns of neurons of the dorsal spinocerebellar tract activated by static extension of primary endings of muscle spindles. *J. Neurophysiol.* **29**, 1061–1086.   [503]

— (1966b). Activity in the dorsal spinocerebellar tract induced by muscle stretch. In *Control and Innervation of Skeletal Muscle*, ed. Andrew, B. L. pp. 119–124. Dundee: Thomson.   [503]

Jansen, J. K. S., Nicolaysen, K. & Walløe, L. (1967). On the inhibition of transmission to the dorsal spinocerebellar tract by stretch of various ankle muscles of the cat. *Acta physiol. scand.* **70**, 362–368.   [506]

Jansen, J. K. S. & Rudjord, T. (1965a). Fusimotor activity in a flexor muscle of the decerebrate cat. *Acta physiol. scand.* **63**, 236–246.   [529, 532]

— (1965b). Dorsal spinocerebellar tract: Response pattern of nerve fibres to muscle stretch. *Science, N.Y.* **149**, 1109–1111.   [502]

Koeze, T. H. (1968). The independence of corticomotoneuronal and fusimotor pathways in the production of muscle contraction by motor cortex stimulation. *J. Physiol.* **197**, 87–105.   [522]

Koeze, T. H., Phillips, C. G. & Sheridan, J. D. (1968). Thresholds of cortical activation of muscle spindles and α motoneurones of the baboon's hand. *J. Physiol.* **195**, 419–449.   [522]

Landgren, S. & Silfvenius, H. (1968). Projections of the eye and neck region on the anterior suprasylvian cerebral cortex of the cat. *Acta physiol. scand.* **74**, 340–347.   [491]

— (1969). Projection to the cerebral cortex of group I muscle afferents from the cat's hind limb. *J. Physiol.* **200**, 353–372.   [483, 484]

Landgren, S., Silfvenius, H. & Wolsk, D. (1967). Somato-sensory paths to the second cortical projection area of the group I muscle afferents. *J. Physiol.* **191**, 543–559.   [485]

Laporte, Y., Lundberg, A. & Oscarsson, O. (1956). Functional organisation of the dorsal spino-cerebellar tract in the cat. II. Single fibre recording in Flechsig's fasciculus on electrical stimulation of various peripheral nerves. *Acta physiol. scand.* **36**, 188–203.   [500]

Larson, B., Miller, S. & Oscarsson, O. (1969). Termination and functional organization of the dorsolateral spino-olivocerebellar path. *J. Physiol.* **203**, 611–640.   [509]

Lundberg, A. & Weight, F. (1971). Functional organization of connexions to the ventral spinocerebellar tract. *Expl. Brain Res.* **12**, 295–316. [507]

Lewis, D.M. (1969). The response of primary afferent fibres from cat spindles to single volleys in sensory nerves. *J. Physiol.* **203**, 22–24P. [517]

McIntyre, A. K. (1953). Cortical projection of afferent impulses in muscle nerves. *Proc. Univ. Otago Med. Sch.* **31**, 5–6. [481]

— (1962). Central projections of impulses from receptors activated by muscle stretch. In *Symposium on Muscle Receptors* ed. Barker, D. pp. 19–29, Hong Kong: Hong Kong University Press. [481]

McIntyre, A. K., Holman, M. E. & Veale, J. L. (1967). Cortical responses to impulses from single Pacinian corpuscles in the cat's hindlimb. *Expl Brain Res.* **4**, 243–255. [483]

Mallart, M. A. (1968). Thalamic projection of muscle nerve afferents in the cat. *J. Physiol.* **194**, 337–353. [481, 484]

Malliani, A., Carli, G., Mancia, G., & Zanchetti, A. (1968). Behavioural effects of electrical stimulation of group I muscle afferents in acute thalamic cats. *J. Neurophysiol.* **31**, 210–220. [499]

Megirian, D. & Troth, A. (1964). Vestibular and muscle nerve connections to pyramidal tract neurons of cat. *J. Neurophysiol.* **27**, 481–492. [490]

Merton, P. A. (1964). Human position sense and sense of effort. *Symp. Soc. exptl. Biol.* **18**, 387–400. [495]

Mountcastle, V. B. (1957). Modality and topographic properties of single neurons of cat's somatic sensory cortex. *J. Neurophysiol.* **20**, 408–434. [492, 493]

Mountcastle, V. B., Covian, M. R. & Harrison, R. (1952). The central representation of some forms of deep sensibility. *Res. Publs Ass. Res. Nerv. ment. Dis.* **30**, 339–370. [481]

Mountcastle, V. B., Poggio, G. F. & Werner, G. (1963). The relation of thalamic cell response to peripheral stimuli varied over an intensive continuum. *J. Neurophysiol.* **26**, 807–834. [492]

Mountcastle, V. B. & Powell, T. P. S. (1959). Central nervous mechanisms subserving position sense and kinesthesis. *Bull. John Hopkins Hosp.* **105**, 173–200. [492, 494]

Oscarsson, O. (1965). Functional organisation of the spino- and cuneocerebellar tracts. *Physiol. Rev.* **45**, 495–522. [500, 505, 508]

— (1967). Functional significance of information channels from the spinal cord to the cerebellum. In *Neurophysiological Basis of Normal and abnormal Motor Activities*, ed. Yahr, M. D. & Purpura, D. P. pp. 93–113 New York: Raven Press. [500]

— (1968). Termination and functional organisation of the ventral spinoolivocerebellar path. *J. Physiol.* **196**, 453–478. [509]

Oscarsson, O. & Rosén, I. (1963). Projection to cerebral cortex of large muscle spindle afferents in forelimb nerves of the cat. *J. Physiol.* **169**, 924–945. [482, 484, 489]

Oscarsson, O., Rosén, I. & Sulg, I. (1966). Organisation of neurones in the cat cerebral cortex that are influenced from Group I muscle afferents. *J. Physiol.* **183**, 189–210. [486, 489]

Paillard, J. & Brouchon, M. (1968). Active and passive movements in the calibration of position sense. In *The Neuropsychology of Spatially Oriented Behaviour*, ed. Freedman, S. J. pp. 37–55. Illinois: Dorsey Press.   [497]

Phillips, C. G., Powell, T. P. S. & Wiesendanger, M. (1971). Projection from low-threshold muscle afferents of hand and forearm to area 3a of baboon's cortex. *J. Physiol.* **217,** 419–446.   [486]

Pompeiano, O. & Swett, J. E. (1962). Identification of cutaneous and muscular afferent fibres producing EEG synchronization or arousal in normal cats. *Archs ital. Biol.* **100,** 343–380.   [498]

Provins, K. A. (1958). The effect of peripheral nerve block on the appreciation and execution of finger movements. *J. Physiol.* **143,** 55–67.   [495]

Rosén, I. (1969*a*). Afferent connections to group I activated cells in the main cuneate nucleus of the cat. *J. Physiol.* **204,** 209–236. [484–488]

— (1969*b*). Excitation of group I activated thalamocortical relay neurones in the cat. *J. Physiol.* **205,** 237–255.   [484–488]

Schomburg, E. D. (1970). Supraspinal interactions of anesthetic, neuroleptic and analeptic drugs on the fusimotor effects of pinna stimulation in the cat. *Expl Brain Res.* **10,** 182–196.   [533]

Sears, T. A. (1964). Efferent discharges in alpha and fusimotor fibres of intercostal nerves of the cat. *J. Physiol.* **174,** 295–315.   [523, 532]

Sherrington, C. S. (1900). The muscular sense. In *Textbook of Physiology*, ed. Schäfer, E. A. Vol. 2, pp. 1002–1025. Edinburgh: Pentland. [493]

Shimazu, H., Hongo, T. & Kubota, K. (1962*a*). Two types of central influences on gamma motor system. *J. Neurophysiol.* **25,** 309–323.   [530, 532]

— (1962*b*). Nature of central regulation of muscle-spindle activity. In *Symposium on Muscle Receptors*, ed. Barker, D. pp. 49–57. Hong Kong: Hong Kong University Press.   [530, 532]

Silfvenius, H. (1968). Cortical projections of large muscle afferents from the cat's forelimb. *Acta physiol. scand.* **74,** 25–26A.   [486]

Skoglund, S. (1956). Anatomical and physiological studies of knee joint innervation in cat. *Acta physiol. scand.* **36,** Suppl. 124, 1–101.   [492]

Steg, G. (1964). Efferent muscle innervation and rigidity. *Acta physiol. scand.* **61,** suppl. 225, 1–53.   [511]

Swett, J. E. & Bourassa, C. M. (1967*a*). Short latency activation of pyramidal tract cells by group I afferent volleys in the cat. *J. Physiol.* **189,** 101–117.   [490]

— (1967*b*). Comparison of sensory discrimination thresholds with muscle and cutaneous nerve volleys in the cat. *J. Neurophysiol.* **30,** 530–545.   [498]

Vallbo, Å. B. (1970). Slowly adapting muscle receptors in man. *Acta physiol. scand.* **78,** 315–333.   [512]

Vedel, J. P. & Mouillac-Baudevin, J. (1969*a*). Contrôle de l'activité des fibres fusimotrices dynamiques et statiques par la formation réticulée mésencéphalique chez le chat. *Expl. Brain Res.* **9,** 307–324.   [527]

Vedel, J. P. & Mouillac-Baudevin, J. (1969*b*). Étude fontionelle du contrôle de l'activité des fibres fusimotrices dynamiques et statiques par les formations réticulées mésencéphalique, pontique et bulbaire chez le chat. *Expl. Brain Res.* **9**, 325–345.   [517, 527]

— (1970). Contrôle pyramidal de l'activité des fibres fusimotrices dynamiques et statiques chez le chat. *Expl. Brain Res.* **10**, 39–63.
[524, 527–531]

Vedel, J. P. & Paillard, J. (1965). Effet différential des stimulations du noyau caudé et du cortex frontal sur la sensibilité dynamique des terminaisons fusoriales primaires chez le chat. *J. Physiol, Paris* **57**, 716–717.   [527]

Voorhoeve, P. E. (1960). Autochthonous activity of fusimotor neurones in the cat. *Acta physiol. pharmacol. néerl.* **9**, 1–43.   [529]

Walløe, L. (1970*a*). Information loss during synaptic transfer. In *Excitatory Synaptic Mechanisms*, ed. Andersen, P. & Jansen, J. K. S. pp. 275–276: Oslo: Universitetsforlaget.   [504]

— (1970*b*). On the transmission of information through sensory neurones. *Biophys. J.* **10**, 745–763.   [504]

Walløe, L., Jansen, J. K. S. & Nygaard, K. (1969). A computer simulated model of a second order sensory neurone. *Kybernetik* **6**, 130–140.
[504]

Yokota, T. & Voorhoeve, P. E. (1969). Pyramidal control of fusimotor neurons supplying extensor muscles in the cat's forelimb. *Expl. Brain Res.* **9**, 96–115.   [524, 528]

10

MUSCLE SPINDLES AND THE SERVO-ASSISTANCE OF MOVEMENT

I T is clearly premature to hope to be able to specify in detail all the various uses made by the CNS of the information that it receives from the muscle receptors. For this to become at all feasible will require an appreciably fuller understanding of central processes than we currently aspire to. At present just 'the fact that the muscle spindles are contractile end organs is still the most challenging observation in the physiology of muscular control' (Merton, 1964). It none the less seems desirable to discuss present views on their role, though these should not be regarded as final. Moreover, it should be remembered throughout that the information which is conveyed by the muscle afferents may be expected to be processed more or less simultaneously at several different levels of the CNS.

Effects of de-afferentation on motor control

The demonstration that muscle afferents have relatively little to contribute to conscious sensation leaves them to operate subconsciously, and everything we know shows that their job is to assist in the regulation of muscle contraction. The effect of de-afferentation of a limb provided the earliest indication that this is so. According to Sherrington (1900), the first observations on the effect of de-afferenting a limb by cutting its dorsal spinal nerve roots were made by Panizza in 1834 in the course of work aimed at confirming the Bell–Magendie law. Panizza was apparently surprised to find, on observing the behaviour of an animal after cutting what he believed to be purely sensory roots, that it had a 'marked impairment of the local motility' with a clumsiness of movement of the affected limb. Repeated confirmation and extension of this observation provides an initial basis for attributing an important motor regulatory role to muscle afferents. No such gross impairment appears to be produced by section of purely cutaneous nerves though the matter does not seem to have been seriously put to the test since Sherrington (1910, p. 77) found that severing 'all the nerve trunks directly distributed to all four feet up to and above the wrists and ankles' produced only a minimal disturbance of walking in the cat.

Mott & Sherrington (1895) made the classical observations in the monkey of the effect both on the forelimb and on the hindlimb of cutting the appropriate dorsal roots. They found that movements of the hand and foot were practically abolished but that movements at the shoulder and hip were much less impaired.

Lassek (1953) later obtained very much the same effects and found no appreciable recovery even when the de-afferentation was performed in the very young animal (Lassek & Moyer, 1953). All other observers have agreed that, whatever the species, local de-afferentation leads to an ataxia; a recent description of this has been given for the lizard (Székely, Czeh & Vörös, 1969). However, there has been considerable controversy about how far the desensitised limb can be used (see review by Nathan & Sears, 1960, who should be consulted for more detailed references). Lassek, like Sherrington & Mott, found so little use to be made of the limb that he considered the functional paralysis to be more severe than that produced by ablating the motor cortex. But with an adequate incentive an animal would appear to be able to come to make more use of a highly inefficient organ than it does when it can better achieve its purpose by using the remaining normal limbs. According to Nathan & Sears, Munk in 1909 induced a monkey to make reasonable use of a de-afferented forelimb by systematically training it to do so and providing sufficient incentive. More recent experiments have entirely borne out this finding and have also shown that the use made by a monkey of a de-afferented hand is greatly increased when the opposite forelimb is also de-afferented (Knapp, Taub & Berman, 1963). Wiesendanger (1964) found that the cat makes moderate use of a de-afferented hindlimb. Konorski (1962) was able to elicit a previously established conditioned reflex from a de-afferented hindlimb, or even to establish a response from it *de novo* (cat, rat, dog). In man, Foerster obtained movements of the arm after de-afferentation, and Sears & Nathan obtained voluntary contraction of the levator scapulae after section of the upper cervical dorsal roots which supply it. In this latter case, however, the contraction was unobtainable for the first fortnight after the operation when the muscle appeared paralysed. Thus there is no question of the α motoneurones becoming completely inaccessible to supraspinal excitation after de-afferentation as would occur if they could only be activated via the 'γ loop'; but their accessibility to their physiologically mediated motor commands would seem to be reduced. On stimulating the motor cortex, however, Mott & Sherrington could detect no difference in the motor responses on the normal and the de-afferented sides. More recently Lewis & Porter (1971) found that local de-afferentation made no difference to the cortical threshold for eliciting a minimum contraction of the foot muscles of the monkey by cortical stimulation; they concluded that the muscular responses produced by brief repetitive trains of stimuli owed nothing to activity transmitted around the γ loop, though this still leaves the matter open for other situations.

It would be interesting to have the nature of the ataxic and other functional deficits occurring after de-afferentation analysed in more detail. But dorsal root section is probably too gross a method, involving too many kinds of afferent fibre from too far apart, for any very precise understanding of the particular role of the muscle receptors to be obtained thereby. It may be noted in this respect that de-afferentation only produces appreciable effects when several contiguous dorsal roots are severed, without allowing any of their filaments to escape. The deficit produced by de-afferentation may well be partly due to elimination of cutaneous and joint afferents, but *a priori* the muscle receptor inputs seem likely to play a major part. This is further indicated by the action of a new drug, an unsymmetrical bis-methonium compound, which has an apparently specific effect in depressing spindle discharges. When given to a normal cat or dog it produces so gross an ataxia that the animals are unable to stand (Matsushita, Yanagisawa, & Shimazu, 1965). The drug had no obvious action on nerve, muscle, the discharge of touch receptors, or the spinal reflexes elicited by electrical stimulation of nerves, but it abolished the response of spindle afferents to stretching or to decamethonium, which causes an intrafusal contraction (primary and secondary spindle afferents, however, do not seem to have been differentiated, nor tendon organs tested).

In man, the interference with normal spindle function produced by a presumed selective block of fusimotor fibres by the intrathecal injection of procaine has been described as producing a feeling of 'weakness' although none was externally detectable; no gross incoordination was described, though this could perhaps have usefully been tested in more detail (Landau, Weaver, & Hornbein, 1960; Nathan, 1969). The 'weakness' is perhaps due to a subjective recognition that the higher motor centres may have to discharge more forcibly to achieve a given result, since they probably have to supply an extra quantity of 'direct' excitation to the α motoneurones so as to compensate for the loss of the servo-assistance normally provided by the indirect 'γ route' (see later).

In the cat, Thulin (1960) considered that normal use of the calf muscles in walking depended upon the presence of fusimotor control. He based this on observations of animals recovering from ablation of a short length of the popliteal nerve when large afferent and efferent fibres appeared to regenerate and establish normal functional connections some weeks earlier than the γ efferents did so.

Ways in which the CNS might use the information it receives from the muscle receptors

There seem to be several separate roles that the muscle receptors might play in the control of movement and which are by no means mutually exclusive. Different regions of the brain can probably operate in-parallel on the same signals to achieve different purposes, that is to say that different kinds of analysis are probably carried on simultaneously at different levels of the CNS. At the lowest conceptual level, spindles may be suggested to be present to maintain central excitability and with it the tone of skeletal muscle. The fact that the spinal cord and other centres receive a tonic spindle input means that when they are deprived of this their 'excitability' will usually be decreased; other centres may, however, perhaps be facilitated by removal of a predominantly inhibitory input. This sort of approach, however, provides no real explanation of the 'usefulness' to the body of having muscle receptors. If they did not exist the appropriate excitabilities could probably be maintained by other means, such as by a variation of neuronal threshold or the introduction of other inputs.

A more profitable way of looking at things is from the point of view of a motor control organ which has to deal with the external world where things are rarely precisely predictable, and where a given effect can never be guaranteed to follow a given muscular contraction. Moreover, the properties of the muscles themselves may vary with time, as in fatigue, and so they may not always produce contractions of the same strength in response to the same motor command. Thus on commanding a movement a higher motor centre could usefully be continuously informed about the progress of the movement so that it could apply a correcting action if the actual movement should differ from the one desired. One way of so assessing the progress of a movement would be to continuously compare the actual with the expected performance and use the difference to initiate correcting action. Such direct servo-compensation would be most expeditiously achieved reflexly in the spinal cord. But with the progressive encephalisation occurring in the higher mammals it might well be appropriate for certain higher centres also to exert such a direct servo-control, in so far as they are concerned with continuously ordering a movement.

A related but different use of a feedback to a higher centre would be to employ it in learning, after the event, to improve the motor performance on the next attempt. This could be done by taking detailed note of just how far the results had departed from those which had been desired and then making the appropriate adjustments to the motor programmes which must be stored somewhere in the CNS. Of course, a movement will often be judged merely by whether or not it achieved its final objective; but if detailed adjustments are to be made to the motor pattern to be issued the next time the movement is required, then a detailed record of what happened previously would appear to be essential. Clearly for this kind of thing to be possible the muscle afferents must send their signals to a part of the CNS which is endowed with memory. Another sort of use for afferent information is to tell a higher centre the present state of affairs in the muscles, for such information is likely to be a pre-requisite for the organisation of a detailed pattern of motor discharges to despatch for the instruction of a lower motor centre.

With one exception there is unfortunately very little that can be said about these and other speculations. The exception is the direct servo-control of movement. Because of the immediacy of its response it has to some extent been possible to analyse such servo-control by experiments restricted to the periphery. The role of the afferents in the servo-control of movement will therefore be dealt with at some length. The future may well show, however, that it is only a small part of their functional role and our present pre-occupation with it to have been a simple consequence of the limited state of current experimental techniques.

The introduction of the idea that movement may be produced by a 'follow-up length servo' with its command signal delivered by the γ efferents

Liddell & Sherrington established the stretch reflex as a mechanism for maintaining the length of a muscle at a constant value in the face of external disturbing forces. Moreover, they saw its un-controlled action in the decerebrate as leading to a caricature of normal standing. This view on its own does not explain how any particular muscle can be adjusted to have more than one length so as to fit in with the requirements of different postures, even though the earlier description of the plastic tone of certain decerebrate preparations had hinted that there were more complicated mechanisms at work as well. Nor does it explain why spindles should be present in all muscles and not just postural ones. Shortly afterwards, Rossi (1927) pointed out that varying degrees of intrafusal contraction might alter the responsiveness of the spindle afferent endings so as to allow a muscle under stretch-reflex control to take up a number of different lengths. Unfortunately this suggestion seems to have passed largely unnoticed at the time. This was presumably partly because it was based on a number of then unproven assumptions, such as that there exists a separate system of fusimotor fibres and that the muscle spindle is responsible for the stretch reflex.

In the early 1950's, with the establishment of the occurrence of specific fusimotor fibres and with the acquisition of a certain amount of knowledge about their properties it became natural to enquire into their functions and the reasons for their existence. Kuffler & Hunt (1952) in reviewing their own work on the effect of stimulating single fusimotor fibres suggested that an important function of the fusimotor fibres was to maintain a steady afferent flow from the spindles in spite of shortening of the muscle in which they lay, so that their reflex function could be preserved at all times. In the absence of fusimotor discharge the primary ending is silenced by a very small release of its muscle and thus by a very small contraction. This view is tantamount to saying that fusimotor action allows the spindle to preserve the same high sensitivity over a wide range of muscle lengths and so is in keeping with some more recent suggestions on the function of the dynamic fusimotor fibres. But in its early simple form Kuffler & Hunt's suggestion did nothing to explain why the spindle could not have been designed so that it did not go silent on release, nor why the fusimotor fibres have become largely separated from the ordinary motor fibres in the higher mammals; evolution would appear to have discarded the simpler shared skeleto-fusimotor innervation found in more primitive forms.

Answers to these questions were provided by Merton (1951, 1953), who unknowingly repeated Rossi when he suggested that the job of the γ motor fibres was to supply the command signal in a 'follow-up length servo' controlling muscular contraction. Figure 10.1 illustrates this idea. Some movements, 'urgent movements'

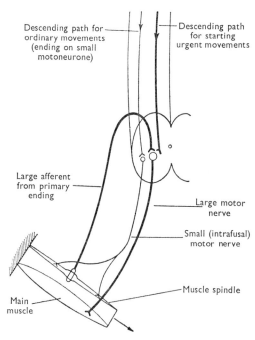

Descending path for ordinary movements (ending on small motoneurone)

Descending path for starting urgent movements

Large afferent from primary ending

Large motor nerve

Small (intrafusal) motor nerve

Muscle spindle

Main muscle

FIG. 10.1. Merton's original diagram of the two possible motor pathways to skeletal muscle. (Merton, 1953, Fig. 3.)

in the diagram, were supposed to be produced in the long-familiar way by impulses from the higher centres impinging straight on to the large α motoneurones, thus directly causing the muscle to contract. Other movements, 'ordinary movements' in the figure, were suggested to be produced rather indirectly by impulses from the higher centres exciting the γ motoneurones rather than the α motoneurones and thereby eliciting a powerless intrafusal contraction, but with excitation of spindle primary endings. The resulting Ia afferent discharge then monosynaptically excites the α motoneurones of the same muscle, and so it contracts. Granit

(1955) subsequently described and popularised these two pathways as the α and the γ routes of motor control.

The suggested advantage of the rather roundabout γ route is that it employs the stretch reflex, which is seen as a powerful servo for automatically holding the muscle at the particular length 'demanded' by the fusimotor discharge and thus unaffected by any disturbances produced by variations in the loading of the muscle or in its strength. A servomechanism may be defined as any automatic control mechanism which is actuated by an 'error signal' occurring in a closed-loop control cycle and which possesses power amplification. The stretch reflex, being independent of the cortex, is clearly automatic and its 'power amplification' is provided by the contraction of the muscle. The closed-loop control cycle may be identified as being: tension on muscle–stretch of muscle–excitation of spindle endings—excitation of the α motoneurones of the same muscle–contraction of muscle–increase in muscle tension. This is a negative feedback loop for the increase in tension in the muscle on its contraction opposes the applied tension, and so tends to maintain the length of the muscle constant in spite of the disturbance. Equally, the muscle tends to maintain the same length when the load on it is reduced.

The way in which fusimotor activity might change the balance point of this servomechanism is illustrated diagrammatically in Fig. 10.2 which shows what would happen to the spindle afferent firing were the command for a new length to be issued solely via the γ route. The top line shows the relation between the frequency of Ia firing and the length of the muscle in the presence of a constant fusimotor discharge of y impulses/sec. The bottom line shows the relationship in the absence of fusimotor firing. Imagine that initially the muscle is at length $L + \Delta L$, that there is no γ discharge, and that the stretch reflex is automatically maintaining the muscle at this length. The Ia discharge will thus be F impulses/sec as given by point A. If the fusimotor discharge is then suddenly increased to y impulses/sec the spindle firing will promptly increase to $F + \Delta F$ (point B) thus producing a more powerful monosynaptic excitation of the α motoneurones than before. As a result the α motor discharge will increase and the muscle will begin to shorten, since the contraction will now be greater than that required to oppose any pre-existing external load. As the muscle shortens the Ia firing will progressively decrease, the frequency of

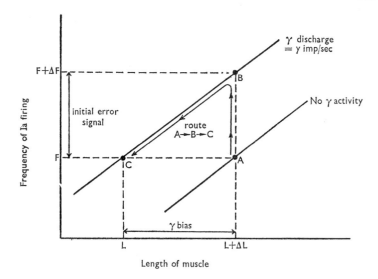

FIG. 10.2. Diagram to illustrate the hypothesis that movement may be produced by a 'follow-up length servo' with its command delivered by the γ efferents. The two straight lines show the relation between the frequency of Ia firing and the length of the muscle in the presence and absence of γ efferent activity. The loop ABC shows what would happen on the servo hypothesis on the arrival of a command to attain length L when the muscle was initially at length $L + \Delta L$ and under the control of the servo-loop, but without any pre-existing γ bias.

firing at any length being given by the upper line. Shortening will continue until point C is reached when the Ia firing will have been restored to its previous value so that the system is once again in equilibrium. Thus a fusimotor discharge of y impulses/sec eventually produces a change of length of ΔL and so may be looked upon as having been the command for this amount of shortening; different frequencies of fusimotor discharge would lead to corresponding differences in the amount of reflex shortening.

The value of ΔL in Fig. 10.2 may be called the 'bias' required to make the Ia firing follow the upper line. The term 'γ bias' was introduced by Eldred, Granit & Merton (1953) and then defined as 'that shortening required to reduce the spindle rate to the same frequency as the unbiassed spindle at the original length' (their p. 500); this corresponds to ΔL. If the lines describing the behaviour of the biassed and the unbiassed spindle are not both straight and parallel the term γ bias loses some of its simplicity, for it will not then be constant at different lengths of the muscle. Even so, in the context of servo-control the 'γ bias' expressed as a length appears a more meaningful measure of activity than the change in the frequency of firing of either the γ fibres or of the Ia fibres (γ and ΔF impulses/sec in Fig. 2). It should be noted, however, that although the term γ bias was originally given this rather precise definition, few later workers have bothered to use it in other than a qualitative sense as a synonym for γ discharge.

The initial increase in Ia firing, ΔF, brought about by the γ discharge may be looked upon as the 'error' or 'misalignment' signal within the servo-loop which brings about an increased motor discharge until it is itself annulled. During the period when the spindle discharge has increased as a result of fusimotor activity the spindle is sometimes said to be 'shorter' than the main muscle; the servo-induced contraction is then seen as continuing to produce shortening of the main muscle until the lengths of the spindle and of the main muscle have been equalised. This helpful terminology should, however, be recognised to be somewhat abstract, and if taken literally may lead to confusion. Intrafusal contraction cannot alter the overall length of the muscle spindle, because it is constrained by its attachments to the much stronger extrafusal fibres. The contraction does, however, lead to a slight shortening of the spindle poles at the expense of a slight elongation of the sensorially innervated equatorial region. Thus it is certainly true that fusimotor firing produces a slight shortening of the spindle poles so that they are 'shorter' than the main muscle. But on then allowing the main muscle to shorten there will be a further shortening of the intrafusal poles. When the servo is in effective command this shortening will continue until the tension in the spindle poles has fallen to the value which allows the sensorially innervated region to be restored to the length that it originally had before the fusimotor discharge increased (A). Thus to say that γ activity makes the spindle 'shorten' is just another way of saying that the frequency-response curve of its afferent has been shifted to the left so that any particular frequency of discharge occurs at a shorter muscle length than before. (It may be noted further that the length of the central Ia innervated region is likely to depend upon the prevailing dynamic conditions as well as the static length.)

A further basic premise of the servo hypothesis is that the stretch reflex is sufficiently powerful (i.e. is sufficiently stiff, has enough gain) to ensure that the shortening commanded by the γ bias occurs irrespective of the value of any load and the variation of the strength of extrafusal fibres with their length; the servo will then produce the appropriate increase in α motor discharge required to compensate entirely for such things. If a movement were to be produced solely by the α route then the command signal to the α motoneurones from the higher centres would of itself have to take account of these factors, whereas a command issued via the γ route does not. Thus the use of the γ route of excitation would save the higher centres a certain amount of effort, as was originally suggested by Rossi for postural control.

Apart from the above sort of theoretical considerations, Merton (1951, 1953) based his suggestion of the servo-control of movement on a careful study of the 'silent period' which occurred in the electrical activity set up by the voluntary contraction of one of his own thumb muscles (the adductor pollicis) when he stimulated its nerve electrically and made the muscle twitch. He particularly emphasised, as shown in Fig. 10.3, that a silent period was still induced by a twitch which was so small that it approached in size the spontaneous fluctuations in tension which occur in a voluntary contraction; these also could therefore be suspected to be accompanied by their own silent periods. The silent period denotes, of course, a temporary cessation of motor discharge and Merton saw it as the response of a length servo to an unexpected shortening of the muscle. He was thus encouraged in his suggestion that the pre-existing voluntary contraction was being produced by a such a servo, with the muscle spindle acting as its peripheral transducer to supply the length feedback. But the mere detection of a silent period during a twitch may now be seen as being largely immaterial in deciding for or against the employment of the γ route by the CNS in eliciting a voluntary contraction. This is because several other factors, in addition to the silencing of spindles, are now recognised to contribute to the silent period elicited by nerve stimulation (i.e. Golgi tendon organ discharge, recurrent inhibition via Renshaw cells, and the synchronisation of the discharge of α motoneurones). Some of these complexities have recently been studied by Granit, Kellerth & Szumski (1966a) using intracellular recording from the silenced motoneurones.

Shortly after Merton made his suggestion Eldred, Granit & Merton (1953) recorded the response of spindle afferents during reflexly induced movements of the soleus muscle of the decerebrate cat. Figure 10.4 illustrates two of their most important findings which have encouraged much subsequent similar work. The first is that when the dorsal roots were intact the spindle firing increased

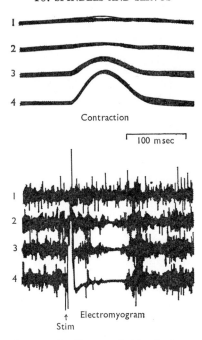

FIG. 10.3. The persistence of a silent period in the human electromyogram for the smallest of twitches. This was part of the original evidence for the servo hypothesis. The records show the response of the adductor pollicis when its nerve was stimulated while the subject was making a steady contraction. The strength of the stimulus was increased from above downwards. It was just subthreshold for the motor fibres for the top traces of each set (1,1) and was just supramaximal for the bottom ones (4,4). The initial tension was always 1 kg and so also was the increase in tension produced by the largest of the twitches. The subject was endeavouring to maintain a constant force by watching a visual display of tension. All four traces of each kind were recorded at the same gain. (Merton, 1951, Fig. 3, reversed in contrast and retouched.)

during the contraction instead of slowing. This showed that there was a concomitant increase in fusimotor firing which was more than enough to offset the unloading effect of the extrafusal contraction. They pointed out that the increased afferent firing provided a possible cause for the α firing which was actually producing the contraction, since the increased afferent discharge would have led to an increased Ia monosynaptic excitation of the α motoneurones. Their second major finding supported this interpretation. It

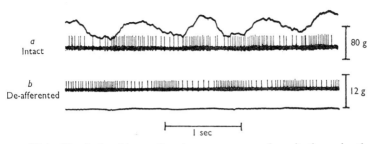

a
Intact

b
De-afferented

80 g

12 g

⊢———— I sec ————⊣

FIG. 10.4. Classical evidence for the occurrence of excitation via the γ route. The contraction of the soleus muscle and the discharge of one of its spindle afferents were recorded in the decerebrate cat while the animal's head was turned rhythmically from side to side. The ventral roots were intact throughout, but the dorsal roots were cut between *a* and *b*. After de-afferentation the frank contraction was absent but the spindle response continued very much as before. The spindle discharge was recorded from a thin dorsal root filament but the remainder of the appropriate dorsal roots were left intact. Isometric recording. (Eldred Granit & Merton, 1953, Fig. 11.)

was that after cutting the dorsal roots and thereby interrupting the γ route the reflex muscle contraction was abolished, but the spindle afferents behaved in the same way as before. Both these findings are those which would be obtained if such tonic reflex movements in decerebrate cats are produced via the γ route. But they are not actually sufficient to prove that the excitation must have been mediated solely in this way, rather than by the co-activation of alpha and gamma neurones by the descending influences. To prove that a contraction is solely dependent on the γ route it also requires to be shown that the afferent firing occurs early enough and is sufficient in degree to be entirely responsible for reflexly eliciting the observed contractions, rather than simply facilitating them. In addition, it requires to be shown that after the de-afferentation the α motoneurones no longer display any increase in their excitability 'in parallel' with the increased afferent discharge. Without these controls de-afferentation has not been excluded as acting partly by removing a steady afferent excitatory input to the α motoneurones, so that their excitability falls sufficiently below threshold for them to fail to discharge in spite of receiving a considerable amount of direct excitation from descending pathways.

None the less, for about the ten years from 1955 onwards it

became widely accepted that the γ route could operate on its own as an independently controllable motor pathway for eliciting gross muscle contraction. This view was perhaps the best known in the form in which it was stated in 1956 in a short but influential review article by Hammond, Merton & Sutton. In the course of it they said that 'while the existence of a follow-up length servo seems to be as well established as most concepts in this field, it is perfectly clear from many experiments on de-afferented limbs (in which the servo is necessarily out of action) that movements can occur without it'. A subsequent author commented that 'in understanding this we have gained considerable insight into the way the nervous system manages its affairs'. But some neurophysiologists remained sceptical (for example, Hunt & Perl, 1960). Since about 1965, however, it has been progressively recognised that the servo hypothesis as expressed above is a considerable simplification, and that it is unlikely that any movements are initiated purely via the γ route. α and γ central co-activation seems to be the rule, though in varying degree, and the muscle control system would appear better described as 'servo-assisted' by the fusimotor fibres rather than as a 'follow-up length servo' with the input restricted to the fusimotor fibres (see later). This is not to doubt that an increase of γ firing, if of sufficient magnitude, is able to reflexly excite α motoneurones 'across the γ loop' by their action on the spindle. As illustrated in Fig. 10.5 such an occurrence was demonstrated at the very outset by Hunt (1952) on stimulating isolated γ efferent fibres. It has also been seen by Granit, Kellerth & Szumski (1966b) on stimulating whole ventral roots at high frequency, particularly after paralysing the extrafusal contractions with gallamine.

Complications arising from the duality of both the sensory and the motor innervation of the spindle

The first problem which has to be faced with the original servo hypothesis is that it is based on too simple a view of structure. There are two kinds of fusimotor fibre and not just one, and there are also two kinds of afferent fibre. This is illustrated in Fig. 10.6 which shows the original simple servo scheme above and the currently more realistic scheme below, incorporating the dualities of sensory and motor innervation. Any discussion of function which ignores this complexity seems doomed from the start to be seriously incomplete. Moreover, the tension feedback provided by

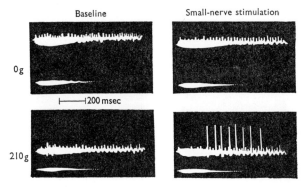

FIG. 10.5. 'Excitation across the γ loop' shown in the decerebrate cat by recording the discharge of an α motor fibre on stimulating the peripheral ends of a number of γ efferent fibres ('small-nerves'). The α motor fibre was isolated from the central end of a cut ventral root and was presumed to supply gastrocnemius because it could be tonically excited by pulling strongly upon the Achilles tendon (830 g). It could also be excited at a moderate initial tension by stimulating about 20 γ efferents to gastrocnemius; these were isolated by subdividing the peripheral end of the ventral root and could be stimulated independently of α motor fibres. The two initial tensions are given by the figures to the left. (Hunt, 1952, Fig. 12.)

the Golgi tendon organs cannot be omitted from any comprehensive scheme, and would appear to be just as important as the length feedback from the spindles. At the least, tension feedback would appear to provide a measure of compensation for the deleterious effects of muscle fatigue; various other more interesting possibilities have recently been raised by Houk, Singer & Goldman (1970).

The role of the secondary endings remains imponderable and one can do little more than reiterate the fact of their existence. It seems likely that their spinal action may be switchable by higher centres so that they may produce sometimes excitation and sometimes inhibition of the motoneurones of their own muscle (see Chap. 8). Further experimental analysis of their central actions is urgent, but perhaps may not be easy to achieve until a suitable stimulation technique can be developed which will allow the activation of the spindle group II fibres in the absence of all others. From the point of view of servo-control it may be emphasised that any static fusimotor action must forcibly activate the secondary endings along with the primary endings, so the signals from the

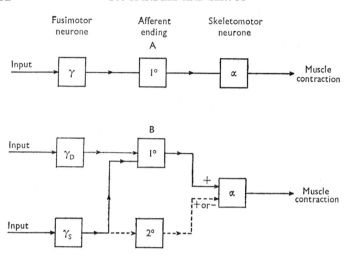

FIG. 10.6. Block diagram of the γ route for muscle activation. A, the original scheme. B, currently more realistic scheme including both kinds of fusimotor fibre and both kinds of afferent ending. As discussed in the text the dynamic fibres are thought to control the 'sensitivity' of the primary ending rather than providing a way of injecting 'commands' into the servo-loop. The static fibres, moreover, appear rarely if ever to be used for command signals in the absence of a corresponding direct central activation of α motoneurones. (Brown & Matthews, 1966, Fig. 9.)

two kinds of efferent are not entirely independent (and of course they are also linked by virtue of being excited by the same mechanical stimuli). An example of their linked activation occurring in the course of a reflexly induced contraction is shown in Fig. 10.7. In this example any 'error signal' of muscle misalignment would appear to be carried equally by the two kinds of afferent. Hongo & Shimazu (1965) observed similarly linked excitation of primary and secondary endings on stimulating various sites within the CNS. Indeed, taking other things into consideration it would appear to be only the secondary ending which provides a direct misalignment signal between the absolute values of the actual and the demanded lengths of the muscle. During any except an isometric contraction the primary ending gives a signal which will usually depend as much upon velocity stimuli as upon the absolute value of the muscle length. It would be remarkable if the signal from the secondary were not used to some extent in the servo-

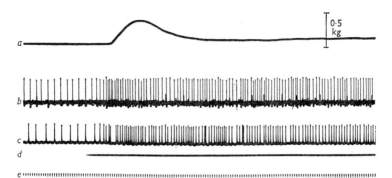

FIG. 10.7. The almost indistinguishable responses of a primary and of a secondary ending during a crossed extensor reflex of the soleus muscle in the decerebrate cat. Both accelerate, showing both have been activated by a fusimotor discharge. a, isometric tension; b, discharge of secondary ending. c, discharge of primary ending. d, signal marker indicating repetitive stimulation of contralateral popliteal nerve. e, 10 msec time marks. (Jansen & Matthews, 1962, Fig. 2.)

control of muscle, and also for informing higher centres how any movement has progressed.

Role of dynamic fibres. An immediate reaction to the more complicated scheme with a dual fusimotor control is that the simplicity of the γ route of the original scheme would be preserved if only the dynamic fibres were supposed to be entrusted with the job of injecting a command signal into the reflex loop. The primary endings would then be activated on their own, and the complications arising from the uncertainty of the central action of the spindle group II fibres would be by-passed. But this mode of operation simply will not work, because, as emphasised by Lennerstrand & Thoden (1968b), an increasing frequency of dynamic fusimotor stimulation appears to be incapable of overcoming the effects of muscle shortening and increasing the Ia discharge above the value pre-existing before shortening begins. Yet the production of an increased afferent discharge during muscle contraction is precisely what is required of the command signal operating a follow-up length servo. The dynamic fibres would seem to produce an intrafusal contraction which is just too slow for this purpose and which is unable to keep up with the more rapid contraction of the extrafusal muscle fibres. Figure 10.8 illustrates the inability of

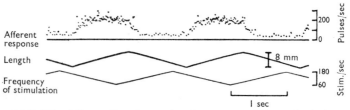

FIG. 10.8. The failure of an increasing frequency of dynamic fusimotor stimulation to overcome the depressing effects of muscle shortening on the discharge of a spindle primary ending. Top, instantaneous frequency of firing of a single afferent. Middle, stretch marker showing 'triangular' stretching, with stretch and release of 8 mm alternating at 1 second intervals. Bottom, stimulus marker showing the frequency of stimulation of a single dynamic fusimotor fibre which was varied 'triangularly between 60 and 180/sec. This stimulation was nearly completely out of phase with the stretching, so that as the stretch was increasing the stimulation was decreasing, and vice versa. Records from a primary ending of a hindlimb flexor muscle of the anaesthetised cat. (Lennerstrand & Thoden, 1968b, Fig. 2.)

dynamic fusimotor stimulation to overcome the unloading effect of a large release. It may be noted, however, that dynamic fibres might be somewhat more effective at counteracting the effect of releases which were of smaller extent and at a lower velocity.

The function of the dynamic fibres seems likely to be to control the parameters of response of the primary ending so that it gives a greater or lesser response to any given stimulus. This would provide one way of controlling the sensitivity of the stretch reflex loop to external disturbances. The most important parameter controlled by the dynamic fibres may well be the sensitivity of the primary ending to stretches of small amplitude (see Chap. 5) thus increasing the effectiveness with which the servo-loop can deal with small deformations. Dynamic action also increases the velocity responsiveness of the primary endings to stretches of large amplitude. This should further help the muscle to reflexly resist stretch and also help improve the damping and thus the stability of the stretch reflex loop (see later). Small deformations, however, seem likely to be the ones which the stretch reflex servo can most successfully deal with. By their very occurrence large sudden extensions of the muscle show that the stretch reflex has failed to achieve its purpose, namely the maintenance of a constant length of the muscle.

These effects of dynamic fibres would both appear chiefly important while the stretch reflex is performing a static holding action, and it remains an open question as to how far they are effective while the muscle is shortening. Because of the slowness of their contraction it seems possible that the nuclear bag intrafusal muscle fibres may then go slack so that the branches of the primary ending upon them then cease to contribute to the overall afferent discharge occurring in the Ia fibre. If the small-amplitude sensitivity and the velocity-sensitivity of the primary ending are derived from its bag branches then its sensitivity to these stimuli might be lost during rapid shortening. However, in postural contractions or in slow tracking movements dynamic fibre activity should probably be able to exert a continuous control over the responsiveness of the primary endings. It may be noted also, as is obvious, that a rapid contraction of one skeletal muscle entails a forcible rapid extension of its antagonist and any pre-existing dynamic bias on the antagonistic spindles will largely determine their response to this stimulus. The whole matter of the effect of dynamic stimulation during shortening and also during concomitant static fusimotor activation could usefully be explored in more detail. During the combined stimulation of static and dynamic fibres the usual dynamic sensitising action is seen on the response of the primary ending to a large stretch, but on release the ending keeps on firing because of the static fusimotor action; it then usually falls nearly silent when the dynamic fibres are acting on their own. It remains uncertain whether or not static fusimotor action obscures the sensitising of the primary ending to small amplitude stretching normally produced by the dynamic fibres.

Role of static fibres. On the other hand, stimulation of static fusimotor fibres at an increasing frequency can still increase the discharge of both the primary and the secondary endings during muscle shortening. The static fibres may thus reasonably be suggested to transmit a command signal for muscle contraction and to form a part of a follow-up servo system for producing movement. Whether they actually do so is a matter for experiment. It should be noted, however, that Lennerstrand & Thoden (1968b) found considerable differences in the effectiveness with which different static fibres could increase spindle firing during muscle shortening.

It remains uncertain whether static fibres are also important for their action in changing the parameters of response of the spindle as well as in altering its bias. They would certainly appear to reduce both the velocity responsiveness of the primary ending and its sensitivity to stretch of small amplitude. Such a reduction in spindle sensitivity would seem a reasonable thing to happen when the CNS switches from using the spindle as an element in a postural servo to using it to provide a degree of servo-assistance in a large rapid movement, which might saturate the transducer if its sensitivity were allowed to remain high. In slower movements the loss of sensitivity produced by static action might be an undesirable side effect which could be overcome by the central co-activation of dynamic fibres along with the static ones; this might also be a useful action of any branches which static fibres put onto the nuclear bag intrafusal muscle fibres in addition to their main ones on the chain fibres. In addition, high-frequency stimulation of static fibres may appreciably increase the positional sensitivity of both primary and secondary endings (i.e. the slope of the relation between frequency of firing and the extension). This effect has been seen under both static conditions and during slow stretching of a muscle, but whether significant effects occur with the more physiological activation of fusimotor fibres at lower frequencies remains uncertain (Lennerstrand & Thoden, 1968a; Brown, Lawrence & Matthews, 1969).

Evidence for the normal occurrence of α and γ co-activation, and hence for the servo-assistance of movement

The next question is whether a movement is ever produced solely by means of the static fusimotor route. The present answer is that no movement has yet been proved to occur in this way. The original evidence for such an occurrence has already been suggested to be inconclusive. The common finding that γ's may be activated before α's in reflex activation or central stimulation certainly shows that they are the more reflexly accessible, but this alone is not enough. What is more important is that α and γ fibres are often activated 'in parallel' and it will be remembered (Chap. 9) that some descending tracts monosynaptically activate both kinds of neurones, possibly by the self-same fibres. Fortunately, there are now four situations in which natural or nearly natural movements have been observed, and in each of which there appears to

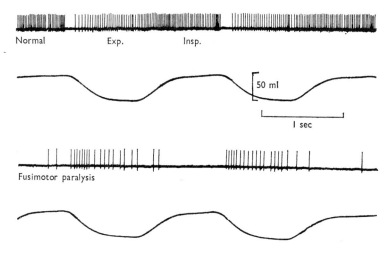

Normal   Exp.   Insp.

50 ml

I sec

Fusimotor paralysis

FIG. 10.9. The demonstration of a powerful fusimotor activation of spindle afferents during normal breathing. The records show the discharge of a single afferent fibre from a spindle in an inspiratory intercostal muscle. This was obtained from a dorsal root filament in the anaesthetised cat with intact ventral roots. It was breathing in the manner shown by the volume trace below. The top records were obtained under normal conditions and show an acceleration of discharge when the muscle contracts. This demonstrates that fusimotor fibres were being excited approximately 'in parallel' with the α motor fibres to the muscle, as the pattern of firing is the reverse of that found with de-afferented spindles (i.e. firing on stretching, silence on shortening). The bottom traces confirm this view by showing the appropriate 'passive' behaviour of the ending when its γ efferents had been paralysed by applying procaine to the appropriate intercostal nerve; this was done without paralysing the α motor fibres so that the muscle continued to contract. (Critchlow & Euler, 1963, Plate 3, retouched.)

be central co-activation of α and γ neurones, presumably including static ones.

Respiration in the cat. The most highly analysed system is that of the respiratory muscles contracting in normal respiration. These have been studied by both Euler and his colleagues and by Sears, with very good general agreement in their findings (Euler, 1966; Sears, 1964*b*). Recording from spindle afferents both of inspiratory and of expiratory muscles shows that the discharge of any particular afferent increases when its muscle is contracting and decreases

TM

when it is relaxing, as shown in Fig. 10.9. This indicates that the α and γ fibres are firing in sympathy, for otherwise the spindles would tend to be silenced during contraction. Recording from thin nerve filaments confirms that the α and γ fibres are indeed being co-activated, as illustrated in Fig. 10.10. Moreover, this still occurs after cutting the dorsal roots so there is no question of the α fibres being dependent upon the γ loop for their activation (Sears, 1964a; Eklund, Euler, & Rutkowski, 1964). Intracellular recording from α motoneurones shows moreover that they are rhythmically depolarised in time with respiration even after local de-afferentation. Detailed study of the firing patterns of individual respiratory fusimotor neurones shows that they do not all fire rhythmically in time with respiration; some of them fire more or less steadily irrespective of the phase of the respiratory cycle. Slightly indirect arguments suggest that static and dynamic fusimotor fibres fall into both these classes of rhythmic and tonic fusimotor neurones, and the significance of this latter yet further subdivision is still uncertain (Euler & Peretti, 1966). Possibly it arises because the intercostal muscles have the dual function of producing rhythmic contractions to ventilate the lungs and tonic contractions to assist in postural fixation of the trunk. Anyhow, for rhythmic respiratory movements it is indubitable that the central co-activation of α and γ neurones is what happens, rather than an indirect activation of α

FIG. 10.10. The parallel activation of α and γ fibres during breathing. The upper trace is a recording from the central end of a filament to an inspiratory intercostal muscle; the large spikes are from α fibres and the small spikes from γ fibres. The lower trace is an electromyographic record from the diaphragm which provides an indication of the timing of the respiratory cycle. Anaesthetised cat. (Sears, 1964a, Fig. 8.)

fibres via the γ loop. The diaphragm, it may be noted, is largely devoid of spindles and so cannot depend for activation of its own γ loop at any rate.

Walking movements in the decerebrate cat. Two further situations have been investigated in the cat with a similar finding of central

$a-\gamma$ co-activation, though they have as yet been less intensively studied than the respiratory system. Severin, Orlovskii & Shik (1967) recorded spindle afferent discharge in the usual way from dorsal root filaments during walking movements in the high decerebrate cat. This preparation can be made to walk more or less normally by stimulating a circumscribed region in the mesencephalon and placing the animal's feet on a moving treadmill, while supporting most of its weight from above. The walking movements would appear to be initiated and controlled by the normal mechanisms for they change in sympathy with any change in the speed of the treadmill. The movements were further shown to depend on a rhythmic afferent feedback for their genesis, because on stimulating the same mesencephalic region in preparations in which movement had been abolished by curarisation the motor discharge recorded from the ventral roots was steady instead of rhythmic.

As with the respiratory muscles, the spindle afferents were found to play their part in the normal movements by increasing their discharge when their own muscle was contracting and slowing down again as it relaxed, even though the muscle in question was then being stretched by the action of its antagonist. This again indicates that the γ fibres increased their firing in sympathy with that of the a fibres. Once again there was no question of the movement depending primarily upon the γ loop, for the muscle began to contract, as shown electromyographically, somewhat before the spindles began to increase their discharge. Moreover, when the hindlimbs were de-afferented they continued to make walking movements, as long as the normally innervated forelimbs were allowed to do so to keep the cycle in motion, but there was then no possibility of the hindlimb movement being γ driven (Shik, Orlovskii & Severin, 1966). It may be noticed in line with all this that the massive extensor contraction which occurs during the 'stance' phase of a stretch, when the foot is on the ground, is not initiated by any stretch reflex resulting from the extensor muscles being stretched as they begin to take the weight of the body. Electromyographic recording has shown that the extensors begin to contract some 10 msec before the foot touches the ground. (Engberg & Lundberg, 1969.)

Jaw movements in the anaesthetised cat. Taylor & Davey (1968) recorded the response of spindle afferents from the jaw muscles

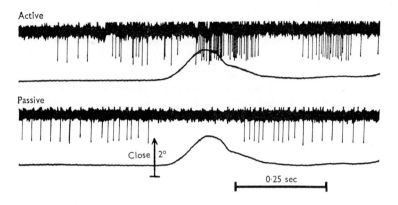

FIG. 10.11. The contrasting patterns of firing of a spindle primary ending during a particular movement depending upon whether the movement was produced actively (above) or passively (below). The fact that the spindle firing increased during the active movement shows that there must then have been an increase in fusimotor firing. The records were taken in the anaesthetised cat from a spindle afferent fibre to one of the muscles which act to close the jaw. All motor fibres were intact. The upper record was obtained by inducing the animal to swallow by putting fluid in its mouth; the movement is fairly small because the jaw was constrained by a stiff spring. The lower record was obtained by moving the jaw passively with a servo-controlled stretching device. The command signal for the servo was derived from a tape recording of the reflexly induced movement. This ensured the equivalence of the two movements. (Taylor & Davey, 1968, Fig. 2.)

during jaw movements in the lightly anaesthetised cat. The movements were induced by getting the animal to swallow by putting saline in its mouth. The recordings were made extracellularly, with a metal microelectrode, from afferent cell bodies lying in the mesencephalic nucleus of the Vth nerve. The upper part of Fig. 10.11 shows the increased spindle discharge occurring during the muscle contraction. When the same movement was produced by passive manipulation of the jaw the spindle was silenced thereby showing that during the active movement its γ fibres had been co-activated with the α fibres. Again the increase in spindle firing sometimes began slightly after the beginning of the movement and so would seem excluded as its sole cause, though sometimes the spindle firing increased beforehand.

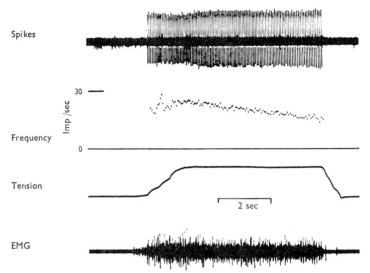

FIG. 10.12. The discharge in man of a presumed spindle afferent during
a weak voluntary isometric contraction of the muscle which it supplied
(flexor of index finger). The recordings were made with a tungsten microelectrode of about 10 μm diameter at its tip which was inserted into the
median nerve somewhat above the elbow. The electromyogram was
recorded with surface electrodes. (Vallbo, 1970a, Fig. 6.)

Finger movements in conscious man. Finally, Vallbo (1970a,b) has
succeeded in recording from single spindle afferents in conscious
man by means of a microelectrode inserted into a nerve trunk.
Figure 10.12 is one of his records and shows an increase in the discharge of a spindle afferent during a willed voluntary contraction.
This again demonstrates that the fusimotor fibres must have
increased their discharge during the contraction, but as the contraction began slightly before the increase in firing it cannot have
been initiated solely by the γ route. Broadly similar results were
obtained for 51 of the 63 units most recently studied; the remaining 12 units showed small increases or decreases in firing which
were attributed to the effects of the extrafusal contraction rather
than to fusimotor action. Because of the difficulty of preventing
the microelectrode from being dislodged, a fairly limited range of
isometric contractions have so far been studied and it is somewhat
tantalising to have to await description of the discharges occurring
during a wider variety of movements.

It may reasonably be concluded for both animals and man that any central activation of skeletal muscles is normally accompanied by sufficient extra fusimotor activity to ensure that the spindle primary endings increase rather than decrease their firing during the contraction; but none the less the increased afferent discharge is not the prime cause of the contraction. There seems little doubt, however, that the increase in afferent firing produced by the γ route must play a part in the production of the increased α motoneurone discharge, if only because of the monosynaptic connections of the Ia fibres.

Thus the idea of a 'follow-up length servo' with the input restricted to the fusimotor fibres seems now best discarded. Fortunately it can be immediately replaced by the idea of the 'servo-assistance' of movement which will occur by virtue of the coupled inputs to the α and to the γ motoneurones. Such a view would seem to have become accepted by the majority of workers in the field. The essential difference between a 'follow-up servo' and 'servo-assistance' lies in the gain required of the feedback system. For a follow-up servo to work successfully the gain of the feedback loop must be rather high so as to ensure that there is always an adequate muscle contraction to overcome any resisting external force. Only thus can it be guaranteed that the command for a particular new length will be faithfully obeyed. In contrast, in a servo-assisted system even quite a moderate gain would help to deal with any unexpected disturbance. Moreover, it becomes irrelevant that the increase in spindle firing observed during a movement is insufficient to produce the whole of the α firing by means of its reflex action. The term 'servo-assistance' seems to have been first used in the present sense by Matthews (1970) following a suggestion by R. B. Stein; it should be taken as a colloquial rather than as an analytical description of how the system works.

The acceptance of central co-activation of α and γ fibres as the normal mode of producing a movement removes the difficulty of the slowness inherent in the excitation of muscle by the γ route alone, while still preserving most of the advantages of servo-control. The slowness of the γ route arises inevitably from the time consumed in conduction between the spindle and the spinal cord, and more particularly, from the slowness of the spindle afferent discharge in response to a change in fusimotor firing. On the evidence of the frequencygram (see Chap. 5) the speed of static activation of the primary ending is much greater than that of its dynamic activation, as would be appropriate if the static fibres were the ones which primarily supplied the command signal to the servo. Rather oddly, however, an assessment of these intrafusal delays by determination of a 'transfer function' for the activation of the spindle by the two kinds of fusimotor fibre gave similar results, with parameters of the same values (Andersson, Lennerstrand & Thoden, 1968).

It may next be asked why, when the α and γ motoneurones are commonly co-activated, the body should have bothered to improve on the shared skeleto-fusimotor innervation found in lower animals such as the frog. One possible answer is that it is probably advantageous to keep the spindles firing at much the same rate throughout the course of a movement when it is proceeding in the manner anticipated by the controlling higher centre. In line with the original idea of Kuffler & Hunt it may be suggested that the spindles might then be at their best in reflexly compensating for any deviation of the movement from its planned course. As said earlier (Matthews, 1964) 'this would be achieved if the relative amounts of α and γ activity were adjusted to be appropriate for the velocity of shortening "expected" under any particular set of conditions. Then if the shortening proceeded faster than "intended" by the higher centres it would be slowed by servo action, and if shortening were hindered by some unexpected load it would be speeded up by servo action'. The independence of the fusimotor pathway from the ordinary α pathway provides the essential degree of freedom which would allow the fusimotor discharge to be appropriate primarily to the trajectory of the planned movement. The direct motor discharge would, in addition, have to be appropriate to the external load. In other words, for a given movement the command signal despatched by the higher centres to the fusimotor fibres would always be the same, but the signal to the α motor fibres would increase with the mass to be moved or the resistance to be overcome. However, such suggestions are clearly speculative until more can be found out about the behaviour of spindle afferents during various movements and also about the switching of the reflex actions of the spindle secondary endings, for they will also be affected by the command. It is interesting to note in this respect that the extrinsic eye muscles show no sign of being

under direct stretch reflex servo-control. These are virtually the
only muscles whose load remains constant, therefore making it
easier for the controlling centres always to produce the α motor
discharge appropriate to the planned movement. But the role of
their spindles remains mysterious.

The problem of the maintenance of stability in a servo-loop

Human-engineered servos are usually provided with a rather
high gain so that within reason they can continue to achieve their
objective whatever external forces stand in the way of their doing
so, or whatever changes take place in the strength of the effector.
Figure 10.13 illustrates the latter point by reference to a simple

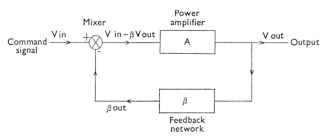

FIG. 10.13. Block diagram of a voltage amplifier stabilised by negative
feedback. The gain of the amplifier on its own is A. The fraction of the
output which is fed back to the input is β. As A increases so the gain of
the stabilised loop tends to $1/\beta$, thus making its behaviour independent
of any small variations in A.

voltage amplifier stabilised by means of voltage feedback. By
inspection it can be seen that when the loop is closed $V_{out} = A(V_{in}
- \beta V_{out})$. From this it can be immediately shown that the gain of
the system, that is V_{out}/V_{in}, is simply $A/(1 + A\beta)$. This tends to
$1/\beta$ when A becomes large enough to make $A\beta$ very much greater
than 1. Thus, provided that the feedback element is accurate (i.e.
β constant), it does not matter if the gain of the amplifier changes.
Likewise, it may be suggested to be easier for the body to make
accurate muscle spindles and tendon organs than to hold the
strength of a muscle constant, particularly in the face of fatigue.
The higher its gain, however, the greater becomes the possibility
of instability of a servo. Instability shows itself as a tendency for
the system to overshoot the final goal and then return to it in an

oscillatory manner or, in the extreme, for the servo to break away into spontaneous oscillations, thereby becoming quite unusable. Instability primarily arises because of time delays between the initiation of an error signal and the development of the appropriate correcting action. The more vigorous the correcting action the more serious it becomes from the point of view of stability that the response occurs with an undue delay.

In the case of the stretch reflex the delay arises partly through the time taken in conduction to and from the spinal cord and transmission within it, and partly through the slowness of skeletal muscle to develop its full tension on its activation. The large size of the Ia afferent fibres and the α motor fibres, and the mono-synaptic link between them, would appear to be designed to mini-mise these so-called 'transport' delays. Such absolute 'dead times' before any response occurs at all are the most difficult for a control system to live with. They must become very large in large animals, but without the invention of a new kind of nerve fibre little improvement would appear to be readily achievable in this respect since the fibres concerned are already the largest in the body. In the common laboratory animals, however, the slowness of muscle contraction would appear likely to be the more serious factor in practice; fortunately such an approximately 'exponential delay' should have less tendency to produce oscillation than does a transport delay. From this point of view the faster the speed of contraction of a muscle the less would be its tendency to go into a reflexly induced oscillation. But for the body to indulge in a general up-grading of the speed of muscle contraction could well prove uneconomical since quickness of muscle contraction appears to be associated with a high expenditure of energy in the mainten-ance of a steady or slowly changing contraction. Thus in develop-ing its various control systems the body has to accept the existence of various time delays in its feedback loops and must take appro-priate steps to minimise their harmful effects.

One way in which the deleterious effects of time delays may be counteracted in an inanimate control system is the inclusion in the servo-loop of an element which gives a response proportional to the rate of change of the incident signal as well as to its absolute value. The spindle primary endings, by responding both to the length of a muscle and to the velocity at which it is being stretched, behave in just the way required to help stabilise the postulated muscle servomechanism. Crudely put, the mechanism of compensation is that the velocity response of the primary ending enables it to 'predict' the length of the muscle after the delay time of the reflex and so ensure that the response will be appropriate to the time when it was initiated. Put another way, the primary ending may be said to give a signal which is phase-advanced on the mechanical stimulus by just the amount required to cancel out the phase lags produced by other parts of the system. Figure 8.16 suggests that the primary ending does this effectively for small amplitudes of sinusoidal stretching at relatively low frequency, for the stretch reflex shows no significant lag in its response to such stimuli. In the mathematical description of servomechanisms such compensation for delay by means of a velocity-sensitive element is similar in many respects to that obtained by damping the moving system with a viscous element, but it has the practical advantage that it does not lead to the loss of power that occurs when an external dash-pot or any related and otherwise useless element is included in the system. The primary ending may thus be said to provide damping for the stretch reflex. Additional damping is probably achieved by the production of a further degree of phase-advance of the nervous signals in their transmission through the spinal cord (Westbury, 1970). Damping is also provided by the 'viscous' properties of contracting muscle fibres themselves, since for a constant degree of activation they develop more tension than the isometric value while they are being stretched, and less while they are shortening. Thus the force available for accelerating the mass of a limb or any external load is reduced in just the same way as it would be by an externally coupled dash-pot and with the same sort of advantage in improving the stability of the system.

The need of a positional servo for damping is increased when the mass which it acts upon is increased. This is because any extra load also requires to be appropriately decelerated as the correcting movement nears its goal, since otherwise the target will be overshot and oscillation occur. An early suggestion for the function of the dynamic fusimotor fibres was to adjust the velocity sensitivity of the primary ending so as to alter the damping of the stretch reflex arc to suit the particular type of movement being undertaken; in particular, they were suggested to increase the damping when a limb and its muscles are operating on an external inertial load, such as in picking up an object or carrying something. It has yet to be established, however, that the dynamic fibres do indeed produce the appropriate phase advance in the response of a primary ending to a sinusoidal stimulus and it seems quite likely that they do not do so. In addition, the dynamic fibres seem to be activated in rather a non-specific manner, including in the course of a variety of spinal reflexes, to be performing such a fine adjustment; computation by the nervous system of the optimum damping appropriate for any particular condition might be expected to be a specialised affair. Indeed, from the point of view of stability it seems as appropriate to concentrate attention on the action of the dynamic fibres in increasing the responsiveness of the primary endings to small-amplitude stimuli. This would be expected to lead dynamic fusimotor activity to have an unstabilising rather than a stabilising action on the stretch reflex arc, at any rate in the small signal range. As already noted an increase in gain tends to unstabilise a previously stable servo, and so an increase in the stretch sensitivity of the spindle will have this effect unless it is accompanied by an appropriate increase in the 'phase advance' of the response (i.e. of the velocity-sensitivity of the ending). The whole matter of just how stability is achieved would appear to be ripe for a more quantitative study accompanied by the development of appropriate models of the stretch reflex system. All that has just been said is essentially qualitative and based on 'linear' servo theory. It may not be entirely relevant to a system which includes several non-linear components such as the primary ending of the spindle.

Evidence for the existence of a controlling servo from the study of human tremor

The liability of servo-controlled systems to go into oscillation has often been suggested as providing a basis for tremors of all kinds. In patients with pathologically brisk knee jerks followed by clonic contractions, an inadequate degree of stabilisation of the stretch reflex system is widely accepted as a sufficient explanation for the oscillatory behaviour; an increase in gain of some part of the reflex arc would appear most likely to be the responsible factor. Such a view has, however, been recently questioned (Walsh, 1971). The tremor of Parkinson's disease would appear to depend upon a purely central generator and not upon the oscillation of a feedback loop involving muscle, for among other things it appears to continue on its way in spite of forcibly oscillating the shaking limb (Walsh, 1969).

In normal human subjects the maintenance of any muscular contraction is naturally accompanied by a small amount of unsteadiness which can be detected by the appropriate instrumental means. When such 'physiological tremor' is subjected to frequency analysis these irregularities are commonly found to have a peak of activity at around 8–10 Hz (cf. most recently, Sutton & Sykes, 1967; Dymott & Merton, 1968). This apparent resonance is often directly apparent in records of the position of a part or of its acceleration. For at least the last 15 years there has been a running controversy as to whether or not the accentuation of the tremor at certain frequencies is due to 'oscillation in the stretch reflex loop'. The proposed alternatives have included transmission of the cardiac impulse, a purely central genesis of the rhythm, oscillation in a servo-loop including visual feedback, a chance synchronisation of the firing of different motor units, the filtering out of the mechanical response to all higher frequencies occurring in the discharge of individual motor units by the occurrence of 'tetanic fusion', and a simple mechanical resonance of the part moved by muscle action. Recent discussions of the often contradictory findings are provided by Marsden, Meadows, Lange & Watson (1969), who showed that the ballistocardiac impulse was only important when there was no muscle contraction, and by Lippold (1970), who produced clear evidence that the tremor seen in an outstretched finger was indeed reflexly mediated. This conclusion cannot, however, be transferred without further experiment to tremors observed under different conditions.

Lippold recorded the position of the finger with a photo-electric arrangement and saw the usual physiological tremor. Under his conditions it had an amplitude of movement of up to about 0·5 mm total extent (0·1–2% of normal range of movement). He then applied a brief tap (about 30 msec duration and 1·5 mm extent) to the tip of the finger and found that it initiated a damped oscillation with the same frequency as the normal tremor of the subject. These shock-excited oscillations are shown in Fig. 10.14 along with the electromyogram from the finger extensor muscles. The records exclude the oscillations being due to a simple mechanical resonance of the moving parts, both because of the accompanying rhythmic changes in motor firing and because, in the middle of the

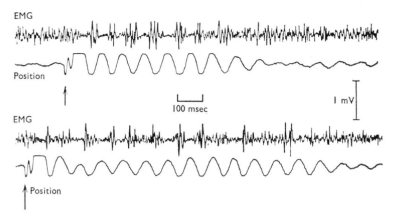

FIG. 10.14. Shock-initiated 'physiological tremor' of the outstretched index finger in conscious man. The top record of each pair is the electro-myogram of the extensors of the index finger, taken with surface electrodes. The bottom records show the position of the finger recorded photo-electrically; the total excursion is approximately 0·5 mm, and upwards movement is shown upwards. The finger was tapped at the arrows. The upper pair of records shows well-marked modulation of the EMG in phase with the movement. The bottom pair of records shows an unusual increase in the response at a time when it was normally dying out. (Lippold, 1970, Fig. 10, reversed in contrast.)

lower record, the oscillations temporarily increased in size showing that energy was being fed into the system. The small rapid initial oscillations were, however, attributable to a mere mechanical resonance. The oscillations were further suggested to be generated by the same mechanisms as the spontaneous physiological tremor because both were grossly depressed by a few minutes of ischaemia produced by inflating a sphygmomanometer cuff around the arm. The responses to prodding were particularly well displayed by averaging a number of successive trials and this confirmed that there was a constant phase relation between the prod and the resulting oscillations. Thus there seems little doubt that the voluntarily outstretched finger is helped to maintain its position by feedback from peripheral receptors, presumably predominantly the spindle primary endings, and that the system is often suffici-ently lightly damped to be near the point of oscillation. Visual feedback was excluded as the responsible factor because similar responses were obtained when the eyes were shut.

It is notable that the total extent of physiological tremor is invariably small whereas when a simple linear servo goes into oscillation the amplitude of movement tends towards the largest the system is capable of. Quite possibly, the restriction of the physiological oscillatory response occurs because the muscle control system behaves non-linearly. If so, the amplitude of the tremor may perhaps correspond to the prevailing extent of the linear range of the spindle primary endings, for over this range their sensitivity to displacement is very much greater than it is for larger displacements. Indeed, if the spindle primaries are involved in the genesis of tremor it seems almost inevitable that as the whole system tends to oscillatory behaviour, the movement will in the first instance be restricted to the range in which the gain of the primary endings is greatest. In the cat's soleus muscle the linear range of the primaries is often around 1% of the physiological range of movement, just as it is for human physiological tremor in man. Be that as it may, these recent experiments on the finger fortify the belief that the stretch reflex servo is in continuous operation modulating the motor discharge occurring during a normal voluntary contraction. In the cat, there has also been moderately extensive study of rhythmical behaviour (see Lippold, 1970, for refs.) and among other things there is evidence that the tremor of shivering is partly controlled by an oscillatory behaviour of the stretch reflex arc (Eldred, Ott, Ishikawa & Stuart, 1966). Indeed it seems possible that the shivering tremor is sometimes initiated by an increase in the gain of some part of the reflex arc, whether centrally or by peripheral fusimotor action on the spindle.

A tendency to oscillation in man has also been shown by Berthoz & Metral (1970) who studied the effect of applying sinusoidally varying forces to the wrist while the subject endeavoured to keep his elbow joint at a right angle. For low frequencies of oscillation the subject could counteract the applied force rather effectively and prevent significant movement occurring, at any rate when his eyes were open. But at frequencies of 2–5 Hz he could not prevent a very considerable movement occurring, irrespective of whether his eyes were open or shut. At higher frequencies the movement again became small. At about 4 Hz an oscillatory tension of ± 1 kg superimposed on a steady voluntary contraction of 2 kg produced a movement of nearly ± 2 cm (all values measured at the wrist), in spite of the fact that the elbow flexors had ample strength to have stopped the movement if they could have discharged at the appropriate time (30 kg tetanic tension). The occurrence of such large amplitudes of movement over a narrow range of frequencies appeared to be due to the activation of a latent resonance in the reflex control system. It was certainly dependent upon uncontrolled muscle action as well as any simple mechanical resonances for electromyographic recording showed that large changes in motor firing occurred in sympathy with the stretching.

Effects of release of a muscle during its voluntary contraction

In addition to occasionally manifesting itself in a tremor, a controlling servo would be expected to declare its existence by responding to any attempt to alter the position of a limb which was being voluntarily held still. Indeed, the earliest evidence that the muscle afferents are continuously contributing reflexly to the maintenance of voluntarily initiated motor discharge was provided by Hansen & Hoffman in 1922 when they described the 'let go' reflex (*Entspannungsreflexe*). They showed that if a voluntary contraction was made against an external obstacle which suddenly gave way so that the contracting muscle could shorten, then there was a temporary period of silence in its electromyogram, as recorded with surface leads. In their experiments the subject held up a weight which was suddenly released by turning off the current in an electromagnet.

Unaware of this classical finding, Angel, Eppler & Iannone (1965) repeated the experiment to obtain the same result, as illustrated in Fig. 10.15 from a later paper. They argued that this removed the obstacles to accepting Merton's ascription of the silent period evoked by motor stimulation to the action of a servo which controlled voluntary contraction by means of feedback from the muscle spindles. The silent period as observed by Merton on nerve stimulation could be due to several things, but of these only the decrease of spindle firing could also be responsible for the silence seen on letting the muscle go. There is then no antidromic volley to produce motor synchronisation or Renshaw inhibition, and there is no increase in muscle tension to excite the tendon organs. There is, of course, now a stretch of the antagonistic muscle caused by the release of the initially contracting muscle and so the silent period of the latter might have been due to an inhibition mediated by the usual 'direct' Ia inhibitory pathway. Any such

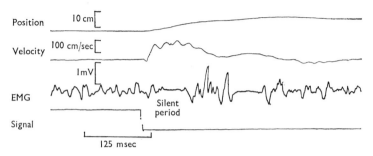

FIG. 10.15. The silent period following the unloading of a voluntarily contracting muscle. At the beginning of the traces the subject was using the flexor muscles of his forearm to hold up a weight of 4·5 kg. At the point shown in the bottom trace the weight was suddenly released by cutting the loop of wire from which it was suspended. The subject's elbow then began to flex, as shown in the upper two traces. The EMG trace shows the electrical activity of his biceps muscle while all this was taking place; it was recorded with surface electrodes. About 40 msec after the beginning of the release the previous continuous electrical activity is replaced by a 'silent period' which lasts about 40 msec. It is followed by a further outburst of muscle activity, even though the shortening continues. (Alston, Angel, Fink & Hoffmann, 1967, Fig. 1.)

inhibition was argued, however, to have been insignificant because the discharge of the antagonistic motoneurones evoked by the stretching had a longer latency than the silencing of the muscle which had been released. In any case the existence of a degree of Ia inhibition from the antagonist would still fit in with the idea of a servo-control of limb position, but now mediated by the control of the angle of a joint by the coupled activity of antagonistic muscles rather than just by the control of the length of an individual muscle. It would, however, be interesting to have a 'let go' experiment performed on a muscle with a detached tendon, as after amputation, or with a tendon pulled upon through a skin incision so as to be partly slack at its distal end, as in the experiments of Gelfan & Carter (see p. 496). There seems little doubt of the result since Hagbarth (1967), in reporting experiments like those described above, stated that the silence occurs as usual in patients in whom the antagonists are totally denervated.

The 'let go' experiments provide very reasonable evidence for the existence of a controlling servo which is continuously in operation during a steady voluntary contraction, for they seem to show it shutting off power the moment the muscle shortens un-expectedly. Moreover, as the silence begins within 40 msec of the release, the control would appear to be mediated by the spinal cord; the latency to full silence includes the duration of the externally recorded muscle action potential as well as the reflex time proper. The experiments do not show, however, that a voluntary contraction is entirely dependent upon such a servo. It should be especially noted that a short time after releasing a contracting muscle its motor units begin firing again even though the shortening continues. This may be seen in Fig. 10.15 (Alston, Angel, Fink & Hofman, 1967; Angel, Garland & Alston, 1970). A decent positional servo might be expected to keep the power shut off until the disturbance had been more effectively counteracted. The cessation of silence seems most likely to have been due to continued excitation reaching the α motoneurones directly from higher centres; the authors argued that it was due to a resumption of afferent firing, which they attributed to an unexplained and hypothetical increase in fusimotor firing (untestable under their conditions in man). If the shortening was suddenly arrested by a stop, the resumption of motor firing occurred earlier; the resumption may now be attributed to an increased afferent discharge for this will occur even though the fusimotor discharge is constant. Whatever is precisely happening, none of these observations support the idea that the position of the limb was initially maintained by an entirely effective positional servo; possibly, however, the servo would have been able to show itself to better effect and have had a higher gain if the subject had been initially performing some different kind of task.

The acceptance of the idea that some kind of feedback regulation helps to maintain a steady 'postural' type of contraction does nothing to show whether or not a similar system remains in command during the course of a movement. This gap has recently been filled by Newsom Davis & Sears (1970) who performed a 'let go' experiment on the intercostal muscles while the subject was inspiring or expiring at a constant rate. They again found a temporary electromyographic silence. The subject was required either to sing steadily or to maintain a constant inspiratory or expiratory inflow. At a predetermined moment the pressure of the chamber into which he was breathing was suddenly reduced so as to lower temporarily the force against which the muscles were working. Electrical activity was recorded with a needle electrode inserted into the appropriate intercostal muscle. The variation inherent in using such a comparatively limited sample of motor unit activity was overcome by averaging the responses to several repetitions of the whole procedure. Figure 10.16 shows the

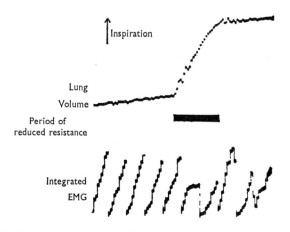

FIG. 10.16. The response to unloading seen in a human inspiratory muscle on temporarily changing the load against which it was working. The top trace is a record of lung volume displayed on a large scale; the step in the middle represents about 5 % of the vital capacity. The bottom trace is an averaged and integrated record of the electromyographic response of an inspiratory intercostal muscle, obtained with a needle electrode. The integrator was reset every 50 msec so that the height of each of the vertical deflections gives the average of the EMG over a 50 msec period; a sudden decrease in the slope of one of the deflections indicates a decrease of activity occurring within the integrating period. The subject was initially inspiring steadily through a high-resistance pathway and endeavouring to maintain a constant pressure inside his mouth (-40 cm H_2O). During the marker the high resistance was by-passed for 100 msec thus allowing the subject's pre-existing muscular effort to have a much greater inspiratory effect. This led to a shutting off of muscle activity, just as occurs on unloading a contracting limb muscle. The present figure shows this response taking place during a voluntarily controlled shortening of a muscle, whereas the previous figure (10.15) illustrated it on letting go a muscle which was initially contracting isometrically. (Newsom Davis & Sears, 1970, Fig. 11D. re-arranged.)

result, which provides clear evidence for a degree of servo control of the movement, probably a spinal one, because the minimal latency for the unloading response was between 22 and 25 msec. It would be valuable to have this type of experiment repeated for a variety of movements for a variety of muscles.

Effects of forcible stretch of a muscle during its voluntary contraction

The converse experiment of applying a stretch to a contracting muscle has naturally also been performed, but unfortunately the results are far from clear cut. The existence of the tendon jerk in response to a sudden tap provides, of course, classical evidence that some sort of controlling system is standing on the alert to resist muscle elongation; this system is now readily equated with the Ia fibres acting via the monosynaptic reflex. However, Hammond, Merton & Sutton (1956) emphasised that on its own the existence of a jerk can tell one very little about the properties and importance of the controlling system. In clinical neurology it is commonplace that the briskness of the jerk bears no simple relation to the power with which a muscle resists more prolonged elongation (i.e. tone). Because of its suddenness, the synchronous Ia volley set up by a tap is able to excite the motoneurones before they have had time to be inhibited by feedback from the Renshaw cells or by the discharges of other afferents. A more prolonged asynchronous afferent barrage might find the motoneurones much less responsive, that is to say it might find the central gain much lower.

Hammond (1954, 1956, 1960) analysed the response of human muscle to a prolonged forcible stretch applied at constant velocity to the forearm when the biceps muscle was contracting voluntarily so as to initially maintain a constant tension. Figure 10.17 shows the typical result. At the beginning of the extension there is a rapid rise in the tension exerted on the wrist; this increase in tension is required to accelerate the arm up to velocity of the stretching device. The tension record then runs nearly flat, except for a small peak which was attributed merely to an instrumental oscillation. Finally, near the end of the record the tension increases abruptly as the neural control system comes into action. The electromyographic record shows an initial steady asynchronous activity, followed by a synchronous wave which corresponds to the tendon jerk. Then a short period of silence is terminated by a tremendous increase in activity which is responsible for the rise in contractile tension seen above.

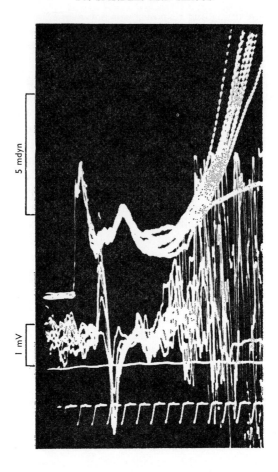

FIG. 10.17. The response of a voluntarily contracting muscle to forcible extension. As in Fig. 10.15 the subject was initially using his biceps brachii to develop a constant force at the wrist (now 3 kg wt.), but in the present figure the elbow was suddenly extended by pulling the wrist away at 40 cm/sec rather than being released as previously. The top record shows the tension developed at the wrist; its zero is given by the straight line below the next record. The middle record shows the electromyogram recorded from biceps with surface electrodes. The bottom trace is a 10 msec time marker. The manoeuvre was repeated ten times and the responses superimposed. The subject was initially maintaining a constant isometric contraction by observing a recording of tension; he was instructed to endeavour to resist any displacement of his arm from its initial position. (Hammond, Merton & Sutton, 1956, Fig. V.)

At first sight all seems well, and the findings might be taken to confirm that the muscle was under a continuous and powerful servo control mediated reflexly. In fact there are several difficulties with this interpretation and the responses have not yet been fully explained. To begin with, no counterpart could be found in the tension record for the early synchronous electrical wave and so the 'tendon jerk' seemed to be making no significant mechanical contribution to servo control. One possibility was that the wave merely represented the synchronisation of discharges of motor units which were about to fire anyway so as to maintain the pre-existing steady tension. The next problem was the surprisingly long latency of the main EMG response, which was responsible for the large increase in tension. This was 45 msec which seems quite unnecessarily long when the Ia pathway was able to elicit a tendon jerk EMG with a latency of only 15–20 msec. One early suggestion was that the silence after the tendon jerk might have been due to a Renshaw inhibition of the motoneurones as a result of the initial motor discharge. But Hammond (1960) later felt that it was equally logical to suppose that the two responses had 'their origin in separate receptors' and that even though muscle was provided with a fast conducting feedback pathway 'the advantage which this could confer in speed of response is not used'.

There seems no doubt that the main response occurring with a latency of some 45 msec was an involuntary response and not a willed one. When the subject was instructed to give a pull with his arm the moment he felt a tap upon his wrist the latency of the resultant voluntary response was always appreciably greater (90 msec or above) than that of the stretch-evoked one (45 msec) even though the initial electromyographic 'jerk' response was the same in both cases. None the less, the main response to stretch did depend in part upon the subject's will, for it varied in form with the subject's intention. When he was told to resist the stretching then the late response was well-developed as in Fig. 10.17. When he was told to 'let go' the moment he felt his arm being stretched then the main response failed to develop its full size and occasionally was apparently altogether absent. These differences began to manifest themselves some 50–60 msec after the beginning of the pulling and so were felt unable to be mediated by a voluntary action initiated on receipt of the stretching stimulus; as just noted the latency of the voluntary response to a tendon tap was appreciably greater. Instead, it was suggested that the sensitivity of the appropriate controlling centres had been preset by voluntary intent so that they should be ready to respond appropriately to the afferent input elicited by the stretching, irrespective of precisely when it should happen to arrive. Because of the great latency of the main response it was impossible to decide whether the controlling centres resided in the spinal cord or above. The initial electromyographic wave, was, however, quite unaffected by the way the subject had made up his mind to act, and so the control would seem unlikely to have been exerted presynaptically on Ia fibres. However, a single record in a brief note by Hagbarth (1967) appears to show an alteration in the initial wave in accordance with the subjects intention.

Understanding of the situation has been made even worse by the more recent similar sort of experiments of Newsom Davis & Sears (1970) on the intercostal muscles; these were performed, as just described, during singing or during the maintenance of a steady expiratory pressure and the stretch was applied by temporarily increasing the pressure against which the subject was breathing. In the first place, the tendon jerk was then absent, though this in itself is not particularly material. But an electromyographic silence of the intercostal muscles, like that seen after the jerk in the biceps, was now found to occur on its own without a preceding jerk and so could no longer be attributed to a Renshaw inhibition. Following the silence there was an excitatory response with a latency of some 50 msec like that in the biceps; and again this seems unduly long to have depended upon simple Ia monosynaptic excitation.

Newsom Davis & Sears quite reasonably attributed the initial silence to a peripherally evoked afferent inhibition of sufficient power and speed of action to overwhelm the expected initial Ia excitation. On this view any measurement of the actual latency of the stretch response becomes irrelevant for deciding upon the length of its central pathway, for the excitatory response can only manifest itself overtly at the moment that it succeeds in overcoming the inhibition. It would then remain allowable to think of the stretch response as being mediated monosynaptically in spite of its tremendously long latency. They suggested further that in the biceps experiments also the latency of the stretch response might have been largely determined by the duration of an afferent inhibition rather than a Renshaw inhibition. Newsom Davis & Sears attributed their initial inhibition to the action of Ib fibres. They were then faced with the problem as to why there is no corresponding brief phase of excitation on letting a muscle go; there should then be removal of pre-existing tonic Ib inhibition to produce an excitatory effect of disinhibition. This led them to postulate a control system of such complexity that it would appear to completely defy analysis by the few techniques which are currently available. However, before accepting that things are quite so difficult it would be desirable to have the limb control systems investigated in greater detail and particularly for different initial tasks so as to give the opportunity for different settings of the servo. The respiratory muscles might perhaps be a special case, and a sudden puff of air into the lungs might excite a non-specific inhibitory response from receptors which had nothing to do with the moment-to-moment control of muscle contraction.

A completely new kind of difficulty has been raised by some recent experiments performed by Marsden, Merton & Morton (1971) on the effect of mechanically interfering with the progress of the movement of the thumb. The thumb was being used to make a slow tracking movement at a constant velocity against a steady external force. In one type of experiment the movement was unexpectedly hindered by suddenly increasing the force against which the thumb was pushing. As a result, the flexor pollicis longus, which was doing the work, was momentarily stretched instead of being able to continue with its shortening. Electromyographic recording demonstrated that the manoeuvre produced the expected stretch reflex with a latency of about 40 msec. In another type of experiment the movement was hindered by suddenly introducing a spring-like resistance to increasing movement, but unaccompanied by any initial increase in force; this was done by means of an electric motor. The muscle was not then actually stretched at all, but it almost completely failed to continue with its shortening because the slight further shortening which did occur greatly increased the force against which the muscle was working. Again there was an increased electromyographic discharge beginning some 40 msec after the force began to increase. This response, however, cannot be properly described as a 'stretch reflex' for there is now no stretching of the muscle. Rather it would appear to be the response of a controlling servo which increases the motor output the moment a misalignment appears between the actual length of the muscle and that which had been intended. Neither response was mediated visually for both occurred in the absence of all visual clues of thumb position. Thus both responses would naturally be taken to depend upon feedback from the muscle spindles and so by their very existence to support the idea that the spindles play a part in the servo-assistance of movement.

Unfortunately things are not so simple and doubt arises because of the effect of anaesthetising the thumb with a xylocaine ring block. The servo-type response was then completely abolished and the stretch response was very greatly reduced in size. The difficulty arises from the fact that the nervous pathways to and from the muscle remained completely untouched by the local anaesthetic and so would still appear to be able to continue to mediate the reflex responses if they had indeed being been doing so in the first place. Thus the experiments can hardly be taken to favour the idea that the spindles have anything to do with the observed reflex actions. It would, however, be premature to believe that the spindles have been excluded from taking part in the observed reactions and to conclude that they do not play a part in the servo-assistance of movement. The paralysis of cutaneous and joint afferents might be important for its action in removing a tonic barrage which is normally responsible for maintaining the excitability of spinal centres, rather than for any action the paralysis has in removing a phasic sensory signal related to the progress of the movement and used for its servo-control. In particular, a reflex dislocation of the normal pattern of fusimotor firing might well prevent the spindles from behaving normally and carrying out their proper work.

In spite of all the difficulties these various experiments with forcible stretch and release of a contracting muscle may reasonably be accepted as having shown two things. First, that voluntary muscle contraction is indeed under some sort of servo-control. Second, the servo appears unlikely to depend exclusively upon monosynaptic feedback from the Ia fibres, though this may still be presumed to be making an important contribution to the control. In attempting to clarify the precise role of the Ia fibres it should be remembered that the way they behave at any particular time will depend upon the prevailing level of γ bias, particularly the relative preponderance of static and dynamic effects. The whole matter requires further experiment before anything final can be said about the central mechanisms responsible for servo-control and even how far they are located spinally rather than supraspinally. The preoccupation with the monosynaptic reflex of the early electro-physiological work on the spinal cord has done rather little to prepare one to meet the complexity of the central mechanisms responsible for reflexly regulating voluntary movement.

The apparent moderate value of the gain of the servo

The gist of the earlier discussion on stability and tremor was that to be effective a follow-up servo requires to have a high gain, but that a high gain brings with it an unwanted tendency to instability. Moreover, at some point on increasing the gain instability will no longer be rectifiable by ancillary controls. Thus there must clearly be a practical limit to the gain that the body can usefully employ in the stretch reflex servo. In addition, because of the compliance of the tendons, a servo which is dependent upon receptors placed entirely in the muscle has an automatic limit set to its effectiveness in controlling limb position, irrespective of how great a gain it is granted. This approach leads to an *a priori* argument against expecting to find the initiation of movement entrusted to a 'follow-up servo' triggered solely by fusimotor action, for even without measurement the stretch reflex could be suspected to have insufficient gain to ensure precision of movement under varying conditions. Moreover, if movement were to be produced by an efficient follow-up servo with a high gain then on meeting an obstacle this might lead to the development of forces which were unduly great from some other point of view, such as the safety of an object being manipulated.

A related argument against expecting the existence of an efficient follow-up servo may be based on the way in which we set about handling various objects. For example, in picking up a weight we rely upon previous experience of approximately how heavy it should be and if we make a mistake in our judgement, as in the case of an opaque bottle unexpectedly containing mercury, then we fail to achieve the desired result. This would not be the case if we had at our command a peripheral servo with a high gain, for the same movement would then follow the same command irrespective of the actual α motor discharge required. In fact, the commands dispatched to the α motoneurones from higher centres would seem

likely to be matched to the anticipated load. This view is
favoured by Evarts' (1968) results on recording from single units
in the pyramidal tract of the monkey while it was performing a
stereotyped movement against different loads. He found that these
particular descending signals were related to the required muscle
effort (tension and rate of change of tension, both of which require
more motor discharge) rather than to the required muscle length,
as he had originally expected to find.

On observing the effect of sudden loading of animals and ourselves it is also obvious that we are not at the mercy of an invari-
antly stiff servo. We yield far more than we would if the full power
of our muscles were to be suddenly turned on by a small displacement. For example, Lundberg (1969, p. 20) has emphasised that
the 'characteristic soft spring of the feline gait' could not occur if
the muscles failed to yield somewhat under the weight of the body,
and that a stretch reflex with a very high gain would lead to an
inappropriately 'stiff gait'. These arguments are all in accord with
the direct experimental evidence against the existence of a purely
γ operated follow-up servo. But they help raise the question as to
just how much gain the muscle servo actually has, and so just how
effective it is at resisting external disturbances and helping along a
movement produced by central co-activation of α and γ motoneurones. Strangely, there is as yet very little definite information
on such things. This is probably partly because of the difficulties
just described of separating involuntary servo-controlled responses,
which are mediated reflexly, from 'voluntary' responses which are
mediated by higher parts of the nervous system.

Experiments on the finger. Tardieu, Tabary & Tardieu (1968) set
out to fill the gap and observe the effectiveness of the postural servo
in maintaining the position of the outstretched index finger when
it was suddenly loaded. They found that its position was surprisingly ineffectively preserved by whatever control systems were
then in operation. Figure 10.18 illustrates the effect of a force of
120 g wt. When this was applied as a pure force by means of an
electromagnet (A) the displacement of the tip of the finger was
nearly 4 cm and there were no oscillations. When the same force
was applied by a weight on the finger (B) the accompanying mass
made the system oscillatory but had little effect on the final
equilibrium position. The subject was instructed to hold his finger

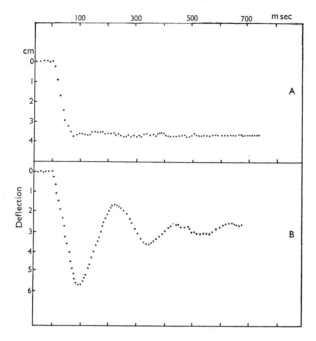

FIG. 10.18. The rather appreciable displacement of the voluntarily out-stretched index finger which occurs when it is suddenly loaded. The graphs show the position of the tip of the finger. A, the application a pure force of 120 g wt. by an electromagnet. B, the application of the same force but accompanied by the addition of an equivalent mass; this was done by loading the finger with a weight of 120 g. The points were determined by measurements of high-speed cinephotographs. Initially, the subject was keeping his finger extended with the minimum of effort and he was asked not to make any particular voluntary effort to return his finger to its original position if it should be displaced. The addition of mass not unnaturally leads to an oscillatory response, but in neither case did the position of the finger appear to be maintained by a particularly powerful positional servo. (Tardieu, Tabary & Tardieu, 1968, Fig. 1.)

up with the minimum of muscular effort, but not specifically to return it to its original position if it should be displaced. Clearly, the finger was under a certain amount of central positional control for otherwise it would have fallen much further, but equally clearly the gain of the system would not appear to have been particularly high. Pouliquen & Richalet (1968) endeavoured to match the physiological response by the response of a linear servo relying exclusively on positional feedback, but they could not do so in spite of extensive adjustment of the parameters of the model. As a result of their failure they felt that velocity and tension signals were probably also important for the physiological servo.

Before accepting that the physiological servo is largely ineffective, however, it should be noted that the finger experiments may have tested its performance under more severe conditions than those it was designed to deal with; the servo might perhaps be relatively much better at resisting small disturbances. It would be illuminating to have these experiments repeated with a wider range of forces, particularly small ones. In addition, it may be noted that the sensitivity of the muscle servo seems likely to be under higher control and may not have been set to its highest value in the conditions of these particular experiments. When the same experiment was performed with the finger held more rigidly in position by tensing both flexors and extensors, then the displacement produced by the same loading was very much less. Pouliquen & Richalet suggested that motion away from a desired position is largely prevented by keeping the velocity of movement at zero by appropriate feedback, and that once a displacement has occurred it is not particularly effectively counteracted by positional feedback from the muscles themselves.

Measurements on the stretch reflex of the decerebrate cat. As already noted in Chap. 8 the stiffness presented by a single muscle under tonic stretch reflex control in the decerebrate is comparatively low in relation to the full strength of the muscle. Yet the stretch reflex provides the basis upon which the whole idea of servo control was founded and upon which the hypothesis is still largely based. For example, the soleus muscle rarely develops more than 200 g wt. of maintained reflex tension per mm of extension. This means that it has to be stretched through about half its physiological range of movement in order to be reflexly induced to give its maximum output (2·5 cm and 2·5 kg wt. respectively). Moreover, in contradiction to the classical belief, it seems likely that much of the reflexly induced stiffness depends on the excitation of secondary endings as well as primary endings; this of course does not alter the importance of the value of the stiffness from the point of view of servo-control. The primary ending would appear to make its major contribution to servo-control both by its great sensitivity to small displacements and by its very considerable velocity sensitivity to large stimuli. The experimentally observed values for the stiffness of the stretch reflex would be somewhat greater if it were not for the restraining influence of the autogenetic inhibition from the tendon organs. Under appropriate conditions in the whole animal this inhibition could perhaps be partly switched off so as to improve control by the servo; but on the figures given in Chap. 8 this would no more than double the stiffness of the stretch reflex. The foregoing figures all apply to a single isolated muscle. In the whole animal somewhat larger values of gain might be expected and the reflex therefore the more effective. This is partly because simultaneous stretch of several synergistic muscles will probably lead each to respond more powerfully than it would on its own, and partly because the relaxation of the antagonistic muscles will decrease their spindle firing and so facilitate the motoneurones of the stretch muscles by disinhibition. Even with these advantages the servo-control seems unlikely to become very much more powerful in the whole animal. In addition, it may be reiterated that in so far as the servo reactions are mediated by Ia monosynaptic connections onto α motoneurones, the pattern of the Ia distribution appears rather too widespread to allow for the ready activation of single muscles via the γ loop (see Chap. 7, p. 353). This, however, need not interfere with servo control in so far as the motor system is organised to think in terms of movements rather than in terms of individual muscles.

Occlusion of respiratory movements in the cat. A more direct test of the efficacy of the servo was made for respiratory movements in the anaesthetised vagotomised cat by Corda, Eklund & Euler (1965). They recorded the α motor discharges in a fine nerve filament to an inspiratory intercostal muscle, first during a normal inspiration, and then again during an attempt at inspiration made during closure of the trachea. In the latter case the normal inspiratory intercostal shortening would have been unable to occur, and so the inspiratory γ drive would produce a greater acceleration of spindle firing than it would have done if the muscle had been allowed to shorten; control recordings from afferent fibres showed that such an increased afferent firing actually occurred. As Fig. 10.19 shows the motor discharge was indeed increased on preventing the movement from occurring, indicating that some sort of

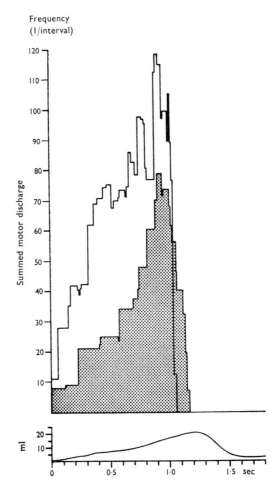

FIG. 10.19. The load compensation reflex in action boosting the inspiratory α motor discharge on occlusion of the trachea. Recordings were taken of the multi-unit α motor discharge in a thin nerve filament to an inspiratory intercostal muscle in the anaesthetised cat. This was first done during normal breathing to obtain the curve indicated by stippling; and second after preventing any appreciable inspiratory movement by occluding the trachea to obtain the upper curve. The lowest trace shows the time-course of a normal breath. The frequency was determined simply by measuring the interval between successive α spikes, even though they came from different units: about 6 units were firing. (Corda, Eklund & Euler, 1965, Fig. 2.)

servo did exist; the augmentation of motor discharge was guaranteed to be reflexly mediated for it did not occur after cutting the dorsal roots. But on the other hand, the increase in motor discharge was not an especially large one, suggesting that the servo was not a particularly powerful one. In the extreme with no shortening, the γ route of excitation would appear to have contributed only about as much extra excitation as did the α activation on its own. (This assumes that when the normal shortening occurred the γ contribution was very small; more quantitative estimates could usefully be made in the light of measurements of the frequency of afferent firing occurring in the two cases.) However, such a γ mediated contribution to dealing with an obstruction to movement is far from insignificant and thus its existence shows the value of servo-assistance.

Euler and his colleagues have called this useful degree of servo-assistance of respiratory movement 'the load compensation reflex'. Using electromyographic recording of intercostal activity Sant'-Ambrogio & Widdicombe (1965) observed similar, though possibly smaller, servo-assisted responses in the rabbit. Likewise, Newsom Davis & Sears' (1970) findings in man also support the existence of a moderate amount of servo-assistance of intercostal muscle activity in man. As with the finger, it seems possible that the efficacy of the servo can only really be assessed by observing its response to the kind of disturbance it is primarily designed to deal with, and which might be rather different from the gross obstructions so far tested in the animal. This is unfortunately, however, a circular approach; the normal function of the servo is still far from clear and might perhaps first become recognisable by establishing the kinds of input that it can best deal with.

Action of vibration in man. The effects of high-frequency vibration in man provide a further indication that the Ia fibres are not normally employed to operate an all-powerful servo. As first described by Hagbarth & Eklund (1966) vibrating the tendon of practically any muscle in the conscious human subject leads to the development of a slow contraction in it. On the evidence of the corresponding animal work the contraction would appear to be reflexly initiated by the vibratory excitation of the Ia fibres from the spindle primaries. A notable thing about the vibration response is that, as may be seen in Fig. 10.20, it builds up and decays rather

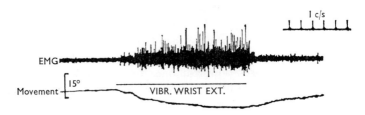

FIG. 10.20. The contraction induced by vibration in the normal human subject. During the signal marker a vibrator oscillating at 100 Hz was applied just above the wrist to the tendons of the wrist extensors. This caused a slow dorsiflexion of the wrist accompanied by an increased electromyographic activity of the appropriate muscles. The hand was unloaded and was initially hanging passively in volar flexion. The recordings are thus approximately isotonic. The subject's eyes were closed. The EMG was recorded with surface electrodes. (Hagbarth & Eklund, 1966, Fig. 1.)

slowly. It does not immediately lead to the development of at all a large muscle force and even the final tension is usually very far from the maximum that the muscle is capable of developing. This again argues against the existence of an overwhelmingly powerful Ia-driven servo; even if the vibration fails to excite fully every primary ending in the muscle studied a violent contraction would still be expected from an outstandingly powerful servo. Repeated short periods of vibration may, however, lead to a potentiation of the response so that eventually the vibration elicits 'the maximum force the subject could exert voluntarily' (Marsden, Meadows & Hodgson, 1969). The slowness of the vibration-induced responses suggests, moreover, that they may perhaps depend partly upon polysynaptic spinal pathways or even supraspinal pathways involving higher centres, as well as upon the simple monosynaptic excitation of motoneurones.

The limited central power of the Ia fibres is further shown by the ability of the subject to override the tonic vibration reflex by voluntary effort. However, not unnaturally he cannot prevent small phasic changes in contraction occurring on starting and stopping the vibration. This is illustrated in Fig. 10.21; the initial failure of voluntary control further supports the idea that the Ia fibres do have a real part to play in controlling muscle contraction, albeit not an exclusive one. A voluntary inhibition can also be exerted

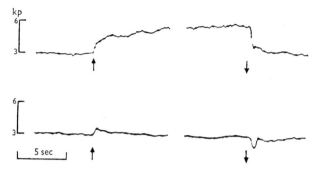

FIG. 10.21. The voluntary suppression of the tonic response to vibration. But voluntary control could not prevent an intial phasic response. The top trace shows the typical response of the elbow flexors to vibration when recorded under isometric conditions (start ↑, stop ↓). It is rather more rapid in onset and cessation than that recorded isotonically (cf. Fig. 10.20). The subject had his eyes closed and attempted to maintain a constant effort. In the bottom trace the subject had his eyes open and was trying to maintain a constant degree of contraction by watching a meter displaying the tension that he was developing. Vibration at 160 Hz. Twelve second portion of more or less steady contraction omitted in the middle of each record. (Eklund & Hagbarth, 1966, Fig. 3.)

upon the rather similar tonic reflex set up by repetitive stimulation of the popliteal nerve. Thus the inhibition of the vibration response seems likely to be due to a genuine central inhibitory antagonisation of the Ia input, rather than to a reduction of γ bias decreasing the sensitivity of the spindle endings to vibration (Marsden, Meadows & Hodgson, 1969). However, a note of caution is necessary in considering all the above arguments based on human experiments. Man cannot be widely denervated as is the experimental animal and so vibration may be exciting a widespread afferent input which will have correspondingly complex central actions, probably including the presynaptic inhibition of the Ia fibres of the muscles studied (cf. Gillies, Lance, Neilson & Tassarini, 1969).

A final pointer to the ability of the body to perform movements independently of the Ia pathway is provided by the ability of humans to work with vibrating tools, such as in the extreme the pneumatic drill. These presumably produce a massive and fairly constant Ia input from a variety of muscles. Even so, though the delicacy of voluntary control may be impaired, voluntary control is certainly not lost as it would be if the pathways upon which it depended were saturated.

Likely complexity of 'command signals' descending to the spinal cord from higher centres

In view of all that has been said it seems clear that the follow-up servo hypothesis is no longer acceptable in its original simple form. But its promulgation has had an entirely healthy effect on scientific progress, for by its very simplicity and dogmatism it has the more readily encouraged further experimentation. It should now be granted that there is still no real evidence that movements can ever normally be produced solely by the γ route, but that central co-activation of α and γ motoneurones appears to be the rule, though probably in varying proportions. This should provide for a useful degree of servo-assistance of movement, which may perhaps also be partly mediated by the spindle group II fibres which are excited along with the Ia fibres by static fusimotor action. In postural reactions the servo may well be at its best in dealing with small rapidly applied deformations. Even the contribution of the Ia fibres to servo-control seems unlikely to depend solely upon their monosynaptic action, though this will be important in mediating rapid responses.

The behaviour of the servo under any particular conditions seems likely to depend crucially on the state of the variety of spinal interneurones mediating Ia, Ib and II reflexes as well as those controlling the excitability of motoneurones. In this respect it may be noted that the intuitive idea that the descending command for muscle action consists just of instructions for certain motoneurones to fire at certain times is almost certain to prove too simple. The message seems likely also to contain instructions for the gain of a variety of reflex pathways to be set to appropriate values. For example, on the basis of studying the H reflex in the course of a willed contraction of the calf muscles, Gottlieb, Argawal & Stark (1970) felt it necessary to postulate that the descending command signals also increased the gain of the monosynaptic Ia pathway, conceivably by removal of a pre-existing presynaptic inhibition. Again, a brief jerk applied to the wrist produces a different response depending upon whether the wrist is initially at rest or is being slowly moved so as to track a target; moreover, the precise form of the response depends upon the direction of motion of the wrist relative to the tap (Denier van der Gon & Wieneke, 1969). All this suggests that the sensitivity of the spinal control centres has been altered by higher command.

In the cat, Lundberg (1970) has recently emphasised that a number of descending pathways which excite a motoneurones also excite the interneurones lying on the Ia inhibitory pathway to antagonist muscles. Such an arrangement would ensure that the increase in spindle firing from the contracting muscle is facilitated in its inhibitory action on the antagonist; in particular, this will see to it that when the movement meets an obstacle and the contracting muscle is helped along by servo action then its antagonist will be further discouraged. Indeed, in the search for conceptual clarity it is too easy to forget that the contraction of one muscle always entails the relaxation of its opponent and that the two need to be thought about together. This was emphasised by Lloyd when he promulgated the concept of the myotatic unit consisting of an antagonistic pair of muscles linked together by reflex action as well as by anatomical connections. Such linkage will be particularly important for movements of large amplitude; other things being equal the increase in the discharge of the spindle primary endings in the muscle which is stretched by an accidental external force may then be greater than the decrease of discharge of those in the released muscle, for this can only fall to zero. In contrast, as already described, in the few slow active movements which have so far been studied a modulation of fusimotor firing leads to an increase in spindle firing for the muscle which is shortening by means of its own contraction, whereas the spindles of the muscle which is being stretched decrease their firing. Thus a judicious combination of reduced fusimotor firing, inhibition of their a motoneurones, and blocking of the central action of their afferents, seems able to stop the stretching of antagonistic muscles interfering by their servo action with the contraction of the wanted muscle. We have now passed beyond expecting movement to be produced by a single command issued to either a or γ motoneurones, but we have a long way to go before we have sorted out all the various things which are taking place in the spinal cord during a voluntary movement.

Résumé of the evidence relating to the servo-control of movement
General considerations. The importance of muscle afferents for

motor control was first suggested by observations on the effects of local de-afferentation of a limb. This leads to a gross ataxia accompanied by a lack of use of the affected part. There is not, however, a complete paralysis and with adequate incentive an animal can be brought to make moderate use of a completely de-afferented limb. The response of the part to electrical stimulation of the motor cortex appears to be unchanged on de-afferentation. The motor effects of de-afferentation appear likely to be mainly due to interrupting proprioceptive rather than the cutaneous afferents, though the matter has not been properly put to the test.

There seem to be several quite separate sorts of way in which the information provided by the muscle receptors might be used by the CNS. Higher levels of the nervous system might use the information to assess the current state of affairs at the periphery so as to be able to despatch the appropriate motor commands to the spinal cord. In addition, they might perhaps use the signals in learning to improve a particular motor act by seeing how far the actual course of a movement differed from that which had been desired. At the lower levels of the nervous system the information may be used for the reflex regulation of muscle, and most notably for its servo-control. This facet of the use to which proprioceptive information may be put has been the most intensively studied. This is simply because it has lent itself to analysis by experiments restricted to the periphery.

The introduction of the follow-up servo hypothesis. The stretch reflex has long been recognised as a system for holding the length of a muscle constant in the face of external disturbances. In modern parlance, this is to recognise it as a servomechanism. In the early 1950's the γ efferents were proved to provide a functionally specific pathway to the muscle spindles. It was then suggested that this enabled them to reset the length of the muscle at which the stretch reflex came into equilibrium. The fusimotor discharge was seen as supplying the command signal for the muscle servo by increasing the Ia firing and producing an excess of α motor discharge until the muscle had shortened sufficiently to reduce the Ia discharge back to its original value. The higher centres were thus suggested to be able to produce a movement in either of two rather different ways, that is either 'directly' by sending descending activity straight onto the α motoneurones themselves, or 'indirectly' by sending the descending activity onto the γ motoneurones in the first place and leaving the servo-loop to produce the desired contraction. The supposed advantage of the indirect γ route was that it makes use of the valuable servo properties of the stretch reflex and is thereby unaffected by muscle fatigue or the size of the external load.

The evidence originally adduced in favour of contraction being mediated in such a roundabout way was the occurrence of a silent period in the electromyogram of a voluntarily contracting muscle when it was induced to twitch by stimulating its nerve. Such silence was found for the smallest of twitches and so was believed to be occurring also in response to the irregularities which are always present in any voluntary contraction. The findings were thus taken to show that servo-control is continuously present during voluntary contraction, and standing ready to shut off muscle power the moment the slightest unwanted muscle shortening occurs. The view that the fusimotor fibres normally supply the command was further supported by experiments on the decerebrate cat. During certain reflexly induced contractions the spindle afferents increased their discharge instead of slowing as might have been expected. This showed that the fusimotor fibres must have been increasing their firing during the contraction in the way required on the servo hypothesis. In addition, it was shown that interrupting the servo-loop by de-afferentation prevented the contraction from taking place, whereas the spindles still behaved in the same way as before. Unfortunately, however, neither the human nor the cat experiments are sufficient to establish that the contractions studied really were solely mediated via the γ route, as sometimes seems to have been supposed. None the less and quite properly the servo hypothesis attracted widespread interest and provided a valuable stimulus to further work.

Anatomical complications. The original servo hypothesis was developed in terms of a single kind of fusimotor fibre and a single kind of afferent ending, namely the primary ending. In fact, of course, there are secondary endings as well as primary endings and there are two kinds of fusimotor fibre. No realistic scheme for the servo control of muscle can ignore this extra complexity of the muscle spindle nor can the tendon organs be omitted. Unfortunately, there is still really nothing useful to say about the secondary ending except to reiterate the fact of its existence and to note that it can probably reflexly elicit autogenetic excitation when the central synapses have been appropriately preset by supraspinal action. Tendon organs are also undoubtedly continuously modulating the motor discharge by means of their reflex action and by virtue of the lowness of their threshold to contractile tension.

On the motor side, however, it can immediately be asked whether one or other of the two kinds of fusimotor fibre is primarily responsible for injecting the command signal into the servo-loop. The answer appears to be that the static fibres are chiefly if not wholly responsible. This can be said because they alone seem able to make the spindle fire faster during shortening of the main muscle, and thereby still allow it to continue to excite the α motoneurones reflexly. The dynamic fusimotor fibres would appear to produce an intrafusal contraction which is too slow to keep up with that of the extrafusal muscle fibres. The evidence for this is that during muscle shortening an increasing frequency of dynamic fusimotor stimulation fails to compensate for the unloading and manage to increase the spindle firing above its previous value, yet such an action is necessarily required of the command signal in order for the muscle servo to work. Static fusimotor stimulation can increase spindle firing in spite of a concomitant muscle shortening and so may reasonably be allocated the role of providing a command signal for muscle shortening. But by causing the contraction of the nuclear chain fibres the static fibres inevitably excite the secondary endings along with the primary endings and the significance of this for servo-control is still largely unfathomed. The dynamic fusimotor fibres may be allocated the role of sensitising the primary ending and thereby controlling the sensitivity of the stretch reflex. In this respect, equal importance may be attached to their increasing the velocity responsiveness of the primary ending to large stretches and their parallel action in increasing the absolute value of its sensitivity to small amplitude stretching.

Co-activation of α and γ motoneurones. The 20 years since the inception of the servo hypothesis have failed to produce any proper evidence for movement ever being mediated solely via the indirect route, and thus of movement being produced by means of a follow-up servo. Instead, there has been an accumulation of evidence showing that α and γ motoneurones are normally co-activated by descending influences to give what may be termed a 'servo-assistance' of movement. As with the reflex example already quoted such γ activation causes an increase of spindle firing above its pre-existing level; but this cannot be held solely responsible for the concomitant α firing because the main contraction normally begins slightly before the spindle accelerates its firing. This sort of thing has been found in each of the four experimental situations which have now been explored in reasonable detail. They are the respiratory movements, the jaw movements and the walking movements of the cat, and the finger movements of the conscious human subject.

Evidence for the presence of servo action in man. An outstretched finger shows a fine tremor which has a prominent component of movement at about 10 Hz. There has been a long-continued controversy as to how far this depends upon an incompletely suppressed tendency to 'oscillation in the stretch reflex loop'. Recent experiments support the idea that there is such a tendency by showing that a tap to the finger sets up a damped train of oscillations which are at the same frequency as the natural tremor and which are indubitably reflexly mediated. Their presence supports the idea of the existence of some sort of servo for controlling limb position in man. Its existence is further indicated by the effect of unexpectedly allowing a muscle to shorten when it is being used to pull against a fixed resistance which suddenly gives way. Such a 'let go' of a voluntary contraction promptly leads to a silent period in the electromyogram of the shortening muscle. When elicited under such circumstances the silence can only be attributed to a diminution of a pre-existing spindle afferent firing. The occurrence of the silent period thus demonstrates that spindle firing must normally contribute importantly to the maintenance of α motor firing. But the EMG silence normally comes to an end while the shortening is still continuing and so the α motoneurones cannot be held to be entirely dependent upon spindle feedback for their excitation. Forcible stretch of a voluntarily contracting muscle quite properly produces a reflex response as would be expected from a servo. It is puzzling, however, that the latency of the response is some 40 msec which is appreciably longer than that for the tendon jerk of the same muscle; but it would not appear to be a voluntary reaction for the latency of the voluntary response to a pull is nearly twice as long. Such responses on stretch and on release have been found to be broadly similar for the elbow flexors, for the thumb flexors, and for the intercostal muscles. They have been observed both when the muscle studied is initially shortening at a constant velocity as well as when it is initially being used to maintain a constant position or a constant tension. The results may be taken to support the view that human muscles are normally under a certain amount of servo-control, but the responses appear to be too complex to be attributable simply to a monosynaptic feedback by the Ia fibres.

Moderateness of gain. In standard engineering practice the gain of a servo is usually made rather high so as to ensure that it obeys its commands in the face of any obstruction that is likely to be normally put in its way. Several general arguments may be adduced against expecting to find such a stiff servo in man and animals. Moreover, the limited experimental evidence that is available supports the view that the gain of the biological servo is comparatively modest and is too low for it to be able to act as an efficient follow-up system. This relative ineffectiveness of control is shown by the fact that a load of 120 g applied to the lightly out-stretched finger produces a displacement of some 4 cm. In the cat, measurements on the stretch reflex and experiments on the effect of tracheal occlusion also suggest a relatively modest value for the gain of the servo when it is presented with a large disturbance. This is further indicated by the comparatively modest reflex effect produced on using high-frequency vibration to excite the Ia fibres in man. However, if the system is used for servo-assistance rather than for follow-up then quite a moderate gain could still provide a useful access of muscle force in the face of an unexpected obstacle. Moreover, the system is quite possibly a non-linear one and better at resisting small disturbances than large ones; this may well be its normal physiological role. In addition, the value of the gain can probably be adjusted by supraspinal action so as to suit the prevailing conditions. All in all, we would appear to be only just getting started in finding out how the CNS uses the continuous flow of information that it receives from the muscle afferents.

References

Alston, W., Angel, R. W., Fink, F. S. & Hoffman, W. W. (1967). Motor activity following the silent period in human muscle. *J. Physiol.* **190**, 189–202.   [582, 583]

Angel, R. W., Eppler, W. & Iannone, A. (1965). Silent period produced by unloading of muscle during voluntary contraction. *J. Physiol.* **180**, 864–870.   [581]

Angel, R. W., Garland, H. & Alston, W. (1970). Interaction of spinal and supraspinal mechanisms during voluntary innervation of human muscle. *Expl. Neurol.* **28**, 230–242.   [583]

Andersson, B. F., Lennerstrand, G. & Thoden, U. (1968). Response characteristics of muscle spindle endings at constant length to variations in fusimotor activation. *Acta physiol. scand.* **74**, 301–318.
                                                                           [573]

Berthoz, A. & Metral, S. (1970). Behaviour of a muscular group subjected to a sinusoidal and trapezoidal variation of force. *J. Appl. Physiol.* **29**, 378–384.   [580]

Brown, M. C., Lawrence, D. G. & Matthews, P. B. C. (1969). Static fusimotor fibres and the position sensitivity of muscle spindle receptors. *Brain Res.* **14**, 173–187.   [566]

Brown, M. C. & Matthews, P. B. C. (1966). On the subdivision of the efferent fibres to muscle spindles into static and dynamic fusimotor fibres. In *Control and Innervation of Skeletal Muscle*, ed. Andrew, B. L. pp. 18–31. Dundee: Thomson.   [562]

Corda, M., Eklund, G. & Euler, C. von. (1965). External intercostal and phrenic α motor responses to changes in respiratory load. *Acta physiol. scand.* **63**, 391–400.   [595, 596]

Critchlow, V. & Euler, C. von (1963). Intercostal muscle spindle activity and its γ-motor control. *J. Physiol.* **168**, 820–847.   [567]

Denier van der Gon, J. J. & Wieneke, G. H. (1969). The concept of feedback in motorics against that of preprogramming. In *Biocybernetics of the Central Nervous System*, ed. Proctor, L.D. pp. 287–296. Boston: Brown, Little & Co.   [601]

Dymott, E. R. & Merton, P. A. (1968). Visually and non-visually determined peaks in the human tremor spectrum. *J. Physiol.* **196**, 62–64P.   [578]

Eklund, G., Euler, C. von & Rutkowski, S. (1964). Spontaneous and reflex activity of intercostal gamma motoneurones. *J. Physiol.* **171**, 139–163.   [568]

Eklund, G. & Hagbarth, K.-E. (1966). Normal variability of tonic vibration reflexes in man. *Expl. Neurol.* **16**, 80–92.   [599]

Eldred, E., Granit, R. & Merton, P. A. (1953). Supraspinal control of the muscle spindles and its significance. *J. Physiol.* **122**, 498–523.
                                                                           [555–559]

Eldred, E., Ott, K., Ishikawa, K. & Stuart, D. (1966). Proprioceptive contributions to shivering. In *Muscular Afferents and Motor Control*, ed. Granit, R. pp. 151–163. Stockholm: Almqvist & Wiksell. [580]

Engberg, I. & Lundberg, A. (1969). An electromyographic analysis of muscular activity in the hindlimb of the cat during unrestrained locomotion. *Acta physiol. scand.* **75**, 614–630. [569]

Euler, C. (1966). Proprioceptive control in respiration. In *Muscular Afferents and Motor Control*. ed. Granit, R. pp. 197–207. Stockholm: Almqvist & Wiksell. [567]

Euler, C. von & Peretti, G. (1966). Dynamic and static contributions to the rhythmic γ activation of primary and secondary spindle endings in external intercostal muscle. *J. Physiol.* **187**, 501–516. [568]

Evarts, E. V. (1968). Relation of pyramidal tract activity to force exerted during voluntary movement. *J. Neurophysiol.* **31**, 14–27. [592]

Gillies, J. D., Lance, J. W., Neilson, P. D. & Tassinari, C. A. (1969). Presynaptic inhibition of the monosynaptic reflex by vibration. *J. Physiol.* **205**, 329–339. [599]

Gottlieb, G. L., Agarwal, G. C. & Stark, L. (1970). Interactions between voluntary and postural mechanisms of the human motor system. *J. Neurophysiol* **33**, 365–381. [600]

Granit, R. (1955). *Receptors and Sensory Perception.* 369 pp. New Haven: Yale University Press. [554]

Granit, R., Kellerth, J. O. & Szumski, A. J. (1966a). Intracellular autogenetic effects of muscular contraction on extensor motoneurones. The silent period. *J. Physiol.* **182**, 484–503. [557]

— (1966b). Intracellular recording from extensor motoneurons activated across the gamma loop. *J. Neurophysiol.* **29**, 530–544. [560]

Hagbarth, K.-E. (1967). EMG studies of stretch reflexes in man. *EEG Clin Neurophysiol. Suppl.* **25**, 74–79. [582, 588]

Hagbarth, K.-E. & Eklund, G. (1966). Motor effects of vibratory muscle stimuli in man. In *Muscular Afferents and Motor Control*. ed. Granit, R. pp. 177–186. Stockholm: Almqvist & Wiksell. [597, 598]

Hammond, P. H. (1954). Involuntary activity in biceps following the sudden application of velocity to the abducted forearm. *J. Physiol.* **127**, 23–25P. [585]

— (1956). The influence of prior instruction to the subject on an apparently neuromuscular response. *J. Physiol.* **132**, 17–18P. [585]

— (1960). An experimental study of servo action in human muscular control. *Proc. III Int. Conf. med. Electron.* pp. 190–199. London: Institution of Electrical Engineers. [585, 587]

Hammond, P. H., Merton, P. A. & Sutton, G. G. (1956). Nervous gradation of muscular contraction. *Brit. Med. Bull.* **12**, 214–218. [560, 585, 586]

Hansen, K. & Hoffman, P. (1922). Weitere Untersuchungen über die Bedeutung der Eigenflexe für unsere Bewegungen. I. Anspannungs- und Entspannungsreflexe. *Z. Biol.* **75**, 293–304. [581]

Hongo, T. & Shimazu, H. (1965). Centrifugal modifications of discharge rates of primary and secondary endings of muscle spindles in the hind limb of the cat. *J. Neurophysiol.* **28**, 724–741. [562]

Houk, J. C., Singer, J. J. & Goldman, M. R. (1970). An evaluation of length and force feedback to soleus muscles of decerebrate cats. *J. Neurophysiol.* **33**, 784–811. [561]

Hunt, C. C. (1952). The effect of stretch receptors from muscle on the discharge of motoneurones. *J. Physiol.* **117**, 359–379. [560, 561]

Hunt, C. C. & Perl, E. R. (1960). Spinal reflex mechanisms concerned with skeletal muscle. *Physiol. Rev.* **40**, 538–579. [560]

Jansen, J. K. S. & Matthews, P. B. C. (1962). The effects of fusimotor activity on the static responsiveness of primary and secondary endings of muscle spindles in the decerebrate cat. *Acta physiol. scand.* **44**, 376–386. [563]

Konorski, J. (1962). Changing concepts concerning physiological mechanisms of animal motor behaviour. *Brain,* **85**, 277–294. [548]

Knapp, J. D., Taub, E. & Berman, A. J. (1963). Movements in monkeys with de-afferented forelimbs. *Expl. Neurol.* **7**, 305–315. [548]

Kuffler, S. W. & Hunt, C. C. (1952). The mammalian small-nerve fibres; a system for efferent nervous regulation of muscle spindle discharge. *Res. Publs Ass. Res. nerv. ment. Dis.* **30**, 24–37. [552]

Landau, W. M.. Weaver, R. A. & Hornbein, T. F. (1960). Fusimotor function in man. *Archs. Neurol. Psychiat, Chicago* **3**, 10–23. [549]

Lassek, A. M. (1953). Inactivation of voluntary motor function following brachial rhizotomy. *J. Neuropath. exp. Neurol.* **12**, 83–87. [548]

Lassek, A. M. & Moyer, E. K. (1953). An ontogenetic study of motor deficits following dorsal brachial rhizotomy. *J. Neurophysiol.* **16**, 247–251. [548]

Lennerstrand, G. & Thoden, U. (1968a). Position and velocity sensitivity of muscle spindles in the cat. III. Static fusimotor single-fibre activation of primary and secondary endings. *Acta physiol. scand.* **74**, 30–49. [566]

— (1968b). Muscle spindle responses to concomitant variations in length and in fusimotor activation. *Acta physiol. scand.* **74**, 153–165. [563–565]

Lewis, M. McD. & Porter, R. (1971). Lack of involvement of fusimotor activation in movements of the foot produced by electrical stimulation of monkey cerebral cortex. *J. Physiol.* **212**, 707–717. [548]

Lippold, O. C. J. (1970). Oscillation in the stretch reflex arc and the origin of the rhythmical 8–12 c/s components of physiological tremor. *J. Physiol.* **206**, 359–382. [578–580]

Lundberg, A. (1969). *Reflex control of stepping.* Nansen Memorial Lecture. 42 pp. Oslo: Universitetsforlaget. [592]

— (1970). The excitatory control of the Ia inhibitory pathway. In *Excitatory Synaptic Mechansims,* ed. Andersen, P. & Jansen, J. K. S. pp. 333–340. Oslo: Universitetsforlaget. [601]

Marsden, C. D., Meadows, J. C. & Hodgson, H. J. F. (1969). Observations on the reflex response to muscle vibration in man and its voluntary control. *Brain* **92**, 829–846. [598, 599]

Marsden, C. D., Meadows, J. C., Lange, G. W. & Watson, R. S. (1969). The role of the ballistocardiac impulse in the genesis of physiological tremor. *Brain* **92**, 647–662. [578]

Marsden, C. D., Merton, P. A. & Morton, H. B. (1971). Servo action and stretch reflex in human muscle and its apparent dependence on peripheral sensation. *J. Physiol.* **216**, 21–23 p.   [589]

Matsushita, A., Yanagisawa, N. & Shimazu, H. (1965). A study of ataxia and muscle spindle depression produced in mammals by a new unsymmetrical bis-methonium compound. *J. Pharmac. exp. Ther.* **157**, 343–349.   [549]

Matthews, P. B. C. (1964). Muscle spindles and their motor control. *Physiol. Rev.* **44**, 219–288.   [573]

— (1970) The origin and functional significance of the stretch reflex. In *Excitatory Synaptic Mechanisms*, ed. Andersen, P. & Jansen, J. K. S. pp. 301–315. Oslo: Universitetsforlaget.   [572]

Merton, P. A. (1951). The silent period in a muscle of the human hand. *J. Physiol.* **114**, 183–198.   [553, 557, 558]

— (1953). Speculations on the servo-control of movement. In *The Spinal Cord*, ed. Wolstenholme, G. E. W., pp. 247–255. London: Churchill.   [553, 557]

— (1964). Human position sense and sense of effort. *Symp. Soc. exp. Biol.* **18**, 387–400.   [547]

Mott, F. W. & Sherrington, C. S. (1895). Experiments upon the influence of sensory nerves upon movement and nutrition of the limbs. Preliminary communication. *Proc. R. Soc.* **57**, 481–488.   [547]

Nathan, P. W. (1969). Motor effects of differential block of spinal roots in spastic patients. *J. neurol. Sci.* **8**, 19–26.   [549]

Nathan, P. W. & Sears, T. A. (1960). Effects on posterior root section on the activity of some muscles in man. *J. Neurol. Neurosurg. Psychiat*, **23**, 10–22.   [548]

Newsom Davis, J. & Sears, T. A. (1970). The proprioceptive reflex control of the intercostal muscles during their voluntary activation. *J. Physiol.* **209**, 711–738.   [583, 584, 588, 597]

Pouliquen, R. & Richalet, J. (1968). Analyse d'une expérience de maintien postural. *J. Physiol., Paris* **60**, 261–273.   [593]

Rossi, G. (1927). Asimmetrie toniche posturali, ed asimmetrie motorie. *Arch. Fisiol.* **25**, 146–157.   [552]

Sant'Ambrogio, H. & Widdicombe, J. G. (1965). Respiratory reflexes acting on the diaphragm and inspiratory intercostal muscles. *J. Physiol.* **180**, 766–779.   [597]

Sears, T. A. (1964a). Efferent discharges in alpha and fusimotor fibres of intercostal nerves of the cat. *J, Physiol.* **174**, 295–315.   [568]

— (1964b). Investigations on respiratory motoneurones of the spinal cord. In *Progress in Brain Research*, Vol. 12, ed. Eccles, J. C. & Schadé, J. P. pp. 259–274. Amsterdam: Elsevier.   [567]

Severin, F. V., Orlovskii, G. N. & Shik, M. L. (1967). Work of the muscle receptors during controlled locomotion. *Biophysics* **12**, 575–586 (translation of *Biofizika* **12**, 502–511).   [569]

Sherrington, C. S. (1900). In *Textbook of Physiology*, ed. Schäfer, E. A. Vol. 2, p. 801. Edinburgh: Pentland.   [547]

Sherrington, C. S., (1910). Flexion-reflex of the limb, crossed extension reflex, and reflex stepping and standing. *J. Physiol.* **40**, 28–121. [547]

Shik, M. L., Orlovskii, G. N. & Severin, F. V. (1966). Organization of locomotor synergism. *Biophysics* **11**, 1011–1019 (translation of *Biofizika* **11**, 879–886). [569]

Sutton, G. G. & Sykes, K. (1967). The effect of withdrawal of visual presentation of errors upon the frequency spectrum of tremor in a manual task. *J. Physiol.* **190**, 281–293. [578]

Székely, G., Czeh, G. & Vörös, G. (1969). The activity pattern of limb muscles in freely moving normal and de-afferentated newts. *Exptl. Brain Res.* **9**, 53–62. [548]

Tardieu, C., Tabary, J. C. & Tardieu, G. (1968). Etude mécanique et électromyographique de réponses à différentes pertubations du maintien postural. *J. Physiol., Paris* **60**, 243–259. [592, 593]

Taylor, A. & Davey, M. R. (1968). Behaviour of jaw muscle stretch receptors during active and passive movements in the cat. *Nature, Lond.* **220**, 301–302. [569, 570]

Thulin, C. A. (1960). Electrophysiological studies of peripheral nerve regeneration with special reference to the small diameter (gamma) fibres. *Exptl. Neurol.* **2**, 598–612. [550]

Vallbo, Å. B. (1970*a*). Slowly adapting muscle receptors in man. *Acta physiol. scand.* **78**, 315–333. [571]

— (1970*b*). Discharge patterns in human muscle spindle afferents during isometric contractions. *Acta physiol. scand.* **80**, 552–566. [571]

Walsh, E. G. (1969). Interference with the tremor of Parkinsonism by the application of a rhythmic muscle force. *J. Physiol.* **202**, 109–110P. [578]

— (1971). Ankle clonus—an autonomous central pace-maker? *J. Physiol.* **212**, 38–39P. [577]

Westbury, D. R. (1970). The response of α-motoneurones of the cat to sinusoidal movements of the muscles they innervate. *Brain Res.* **25**, 75–86. [576]

Wiesendanger, M. (1964). Rigidity produced by de-afferentation. *Acta physiol. scand.* **62**, 160–168. [548]

Author Index

The references are grouped at the end of each chapter. Each reference is followed by the page number of the place at which it is quoted in the main text. The present index of authors gives the page numbers of the places in the reference lists where there is a paper by the cited author. All papers by a particular author are referred to, irrespective of whether they were written alone or in collaboration.

Subject Index

No references are here given to the mention of a topic in the résumés at the end of each chapter.

A1/A2 classification of spindle endings, 110–113

A/B classification of stretch receptors, 106–110

Acceleration response of spindle afferents, 167–169, 182, 283–285

Acetylcholine action on spindle, 242, 298

Accommodation of afferent fibres to current, 268–271

Adaptation:
  equivalence to dynamic sensitivity, 266
  contribution of mechanical factors to, 265–274

Adrenaline action on spindle, 246–248

Afferent fibres:
  classification into groups I to IV, 78–81
  into Ia and Ib, 85, 340
  See also group I, etc.

Alpha fibres:
  branching of, 72–73
  definition of, 73–75
  diameters of, 69–73, 90

Alpha-gamma co-activation:
  in reflex action, 533
  on central stimulation, 522–525
  during movement, 566–574
  significance, 572–574

Alpha-gamma linkage, imprecision of term, 523, *see* co-activation

Alpha rigidity, 455, 456

Anaemic decerebration, 413, 455

Anaesthetics:
  general on muscle spindle, 246
  local, on γ efferents, 248–251, 467, 549, 567
  local, on joints, 495
  local, on stretch reflex in cat, 433–435
  local, on stretch reflex in man, 589

Ankle jerk, monosynaptic mediation (*see also* tendon jerk), 324–328

Annulo-spiral ending, as synonym for spindle primary ending, 17

Anoxia of muscle spindle, 246–248

Arousal, absence on group I stimulation, 497–499

Asphyxia of muscle spindle, 246–248

Ataxia:
  on dorsal root section, 547–549
  on spindle paralysis, 549

Autogenetic excitation:
  from spindle primaries, 334–361, 423–426
  probability of from spindle secondaries, 428–434

Autogenetic inhibition:
  from group II afferents, 367–371
  from tendon organs, 336–346

Averaging methods for studying sinusoidal stretching, 173–176

Baboon:
  cortical area receiving Ia input, 486, 490
  cortical control of fusimotor neurones, 524
  sizes of afferent fibres, 91

Beta (β) fibres:
  definition of, 42
  anatomical demonstration of existence, 42–44
  dubious relation to early discharge, 237
  dynamic actions of, 237
  physiological proof of existence, 234–237
  static action of, in rabbit, 237
  supplying p_1 plates, 42–43

Blood-pressure, reflex effects of various afferents on, 376–380

Branching (peripheral):
  of α and γ fibres, 73
  of Ia fibres, 88
  of Ib fibres, 88
  of group II fibres, 88